Stanley Gibbons

Great Britain

Specialised Stamp Catalogue
Volume 3

Retail Price

£2·00

Stanley Gibbons

Great Britain

Specialised Stamp Catalogue

Volume 3
Queen Elizabeth II

Second Edition

By Appointment
to H.M. the Queen
Stanley Gibbons Ltd
Philatelists

Stanley Gibbons Ltd 391 Strand London WC2R OLX
Telephone 01-836 9707

©
1971
Stanley Gibbons Ltd
ISBN 0 85259 420 8

1st Edition—August 1970
2nd Edition—October 1971
Printed in Great Britain by The Anchor Press Ltd Tiptree Essex
Bound by the Leighton-Straker Bookbinding Co Ltd NW10

Preface to the Second Edition

In addition to sharing with other S.G. Catalogues in the award of a Gold Medal for Literature at " Philympia " last year, we were gratified that the three-volume G.B. Specialised Catalogue was granted a Silver-Gilt at " RSA 10 " at Capetown this year.

Although published only a year after the first edition, a good deal of work has been put into this new edition affecting every Section and this reflects the interest this volume has aroused amongst specialists of modern G.B.

Wilding Issues. Attention has been given to dates of issue and amendments made, particularly for the whiter papers and inverted watermarks where dates are sometimes governed by the appearance of booklets and coils. All basic dates now relate to stamps in sheet form and where they appeared earlier in booklets or coils these dates are given in footnotes.

Information about coils has been thoroughly checked, particularly as to their existence on cream and/or whiter paper.

Machin £.s.d. Issues. In the first edition we undertook to review the listing of shades as soon as the issue was superseded by decimal stamps. This we have done after careful examination of an exhaustive array of shades which exist for most values. This proved to be difficult as the more shades there are the harder it is to find words to describe them owing to the wide range of intermediates. We have found it possible to add a few of the more marked shades and where practicable to relate these to the listing of cylinder blocks.

Another interesting development during the past year was the introduction of phosphor cylinder numbers on some late printings. Because they are unsynchronised we have recorded them under sheet markings but prices are also quoted there.

Booklet panes are now listed and priced according to their perforation types which are illustrated and described in Appendix O. These are much sought after by specialists.

After studying the numerous specialist articles on the two types of Machin head and the screen variations in the phosphor bands, we decided that it would be carrying specialisation too far to list these out in detail. Instead we have introduced a table recording the incidence of the two heads in combination with the phosphor screens and also the source of the stamps by reference to the sheet cylinder numbers, booklets or coils. The ultra specialist can use this as a basis for going beyond the scope of this Catalogue.

Machin Decimal Issues. In their publicity directed to stamp collectors the Post Office emphasized the point that these issues mark the beginning of a new era and, therefore, make a good starting point for new collectors. We would agree with this, particularly as regards the definitives. There is every indication that these will provide as much philatelic interest as the Wildings.

In the first place there is the innovation of phosphor cylinder numbers so that now cylinder blocks have to be collected so as to include changes in phosphor cylinder numbers. Right from the outset there were experiments

5

in the positioning and size of the phosphor numbers resulting eventually in large figures synchronised with the ink cylinder block.

Then the four booklet compositions have given rise to no less than ten different booklet panes, each obtainable in two or three different perforation types. Furthermore, a new perforator is being introduced for booklets containing labels. In future the labels will not be perforated in the binding margin to prevent blind people using them as stamps.

Moreover, gum arabic is still with us as it continues to be used for the multi-value coil. Missing phosphor varieties are becoming commonplace, but worth looking for none the less. Specialists are already writing about variations in multipositives which we shall doubtless have to cover in a future edition.

As we are imminently threatened with further rises in postal rates we can expect new colour and phosphor band changes as well as variations in booklet compositions.

Special Issues. As elsewhere, we have been able to add a number of newly discovered errors, varieties and flaws, particularly in the issues of the past year. Issues are included up to the 1971 Ulster Paintings.

Regional Issues. There have been a few additional items in the Wilding £.s.d. stamps and now a new chapter is added to cover the Machin decimals which made their appearance just before we went to press.

Presentation Packs Packs with German text are now listed and sales figures for all packs are given where known.

Booklets. It is clear from the quantities sold and now included that the pictorial booklets introduced for the Machin £.s.d. issues have proved popular with the public and collectors. We predict that the decimal booklets will be even more popular with the innovation of numbered design series drawn by well-known artists. The success of the National Postal Museum's Booklet Exhibition, itself publicised by a special issue of booklets, is another pointer.

Prices. These have been brought into line with the basic prices in the 1972 *British Commonwealth* and *Elizabethan Catalogues*. Some reductions will be noted so that this might be a good time to buy.

STANLEY GIBBONS LTD.

Acknowledgements

Amongst others who have given us help we particularly wish to thank the following:—Mr. R. F. Allen for original work on the Wilding High Values; Dr. A. S. Law for data about Machin £.s.d. phosphor cylinder numbers; Mr. D. G. A. Myall for much assistance in almost every Section but especially for providing data for the Machin £.s.d. table of head types and phosphor screens; Mr. L. F. Newbery for assistance on the decimal booklet perforation types; Mr. J. W. Robinson for the opportunity to examine a remarkable collection of shades of the Machin £.s.d. stamps; Brigadier M. A. Studd for keeping us supplied with new varieties for listing. In addition several members of the trade who specialise in modern Great Britain have been most co-operative in bringing items to our attention and vetting some draft listings.

Preface to the First Edition

The following shortened version of the original Preface is reprinted as the information is still relevant.

In this volume the Wilding, Machin and Regional issues are dealt with value by value, taking them through the remarkable series of changes involving the three watermarks and the unwatermarked stamps; the cream, whiter and chalky papers; the graphite, phosphor-graphite and the three colour reactions of the phosphor bands, together with their variations in width, method of application and missing phosphor varieties; and finally the introduction of PVA gum.

The listing of each stamp is followed by the cylinder numbers which are priced according to the type of perforator used, and this takes account of the state of the perforations on all four sides of the sheet, not just the corner where the cylinder number appears. We have worked out what we believe to be a better and simpler method of describing the numerous types of perforators.

Another feature is the detailed descriptions of all the marginal markings on each stamp. This is useful, partly because marginal multiples help to establish the position of varieties and also because the markings can be an aid in establishing the cylinder or pane.

Whilst listed varieties are fully illustrated and priced, we have also recorded minor constant flaws, indicating their position by reference to the S.G. "Thirkell" Position Finder. Although not priced individually, we quote minimum prices for minor flaws. It should be remembered that these flaws, even when described as being constant, are sometimes transient, starting during the course of printing and possibly developing in size so as to be sufficiently noticeable to be worth retouching.

In dealing with varieties and minor flaws we were faced with the choice of including everything that has been recorded or only what we have seen. Since there are also many flaws which are not constant, we decided to follow a cautious policy of recording only what we have been able to verify from the examination of more than one sheet, or else flaws that have been recorded elsewhere and confirmed in our own stock. Hence the list is necessarily incomplete, but at least we can vouch for what we have included and others can be added in future editions as they come to our notice.

The figures for quantities issued or sold have all been obtained from the Post Office except for some figures for the Regionals which came from an article by Mr. E. C. Ehrmann in *Stamp Collecting*.

We decided to omit from this volume the stamps of Guernsey and Jersey issued by the present independent postal administrations. We will reconsider this at some future date and decide whether to include them or possibly publish a separate volume for them.

STANLEY GIBBONS LTD.

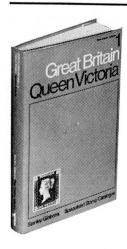 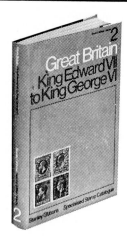

The Stanley Gibbons
Great Britain Specialised Catalogue

Volume 1—Queen Victoria

The authoritative Catalogue of the Victorian issues in a new, completely revised edition embodying over fifty extra pages and 900 new illustrations.

In the Line-Engraved stamps the chapter relating to Die Proofs, Essays and Colour Trials, etc. has been completely rewritten and many recently discovered constant varieties in these issues are listed for the first time. Much new material added to the Surface-Printed issues, particularly in the Die Proofs, etc., derived from research at the National Postal Museum and study of the famous Maximus Collection. This new edition also contains much additional historical data and we have added a General Index as well as tabulated tables of all issues, giving essential descriptions of each stamp together with its Specialised and S.G. catalogue numbers and page reference.

3rd Edition. July 1970. Uniform binding. 269 Pages.
Price £2·25. Postage extra.

Volume 2—The Four Kings

A priced listing continuing in fascinating detail the philatelic story of British stamps through the reigns of King Edward VII, King George V, King Edward VIII and King George VI. Includes an ingenious tabulated record of the plate-markings of the typographed issues. Appendices cover Watermark varieties, "Specimens," Perforators, Booklets, Cylinder Numbers, Controls, etc.

2nd. Edition. July 1970. Uniform binding. 266 pages.
Price £2·25. Postage extra.

Contents

9

Notes

The aim of this catalogue is to classify in specialised form the stamps of Great Britain, to give distinguishing numbers to them and to quote prices which are current with the Publishers at the time of going to press and at which they will supply if in stock.

To Quote or Order from this Catalogue

Always quote the *Specialised Catalogue* number, mentioning *Vol. 3, 2nd Ed.*, and where necessary specify additionally the precise item wanted.

All *Specialised Catalogue* numbers include a prefix letter or letters; shades have a number in brackets where there is more than one and subsequent varieties have letter identifications. Thus if a variety exists on more than one shade the price quoted will be for the commoner shade and it will be worth correspondingly more on a scarcer shade.

In ordering *cylinder blocks* (from sheets or booklet panes), it is necessary to quote first the basic number of the stamp followed by the cylinder number and to state whether with or without dot, the perforation type, cream or whiter paper, gum arabic or PVA wherever these alternatives are given.

The prices for *varieties and flaws* are for singles and extra stamps required to make up positional blocks will be charged as normals. Prices for cylinder blocks containing listed varieties are indicated by an asterisk and include the cost of the variety.

When ordering *minor flaws* after quoting the basic catalogue number it is necessary to state the cylinder number, whether with or without dot, and the sheet position. Minimum prices for flaws are given and those occurring on scarcer cylinders will be worth more.

Booklets all have catalogue numbers with prefix letters. To avoid introducing a fresh numbering system for these we have used the same numbers as are given in the *Elizabethan Catalogue*. As some of these prefix letters have also been used in the various Sections of the *Specialised Catalogue* it should be made clear on want lists that booklets are required.

Symbols and Abbreviations

†	=	Does not exist.
—	=	Exists, but price cannot be quoted (also blank in used price column).
/		between colours means "on" and the colour following is that of the paper on which the stamp is printed.
P.O.T.S.	=	Post Office Training School
Th.	=	S.G. "Thirkell" Position Finder. The letters and figures which follow indicate the position of the flaw on the stamp.

Watermark Illustrations

These are always shown as seen from the *front* of the stamp. This is important to remember when classifying sideways watermarks which also exist sideways inverted (i.e. Crown to right).

Finally, Please Note—

Reference should be made to the General Notes for Section S for notes on the *arrangement* of this catalogue and also *varieties* and *minor constant flaws* as these apply equally to all other Sections.

Colour shifts due to faulty registration range from minor shifts to quite spectacular varieties but as it is very difficult to draw a line between major and minor shifts we have not listed any.

The Editor will be pleased to examine unlisted *errors* and *varieties* with a view to adding them in a future edition. Before submitting stamps please note that varieties such as doctor blade flaws, paper creases, colour shifts, partially omitted colours and misplaced perforations are outside the scope of this catalogue. All enquiries are expected to be accompanied by a stamped addressed envelope for reply.

May we help?

We would like to help you build your Great Britain collection and therefore remind you that the prices quoted in this catalogue are our selling prices at the time this book went to press. They are for stamps in fine average condition, and in issues where condition varies we may ask more for the superb and less for the sub-standard. In the case of unused stamps, our prices are for stamps lightly hinged and used are for postally used. All prices are subject to change without prior notice and we give no guarantee to supply all stamps priced.

Ideally, we hope you'll visit our 391 Strand Shop or our Specialist and Rare Stamp Department at Romano House, 399 Strand, for here you can see our world-famous stock of Great Britain, but equally, our Approval Service can send you, no matter where you live, attractive selections covering all issues and price ranges of the stamps of Great Britain. For stamps priced at £1 or over in this catalogue we welcome collectors' Want Lists. Our Specialists File can register your special requirements if we cannot offer immediately.

In every way we can help you enjoy a lifetime's hobby—that is just what we are doing for many thousands of collectors throughout the world—so the important thing is to contact us.

STANLEY GIBBONS

Guarantee

All stamps are guaranteed genuine originals in the following terms:—

If not as described, and returned by the purchaser within six years, we undertake to refund the price paid to us and our liability will thereby be discharged. If any stamp is certified as genuine by the Expert Committee of the Royal Philatelic Society, London, or of the British Philatelic Association Limited, the purchaser shall not be entitled to make any claim against us for any error, omission or mistake in such certificate.

Please note

Our terms are cash with order unless you have established a credit account.

We do not give opinions as to the genuineness of stamps, nor do we identify stamps or number them by our Catalogue.

Our Addresses and Business Hours

HEAD OFFICE—
STANLEY GIBBONS LTD.
391 STRAND,
LONDON, WC2R OLX

Telephone: 01–836 9707.
Telegrams: Philatelic, London, W.C.2.
Cables: Stangib, London, WC2B 5HD.
Code: A.B.C. (6th Edition).

SHOP DEPARTMENT—
Our only retail shop is at
391 Strand, London, WC2

Open from Monday to Friday 9 a.m. to
5.30 p.m. and on Saturday 9.30 a.m. to
12.30 p.m.

SPECIALIST AND RARE STAMP DEPARTMENT—
ROMANO HOUSE,
399 STRAND, LONDON, WC2

Open from Monday to Friday 9 a.m. to
5 p.m. and on Saturday 9.30 a.m. to 12
noon (excluding Summer Saturdays).

CATALOGUE AND MAGAZINE EDITORS AND ACCOUNTS—
STANLEY GIBBONS LTD.
DRURY HOUSE,
RUSSELL STREET,
DRURY LANE,
LONDON, WC2B 5HD

Telephones:
01–836 4136 (Editorial)
01–836 2005 (Retail Publications)
01–836 9707 (Stamps and all Depts.)

AUCTIONS—
STANLEY GIBBONS AUCTIONS LTD.
DRURY HOUSE,
RUSSELL STREET,
DRURY LANE,
LONDON, WC2B 5HD

Telephone: 01–836 7941
Cables: Philators, London, WC2.

TRADE PUBLICATIONS DIVISION—
STANLEY GIBBONS LTD.
STANGIB HOUSE, Sarehole Road, Hall Green, Birmingham, B28 8EE

NEW YORK BRANCH—
STANGIB LTD.
595 FIFTH AVENUE,
NEW YORK,
N.Y. 10017, U.S.A.

Telephone: 212–PL8–2210.
Cables: Stangib, New York.

SECTION S
Dorothy Wilding Issues

General Notes

INTRODUCTION. Queen Elizabeth II came to the throne on 6th February, 1952. By contrast with the King George VI series there were five different basic designs from five artists with a common feature consisting of the portrait of the Queen by Dorothy Wilding, Ltd. enclosed in an oval. In this portrait the Queen is shown wearing the Crown Jewels, whilst the policy of embodying various emblems representative of the different parts of the Kingdom was continued. These and the intricacies of the Crown Jewels produced many minor varieties and there are probably more varieties and flaws on this issue than on any other issue since the Victorian Line-engraved stamps.

The stamps came out value by value over a period, the first to be issued being the 1½d. and 2½d. which were placed on sale on the 5th December 1952 but it was not until February 1954 that the series was completed. During this period there was an interesting phase when booklets were issued containing panes of King George VI and Queen Elizabeth II stamps.

ARRANGEMENT. This Section takes each value in turn and follows its history through the various watermarks, graphite lines, phosphors, and papers taking in the booklet panes and coils and on page 18 there is a table setting out which values occurred in each state and quoting their catalogue numbers for easy reference. The general arrangement of the catalogue is to show first the basic listing with errors and varieties in small type, followed by illustrations of the listed varieties, a list of the cylinder numbers, a record of the minor constant flaws, booklet panes and coils and finally ancillary information such as sheet markings, withdrawal dates and quantities issued or sold.

PRINTERS. All the Wilding issues were printed in photogravure by Harrison & Sons. They were printed on continuous reels of paper " on the web " generally in double pane width, i.e. 480 stamps consisting of two panes (no dot and dot) each of 240 stamps arranged in twenty rows of twelve stamps, the panes being guillotined before issue. However, some printings were made from single cylinders printing sheets of 240 stamps (i.e. no dot panes only). Exceptionally, the 1963 2s. Holiday Booklet (No. NR1) stamps were printed on a sheet-fed machine.

PAPER. For the first ten years the definitives were printed on a creamy paper but starting in April 1962 a whiter paper was gradually introduced. It is always a difficult matter to maintain successive supplies of paper in exactly the same colour and so it is not surprising that there is some variation in the degree of whiteness in the " whiter paper " which sometimes makes it difficult to identify. Sometimes knowledge of the cylinder used can be decisive. The whiter paper does not respond to the chalky test (that is applying silver to see if it will produce a black line) but a true coated chalk-surfaced paper was used for the 2s. Holiday Booklet issued in 1963 which affected the ½d. and 2½d. values in the Crowns watermark. In 1964 an experimental paper was used for the 3d. non-phosphor Crowns watermark which was slightly thicker. It can be distinguished by the fact that an additional watermark letter " T " lying on its side occurred about four times in the sheet.

Tudor Crown	St. Edward's Crown	Crowns
W.22	**W.23**	**W.24**

WATERMARKS

The illustrations of the watermarks are as seen from the front of the stamp. The " Tudor Crown " was in use from 1952 to 1954, the " St. Edward's Crown " from 1955 to 1958 and the Multiple Crowns from 1958 onwards. No Wilding issues appeared on paper without watermark.

In the Crowns watermark differences in the spacing of the Crowns have been noticed but it is believed that this is due to variations in the dandy roll and does not represent a different version of the watermark.

Watermark Varieties. As the Wilding issues are all printed " on the web " inverted watermarks cannot occur on the sheet stamps, but they do occur on 50% of the booklet panes owing to the manner in which the sheets are arranged with some rows having the images inverted on the cylinders. The booklets are guillotined before issue resulting in some panes with the watermark inverted. Booklets are the only source of inverted watermarks in the Wilding issues.

Until 1961 all stamps with the watermark sideways came only from coils with left side delivery and these all show the top of the watermark pointing to left as seen from the front of the stamp. From 1961 all 2s. booklets on Crowns watermark had the watermark sideways and these, of course, have 50% of the panes with the crowns pointing to left and 50% to right and they are listed both ways.

GUM.   Only gum arabic has been used for the Wilding issues as PVA gum was not introduced until the Machin series.

PERFORATION.   All stamps are comb perforated 15 × 14 as the King George VI issues However, the horizontal perforation is very close to the three-quarters mark and so is sometimes described as 14½ × 14. Quite a number of different perforators were used and these are described and illustrated in Appendix O which deals with the perforators employed for all the Harrison issues. The cylinder numbers are listed according to the type of perforator used.

Perforation varieties such as double or misplaced perforations are not listed in this Catalogue.

EXPERIMENTAL GRAPHITE ISSUES.   The first Automatic Letter Facing machine (known as ALF) was introduced experimentally in Southampton in 1957. The machine, which prepares letters for the sorting process, is fed with letters having their long edges parallel but with stamps in any of four possible positions. The letters are reorientated to make the addresses all face the same direction the same way up. First and second class items are separated and the stamps are cancelled. Items which cannot be faced, due for example to the absence of a stamp, are rejected to receive manual treatment.

The very first facing machine looked in the stamp corner for an area of dense printing ink, having the characteristics of a stamp, as a means of stamp detection. This system was inefficient as the machine's performance was influenced by stamp design and the occasional presence of misleading writing on the envelope. However, facing machines are still being equipped with this method as a secondary means of stamp detection in order to deal with O.H.M.S. and Business Reply items.

To improve the efficiency of facing it was necessary to give these stamps some unmistakable identity. The first attempt used stamps which were printed with electrically conducting vertical black graphite lines on the back under the gum. One line on the 2d., then the printed paper rate, and two lines on the other values. The use of electrically conducting lines was not a complete success as failures were caused by metallic paper fasteners and damp mail.

There were two graphite issues. The first in November 1957 on the ½d., 1d., 1½d., 2d., 2½d. and 3d. sheet stamps with the St. Edward's Crown watermark and also on coils. The second issue came out during 1958-59 on the same values, plus the 4d. and 4½d. in sheets with the Crowns watermark and here there were also coils and booklets.

PHOSPHOR-GRAPHITE ISSUES.   In November 1959 existing graphite stamps were overprinted on the face with phosphorescent ink which, when exposed to ultra-violet (u.v.) light, releases energy in the form of visible light. The emission of visible light persists for some time after the exposure to u.v. light has ceased. Most countries which handle very large quantities of mail have followed the lead of Great Britain in the use of some form of luminescence on stamps to facilitate automatic facing.

The British Post Office uses organic-resin phosphors containing an activator, the choice of activator affecting the optical properties.

Phosphor bands are not always easy to see, especially on used stamps, and it is usually necessary to hold the stamps up to the light at eye level when they become visible as broad bands.

The graphite lined stamps were overprinted with vertical phosphor bands on the face, again one band for the 2d. and two bands for the others. In sheets they appeared on the ½d., 1d. and 1½d. with St. Edward's Crown watermark and on the 2d., 2½d., 3d., 4d. and 4½d. with Crowns watermark. The substance used is commercially known as Lettalite B1 (the activator being Parahydroxydiphenyl) and it produces a greenish phosphorescence when reacting with u.v. light in the 2000 to 3000 Ångstrom range.

As the phosphor treatment of stamps at Southampton was successful, residual stocks having graphite lines were distributed as normal stock to other areas and a notice was sent to Post Office clerks to say that they should disregard the black lines. This applied also to the 5s. booklets listed under Nos. HG1/3.

PHOSPHOR ISSUES.   More facing machines were brought into use on 6th July 1960 and the ½d. to 4d. and 1s.3d. values with Crowns watermark with phosphor bands only were issued on 22nd June 1960, the 6d. following on 27th June. Coils and booklets came a little later.

The same phosphor reacting green was employed but in 1961 this was superseded by Lettalite B₂ (Carbazole sulphonic acid being the activator) which reacts blue to u.v. in the 2000–4000 Ångstrom range. The advantage of this was that it gave a stronger signal. By this time ALF machines were introduced into other areas and the "blue" phosphor was in use between 1961 and 1966 on the same values as for the "green" phosphor and with the addition of the 4½d. value. This period covered the change-over to the whiter paper and also two changes in postal rates so that the 2d., 2½d. and 3d. were each issued with one and two bands.

With the introduction of address coding and automatic letter sorting, at Norwich in 1965, it became necessary to use a phosphor for stamps which would not interfere with sorting. Thus another change was made, this time to Lettalite B3 (having Terephthalic acid as the activator) which was inert to the u.v. light of wavelength 3650 Angstroms used in sorting machines but which has a bright visible light output when subjected to 2537 Ångstroms in the facing machine. This reacts violet under the lamp.

There are two types of the "violet" phosphor, the first with 8 mm. bands, issued in 1965 (½d., 1d., 1½d., 2d., 3d., 4d., 6d. and 1s.3d., plus coils and booklets) and the second with 9·5 mm. bands issued in 1966-67 (1d., 2d., 3d., 4d., 5d., 6d., 7d., 8d., 9d., 10d., 1s., 1s.3d. and 1s.6d. plus coils and booklets). As the bands overlap the stamps it is easier to distinguish these by measuring the space between the bands, this being approximately 12 mm. for the 8 mm. bands and 10·5 mm. for the 9·5 mm. bands. There is the further complication of identifying the 3d. value which has only one band but in the 8 mm. band series this is at the left or right of the stamp whilst in the 9·5 mm. band series it is in the centre. Both the "green" and the "blue" bands normally measure 8 mm.

Application of Phosphor Bands. The choice of method for applying the phosphor bands is a matter for the printer and three different methods have been used: photogravure, typography and flexography.

To apply bands in photogravure sometimes an additional printing cylinder is brought into use so that it is done in the same operation as printing the stamps. In the case of multicoloured special issues there may not be a spare cylinder available as this would depend upon the colour capacity of the press and the number of colours to be used. The bands may then be applied by typography or photogravure as a separate operation on a sheet-fed press.

Flexography is a typographic process but using a rubber cylinder which picks up the impression from a photo-etched inking cylinder. The screen pattern is usually blurred, although some traces of it remain. This method is usually employed for applying bands to stamps already printed " in the web " before being cut into sheets.

Photogravure bands do not indent the paper, are screened and extend through the top and bottom sheet margins. Bands applied by typography generally indent the paper, as can be seen from the back, are solid and stop short of the edges of the sheet. It is rather difficult to distinguish between flexography and typography and we have made no attempt to do so. However, where a stamp exists with the bands applied in photogravure and typography (including flexography) we list both.

The " green " phosphor was overprinted by typography on the graphite stamps but in photogravure only on the first phosphor only issue. The " blue " phosphor was normally applied in photogravure but some values also exist with typographic overprint. The " violet " 8 mm. bands are normally applied in photogravure but again some values exist with them typographed, but the 9·5 mm. series exist with them only in photogravure.

Phosphor bands frequently appear misplaced in various degrees but such varieties are outside the scope of this Catalogue except where the misplacement affects the number of bands.

Identification of Phosphor Colours. The ordinary philatelic " Black " lamp used for detecting forgeries and repairs is satisfactory for identifying the "blue" phosphors, but it will not serve for the "green" or "violet" as these are outside its range. There are now several ultra-violet lamps on the market which are claimed to detect all types of phosphor but great care is required in using them as exposure to their light is extremely dangerous to the eyes.

BOOKLET ERRORS. Those listed as " Imperf. pane " show one row of perforations either at top or bottom of booklet pane. Those listed as " part perf. pane " have one row of three stamps imperforate on three sides. The *tête-bêche* errors also derive from booklets owing to the way they are made up; this is described in the introductory notes to Appendix P.

. **VARIETIES.** Most of the more prominent varieties are listed and illustrated but we have restricted ourselves to those we have actually seen. Others will be added to future editions as specimens become available for illustration.

The position is always indicated by stating first the cylinder number (and where no full stop is shown this means the " no dot " cylinder, whereas a full stop means the " dot " cylinder) followed by the position indicated first by the vertical row and then the horizontal position. Thus " Cyl. 15, R.10/3 " means cylinder 15 no dot, the third stamp in the tenth row down. Where the same cylinder is used on stamps with different watermark, paper or type of phosphor, etc. the varieties on that cylinder will recur, unless corrected by re-touching, and these are then listed again with footnotes referring back to its first appearance where it is illustrated.

MINOR CONSTANT FLAWS.   These are so numerous that they are merely recorded without illustrations and not individually priced, although a minimum price for minor flaws on each stamp is indicated.   Their location on the stamp is indicated, where helpful, by reference to the S.G. " Thirkell " Position Finder, an essential tool for identifying flaws. The recording of these flaws, often insignificant in themselves, will prove an aid in identifying a particular cylinder and will also serve to show that the flaw has been considered for listing as a variety but rejected as being too minor.   Again we have only recorded what we have actually seen but the picture is necessarily incomplete as we have not been able to view full sheets from every cylinder.

BOOKLET AND COIL VARIETIES.   Varieties and flaws on booklets occur on stamps with watermark either upright or inverted but we do not state which as they can only exist in one form.   As booklets are also printed from double cylinders only half the booklets from a particular position will show the varieties.   Varieties appearing in booklet panes printed from 20-row cylinders will always *only* appear in the top or bottom row of the pane, but varieties appearing in booklet panes printed from 21-row cylinders may appear in either the top or bottom row of the pane.

Similarly coils are generally printed from double cylinders.   In identifying their position the roll number is quoted (this is the number printed on the outer wrapper of the coil which corresponds to the row in the sheet before reeling) but where double cylinders are used only half the coils bearing the roll numbers will contain the variety.   Hence there are twelve rolls (vertical delivery) and ten rolls (sideways delivery) from every sheet and varieties will be repeated on every 21st stamp on vertical rolls and on every 25th stamp on sideways delivery rolls.

SHADES.   Intended changes of colour such as the 2d. red-brown and light red-brown, the 6d. reddish purple and deep claret and the 4d. ultramarine and deep ultramarine are given full numbers and some of the more marked shades which were not made by design are shown as alternatives.   In some cases, however, there is a whole range of shades which it would be meaningless to attempt to list.   The colour descriptions given are based on the Stanley Gibbons Colour Guide.

DATES OF ISSUE.   The dates given in bold type in the headings are those on which stamps in normal Post Office *sheets* were first issued, notwithstanding the fact that they may have appeared earlier in booklet form.   A dagger is added to the sheet date where stamps were issued at an *earlier* date in booklets or coils.   Stamps with inverted or sideways watermarks which appeared either earlier or later than those from ordinary sheets have the dates given after the listing of each item, and for stamps from booklets we have taken the earliest possible dated booklet, i.e. taking into account booklets containing panes with mixed watermarks.

Where there is a change of watermark or type of phosphor or to the whiter paper, the dates given are generally those on which they were first issued by the Supplies Department to Postmasters.

WITHDRAWAL DATE.   All the low value Wilding stamps not previously sold out were withdrawn from issue at the Philatelic Bureaux on 27th February 1970.

SHEET MARKINGS.   Compared with the King George VI period a wide variety of markings of various kinds have been introduced in Elizabethan issues to facilitate new elements such as registration of multicoloured stamps, ensuring that the cylinders are applied in the correct sequence, aids to registration of perforation, colour dots to ease checking for omission of colours and so on.   We give below notes and illustrations of the markings which are used in the Wilding issues and those which apply to other issues are described in the General Notes relating to the other Sections.   They are particularly helpful in establishing the position of varieties in the case of marginal blocks and can also help in identifying the type of perforator used or the type of machine employed for printing, etc.

Cylinder Number

Cylinder Number.   This always occurs in the left-hand margin opposite Row 18 No. 1.   In double pane cylinders the no dot pane is on the left and the dot pane on the right.   Booklet cylinder numbers are described in Appendix P.

| " V " shaped
Hand engraved | " W " shaped Photo etched |

Marginal Arrows. These occur against the middle rows of the sheet as an aid to Post Office Clerks when breaking up the sheets. They may be hand engraved or photo-etched. The earlier cylinders were " V " shaped (hand engraved) at the top and bottom of the sheet and " W " shaped (photo-etched) at both sides. Later cylinders were often " W " shaped (photo-etched) at top, bottom and sides but a number of combinations exist. In some cases they are accidentally missing from the Cylinder and where these are known this is stated.

| Narrow Rule | Wide Rule | Damaged Rule |

Marginal Rules. These are the solid bands of colour which appear below the bottom row of the sheet and which used to be called " Jubilee Lines " because they were first introduced in the so-called " Jubilee " issue of 1887. These are invariably co-extensive (with breaks between each stamp) and come in various widths.

| Unboxed | Boxed | In Double Box | Black Bar |

Perforation Guide Holes. These large circular punched holes occur on all reel-fed printings in various positions as stated in the lists. They are an indication of the type of perforator used and further reference to these is made in Appendix O. They occur unboxed, in a single box and also in double boxes, those illustrated being representative. See also General Notes for Section W. They are liable to be trimmed off almost completely.

Black Bar. This was used alongside the marginal arrows at left on no dot sheets and at right on dot sheets only on the first phosphor only issue reacting green. It was intended for easy recognition of phosphor stocks in the Post Office Supplies Department.

Sheet numbers. Most sheets are serially numbered in black after printing for checking purposes but the numbers are liable to be placed anywhere in the margins and so are of no use for identifying a position. They are not of much help in establishing whether a sheet occurred early or late in a printing either, as a particular printing was not necessarily numbered from 1 and several machines may have been used.

Checkers Marks. These are small encircled numbers applied with a rubber stamp in a variety of colours. They are applied by Post Office checkers when counting the sheets delivered by the printer. As with sheet numbers they are liable to be placed anywhere in the sheet margins.

Varieties in Cylinder Blocks. Where a cylinder block contains a listed variety the price is adjusted accordingly and bears an asterisk.

TABLE OF WILDING ISSUES

References are to Catalogue Numbers

Issue	½d. Red-brown	1d. Red-brown	1½d. Red-brown	2d. Red-brown	2d. Light red-brown	2d. 2 bands	2½d. Type I	2½d. Type II	2½d. Type II 1 band	2½d. Type I 1 band	3d. Ultramarine	4d. Ultramarine	4d. Deep ultramarine	4½d.	5d.	6d. Reddish purple	6d. Deep claret	7d.	8d.	9d.	10d.	11d.	1s.	1s.3d.	1s.6d.
Tudor Crown	S1	S13	S25	S36	..	..	S50	S51	..	..	S67	S81	..	..	S99	S104	..	S114	S119	S124	S129	S134	S136	S141	S150
St. Edward's Crown	S2	S14	S26	S37	S38	..	S52	S53	..	..	S68	S82	..	..	S100	S105	S106	S115	S120	S125	S130	S135	S137	S142	S151
Graphite. St. Edward's Crown	S3	S15	S27	..	S39	..	..	S54	..	..	S69	..	..	..	..	..	..	..	..	..	..	..	..	..	..
Crowns, Cream Paper	S4	S16	S28	..	S40	..	S56	S55	..	..	S70	S83	..	S93	S101	S107	..	S116	S121	S126	S131	..	S138	S143	S152
Crowns, Whiter Paper	S5	S17	S29	..	S41	..	S56b	S57	..	..	S71	S84	S85	S94	S102	S108	..	S117	S122	S127	S132	..	S139	S144	S153
Crowns, Chalky Paper	S6	..	..	..	..	..	..	S58	..	..	..	..	..	..	..	..	..	..	..	..	..	..	..	..	..
Graphite. Crowns	S7	S18	S30	..	S42	..	..	S59	..	..	S72	..	S86	S95	..	..	..	..	..	..	..	..	..	..	..
Phosphor-graphite	S8	S19	S31	..	S43	..	..	S60	..	..	S73	..	S87	S96	..	..	..	..	..	..	..	..	..	..	..
Green Phosphor	S9	S20	S32	..	S44	..	..	S61	..	..	S74	..	S88	..	..	..	S109	..	..	..	..	..	S145	..	..
Blue Phosphor. Cream Paper	S10	S21	S33	..	S45	S46	..	S62	S63	S64	S75	..	S89	S97	..	..	S110	..	..	..	..	..	S146	..	..
Blue Phosphor. Whiter Paper	S11	S22	S34	..	..	S47	..	S66	S65	..	S76	..	S90	S98	..	..	S111	..	..	..	..	..	S147	..	..
Violet Phosphor. 8 mm.	S12	S23	S35	..	..	S48	..	..	..	..	..	..	S91	..	..	..	S112	..	..	..	..	..	S148	..	..
Violet Phosphor. 9·5 mm.	..	S24	..	..	..	S49	..	..	..	..	S80	..	S92	..	S103	..	S113	S118	S123	S128	S133	..	S140	S149	S154
1 Side Band. Blue Phosphor	..	..	..	..	..	..	..	..	..	..	S77	..	..	..	..	..	..	..	..	..	..	..	..	..	..
1 Side Band. Violet Phosphor	..	..	..	..	..	..	..	..	..	..	S78	..	..	..	..	..	..	..	..	..	..	..	..	..	..
1 Centre Band. Violet Phosphor	..	..	..	..	..	..	..	..	..	..	S79	..	..	..	..	..	..	..	..	..	..	..	..	..	..

S1　　　　　　　S2　　　　　　　S3　　　　　　　S4

S5　　　　　　　S6　　　　　　　S7

Portraits of Queen Elizabeth II and National Emblems
(Des. Miss E. Marx **(S1)**, M. C. Farrar-Bell **(S2/3)**, G. Knipe **(S4)**,
Miss M. Adshead **(S5)**, E. Dulac **(S6/7)**
(Portrait by Dorothy Wilding Ltd.)

1953–65.   ½d. Orange-red, Type S1

Cat. No.	S.G. No.	Shades	Unused	Used

1953 (AUGUST 31).   WATERMARK TUDOR CROWN, TYPE W.22

S1　　　　515 　　　　　　　　　　　Orange-red　　　　　　5　　5
a. Watermark inverted (3.54) .. 　30 　15
b. Coil join (horiz. pair) .. 　.. 　35 　　　　　e. Cancelled two vert. black bars
c. A flaw (Vert. coil, Roll 3) 　.. 　75 　　　　　　(P.O. Training School).. 　.. 　8
d. Spot on d (Vert. coil, Roll 5) .. 　75

Listed Varieties

S1c, S2e, S4h 　　　　　　　S1d, S2f, S4i

Cylinder Numbers (Blocks of Six)

Perforation Type B (no dot) and C (dot)　　Perforation Type A

Cyl. No.					No dot	Dot		Cyl. No.					No dot	Dot
1	..	..	..	..	70	70		1	..	..	..	..	40	40
								3	..	..	..	..	45	45

19

Minor Constant Sheet Flaws

Minimum price as singles: 50p

Cyl. 1   4/4 White smudge at left of upper left rose (Th. B1)
         5/6 White spot at end of stem of upper right shamrock (Th. C6)
       13/1 Large concealed retouch on Queen's cheek (Th. D3–4)

Cyl. 1.   1/7 Background retouch below upper left rose (Th. B1)
      1/10 Orange spot at top right of centre cross in crown (Th. A–B3–4)
     15/4 Retouched background between OS of POSTAGE
     18/8 Coloured dot in P of POSTAGE
   19/12 White bulge on upper right sepel of lower right rose (Th. E5–6)

Cyl. 3   4/4 As cyl. 1
       5/6 As cyl. 1

Cyl. 3.   18/8 As cyl. 1.
   19/12 As cyl. 1.

Booklet Panes of Six

From 2/6 Booklets F14/34 and 5/- Booklets H6/16

SB1 Watermark upright   25   SB1a Watermark inverted   1·50

Booklet Panes of Four

From 1/- Booklet K1 for use in "E" machines

SB2 Watermark upright   20   SB2a Watermark inverted   1·10
   No cylinder numbers were used.

Booklet Pane of Two

From 1/- Booklet E1 for use in experimental "D" machines

SB3 Watermark upright   12
   Made up from vertical rows 1 and 2 from sheets.

Booklet Cylinder Numbers

Panes of six (20-row cylinders)

Cyl. No.			No dot	Dot	Cyl. No.				No dot	Dot
E1 ..	..	..	..	.. 1·50	1·50	E4*	..	..	..	.. 1·40	1·40
E2 ..	..	..	..	.. 1·40	1·40						

Panes of two (from sheets)

1 ..	..	..	..	.. 1·00	1·00	3 ..	..	..	..	.. 1·00	1·00

*The no-dot pane of cylinder E4 originally had a dot inserted in error. This can be distinguished from the true dot cylinder in which the "4" is broader and farther from the "E", and the dot is more circular than the erroneous dot.

The erroneous dot was not noticed until the Crowns watermark which exists in three states: I with the erroneous dot; II with dot removed leaving a smudge; and III with smudge removed. These are shown in the following illustration:—

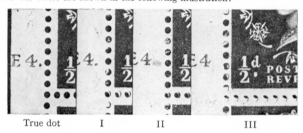

     True dot   I   II   III

Coils

All coils have the watermark upright and Cylinder A1 or A2 was used.

Vertical delivery printed in continuous reels

Code No.	Number in roll	Face value
AA	240	10/-
G	480	£1
W	960	£2
D	960	£2
Y	1920	£4

Sideways delivery made up from sheets with sheet margin joins

P	480	£1

Sheet Markings

Guide holes: Boxed opposite rows 14/15, at left (no dot) or right (dot)
Others: As given in General Notes

Cat. No.	S.G. No.			Shades	Unused	Used

1955 (DECEMBER 12).† WATERMARK ST. EDWARD'S CROWN, TYPE W.23

S2	540			Orange-red	5	5

a. Part perf. pane* .. .. 70·00
b. Watermark inverted (9.55) .. 20   15
c. Coil join (horiz. pr.) 35
d. Major retouch (Cyl. 2., R.19/2)   70
e. A flaw (Vert. coil, Roll 3) .. 60
f. Spot on d (Vert. coil, Roll 5)   60

g. Shamrock flaw (Vert. coil, Roll 11) 75
h. R flaw (Vert. coil, Roll 11) .. 75
i. Cancelled two vert. black bars (P.O.T.S.) 8

*Booklet error. See General Notes.

Listed Varieties

For illustrations of Nos. S2*e*/*f*, see Nos. S1*c*/*d*.

S2*d*, S4*g*   S2*h*, S4*k*, S5*h*, S9*c*, S10*f*,
                                   S11*e*, S12*e*

Cylinder Numbers (Blocks of Six)

Perforation Type B (no dot) and C (dot)   Perforation Type A

Cyl. No.					No dot	Dot		Cyl. No.					No dot	Dot
1 ..	..	..	..	..	35	35		2 ..	..	..	..	..	35	90*
								3 ..	..	..	..	..	35	35

Minor Constant Sheet Flaws

Minimum price as singles: 50p
Cyl. 1 no dot and dot. As for No. S1, cyl. 1
Cyls. 2 and 3 no dot and dot. As for No. S1, cyl. 3 except that flaw on 4/4 is retouched on **cyl. 3 no dot.**
Cyl. 2. 20/2 Retouch by lower right thistle and rose (Th. F5-6)

Booklet Panes of Six

From 2/6 Booklets F34/61, 3/- Booklets M1/9 and 5/- Booklets H17/36
SB4 Watermark upright   25   SB4a Watermark inverted   1·10

Booklet Panes of Four

From 1/- Booklet K2 for use in "E" machines and 2/- Booklet N1
SB5 Watermark upright   20   SB5a Watermark inverted   90
    No cylinder numbers were used.

Booklet Pane of Two

From 1/- Booklet E2 for use in experimental "D" machines
SB6 Watermark upright   12
    Made up from vertical rows 1 and 2 from sheets

Booklet Cylinder Numbers

Panes of six (20-row cylinders)

Cyl. No.				No dot	Dot		Cyl. No.				No dot	Dot
4 *	..	..	..	.. 1·00	1·00		E4 T*	..	..	..	.. 1.00	1·00

Panes of two (from sheets)

3	..	..	..	.. 1·00	1·00

*See notes after booklet panes of No. S1.

The ½d. double pane cylinders E1, E2 and E4 contained 20 rows and the cylinder number always occurred opposite row 18 so that it always appears next to the bottom row of the pane.

Cylinder E4 was later modified by adding another row of 24. In this and later 21-row cylinders, which are printed continuously in the web, the perforated web is cut at every 20th row to make sheets of 480. Consequently on successive sheets the cylinder number appears one row lower and thus a pane can have it adjoining the top or bottom row. Where the cylinder number adjoins the top row of the pane it is designated by the letter "T".

Coils

All coils have the watermark upright and it is believed that the cylinder number used was A3 in double panes as well as cylinder A1 or A2.

Vertical delivery printed in continuous reels

Code No.	Number in roll	Face value
AA	240	10/-
G	480	£1
W	960	£2
D	960	£2
Y	1920	£4

Sideways delivery made up from sheets with sheet margin joins

P	480	£1

Sheet Markings

All the same as for No. S1

Graphite-lined Issues

The graphite lines were printed in black on the back, beneath the gum. Two lines per stamp, except for the 2d. value which only have one line.

S8

Cat. No.	S.G. No.		Shades	Unused	Used

1957 (NOVEMBER 19). WITH GRAPHITE LINES, TYPE S8. WMK. ST. EDWARD'S CROWN

S3	561		Orange-red	8	8
a. E flaw (Cyl. 5, R.17/9)..	..	1·10			
b. Extra stem to thistle (Cyl. 5, R.18/10)	.. ..	1·10			

Listed Varieties

S3*a*, S8*a*

S3*b*, S8*b*

Cylinder Numbers (Blocks of Six)
Single pane cylinders

Cyl. No.	Perforation Type		No dot	Cyl. No.	Perforation Type		No dot
4	B	..	80	5	B	..	1·00
4	C	..	80	5	C	..	1·00

Minor Constant Sheet Flaws
Minimum price as singles: 55p
Cyl. 4   12/8   Orange spot in top thistle (Th. A4)

Coils
All have watermark upright, sheet cylinder 4 having been converted to a 21-row cylinder.
Vertical delivery printed in continuous reels

Code No.	Number in roll	Face value
G	480	£1
W	960	£2
Y	1920	£4

Sheet Markings
Guide holes: Boxed opposite rows 14/15, at both sides and unboxed opposite rows 1 and 7/8 at both sides
Others: As given in General Notes

Quantity Issued   22,748,400

Cat. No.	S.G. No.		Shades	Unused	Used

1958 (NOVEMBER 25).   WATERMARK CROWNS, TYPE W.24

A. Cream Paper

S4   —   Orange-red   5   5

a. Part perf. pane*	..	.. 70·00	*h.* A flaw (Vert. coil, Roll 3) ..	50	
b. Tête-bêche (vert. pair)		.. £300	*i.* Spot on d (Vert. coil, Roll 5)	50	
c. Watermark inverted (11.58) ..	15	15	*j.* Shamrock flaw (Vert. coil,		
d. Watermark Crown to left (26.5.61)	15	15	Roll 11)	35	
e. Watermark Crown to right ..	15	15	*k.* R flaw (Vert. coil, Roll 11) ..	35	
f. Coil join (horiz. pair) ..	15	15	*l.* Cancelled two vert. black bars		
g. Major retouch (Cyl. 2., R.19/2)	50		(P.O.T.S.)	8	

B. Whiter Paper (27 May 1962)†

S5   570   Orange-red   5   5

a. Watermark Crown to left (5.6.62) ..	..	12	12	*f.* Large dot by daffodil (Vert. coil, Roll 4)	50
b. Watermark Crown to right ..	12	12	*g.* d joined to shamrock (Vert. coil, Roll 11)	65	
c. Watermark inverted (29.7.62)	12	12	*h.* R flaw (Vert. coil, Roll 11) ..	25	
e. Shamrock flaw (Vert. coil, Roll 11)	25				

C. Chalky Paper   Booklets only (15 July 1963)

S6   570k   Orange-red   35   35
   a. Watermark inverted ..   35   35

   *Booklet error—See General Notes.
   †The earliest issue was in vertical coils on 30 April 1962.

Listed Varieties

For illustrations of No. S4*g*, see No. S2*d*, for No. S4*h* see No. S1*c*, for No. S4*i* see No. S2*f* and for Nos. S4*j/k* and S5*g/h* see Nos. S2*g/h*.

S5*f*, S12*c*

S5*g*, S12*d*

Cylinder Numbers (Blocks of Six)

A. Cream Paper
Perforation Type B (no dot) and C (dot)

Cyl. No.						No dot	Dot
1	..	..	..	..	..	40	40
3	..	..	..	..	..	40	40

Perforation Type A

Cyl. No.						No dot	Dot
2	..	..	..	..	..	40	70*
3	..	..	..	..	..	35	35

B. Whiter Paper
Perforation Type A

1	..	..	..	..	..	35	35
3	..	..	..	..	..	35	35

Minor Constant Sheet Flaws

Minimum price as singles: 30p

Cyl. 1   4/4 White smudge at left of upper left rose (Th. B1)
        5/6 White spot at end of stem of upper right shamrock (Th. C6), rather faint on this cylinder
        13/1 Large concealed retouch on Queen's cheek (Th. D3–4)
Cyl. 1. 1/10 Orange spot at top right of centre cross in crown (Th. A–B3–4)
Cyl. 2. 18/8 Coloured dot in P of POSTAGE (later retouched)
        20/2 Retouch by lower right thistle and rose (Th. F5–6)
Cyl. 3   5/6 White spot at end of stem of upper right shamrock (Th. C6)
Cyl. 3. 18/8 Coloured dot in P of POSTAGE

Booklet Panes of Six

Cream or whiter paper
From 3/– Booklets M9a/74, 5/– Booklets H35a and H37/74 and 10/– Booklets X1/2

SB7 Watermark upright   25   SB7a Watermark inverted   65

Booklet Panes of Four

Cream paper
From 1/– Booklet K3 for use in "E" machines and 2/– Booklets N2/3

SB8 Watermark upright   15   SB8a Watermark inverted   40
    No cylinder numbers were used.

Cream or whiter paper. Sideways watermark
From 2/– Booklets N4/20

SB9 Wmk. Crown to left   40   SB9a Wmk. Crown to right   40

SB10   SB11

Se-tenant Panes of Four from Holiday Booklets

Chalky paper. 3 × ½d. with 1 × 2½d. (No. S58) from 2/– Booklet NR1

SB10 Watermark upright   1·50   SB10a Watermark inverted   1·50
                          ab. Daffodil flaw on ½d. ..   ..   3·50
                          ac. Screen damage on 2½d.   ..   4·25

Whiter paper. Sideways watermark
Pair of ½d. with pair of 2½d. (Nos. S57b/c) from 2/– Booklet NR2

SB11 Wmk. Crown to left   65   SB11a Wmk. Crown to right   65
    b. Comma flaw ..   ..   ..   4·00
    c. Spot right of d ..   ..   3·75
    d. Rose flaw ..   ..   ..   3·00

Listed Booklet Varieties

SB10*ab*
Bottom left stamp of pane
(2½d. to right)

SB10*ac*

SB11*b*
Right stamp of pane

SB11*c*
Left stamp of pane

SB11*d*
Upper right stamp
of pane

Booklet Cylinder Numbers

Panes of six (21-row cylinders)

Cream paper				Cream or whiter paper				
Cyl. No.		No dot	Dot	Cyl. No.			No dot	Dot
E4* With erroneous dot	..	90	65	E12	.. .. ..	..	75	75
E4* No dot with smudge	..	1·00	†	E12 T	.. .. ..	..	75	75
E4* Smudge removed ..	..	80	†					
E4 T* With erroneous dot	..	90	70					
E4 T* No dot with smudge	..	1·00	†					
E4 T* Smudge removed ..	..	80	†					
E11	..	65	65					
E11 T	..	65	65					

*For explanation see notes below booklet panes of No. S1.

Panes of four

In the 2/– Booklets (N4/20) the cylinder numbers were usually trimmed off, but the following exists from the Holiday Booklet NR2 on whiter paper:—

Cyl. No.	Value	No dot	Dot
E14	½d.	} 4·00	4·00
J15	2½d.		

Coils

All have watermark upright and cylinder numbers A1, A2 and A3 were used for cream paper printings and numbers A3 and A4 for whiter paper issues.

Vertical delivery printed in continuous reels. Cream or whiter paper.

Code No.	Number in roll	Face value
AA	240	10/–
G	480	£1
W	960	£2
D	960	£2
Y	1920	£4

Sideways delivery made up from sheets with sheet margin joins. Cream paper

P	480	£1

Sheet Markings

All the same as for No. S1.

Cat. No.	S.G. No.	Shades	Unused	Used

1959 (JUNE 15). WITH GRAPHITE LINES, TYPE S8. WATERMARK CROWNS

This was only issued in booklets and coils.

S7   587   Orange-red   75   75
   a. Watermark inverted (4.8.59)   1·00   1·00

Booklet Panes of Six

From 3/– Booklets MG1/6 and 5/– Booklets HG1/3
SB12 Watermark upright   3·75   SB12a Watermark inverted   5·00

Booklet Cylinder Numbers

Panes of six (21-row cylinder)

Cyl. No.					No dot	Dot	Cyl. No.				No dot	Dot
E4..	..	..	..	..	6·00	6·00	E4 T	..	..	..	6·00	6·00

Coils

All have watermark upright, sheet cylinder 4 having been converted to a 21-row cylinder.

Code No.	Number in roll	Face value
W	960	£2
Y	1920	£4

Quantity Issued   4,181,840

1959 (NOVEMBER 18). PHOSPHOR-GRAPHITE ISSUE. WMK. ST. EDWARD'S CROWN

This has two graphite lines, Type **S8,** on the back and two phosphor bands on the front, which react green under the lamp.

S8   599   Orange-red   1·00   1·00
   a. E flaw (R.17/9)   ..   ..   6·00
   b. Extra stem to thistle (R.18/10)   6·00

These varieties are as illustrated for Nos. S3*a/b.*

Cylinder Numbers (Blocks of Six)

Single pane cylinder

Cyl. No.	Perf. Type		No dot
5	B	..	5·00
5	C	..	5·00

Sheet Markings

All the same as for No. S3

Quantity Issued   707,040

1960 (JUNE 22). TWO PHOSPHOR BANDS REACTING GREEN. WMK. CROWNS

The bands were applied in photogravure.

S9   —   Orange-red   40   30
   a. Watermark inverted (14.8.60)   50   50 | *c.* R flaw (Coil, Roll 11) ..   ..   1·00
   b. Shamrock flaw (Coil, Roll 11)..   1·00 | *d.* Coil join (vert. pair) ..   ..   1·25

For illustrations of Nos. S9*b/c* see Nos. S2*g/h.*

Cylinder Numbers (Blocks of Six)

Perforation Type B (no dot) and C (dot)

Cyl. No.					No dot	Dot
1	..	..	..	..	3·00	3·00

Minor Constant Sheet Flaws

Minimum price as singles: 75p

Cyl. 1   4/4   White smudge at left of upper left rose (Th. B1)
        5/6   White spot at end of stem of upper right shamrock (Th. C6), rather faint on this cylinder
       13/1   Large concealed retouch on Queen's cheek (Th. D3–4)
Cyl. 1.   1/10   Orange spot at top right of centre cross in crown (Th. A–B3–4), later retouched
      19/12   White bulge on upper right sepel of lower right rose (Th. E5–6)

Booklet Panes of Six
From 3/- Booklets MP1/3 and MP6 and 5/- Booklet HP1
SB13 Watermark upright   2·00   SB13a Watermark inverted   2·50

Booklet Cylinder Numbers
Panes of six (21-row cylinder)

Cyl. No.				No dot	Dot		Cyl. No.					No dot	Dot
E11	..	..	..	4·00	4·00		E11 T	..	..	..	..	4·00	4·00

Coils
All have watermark upright and cylinder number A3 was used in double panes.
Vertical delivery printed in continuous reels

Code No.	Number in roll	Face value
G	480	10/-
W	960	£2
Y	1920	£4

Vertical delivery. Made up from sheets with sheet margin joins.

Y	1920	£4

Sheet Markings
Guide holes: Boxed opposite rows 14/14, at left (no dot) or right (dot)
Black bar: This occurs by the marginal arrows opposite rows 10/11, at left (no dot) or right (dot)
Others: As given in General Notes

Cat. No.	S.G. No.		Shades	Unused	Used

1961 (JUNE 5).† TWO PHOSPHOR BANDS REACTING BLUE. WMK. CROWNS
The bands were applied in photogravure.

A. Cream Paper
S10   —   Orange-red   8   8

a. Watermark inverted (3.61) ..	30	30
b. Watermark Crown to left		
(14.7.61)	50	50
c. Watermark Crown to right ..	50	50

d. Single broad band at right ..	25
e. Shamrock flaw (Coil, Roll 11)..	35
f. R flaw (Coil, Roll 11)	35

B. Whiter Paper (21 June 1965)†
S11   —   Orange-red   5   5

a. Watermark Crown to left		
(15.8.62)	40	40
b. Watermark Crown to right ..	40	40

c. Watermark inverted (3.6.63)..	20	20
d. Shamrock flaw (Coil, Roll 11) ..	25	
e. R flaw (Coil, Roll 11)	30	

For illustrations of Nos. S10e and S11d, see No. S2g and for Nos. S10f and S11e see
No. S2h.

Cylinder Numbers (Blocks of Six)
Perforation Type A

	Cream paper				Whiter paper		
Cyl. No.		No dot	Dot	Cyl. No.		No dot	Dot
1		60	60	1		50	50

Minor Constant Sheet Flaws
Minimum price as singles: 20p
As for No. S9

Booklet Panes of Six
Cream or whiter paper
From 3/- Booklets MP4/5, MP6a and MP7/38, and 5/- Booklets HP2/25
SB14 Watermark upright   40   SB14a Watermark inverted   1·00

Booklet Panes of Four
Cream or whiter paper. Sideways watermark
From 2/- Booklets NP1/13
SB15 Wmk. Crown to left   1·20   SB15a Wmk. Crown to right   1·50

Booklet Cylinder Numbers

Panes of six (21-row cylinder)

Cyl. No.				No dot	Dot		Cyl. No.				No dot	Dot
E12	..	..	..	1·00	1·00		E12 T	..	..	..	1·00	1·00

Panes of four (single pane cylinder)

In the 2/– Booklets the cylinder numbers were usually trimmed off.

Coils

All have watermark upright and cylinder number A3 was used in double panes.
Vertical delivery printed in continuous reels. Cream or whiter paper.

Code No.	Number in roll	Face value
G	480	10/–
W	960	£2
Y	1920	£4

Sheet Markings

As for No. S9 except that there are no black bars

Cat. No.	S.G. No.	Shades	Unused	Used

1965 (AUGUST 13). TWO 8 mm. PHOSPHOR BANDS REACTING VIOLET. WMK. CROWNS

The bands were applied typographically on the sheets and in photogravure on the coils.

S12	610			Orange-red		8	8
a.	Typo. bands omitted ..	..	50				
b.	Bands applied photo. (15.10.65)	5	5	d.	d joined to shamrock (Coil, Roll 11)		65
c.	Large dot by daffodil (Coil, Roll 4)		50	e.	R flaw (Coil, Roll 11)		60

No S12a can be distinguished from a non-phosphor stamp by the fact that this shows a clear impression of the typo. plate with no reaction under the lamp.
For illustrations of Nos. S12c/d, see Nos. S5f/g and for No. S12e, see No. S2h.

Cylinder Numbers (Blocks of Six)

Perforation Type A

Cyl. No.						No dot	Dot
1	..	..	..	..	..	60	6·00

Minor Constant Sheet Flaws

Minimum price as singles: 20p
As for No. S9

Coils

All have the watermark upright and it is believed a new double pane cylinder number A4 was used.

Vertical delivery printed in continuous reels

Code No.	Number in roll	Face value
G	480	10/–
W	960	£2
Y	1920	£4

Sheet Markings

All the same as for No. S1

1953–67. 1d. Ultramarine, Type S1

Cat. No.	S.G. No.		Shades	Unused	Used

1953 (AUGUST 31). WATERMARK TUDOR CROWN, TYPE W.22

S13   516   Ultramarine   5   5
  a. Watermark inverted (3.54) .. 35   20
  b. Coil join (horiz. pair) 35   *d.* Cancelled two vert. black bars
  c. Shamrock flaw (Cyl. 2, R.18/2) 2·75   (P.O.T.S.)   8

Listed Variety

White flaw on top shamrock, later retouched on St. Edward's Crown watermark

S13*c*, SB18*a*,
S14*d*, SB24*a*

Cylinder Numbers (Blocks of Six)

Perforation Type B (no dot) and C (dot)			Perforation Type A			
Cyl. No.	No dot	Dot	Cyl. No.		No dot	Dot
1	35	50	2		3·00*	75

Minor Constant Sheet Flaws

Minimum price as singles: 50p

Cyl. 2.   19/8   White flaw between thistle stem and lower right rose (Th. E6)

Booklet Panes of Six

From 5/– Booklets H7/16

SB16 Watermark upright   25   SB16a Watermark inverted   1·75

Booklet Panes of Four

From 1/– Booklet K1 for use in "E" machines

SB17 Watermark upright   15   SB17a Watermark inverted   1·10
  No cylinder numbers were used.

Booklet Pane of Two

From 1/– Booklet E1 for use in experimental "D" machines

SB18 Watermark upright   12
  a. Shamrock flaw (as on No. S13*c*)   2·75
  Made up from vertical rows 1 and 2 from sheets.

Booklet Panes with Printed Labels

Panes of six comprising three stamps and three labels
"MINIMUM INLAND PRINTED PAPER RATE 1½d." from 2/6 Booklet F15
SB19 Watermark upright   10·00   SB19a Watermark inverted   10·00
"PLEASE POST EARLY IN THE DAY" from 2/6 Booklets F16/25
SB20 Watermark upright   1·25   SB20a Watermark inverted   1·25
  b. Modified setting   ..   2·00   *ab.* Modified setting   ..   ..   2·00
  In the modified setting the distance between "IN THE" is 1 mm. and this comes from Booklet F25 only. The normal spacing is 1½ mm.
"PACK YOUR PARCELS SECURELY" (1st label), "ADDRESS YOUR LETTERS CORRECTLY" (2nd label) and "AND POST EARLY IN THE DAY" (3rd label) from 2/6 Booklets F26/34
SB21 Watermark upright   1·25   SB21a Watermark inverted   1·25

Booklet Cylinder Numbers

Panes of six from 5/– Booklets SB16

Cyl. No.		No dot	Dot
F4		2·00	2·00

Panes with printed labels from 2/6 Booklets

Cyl. No.	Cat. No.	No dot	Dot	Cyl. No.	Cat. No.	No dot	Dot
F5	SB19	.. †	25·00	F6	SB20	.. 3·00	3·00
F6	SB19	..15·00	15·00	F6	SB20*b*	.. 4·00	4·00
				F6	SB21	.. 3·00	3·00

Panes of two (from sheets)

1	.. .. 1·00	1·00	2	.. .. 1·00	1·00

Coils

Single pane cylinder B1 was used for the Tudor Crown watermark. The watermark is always upright.

Vertical delivery printed in continuous reels

	Code No.	Number in roll	Face value
	AB	240	£1
	E	480	£2
	X	960	£4
	Z	1920	£8

Sideways delivery made up from sheets with sheet margin joins

	O	480	£2

Sheet Markings

Guide holes: Boxed opposite rows 14/15, at left (no dot) or right (dot)
Others: As given in General Notes

Cat. No.	S.G. No.		Shades		Unused	Used

1955 (SEPTEMBER 19).† WATERMARK ST. EDWARD'S CROWN, TYPE W.23

S14	541	Ultramarine	5	5

a. Tête-bêche (horiz. pr.) .. 75·00
b. Watermark inverted (9.55) .. 15   15
c. Coil join (horiz. pair) .. 35   *e.* Cancelled two vert. black bars
d. Shamrock flaw (Cyl. 2, R.18/2) 2·10   (P.O.T.S.) 8

For illustration of No. S14*d* see No. S13*c.*

†The earliest issue was from E coils in August 1955.

Cylinder Numbers (Blocks of Six)

Perforation Type A | Perforation Type B (no dot) or C (dot)

Cyl. No.				No dot	Dot	Cyl. No.				No dot	Dot
1 ..	..	..	..	40	40	4 ..	..	..	..	50	50
2 ..	..	..	..	2·25*	40						
4 ..	..	..	..	35	35						

Minor Constant Sheet Flaws

Minimum price as singles: 50p

Cyl. 2   19/8   White flaw between thistle stem and lower right rose (Th. E6)
Cyl. 4   11/9   Blue spot in E of POSTAGE
       19/8   As cyl. 2

Booklet Panes of Six

From 3/– Booklets M1/9 and 5/– Booklets H17/36

SB22 Watermark upright	25	SB22a Watermark inverted	75

Booklet Panes of Four

From 1/– Booklet K2 for use in "E" machines and 2/– Booklet N1

SB23 Watermark upright	15	SB23a Watermark inverted	45

No cylinder numbers were used.

Booklet Pane of Two

From 1/– Booklet E2 for use in experimental "D" machines

SB24 Watermark upright	12

a. Shamrock flaw (as on No. S14*d*) 2·10

Made up from vertical rows 1 and 2 from sheets.

Booklet Panes with Printed Labels

Panes of six comprising three stamps and three labels
"PACK YOUR PARCELS SECURELY" (1st label), "ADDRESS YOUR LETTERS CORRECTLY" (2nd label) and "AND POST EARLY IN THE DAY" (third label) from 2/6 Booklets F34/52

SB25 Watermark upright	1·25	SB25a Watermark inverted	1·25

Booklet Cylinder Numbers

Panes of six

Cyl. No.		Cat. No	No dot	Dot	Cyl. No.		Cat. No.	No dot	Dot
F3 ..	..	SB22 ..	.. 1·50	1·50	F6 ..	..	SB25 ..	.. 2·00	2·00
F3 T	..	SB22 ..	.. 1·50	1·50	F9 ..	..	SB25 ..	.. 2·00	2·00
F4 ..	..	SB22 ..	.. 1·00	1·00					

Panes of two

1 ..	..	..	..	..	1·00	1·00

Cylinder F3 contained 21 rows so that cylinder numbers adjoin either the top (T) or the bottom row. It was used in all 3/– Booklets H31/36. The others are all 20-row cylinders. F4 was used for 5/– Booklets H17/30, F6 for the 2/6 Booklets F34/40 and part of F41/52 and F9 for 2/6 Booklets F41/52.

Coils

Single pane cylinder B1 was again used for the St. Edward's Crown watermark. The watermark is always upright.

Vertical delivery printed in continuous reels

Code No.	Number in roll	Face value
AB	240	£1
E	480	£2
B	960	£4
X	960	£4
Z	1920	£8

Sideways delivery made up from sheets with sheet margin joins

O	480	£2

Sheet Markings

All the same as for No. S13

Cat. No.	S.G. No.	Shades	Unused	Used

1957 (NOVEMBER 19). WITH GRAPHITE LINES, TYPE S8. WMK. ST. EDWARD'S CROWN

S15	562	Ultramarine	15	12

a. Daffodil stem flaw (Cyls. 7 & 8, R.15/2) .. .. .. 1·25	
b. Extra stop (Coil, Roll 2) .. 1·50	d. White flaw on shamrock leaf
c. Stop omitted (Coil, Roll 3) .. 1·75	(Coil, Roll 8) .. .. .. 1·75

Listed Varieties

S15a, S19a	S15b	S15c	S15d

Cylinder Numbers (Blocks of Six)

Single pane cylinders

Cyl. No.	Perf. Type	No dot
7	B	.. 1·00
7	C	.. 1·00
8	B	.. 1·75
8	C	.. 1·75

Coils

Single pane cylinder B2 was used and all have the watermark upright.

Vertical delivery printed in continuous reels

Code No.	Number in roll	Face value
E	480	£2
X	960	£4
Z	1920	£8

Sheet Markings

Guide holes: Boxed opposite rows 14/15, at both sides and unboxed opposite rows 1 and 7/8 at both sides
Others: As given in General Notes

Quantity Issued   29,620,080

Cat. No.	S.G. No.	Shades	Unused	Used

1959 (MARCH 24).†   WATERMARK CROWNS, TYPE W.24

A. Cream Paper

S16   —   Ultramarine   5   5

- *a.* Imperf. (vert. pair from coil) .. £150
- *b.* Imperf. pane* £400
- *c.* Part perf. pane* .. .. 50·00
- *d.* Watermark inverted (11.58) .. 15   15

- *e.* Watermark Crown to left (26.5.61)   12   12
- *f.* Watermark Crown to right ..   12   12
- *g.* Daffodil flaw (Cyl. 5, R.10/11)..   85
- *h.* Coil join (horiz. pair)   30

B. Whiter Paper (7 May 1962)

S17   571   Ultramarine   5   5

- *a.* Watermark Crown to left (5.6.62) 10   10
- *b.* Watermark Crown to right ..   10   10
- *c.* Watermark inverted (29.7.62)   5   5

- *d.* Daffodil flaw (Cyl. 5, R.10/11)   75
- *e.* Coil join (horiz. pair)   30

*Booklet errors—See General Notes.

Listed Booklet Variety

S16*g*, S17*d*, S20*b*, S21*e*, S22*d*, S23*e*, S24*d*

Cylinder Numbers (Blocks of Six)

A. Cream Paper

Perforation Type A

Cyl. No.					No dot	Dot
4	..	..	..	..	35	35
5	..	..	..	..	35	35

Perforation Type B (no dot) and C (dot)

Cyl. No.					No dot	Dot
4	..	..	..	..	40	40

B. Whiter Paper

Perforation Type A

					No dot	Dot
4	..	..	..	..	30	30
5	..	..	..	..	30	30

Perforation Type F (L)*

					No dot	Dot
4	..	..	..	..	50	50

Minor Constant Sheet Flaws

Minimum price as singles: 40p

Cyl. 4   11/9   Blue spot on E of POSTAGE
         19/8   White flaw between thistle stem and lower right rose (Th. E6)
Cyl. 5   3/5   Dark patch below bottom right rose (Th. E5)
         19/8   White flaw between thistle stem and lower right rose (Th. E6)
Cyl. 5.   1/12   Small white flaw on top of top left daffodil (Th. A2)

Booklet Panes of Six
Cream or whiter paper
From 3/– Booklets M9b/c, M10/74, 4/6 Booklets L59/65, 5/– Booklets H35b/c, H36a and H37/74 and 10/– Booklets X1/14

SB26 Watermark upright	25	SB26a Watermark inverted	25

Booklet Panes of Four
Cream paper
From 1/– Booklet K3 for use in "E" machines and 2/– Booklets N2/3

SB27 Watermark upright	15	SB27a Watermark inverted	45

No cylinder numbers were used.
Cream or whiter paper. Sideways watermark
From 2/– Booklets N4/20

SB28 Wmk. Crown to left	35	SB28a Wmk. Crown to right	35

Se-tenant Panes of Four
Whiter paper. Sideways watermark
Pair of 1d. with pair of 3d. (Nos. S71a/b) from 2/– Booklets N21/27

SB29 Wmk. Crown to left with 3d. at right	60	SB29a Wmk. Crown to right with 3d. at right	60
b. Wmk. Crown to left with 3d. at left	60	ab. Wmk. Crown to right with 3d. at left	60
		ac. Do. with R flaw	1·50

Listed Booklet Variety

Flaw on P which appears as R and occurs on bottom right stamp of pane with 3d. at left

SB29ac, SB34ac,
SB36ac, SB38ad,
SB38af

Booklet Cylinder Numbers
Panes of six (21-row cylinders)

	Cream paper			Cream or whiter paper		
Cyl. No.		No dot	Dot	Cyl. No.	No dot	Dot
F3		75	75	F10	75	75
F3 T		75	75	F10 T	75	75

Panes of Four (20-row cylinder)
In the 2/– Booklets (N4/20) the cylinder numbers were usually trimmed off, but the following exists from the *se-tenant* pane booklets on whiter paper:—

Cyl. No.	Value	No dot	Dot
F13	1d.	} 2·50	2·50
K22	3d.		

Coils
Double pane cylinder B1 was used for cream paper printings and cylinder B3 was used for both cream and whiter paper issues with the watermark always upright.
Vertical delivery printed in continuous reels. Cream or whiter paper

Code No.	Number in roll	Face value
AB	240	£1
E	480	£2
B	960	£4
X	960	£4
Z	1920	£8

Sideways delivery made up from sheets with sheet margin joins. Cream or whiter paper

O	480	£2

Sheet Markings
Guide holes: Boxed opposite rows 14/15, at left (no dot) or right (dot) but in the case of perforation Type F (L)* the boxes remain on both panes but the holes are unboxed above and below the eighth vertical row on the no dot pane only
Others: As given in General Notes

Cat. No.   S.G. No.   Shades   Unused Used

1958 (DECEMBER 18). WITH GRAPHITE LINES, TYPE S8. WATERMARK CROWNS

This was only issued in booklets and coils.

S18	588						(1) Ultramarine (coils)	25	25
a.	Watermark inverted (4.8.59) ..	50	50				(2) Bright ultramarine (booklets)	35	35
b.	Two lines at left (7.61) ..	30	30						
c.	Two lines at right	30	30	e.	One line at right			40	40
d.	One line at left	40	40	f.	Three lines			50	50

The misplaced graphite lines (varieties b/f) came from the Z coils. They were printed after the graphite line experiment had ended to use up residual stock of graphite-lined paper which had been prepared for booklets.

Booklet Panes of Six

From 3/– Booklets MG1/6 and 5/– Booklets HG1/3

SB30 Watermark upright   1.25   SB30a Watermark inverted   2·50

Booklet Cylinder Numbers

Panes of six (21-row cylinder)

Cyl. No.				No dot	Dot	Cyl. No.				No dot	Dot
F3 ..	..	..	..	.. 3·50	3·50	F3 T	..	..	..	.. 3·50	3·50

Coils

Double pane cylinder B3 was used only for the Z coils with misplaced lines (issued July 1961); other coils were from sheet cylinder 7 converted to 21 rows. The watermark is always upright.

Vertical delivery printed in continuous reels

Code No.	Number in roll	Face value
E	480	£2
X	960	£4
Z	1920	£8

Quantity Issued   12,448,880 including 3,400 Z coils with misplaced lines

1959 (NOVEMBER 18). PHOSPHOR-GRAPHITE ISSUE. WMK. ST. EDWARD'S CROWN

This has two graphite lines, Type S8, on the back and two phosphor bands on the front, which react green under the lamp.

S19	600	Ultramarine	1·00	1·00
a.	Daffodil stem flaw (Cyl. 8, R.15/2) .. .. .. 3·50			

For illustration of No. S19a, see No. S15a.

Cylinder Numbers (Blocks of Six)

Single pane cylinder

Cyl. No.	Perf. Type	No dot
8	B	.. 6·00
8	C	.. 6·00

Sheet Markings

All the same as for No. S15.

Quantity Issued   709,680

1960 (JUNE 22). TWO PHOSPHOR BANDS REACTING GREEN. WMK. CROWNS

The bands were applied in photogravure.

S20	—	Ultramarine	50	40
a.	Watermark inverted (14.8.60)	75	65
b.	Daffodil flaw (Cyl. 5, R.10/11)	1·00	

For illustration of No. S20b, see Nos. S16g.

Cylinder Numbers (Blocks of Six)

Perforation Type B (no dot) and C (dot)

Cyl. No.					No dot	Dot
5	..	..	..	..	.. 3·00	3·00

Minor Constant Sheet Flaws

Minimum price as singles: £1

Cyl. 5　　3/5　Dark patch below bottom right rose (Th. E5)
　　　　　19/8　White flaw between thistle stem and lower right rose (Th. E6)
Cyl. 5.　1/12　Small white flaw on top of top left daffodil (Th. A2)

Booklet Panes of Six

From 3/– Booklets MP1/3 and MP6 and 5/– Booklet HP1

SB31 Watermark upright　　　2·50　　　　　SB31a Watermark inverted　　4·00

Booklet Cylinder Numbers

Panes of six (21-row cylinder)

Cyl. No.					No dot	Dot	Cyl. No.					No dot	Dot
F3 ..	..	..	..	..	4·00	4·00	F3 T ..	..	..	..	..	4·00	4·00

Coils

Double pane cylinder B3 was used with the watermark always upright.

Vertical delivery printed in continuous reels

Code No.	Number in roll	Face value
E	480	£2
X	960	£4
Z	1920	£8

Sheet Markings

Guide holes: Boxed opposite rows 14/15, at left (no dot) or right (dot)
Black bar: This occurs by the marginal arrows opposite rows 10/11, at left (no dot) or right (dot)
Others: As given in General Notes

Cat. No.	S.G. No.	Shades	Unused	Used

1961 (JUNE 5). TWO PHOSPHOR BANDS REACTING BLUE. WMK. CROWNS

The bands were applied in photogravure.

A. Cream Paper

S21　　　　—　　　　　　　　　　　Ultramarine　　　　　　8　　8
　a. Watermark inverted (3.61) ..　30　25
　b. Watermark Crown to left
　　　(14.7.61)　..　..　..　30　25　　*d.* Single broad band at right　..　25
　c. Watermark Crown to right ..　30　25　　*e.* Daffodil flaw (Cyl. 5, R.10/11)　1·00

B. Whiter Paper (21 May 1965)†

S22　　　　—　　　　　　　　　　　Ultramarine　　　　　　8　　8
　a. Watermark Crown to left
　　　(15.8.62)　..　..　..　25　20　　*c.* Watermark inverted (3.6.63)　25　20
　b. Watermark Crown to right ..　25　20　　*d.* Daffodil flaw (Cyl. 5, R.10/11)　85
For illustrations of Nos. S21*e* and S22*d*, see No. S16*g*.

Cylinder Numbers (Blocks of Six)

A. Cream paper
Perforation Type B (no dot) and C (dot)

Cyl. No.					No dot	Dot
5 ..	..	..	..	..	60	60

B. Whiter paper
Perforation Type A

Cyl. No.					No dot	Dot
4 ..	..	..	..	..	50	50
5	..	..	..	..	50	50

Minor Constant Sheet Flaws

Minimum price as singles: 60p

Cyl. 4　　11/9　Blue spot on E of POSTAGE
　　　　　19/8　White flaw between thistle stem and lower right rose (Th. E6)
Cyl. 5　　3/5　Dark patch below bottom right rose (Th. E5)
　　　　　19/8　As for cyl. 4
Cyl. 5.　1/12　Small white flaw on top of top left daffodil (Th. A2)

Booklet Panes of Six
Cream or whiter paper
From 3/– Booklets MP4/5, MP6a and MP7/38, 4/6 Booklets LP32/3, LP34 or LP35 and
5/– Booklets HP2/25

SB32 Watermark upright	40	SB32a Watermark inverted	1.25

Booklet Panes of Four
Cream or whiter paper. Sideways watermark
From 2/– Booklets NP1/13

SB33 Wmk. Crown to left	75	SB33a Wmk. Crown to right	75

Se-tenant Panes of Four
Whiter paper. Sideways watermark
Pair of 1d. with pair of 3d. (Nos. S77b/e) from 2/– Booklets NP14/15 and NP16

SB34 Wmk. Crown to left with
    3d. at right   ..   ..   1·25
  b. Wmk. Crown to left with 3d.
    at left   ..   ..   1·25

SB34a Wmk. Crown to right
    with 3d. at right   ..   1·25
  ab. Wmk. Crown to right with 3d.
    at left   ..   ..   ..   1·25
    ac. Do. with R flaw   ..   2·25

For illustration of No. SB34ac, see No. SB29ac.

Booklet Cylinder Numbers
Panes of six (21-row cylinders)

	Cream paper				Cream or whiter paper		
Cyl. No.		No dot	Dot	Cyl. No.	..	No dot	Dot
F3	.. ..	1·50	1·50	F10	.. ..	1·50	1·50
F3 T	.. ..	1·50	1·50	F10 T	.. ..	1·50	1·50

Panes of four (20-row cylinder)
In the 2/– Booklets the cylinder numbers were usually trimmed off, but the following
exists from the se-tenant pane booklets on whiter paper:—

Cyl. No.	Value	No dot	Dot
F13	1d.	}	
K22	3d.	4·00	4·00

Coils
Double pane cylinder B3 was used with the watermark always upright.
Vertical delivery printed in continuous reels. Cream or whiter paper

Code No.	Number in roll	Face value
E	480	£2
X	960	£4
Z	1920	£8

Sheet Markings
As for No. S20 except that there are no black bars

Cat. No.	S.G. No.	Shades	Unused	Used

1965 (AUGUST 13). TWO 8 mm. PHOSPHOR BANDS REACTING VIOLET. WMK. CROWNS
The bands were originally applied typographically on sheets and later in photogravure
on sheets, coils and booklets.

S23   —   Ultramarine   8   8
  a. Bands applied photo. (1966) ..   8   8
  b. Watermark inverted (9.65) ..   20   20
  c. Watermark Crown to left
    (10.65)   15   15   d. Watermark Crown to right ..   15   15
                                      e. Daffodil flaw (Cyl. 5, R.10/11)   75
For illustration of No. S23e, see No. S16g.

Cylinder Numbers (Blocks of Six)
Perforation Type A

	Bands typo.				Bands photo.		
Cyl. No.		No dot	Dot	Cyl. No.		No dot	Dot
5 ..	.. ..	3·50	3·50	5 ..	.. ..	50	50

Minor Constant Sheet Flaws

Minimum price as singles: 60p

Cyl. 5   3/5   Dark patch below bottom right rose (Th. E5)
       19/8   White flaw between thistle stem and lower right rose (Th. E6)

Cyl. 5.   1/12   Small white flaw on top of top left daffodil (Th. A2)

Booklet Panes of Six

From 4/6 Booklets LP33a, LP34a and LP35a/38 and 10/– Booklet XP1

SB35 Watermark upright   40   SB35a Watermark inverted   1·00

Se-tenant Booklet Panes of Four

Sideways watermark

Pair of 1d. with pair of 3d. (1 side 8 mm. violet band, Nos. S78b/e) from 2/– Booklets NP15a, NP16a, NP17/23.

SB36 Wmk. Crown to left	SB36a Wmk. Crown to right	
with 3d. at right .. 65	with 3d. at right 65	
b. Wmk. Crown to left with 3d.	*ab.* Wmk. Crown to right with 3d.	
at left 65	at left 65	
	ac. Do. with R flaw .. 1·50	

For illustration of No. SB36ac, see No. SB29ac.

The following illustration shows how the *se-tenant* stamps with one phosphor band on 3d. are printed and the arrows indicate where the guillotine falls. The result gives 1d. stamps with two bands and 3d. stamps with one band, either at left or right.

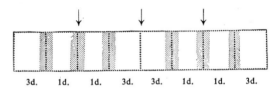

3d.   1d.   1d.   3d.   3d.   1d.   1d.   3d.

Booklet Cylinder Numbers

Panes of six (21-row cylinder)

Cyl. No.				No dot	Dot	Cyl. No.				No dot	Dot
F10	..	..	..	.. 75	75	F10 T	..	..	..	.. 75	75

Se-tenant panes of four (20-row cylinder)

Cyl. No.	Value	No dot
F13	1d. }	3·00
K22	3d. }	

Coils

Double pane cylinder B3 was used with the watermark always upright.

Vertical delivery printed in continuous reels

Code No.	Number in roll	Face value
E	480	£2
X	960	£4
Z	1920	£8

Sheet Markings

Guide holes: Not known
Others: As given in General Notes

Cat. No.	S.G. No.		Shades	Unused	Used

1967 (EARLY).   TWO 9·5 mm. PHOSPHOR BANDS REACTING VIOLET. WMK. CROWNS

The bands were applied in photogravure only.

S24   611

a. Watermark inverted (2.67)   ..   10   5
b. Watermark Crown to left
   (15.9.67)   10   8
For illustration of No. S24*d*, see No. S16*g*.

Ultramarine   5   5

c. Watermark Crown to right   ..   10   8
d. Daffodil flaw (Cyl. 5, R.10/11)   60

Cylinder Numbers (Blocks of Six)

Perforation Type F (L)*

Cyl. No.						No dot	Dot
4 ..	..	..	..	..	..	35	35

Perforation Type A

Cyl. No.						No dot	Dot
5 ..	..	..	..	..	..	35	35

Minor Constant Sheet Flaws

Minimum price as singles: 50p

Cyl. 4   11/9   Blue spot on E of POSTAGE
        19/8   White flaw between thistle stem and lower right rose (Th. E6)
Cyl. 5   3/5   Dark patch below bottom right rose (Th. E5)
        19/8   As for Cyl. 4
Cyl. 5.   1/12   Small white flaw on top of top left daffodil (Th. A2)

Booklet Panes of Six

From 4/6 Booklets LP38*a*/44 and 10/– Booklets XP1*a*, XP2/3
SB37 Watermark upright   25   SB37*a* Watermark inverted   50

Se-tenant Booklet Panes of Four

Sideways watermark

Pair of 1d. with pair of 3d. (two 9·5 mm. violet bands, Nos. S80/*a*) from 2/– Booklets NP23*a*/26

SB38 Wmk. Crown to left
   with 3d. at right   1·25
b. Error, 1 band on 3d. ..   ..   1·50
c. Wmk. Crown to left with 3d.
   at left ..   ..   1·25
e. Error, 1 band on 3d. ..   ..   1·50

SB38*a* Wmk. Crown at right
   with 3d. at right   1·25
ab. Error, 1 band on 3d. ..   ..   1·50
ac. Wmk. Crown to right with 3d.
   at left ..   ..   1·25
ad. Do. with R flaw   ..   ..   2·00
ae. Error, 1 band on 3d. ..   ..   1·50
af. Do. with R flaw   ..   ..   4·00

Part of the October 1967 2/– Booklets NP23/4 had 8 mm. bands and part 9·5 mm. bands and of the latter some had only a single line band on the 3d. value (NP23*a*), at right or left as listed above.   As these bands are applied across the perforations and are liable to shift, it is not possible to distinguish the 3d. one-band errors 9·5 mm. bands from the 8 mm. bands of Nos. SB36, etc. *in singles,* and hence these are not listed as varieties under the 3d. value.

For illustrations of the R flaw, see No. SB29*ac.*

Booklet Cylinder Numbers

Panes of six (21-row cylinder)

Cyl. No.					No dot	Dot
F10..	..	..	..	..	75	75

Cyl. No.					No dot	Dot
F10 T	..	..	..	..	75	75

Se-tenant panes of four (20-row cylinder)

Cyl. No.	Value		No dot	Dot
F13	1d. ..⎫			
K22	3d. ..⎭		2·00	2·00

Coils

Double pane cylinder B3 was used with the watermark always upright.

Vertical delivery printed in continuous reels

Code No.	Number in roll	Face value
E	480	£2
X	960	£4
Z	1920	£8

Sheet Markings

Guide holes: Boxed opposite rows 14/15, at left (no dot) or right (dot) but in the case of peforation Type F (L)* the boxes remain on both panes but the holes are unboxed above and double-boxed below the eighth vertical row in the no dot pane only
Others: As given in General Notes

1952–65. 1½d. Green, Type S1

Cat. No.	S.G. No.	Shades	Unused	Used

1952 (DECEMBER 5). WATERMARK TUDOR CROWN, TYPE W.22

S25	517			(1) Green	8 5
a.	Imperf. pane* £200			(2) Deep green	40 10
b.	Watermark inverted (5.53) ..	30	25	h. Flaw over O of POSTAGE	
c.	Watermark sideways (15.10.54)	20	20	(Sideways coil, Roll 2) ..	1·50
d.	Butterfly flaw (Cyl. 6., R.19/1) 75·00			i. Dot over rose (Sideways coil,	
e.	Flaw on daffodil stem (Cyl. 9.,			Roll 10)	1 60
	R.18/1)	2·00		j. Daffodil flaw (Sideways coil,	
f.	Extra dot (Cyl. 13., R.17/10) ..	1·25		Roll 8)	1·25
g.	Rose and thistle joined at right			k. Cancelled two vert. black bars	
	(Cyl. 13., R.19/1)	1·25		(P.O.T.S.)	8

*Booklet error.—This pane of six stamps is *completely* imperf. (cf. General Notes).
Stamps with sideways watermark are from N coils with sideways delivery.

Listed Varieties

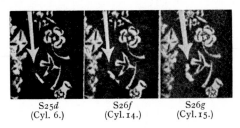

S25d	S26f	S26g
(Cyl. 6.)	(Cyl. 14.)	(Cyl. 15.)

Of the first thirteen cylinders used, numbered 1 to 15 (with the exception of Nos. 3 and 7 which were not used), the following is a record of the development of the above illustrated flaws:

Cyl. 1. No flaws

Cyls. 2., 4. and 5. Disturbed background

Cyl. 6. This is found in two states. One with disturbed background and the other with a short white flaw as illustrated, the latter being the first of the clear defects in this position

Cyls. 8. to 13. Disturbed background

Cyl. 14. Found in two states, one with disturbed background and the other with a long white flaw as illustrated

Cyl. 15. Also found in two states, one with disturbed background and the other with a larger white flaw as illustrated, the latter only occurring on the St. Edward's Crown watermark

The most plausible explanation of the development of this flaw is that prior to the making of cylinder 2, the multipositive was damaged and imperfectly retouched with the result that cylinders 2, 4 and 5 show an uneven background. Before the making of cylinder 6 the opaque retouching medium appears to have partly peeled off from the multipositive leaving a transparent area which produced the small white flaw on the stamp. This was evidently discovered during the run and the cylinder retouched with the result that we have cylinder 6 with uneven background.

The multipositive was again retouched and this time continued to be used uneventfully for cylinders 8. to 13. After this the retouching medium appears to have peeled off again before making cylinders 14. and 15., each time being discovered and retouched during the printing run. Cylinder 22. is normal, showing no trace of the flaw or a retouch.

Prices are for cylinder blocks of six.

S25e, SB41a
Price is for
cylinder block of six,
except when in
booklet pane

S25f, S26d
Later retouched on
St. Edward's Crown
watermark

S25g, S26e

Listed Varieties (contd.)

S25*h*, S26*j*　　　　　　S25*i*, S26*k*　　　　　　S25*j*, S26*l*

From sideways delivery N coils

Cylinder Numbers (Blocks of Six)

Perforation Type A									Perforation Type B (no dot) or C (dot)							
Cyl. No.					No dot	Dot		Cyl. No.					No dot	Dot
1	..	..	..	..	.. 60	60		1	..	..	..	..	.. 75	75
2	..	..	..	..	.. 60	60		2	..	..	..	..	..1·00	1·00
4	..	..	..	..	.. 60	60		6	..	..	..	..	.. 75	80
5	..	..	..	..	.. 60	60		9	..	..	..	..	.. 75	2·25*
6	..	..	..	..	.. 65	75								
8	..	..	..	..	.. 75	75								
9	..	..	..	..	.. 50	2·25*								
10	..	..	..	..	.. 60	60								
11	..	..	..	..	.. 60	60								
12	..	..	..	..	.. 60	60								
13	..	..	..	..	.. 75	1·75*								

Booklet Panes of Six

From 2/6 Booklets F1/34 and 5/– Booklets H1/16

SB39 Watermark upright　　　　40　　　　SB39a Watermark inverted　　　1·50

Booklet Panes of Four

From 1/– Booklet K1 for use in "E" machines

SB40 Watermark upright　　　　25　　　　SB40a Watermark inverted　　　90

No cylinder numbers were used.

Booklet Pane of Two

From 1/– Booklet E1 for use in experimental "D" machines

SB41 Watermark upright　　　　20

a. Flaw on daffodil stem (as on
No. S25*e*) .. .. .. 2·00

Made up from vertical rows 1 and 2 from sheets.

Booklet Cylinder Numbers

Panes of six (20-row cylinders)

Cyl. No.				No dot	Dot		Cyl. No.				No dot	Dot
G2	..	..	..	.. 2·00	2·00		G6	..	..	..	.. 3·00	3·00
G3	..	..	..	.. 2·00	2·00							

Panes of two (from sheets)

2	..	..	..	.. 1·00	1·00		9	..	..	..	.. 1·00	1·00
6	..	..	..	.. 1·00	1·00		12	..	..	..	.. 1·00	1·00

Coils

Printed in continuous reels

Double pane cylinders C1 and C2 were used for the vertical delivery coils and single pane
cylinder number C3 for the sideways delivery coils.

	Code No.	Number in roll	Face value
(a) Vertical delivery. Watermark upright			
	L	480	£3
	K	960	£6
(b) Sideways delivery. Watermark sideways			
	N	480	£3

Sheet Markings

Guide holes: Boxed opposite rows 14/15, at left (no dot) or right (dot)
Others: As given in General Notes

Cat. No.	S.G. No.		Shades	Unused	Used

1955 (OCTOBER 11).† WATERMARK ST. EDWARD'S CROWN, TYPE W.23

S26	542		(1) Green	8	5
a.	Tête-bêche (horiz. pair) ..	£300	(2) Deep green	15	8
b.	Watermark inverted (8.55) ..	25	15		
c.	Watermark sideways (7.3.56)	15	10		
d.	Extra dot (Cyl. 13., R.17/10)..	1·00			
e.	Rose and thistle joined at right		j. Flaw over O of POSTAGE		
	(Cyl. 13., R.19/1)	1·00	(Sideways coil, Roll 2) ..	1·25	
f.	Butterfly flaw (Cyl. 14., R.19/1)	7.00	k. Dot over rose (Sideways coil,		
g.	Butterfly flaw (Cyl. 15., R.19/1)	1·50	Roll 10)	1·25	
h.	Spot between rose and		l. Daffodil flaw (Sideways coil,		
	shamrock (Cyl. 15, R.20/3) ..	1·25	Roll 8)	1·25	
i.	"Rabbit's ears" (Booklet pane		m. Cancelled two vert. black bars		
	R.1/2 or 2/2)	1·00	(P.O.T.S.)	8	

Stamps with sideways watermark are from N coils with sideways delivery.

Listed Varieties

For illustrations of Nos. S26d, S26e, S26f/g and S26j/l, see Nos. S25f, S25g, S25d and S25h/j respectively.

S26h, S28e, S29e, S32b, S33e, S34d
Later retouched on Crowns Watermark.
Prices are for cylinder blocks of nine

S26i
Two white dots extending upwards from shamrock at left appearing as rabbit's ears

Cylinder Numbers (Blocks of Six)
Perforation Type A

Cyl. No.					No dot	Dot	Cyl. No.					No dot	Dot
11 ..	..	..	..	..	50	65	14 ..	..	..	..	..	50	65
13 ..	..	..	..	..	50	1·50*	15 ..	..	..	..	..	50	65

Minor Constant Sheet Flaws
Minimum price as singles: 75p
Cyl. 15. 1/4 Green dot in lower half of 1 of left ¼ (Th. G1)

Booklet Panes of Six
From 2/6 Booklets F33b and F34/52, 3/– Booklets M1/9 and 5/– Booklets H17/31

SB42 Watermark upright	40	SB42a Watermark inverted	1·25

Booklet Panes of Four
From 1/– Booklet K2 for use in "E" machines and 2/– Booklet N1

SB43 Watermark upright	25	SB43a Watermark inverted	75

No cylinder numbers were used.

Booklet Pane of Two
From 1/– Booklet E2 for use in experimental "D" machines

SB44 Watermark upright   20

Made up from vertical rows 1 and 2 from sheets.

Booklet Cylinder Numbers
Panes of six (G6 and G7 20-row cylinders, others 21-row cylinders)

Cyl. No.					No dot	Dot	Cyl. No.					No dot	Dot
G6 ..	..	..	..	..	1·25	1·25	G9 T	..	..	..	..	1·75	1·75
G7 ..	..	..	..	..	1·50	1·50	G10	..	..	..	..	2·00	2·00
G9 ..	..	..	..	..	1·75	1·75	G10 T	..	..	..	..	2·00	2·00

Panes of two (from sheets)

14	..	..	..	..	1·00	1·00

Coils

Printed in continuous reels

Double pane cylinders C1 and C2 were again used for the vertical delivery coils and single pane cylinder number C3 for the sideways delivery coil.

Code No.   Number in roll   Face value

(a) Vertical delivery. Watermark upright

L	480	£3
K	960	£6

(b) Sideways delivery. Watermark sideways

N	480	£3

Sheet Markings

All the same as for No. S25

Cat. No.	S.G. No.	Shades	Unused	Used

1957 (NOVEMBER 19). WITH GRAPHITE LINES, TYPE S8. WMK. ST. EDWARD'S CROWN

S27   563   Green   20   15
a. Both lines at left   ..   ..   —   60·00
b. Horiz. pair, one stamp with
    only one line ..   ..   .. 90·00   *d.* Green stroke below E (Cyl. 21,
c. Coil join (horiz. pair) ..   ..   1·50   R.13/8) ..   .. 1·00
Nos. S27*a/b* result from a misplacement of the graphite lines.

Listed Variety

Diagonal green stroke below middle E of REVENUE in bottom margin of stamp

S27*d*, S31*a*

Cylinder Numbers (Blocks of Six)

Single pane cylinder

Cyl. No.	Perf. Type	No dot
21	B	2·00
21	C	2·00

Coils

Sideways delivery made up from sheets with sheet margin joins

Code No.	Number in roll	Face value
N	480	£3

Sheet Markings

Guide holes: Boxed opposite rows 14/15, at both sides and unboxed opposite rows 1 and 7/8, at both sides
Others: As given in General Notes

Quantity Issued   10,506,720

Cat. No.	S.G. No.	Shades	Unused	Used

1960 (AUGUST 30).† WATERMARK CROWNS, TYPE W.24

A. Cream Paper

S28 —
a. Watermark inverted (12.58) .. 30 30
b. Watermark Crown to left (26.5.61) 40 40
c. Watermark Crown to right .. 40 40
d. Coil join (vert. pair) 35

(1) Green 8 5
(2) Deep Green 12 10

e. Spot between rose and shamrock (Cyl. 15, R.20/3) .. 1·00

B. Whiter Paper (7 May 1962)

S29 572
a. Watermark Crown to left (5.6.62) 35 35
b. Watermark Crown to right .. 35 35
c. Watermark inverted (18.9.62) 20 20
d. Coil join (horiz. pair) .. 20
e. Spot between rose and shamrock (Cyl. 15, R.20/3) .. 90

(1) Green 5 5
(2) Deep green 10 8

f. Thistle flaws (Cyl. 22, R.12/1) 75
g. Daffodil flaw (Cyl. 22., R.1/12) 75

Listed Varieties

For illustration of Nos. S28*e* and S29*e* see No. S26*h*

White flaws in and around thistle at upper left
S29*f*, S34*e*

White spot by upper left daffodil
S29*g*, S34*f*

Cylinder Numbers (Blocks of Six)

A. Cream paper
Perforation Type A

Cyl. No.					No dot	Dot
15 ..	..	..	..	..	40	40

B. Whiter paper
Perforation Type A

Cyl. No.					No dot	Dot
15 ..	..	..	..	..	35	35
22 ..	..	..	..	..	50	50

Minor Constant Sheet Flaws

Minimum price as singles: 60p

Cyl. 15 13/9 White spur on top left daffodil stem (Th. A2)
Cyl. 15. 1/4 Green dot in lower half of 1 of left ½ (Th. G1)

Booklet Panes of Six

Cream or whiter paper
From 3/– Booklets M10/74 and 10/– Booklets X1/9
SB45 Watermark upright 25   SB45a Watermark inverted 1·00

Booklet Panes of Four

Cream paper
From 1/– Booklet K3 for use in "E" machines and 2/– Booklets N2/3
SB46 Watermark upright 25   SB46a Watermark inverted 90
    No cylinder numbers were used.

Cream or whiter paper. Sideways watermark
From 2/– Booklets N4/20
SB47 Wmk. Crown to left 1·10   SB47a Wmk. Crown to right 1.10

Booklet Cylinder Numbers

Panes of six (21-row cylinders)

Cream paper							Whiter paper					
Cyl. No.					No dot	Dot	Cyl. No.				No dot	Dot
G10	..	..	..	..	1·25	1·25	G15	..	..	..	.. 1·00	1·00
G10 T	..	..	..	..	1·25	1·25	G15 T	..	..	..	.. 1·00	1·00
G11	..	..	..	..	1·00	1·00	G16	..	..	..	.. 2·00	2·00
G11 T	..	..	..	..	1·00	1·00	G16 T	..	..	..	.. 2·00	2·00
G15	..	..	..	..	1·00	1·00						
G15 T	..	..	..	..	1·00	1·00						

Panes of four

In the 2/– Booklets (N4/20) the cylinder numbers were usually trimmed off.

Coils

Made up from sheets with sheet margin joins. Watermark upright

Code No.	Number in roll	Face value	
L	480	£3	Vertical delivery (Cream paper)
N	480	£3	Sideways delivery (Whiter paper

Sheet Markings

	Cylinder 15	Cylinder 22
Guide holes:	Boxed opposite rows 14/15, at left (no dot) or right (dot)	Boxed opposite rows 14/15, at left (no dot) or right (dot)
Marginal arrows:	"V" shaped, hand-engraved, at top and bottom; "W" shaped, photo-etched, at both sides	"W" shaped, hand-engraved, at top; "W" shaped, photo-etched at bottom and at both sides
Marginal rule:	At bottom of sheet (1½ mm. wide)	At bottom of sheet (2 mm. wide
Others:	As given in General Notes	As given in General Notes

Cat. No.	S.G. No.	Shades	Unused Used

1959 (AUGUST 4). WITH GRAPHITE LINES, TYPE S8. WATERMARK CROWNS

This was only issued in 3s. Booklets.

S30	589	Green	2·50 **2·50**
a. Watermark inverted (4.8.59) ..	2·00	2·00	

Booklet Panes of Six

From 3/– Booklets MG1/6

SB48 Watermark upright	12·00	SB48a Watermark inverted	10·00

Booklet Cylinder Numbers

Panes of six (21-row cylinder)

Cyl. No.				No dot Dot	Cyl. No.				No dot Dot
G11 ..	..	..	..	.. 20·00 20·00	G11 T	..	..	..	.. 20·00 20·00

Quantity Issued   1,864,800

Cat. No.	S.G. No.	Shades	Unused	Used

1959 (NOVEMBER 18). PHOSPHOR-GRAPHITE ISSUE. WMK. ST. EDWARD'S CROWN

This has two graphite lines, Type **S8**, on the back and two phosphor bands on the front, which react green under the lamp.

S31	601		Green		1.00	1·00
a.	Green stroke below E (Cyl. 21,					
	R.13/8)	4·00				

For illustration of No. S31*a* see No. S27*d.*

Cylinder Numbers (Blocks of Six)

Single pane cylinder

Cyl. No.	Perf. Type	No dot
21	B	.. 6·00
21	C	.. 6·00

Sheet Markings

All the same as for No. S27

Quantity Issued 704,160

1960 (JUNE 22). TWO PHOSPHOR BANDS REACTING GREEN. WMK. CROWNS

The bands were applied in photogravure.

S32	—		Green		45	40
a.	Watermark inverted (14.8.60)	80	75			
b.	Spot between rose and					
	shamrock (Cyl. 15, R.20/3) ..	1·75				

For illustration of No. S32*b* see No. S26*h.*

Cylinder Numbers (Blocks of Six)

Perforation Type B (no dot) or C (dot)

Cyl. No.					No dot	Dot
15 ..	..	..	..	..	3·00	3·00

Minor Constant Sheet Flaws

Minimum price as singles: £1

Cyl. 15   13/9   White spur on top left daffodil stem (Th. A2)
Cyl. 15.   1/4   Green dot in lower half of 1 of left ½ (Th. G1)

Booklet Panes of Six

From 3/– Booklets MP1/3 and MP6

SB49 Watermark upright	2·25	SB49a Watermark inverted	4·00

Booklet Cylinder Numbers

Panes of six (21-row cylinders)

Cyl. No.				No dot	Dot	Cyl. No.					No dot	Dot
G11	..	..	..	4·50	4·50	G11 T	..	..	..	..	4·50	4·50

Sheet Markings

Guide holes: Not known
Black bar: This occurs by the marginal arrows opposite rows 10/11, at left (no dot) or right (dot)
Others: As given in General Notes

Cat. No.	S.G. No.			Shades	Unused	Used

1961 (JUNE 5).† TWO PHOSPHOR BANDS REACTING BLUE. WMK. CROWNS

The bands were applied in photogravure.

A. Cream Paper

S33	—			Green	12	10

a. Watermark inverted (4.61) ..   1 00   1·00
ab. Do. Single broad band at left   1·25
b. Watermark Crown to left   *d.* Single broad band at right ..   25
    (14.7.61)   85   85   *e.* Spot between rose and
c. Watermark Crown to right ..   85   85   shamrock (Cyl. 15, R.20/3) ..   1·25

B. Whiter Paper (Sept. 1964)†

S34	612			Green	5	5

a. Watermark Crown to left   *d.* Spot between rose and
    (15.8.62)   75   75   shamrock (Cyl. 15, R.20/3) ..   1·00
b. Watermark Crown to right ..   75   75   *e.* Thistle flaws (Cyl. 22., R.12/1)   75
c. Watermark inverted (11.64) ..   75   75   *f.* Daffodil flaw (Cyl. 22., R.1/12)   75

For illustrations of Nos. S33*e* and S34*d* see No. S26*h*; for Nos. S34*e*/*f* see Nos. S29*f*/*g*.

Cylinder Numbers (Blocks of Six)

A. Cream paper   B. Whiter paper
Perforation Type B (no dot) and C (dot)   Perforation Type A

Cyl. No.				No dot	Dot		Cyl. No.				No dot	Dot
15 ..	..	..	..	.. 35	35		15 ..	..	..	..	.. 35	35
							22 ..	..	..	..	.. 45	45

Minor Constant Sheet Flaws

Minimum price as singles: 60p

Cyl. 15   13/9   White spur on top left daffodil stem (Th. A2)
Cyl. 15.   1/4   Green dot on lower half of 1 of left ½ (Th. G1)

Booklet Panes of Six

Cream or whiter paper
From 3/– Booklets MP4/5, MP6*a* and MP7/38
SB50 Watermark upright   40   SB50a Watermark inverted   2·50

Booklet Panes of Four

Cream or whiter paper. Sideways watermark
From 2/– Booklets NP1/13
SB51 Wmk. Crown to left   2·25   SB51a Wmk. Crown to right   2·25

Booklet Cylinder Numbers

Pane of six (21-row cylinders)
Cream or whiter paper

Cyl. No.				No dot	Dot		Cyl. No.				No dot	Dot
G15	..	..	..	.. 1·50	1·50		G15 T	..	..	..	.. 1·50	1·50

Pane of four (Single pane 20-row cylinder)
In the 2/– Booklets the cylinder numbers were usually trimmed off.

Sheet Markings

All the same as for Nos. S28/9

1965 (AUGUST 13). TWO 8 mm. PHOSPHOR BANDS REACTING VIOLET. WMK. CROWNS

The bands were applied typographically.

S35	—			Green	15	15

a. Phosphor bands on back and
    front   ..   ..   1·00

Cylinder Numbers (Blocks of Six)

Perforation Type A

	Cyl. No.				No dot	Dot
	15 ..	..	..	..	.. 1.00	1·00

Sheet Markings

All the same as for Cylinder 15 under Nos. S28/9

1953–67.   2d. Red-brown, Type S1

Cat. No.	S.G. No.		Shades	Unused	Used

1953 (AUGUST 31).   WATERMARK TUDOR CROWN, TYPE W.22

S36   518   Red-brown   12   5

a. Watermark inverted (3.54) ..	1·00 50
b. Watermark sideways (8.10.54)	25 25
c. Rose petal flaw (Cyl. 3, R.4/8)	1·25
d. Tadpole flaw (Cyl. 4., R.17/6)	1·25
e. Retouched (Cyl. 3., R.17/6) ..	1·00
f. Retouched face (Booklet pane R.2/1)	3·50
g. Extra leg to R (Sideways coil, Roll 2)	1·60
h. Retouched left 2 (Sideways coil, Roll 5)	1·40
i. Dot on rose (Sideways Coil, Roll 9)	1·25
j. Cancelled two vert. black bars (P.O.T.S.)	8

Stamps with sideways watermark are from T coils with sideways delivery.

Listed Varieties

S36c, S37e

S36d, S37f, S38f
White flaw

S36e, S37g, S38g, S40d
Retouched darker

S36f, S37j
From booklet pane showing cyl. H1

S36i

S36g, S37k, S38t,
S40i, S41b, S49b

From sideways delivery T coils

Normal

S36h, S37l,
S38u, S40j,
S41c, S49c

Cylinder Numbers (Blocks of Six)

Perforation Type A

Cyl. No.				No dot	Dot	Cyl. No.					No dot	Dot
1 ..	..	..	..	1·50	1·50	3 ..	..	..	..	..	1·25	1·25
2 ..	..	..	..	1·50	1·50	4 ..	..	..	..	..	1·25	1·25

47

Booklet Panes of Six
From 5/– Booklets H8/16
SB52 Watermark upright   60   SB52a Watermark inverted   5.00

Booklet Cylinder Numbers
Panes of six (20-row cylinder)
Cyl. No.   No dot Dot
H1 ..   ..   3·50* 2·50

Coils

   Double pane cylinder number D1 was used for vertical delivery coils and single pane
cylinder D3 for sideways delivery coils.
Printed in continuous reels

	Code No.	Number in roll	Face value
(a) Vertical delivery. Watermark upright			
	R	480	£4
	Q	960	£8
	V	960	£8
(b) Sideways delivery. Watermark sideways			
	T	480	£4

Sheet Markings
   Guide holes: Boxed opposite rows 14/15, at left (no dot) or right (dot)
   Others: As given in General Notes
   Sheets are known with the arrows missing at top and bottom from cylinder 2 (no dot)

Cat. No.	S.G. No.		Shades	Unused	Used

1955 (SEPTEMBER 6).   WATERMARK ST. EDWARD'S CROWN, TYPE W.23
A. Red-brown

S37   543   Red-brown   15   5
 a. Imperf. between pair (from
     vert. coil) £300
 b. Imperf. between pair (from   i. Flaw between shamrock and
     sideways wmk. horiz. coil)   ..   £250   diadem (Cyl. 7., R.1/6)   ..   1·40
 c. Watermark inverted (9.55) ..   70   35   j. Retouched face (Booklet pane
 d. Watermark sideways (31.7.56)   25   25   R.2/1) ..   ..   1·00
 e. Rose petal flaw (Cyl. 3, R.4/8) 1·00   k. Extra leg to R (Sideways coil,
 f. Tadpole flaw (Cyl. 4., R.17/6)   1·00   Roll 2) ..   ..   1·50
 g. Retouched (R.17/6 on Cyls. 3.,   l. Retouched left 2 (Sideways
     6., 7.)   80   coil, Roll 5)   ..   ..   ..   1·25
 h. Tadpole flaw with shamrock   m. Cancelled two vert. black bars
     flaw (Cyl. 9., R.17/6) ..   ..   1·25   (P.O.T.S.)   8

Stamps with sideways watermark are from T coils with sideways delivery.

Listed Varieties

   For illustrations of Nos. S37e/g, see Nos. S36c/e and
for Nos. S37j/l, see Nos. S36g/i. No. S37h comprises the
variety shown for No. S36d but in addition there is a
white flaw to the left of the adjoining shamrock.

S37i, S38j
This was a multipositive flaw
which was retouched on other
cylinders

Cat. No.	S.G. No.		Shades	Unused	Used

B. Light red-brown (17 October 1956)

S38   543*b*   Light red-brown   10   5

a.	Tête-bêche (horiz. pair) ..	75·00	
b.	Imperf. pane*	£130	
c.	Imperf. between stamp and top margin	40·00	
d.	Watermark inverted (1.57) ..	30	25
e.	Watermark sideways (5.3.57)..	30	25
f.	Tadpole flaw (R.17/6 on Cyls. 8., 10., 11.)	1·00	
g.	Retouched (R.17/6 on Cyls. 6., 7., 13., 15.)	75	
h.	Tadpole flaw with shamrock flaw (R.17/6 on Cyls. 9., 12.) ..	1·25	
i.	Tadpole flaw retouched with shamrock flaw (R.17/6 on Cyls. 14., 16.)	1·50	
j.	Flaw between shamrock and diadem (Cyl. 7., R.1/6) ..	1·25	
k.	"Double trumpet" flaw (Cyl. 10, R.11/1)	1·25	
l.	Dot on shamrock (Cyl. 10, R.20/1)	1·40	

m.	Dot over rose stem (Cyl. 14, R.1/1)	1·40
n.	Daffodil flaw (Booklet pane R.1/3 or 2/3)	1·00
o.	D for P (Booklet pane R.1/2 or 2/2)	3·00
p.	Spot after 2 (Booklet pane R.1/2 or 2/2)	3·00
q.	"Dew drop" (Booklet pane R.1/2 or 2/2)	1·00
r.	Shamrock flaw (Booklet pane R.1/3 or 2/3)	1·00
s.	Diadem flaw (Booklet pane R.1/3 or 2/3)	1·00
t.	Extra leg to R (Sideways coil, Roll 2)	1·40
u.	Retouched left 2 (Sideways coil, Roll 5)	1·25
v.	Cancelled two vert. black bars (P.O.T.S.)	8

*Booklet error—See General Notes.

Stamps with sideways watermark are from T coils with sideways delivery.

In December 1956 a completely imperforate sheet was noticed by clerks in a Kent post office one of whom purchased it against P.O. regulations. In view of this irregularity we do not consider it properly issued.

Listed Varieties

Tadpole flaws: Nos. S38*f/h* are as Nos. S37*f/h*; No. S38*i* is a fourth state which combines the shamrock flaw (now grown larger) with the retouched state of the tadpole flaw. For illustrations of No. S38*j*, see No. S37*i*, and for Nos. S38*t/u*, see Nos. S36*g/h*.

S38*k*

S38*n*
Later retouched

S38*l*

S38*m*

S38*o*, S40*g*

S38*p*, S40*h*

Listed Varieties (contd.)

S38q	S38r	S38s
Later retouched	Later retouched	Later retouched

Cylinder Numbers (Blocks of Six)

(a) Red-brown

Perforation Type A

Cyl. No.					No dot	Dot	Cyl. No.	..					No dot	Dot
3 ..	..	..	..	..	1·00	1·00	7 ..	..	..	..	..	..	1·00	1·00
4 ..	..	..	..	..	1·00	1·00	9 ..	..	..	..	..	..	1·25	1·25
6 ..	..	..	..	..	1·00	1·00								

(b) Light red-brown

Perforation Type A

					No dot	Dot							No dot	Dot
6 ..	••	..	..	..	80	80	12 ..	..	..	..	..	..	80	80
7 ..	..	..	..	..	80	80	13 ..	..	..	..	..	..	80	80
8 ..	..	..	..	..	80	80	14 ..	..	..	..	..	..	80	80
9 ..	..	..	..	..	80	80	15 ..	..	..	..	..	..	80	80
10 ..	..	..	..	..	1·50*	80	16 ..	..	..	..	..	..	80	80
11 ..	..	..	..	..	80	80								

Perforation Type E

7 ..	••	••	••	..	1·50	†
9 ..	..	..	..	..	1·50	†

Minor Constant Sheet Flaws

Minimum prices as singles: Red-brown 75p; Light red-brown 70p

Cyl. 7   14/8   White dot above T of POSTAGE
Cyl. 9   20/1   White spur on lower daffodil (Th. G3)

Booklet Panes of Six

(a) Red-brown from 5/- Booklets H17/25

SB53 Watermark upright   75   SB53a Watermark inverted   3·50

(b) Light red-brown from 2/6 Booklets F53/61 and 5/- Booklets H26/31

SB54 Watermark upright   50   SB54a Watermark inverted   1·50

Booklet Cylinder Numbers

Panes of six (21-row cylinders)*

Cyl. No.	Cat. No.		No dot	Dot	Cyl. No.	Cat. No.		No dot	Dot
H1	SB53	..	3·00	3·00	H1 T	SB53	..	3·00	3·00
H6	SB53	..	2·50	2·50	H6 T	SB53	..	2·50	2·50
H6	SB54	..	2·00	2·00	H6 T	SB54	..	2·00	2·00

*Cylinder H1 was originally a 20-row cylinder but it was later converted to a 21-row cylinder so that it exists with the cylinder number adjoining the top row.

Coils

Double pane cylinder number D1 was used for vertical delivery coils of No. S37 and cylinder D2 for No. S38 and single pane cylinder D3 was used for the sideways delivery coils.

Printed in continuous reels

Code No.	Cat. No.	Number in roll	Face value
(a) Vertical delivery. Watermark upright			
R	S37	480	£4
Q	S37	960	£8
V	S37	960	£8
R	S38	480	£4
Q	S38	960	£8
V	S38	960	£8
(b) Sideways delivery. Watermark sideways			
T	S37d	480	£4
T	S38e	480	£4

Sheet Markings

Guide holes: Boxed opposite rows 14/15, at left (no dot) or right (dot)
Others: As given in General Notes

On the 2d. value the single graphite line normally appeared at the right when viewed from the back. It was printed in black under the gum.

S9

Cat. No.	S.G. No.		Shades		Unused	Used

1957 (NOVEMBER 19). WITH GRAPHITE LINE, TYPE S9. WMK. ST. EDWARD'S CROWN

S39	564		Light red-brown		60	60

a. Line at left (as seen from back) 75·00 75·00
b. Horiz. pair, one with line omitted £100
c. Coil join (vert. pair) ..   .. 1·40
d. Coil join (horiz. pair) 80

Nos. S39a/b result from a misplacement of the line.

Cylinder Numbers (Blocks of Six)

Single pane cylinder

Cyl. No.	Perf. Type		No dot
17	B	..	3·75
17	C	..	3·75

Minor Constant Sheet Flaws

Minimum price as singles: £1

Cyl. 17   11/2   White flaw on tail of left d
16/1   White flaw in centre of upper left rose (Th. B1)

Coils

Made up from sheets with sheet margin joins

Code No.	Number in roll	Face value	
V	960	£8	Vertical delivery
T	480	£4	Horizontal delivery

Sheet Markings:

Guide holes: Boxed opposite rows 14/15, at both sides and unboxed opposite rows 1 and 7/8 at both sides
Others: As given in General Notes

Quantity Issued   37,686,480

Cat. No.	S.G. No.	Shades	Unused	Used

1958 (DECEMBER 4).† WATERMARK CROWNS, TYPE W.24
A. Cream Paper

S40 — Light red-brown 8 5

a. Imperf. between stamp and
top margin .. .. .. 35·00
b. Watermark sideways (3.4.59) 8 5
c. Watermark inverted (10.4.61) 6·00 5·00
d. Tadpole retouch (R.17/6 on
Cyls. 15. and others) .. 75
e. Tadpole retouch and shamrock
flaw (R.17/6 on Cyls. 16. and
others) .. .. 1·00
f. "Swan's head" flaw (Cyl. 24.,
R.19/10) .. .. .. 1·25

g. D for P (Booklet pane R.1/2 or
2/2)* .. .. 7·00
h. Spot after 2 (Booklet pane
R.1/2 or 2/2)* .. .. .. 7·00
i. Extra leg to R (Sideways coil,
Roll 2) .. .. 1·00
j. Retouched left 2 (Sideways coil,
Roll 5) .. .. 1·25

B. Whiter Paper (5 September 1963) †

S41 573 Light red-brown 5 5

a. Watermark sideways (27.7.62) 5 5
b. Extra leg to R (Sideways coil,
Roll 2) 75

c. Retouched left 2 (Sideways coil,
Roll 5) .. .. 1·00

†No. S40 was issued in November 1958 in V coils and No. S41 appeared on 20 September 1962 in V coils.

Stamps with sideways watermark are from T coils with sideways delivery.

*Nos. S40g/h are on panes with watermark inverted.

Listed Varieties

Tadpole flaws: No. S40d is as No. S38g and No. S40e as No. S38i. For illustrations of Nos. S40g/h, see Nos. S38o/p and for Nos. S40i/j and S41b/c, see Nos. S36g/h.

S40f

Cylinder Numbers (Blocks of Six)

A. Cream paper

Cyl. No. Perforation Type A	No dot	Dot
15	60	60
19	60	60
20	60	60
21	60	60
22	60	60
23	60	60
24	60	60

Cyl. No. Perforation Type A	No dot	Dot
25	60	60
27	60	60
29	60	60
30	60	60

Perforation Type B (no dot) and C (dot)

	No dot	Dot
22	70	70

B. Whiter paper

Perforation Type A	No dot	Dot
23	60	60
25	60	60

Perforation Type A	No dot	Dot
27	60	60
30	60	60

Booklet Panes of Six

From 10/– Booklets X1/2. Cream paper

SB55 Watermark upright 25   SB55a Watermark inverted 30·00

Booklet Cylinder Numbers

Panes of six (21-row cylinder). Cream paper

Cyl. No.	No dot	Dot
H6	8·00	8·00

Cyl. No.	No dot	Dot
H6 T	8·00	8·00

Coils

Double cylinder D2 was used for vertical delivery coils and cylinders D3 and D4 (single pane) for sideways delivery coils.

Printed in continuous reels. Cream or whiter paper

	Code No.	Number in roll	Face value

(a) Vertical delivery. Watermark upright

	Code No.	Number in roll	Face value
	R	480	£4
	Q	960	£8
	V	960	£8

(b) Sideways delivery. Watermark sideways

	T	480	£4

Sheet Markings

Guide holes: Boxed opposite rows 14/15, at left (no dot) or right (dot)
Others: As given in General Notes

Cat. No.	S.G. No.		Shades	Unused	Used

1958 (NOVEMBER 24). WITH GRAPHITE LINE, TYPE S9. WATERMARK CROWNS

S42	590		Light red-brown	1·00	1·00

a. Line at extreme left (as seen from back) .. .. .. 80·00   *b.* Coil join (vert. pair) .. .. 2·25

Cylinder Numbers (Blocks of Six)

Single pane cylinder

	Cyl. No.	Perf. Type		No dot
	17	B	..	6·50
	17	C	..	6·50

Minor Constant Sheet Flaw

Minimum price as single: £1·50

Cyl. 17   11/2 White flaw on tail of left d

Coil

Vertical delivery. Made up from sheets with sheet margin joins

	Code No.	Number in roll	Face value
	V	960	£8

Sheet Markings

As for No. S39

Quantity Issued 48,419,520

1959 (NOVEMBER 18). PHOSPHOR-GRAPHITE ISSUE. WATERMARK CROWNS

This has one graphite line (Type **S9**), on the back and one phosphor band on the front, which reacts green under the lamp.

S43	605		Light red-brown	1·00	1·00

a. Error, Watermark St. Edward's Crown (3.60) .. .. .. 28·00   25·00

Cylinder Numbers (Blocks of Six)

Single pane cylinder

Watermark Crowns				Watermark St. Edward's Crown		
Cyl. No.	Perforation Type		No dot	Cyl. No.	Perforation Type	No dot
17	B	..	4·00	17	B ..	£170
17	C	..	4·00	17	C ..	£170

Minor Constant Sheet Flaws

Minimum prices as singles: Wmk. Crowns 80p; wmk. St Edward's Crown £30

Cyl. 17   11/2 White flaw on tail of left d
         16/1 White flaw in centre of upper left rose (Th. B1) (on St. Edward's Crown wmk. only)

Sheet Markings

As for No. S39

Quantity Issued 4,509,120 (including both watermarks)

Cat. No.	S.G. No.	Shades	Unused	Used

1960 (JUNE 22). ONE PHOSPHOR BAND REACTING GREEN. WMK. CROWNS

The band was applied in photogravure.

S44   —   Light red-brown   2·00 2·00
　　a. Coil join (vert. pair) ..   ..   4·50

Cylinder Numbers (Blocks of Six)

Single pane cylinder

	Cyl. No.	Perf. Type	No dot
	17	B	.. 14.00
	17	C	.. 14.00

Minor Constant Sheet Flaws

Minimum price as singles: £2·50

Cyl. 17   11/2 White flaw on tail of left d
　　　　16/1 White flaw in centre of upper left rose (Th. B1)

Coil

Vertical delivery. Made up from sheets with sheet margin joins

Code No.	Number in roll	Face value
V	960	£8

Sheet Markings

As for No. S39

1961 (JUNE 5). ONE PHOSPHOR BAND AT LEFT REACTING BLUE. WMK. CROWNS

This exists on cream paper only and the phosphor band was applied in photogravure.

S45   613   Light red-brown   1·75 1·75
　　a. Left band applied typo.   ..   2·50 2·50   *b.* Band at centre applied photo.   2·00

Cylinder Numbers (Blocks of Six)

One band applied photo.
Perforation Type A

Cyl. No.					No dot	Dot		Cyl. No.					No dot	Dot
29	..	..	..	..	.. 12·00	12·00		29	..	..	..	..	.. 12·00	12·00

Perforation Type B (no dot) and C (dot) appear at right.

One band applied typo.
Perforation Type A

	Cyl. No.					No dot	Dot
	29	..	..	..	..	.. 18·00	18·00

Minor Constant Sheet Flaws

Minimum price as singles: £2·25

Cyl. 29.   17/6 There is only a slight shading to the background where the tadpole and shamrock flaws
　　　　　　were

Coil

Double pane cylinder D2 was used.

Printed in continuous reels. Vertical delivery with watermark upright

Code No.	Number in roll	Face value
V	960	£8

Sheet Markings

Guide holes: Boxed opposite rows 14/15 at left (no dot) and right (dot)
Others: As given in General Notes

Cat. No.	S.G. No.	Shades	Unused	Used

1961 (OCTOBER 4). TWO PHOSPHOR BANDS REACTING BLUE. WMK. CROWNS

A. Cream Paper Bands typographed

| S46 | — | Light red-brown | 30 | 30 |

aa. Imperf. three sides*
  a. Bands applied photo. (3.4.62)   12   10

B. Whiter Paper (5 November 1964)† Bands applied in photogravure

| S47 | — | Light red-brown | 10 | 8 |

*This comes from the bottom row of a sheet which is imperf. at bottom and both sides. From cyl. 29 no dot with bands applied photo.

No. S47 appeared earlier from V coils on 21 January 1963.

Cylinder Numbers (Blocks of Six)

Cream paper						Whiter paper		
Cyl. No.				No dot	Dot	Cyl. No.	No dot	Dot

Two bands applied typo.
Perforation Type A

25	..	..	..	..	..	1·50	†
27	..	..	..	..	..	†	1·50
29	..	..	..	..	..	1·50	1·50
30	..	..	..	..	..	1·50	1·50

Two bands applied photo.
Perforation Type B (no dot) and C (dot)

| | | | | | | | Perforation Type A | |
| 29 | .. | .. | .. | .. | 1·25 | 1·25 | 25 .. .. | 80 | 80 |

As the bands were applied on individual sheets and not in the reel, it is possible that the items marked with a dagger may exist.

Minor Constant Sheet Flaws

Minimum prices as singles: Cream paper 75p; whiter paper 60p

Dot cyls. 17/6 There remains only a slight disturbance to the background where the tadpole and shamrock flaws were

Coil

Double pane cylinder D2 was used.

Printed in continuous reels. Vertical delivery with watermark upright. Cream or whiter paper.

Code No.	Number in roll	Face value
V	960	£8

Sheet Markings

As for No. S40

1965 (AUGUST 17). TWO 8 mm. PHOSPHOR BANDS REACTING VIOLET. WMK. CROWNS

The bands were applied in photogravure only.

| S48 | — | Light red-brown | 8 | 5 |

Cylinder Numbers (Blocks of Six)

Perforation Type A

Cyl. No.					No dot	Dot
30	..	..	..	..	50	50

Constant Minor Sheet Flaws

Minimum price as singles: 60p

Cyl. 30. 17/6 There remains only a slight disturbance under the thistle to the original tadpole and shamrock flaws

Coil

Double pane cylinder D2 was used.

Printed in continuous reels. Vertical delivery with watermark upright

Code No.	Number in roll	Face value
V	960	£8

Sheet Markings

As for No. S40

Cat. No.	S.G. No.	Shades	Unused	Used

1967 (SEPTEMBER).† Two 9·5 mm. PHOSPHOR BANDS REACTING VIOLET. WMK. CROWNS

The bands were applied in photogravure only.

S49   613*a*   Light red-brown   5   5
  a. Watermark Crown to left (6.4.67) 8   5
  b. Extra leg to R (Sideways coil,   *c.* Retouched left 2 (Sideways
    Roll 2) .. .. 1·00   coil, Roll 5) .. .. .. 1·00

Stamps with sideways watermark are from T coils with sideways delivery.
For illustrations of Nos. S49*b*/*c*, see Nos. S36*g*/*h*.

Cylinder Numbers (Blocks of Six)

Perforation Type F (L)*					Perforation Type A			
Cyl. No.				No dot Dot	Cyl. No.			No dot Dot
25 ..	..	..	..	.. 35 35	27 ..	..	..	.. 35 35

Minor Constant Sheet Flaws

Minimum price as singles: 60p

Dot panes. 17/6 There remains only a slight disturbance to the background where the tadpole and shamrock
flaws were

Coils

Double pane cylinder D2 was used for the vertical delivery coils and cylinder D3 (single pane) for sideways delivery coils.

Printed in continuous reels

Code No.	Number in roll	Face value
(a) Vertical delivery. Watermark upright		
R	480	£4
V	960	£8
(b) Sideways delivery. Watermark sideways		
T	480	£4

Sheet Markings

Guide holes: Boxed opposite rows 14/15, at left (no dot) or right (dot) but in the case of perforation Type
F (L)* the boxes remain on both panes but the holes are unboxed **above** and below the eighth vertical
row in the no dot pane only

Others: As given in General Notes

1952–65.   2½d. Carmine-red, Type S2

Two Types

I   II

Type I   In the frontal cross of the diadem, the top line is only half the width of the cross.

Type II The top line extends to the full width of the cross and there are signs of strengthening in other parts of the diadem.

Variations in the Multipositives

The original multipositive became damaged and had to be replaced. The original negative consisted of two negatives placed in contact against each other, one for the frame and one for the Queen's head and oval setting. When these two pieces of glass were placed together the position of the two was not exactly the same as when the first multipositive was made, resulting in a slight tilting of the portrait.

The second multipositive (Type B) was used for making cylinder 46 which was employed for No. S53 and the third multipositive (Type C) was used for all later cylinder numbers, i.e. Nos. 49 onwards.

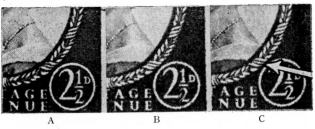

A   B   C

Type A. At the shoulder line above "E" of "POSTAGE" the line dividing the light from the dark material of the dress, if projected, runs level with the second diagonal line of the ribbon on the wreath.

Type B. The line runs between the first and second diagonal line of the ribbon.

Type C. The line runs level with the first diagonal line of the ribbon.

These are not listed as separate varieties because the stamps printed from the cylinders made from the three variations in the multipositives differ in other respects. This is, however, a most interesting development. It also applies to the 3d. value.

Cat. No.	S.G. No.	Shades	Unused	Used

1952 (DECEMBER 5).   WATERMARK TUDOR CROWN, TYPE W.22. TYPE I

S50   519   Carmine-red   10   5
  a. Watermark sideways (15.11.54)   50   50
  b. Broken value circle (Cyl. 8, R.20/2) ..   1·25
  c. Frame retouch (Sideways coil, Roll 7) ..   ..   ..   1·50

  d. Cancelled two vert. black bars (P.O.T.S.)   8
  e. Overprinted "SCHOOL SPECIMEN"   15

Stamps with sideways watermark are from M coils with sideways delivery.

Listed Varieties

S50*b*

S50*c*, S52*e*, S56*ab*, S56*d*

57

Cylinder Numbers (Blocks of Six)

Perforation Type A

Cyl. No.					No dot	Dot	Cyl. No.					No dot	Dot
2	..	..	..	..	1·00	1·00	16	..	..	..	..	1·00	1·00
4	..	..	..	..	1·00	1·00	17	..	..	..	..	1·00	1·00
5	..	..	..	..	1·00	1·00	18	..	..	..	..	1·00	1·00
6	..	..	..	..	1·00	1·00	19	..	..	..	..	1·00	1·00
7	..	..	..	..	1·00	1·00	22	..	..	..	..	1·00	1·00
8	..	..	..	..	1·00	2·00*	23	..	..	..	..	1·00	1·00
9	..	..	..	..	1·00	1·00	24	..	..	..	..	1·00	1·00
10	..	..	..	..	1·00	1·00	25	..	..	..	..	1·25	1·25
11	..	..	..	..	1·00	1·00	27	..	..	..	..	1·00	1·00
12	..	..	..	..	1·00	1·00							
13	..	..	..	..	1·25	1·25							
14	..	..	..	..	1·00	1·00							
15	..	..	..	..	1·00	1·00							

Perforation Type B (no dot) and C (dot)

Cyl. No.					No dot	Dot
14	..	..	..	..	1·00	1·00
24	..	..	..	..	1·00	1·00

Minor Constant Sheet Flaws

Minimum price as singles: 50p

Multipositive flaws

No dot 1/4 Red dot over left of crown (Th. A3)
12/4 Red spot in leaf of shamrock (Th. G1)
18/1 Diagonal scratch from chin to neck (Th. E3–F4)

Dot 11/9 White spot in R of E R (Cyls. 23. onwards)

Cylinder flaws

Cyl. 2. 16/1 Smudge line across top of REVENU
Cyl. 8 19/1 Red spot in 1 of fraction
Cyl. 10. 20/1 Extended top of 2 in value

Coils

Single pane cylinder L1 was used for the vertical delivery coils and L2 for the sideways delivery coils.

Printed in continuous reels

	Code No.	Number in roll	Face value
(a) Vertical delivery. Watermark upright			
	F	960	£10
	U	1920	£20
(b) Sideways delivery. Watermark sideways			
	M	480	£5

Sheet Markings

Guide holes: Boxed opposite rows 14/15, at left (no dot) or right (dot)
Others: As given in General Notes

Cat. No.	S.G. No.	Shades	Unused	Used

1953 (MAY). WATERMARK TUDOR CROWN, TYPE W.22. TYPE II

This issue appeared from booklets only.

S51 519b Carmine-red 25 25
a. Watermark inverted (5.53) .. 35 20
b. R flaw (R.1/1) 75
c. Jewels flaw (R.2/2) 75

Listed Varieties

S51*b*, S52*d*

S51*c*

Booklet Panes of Six

From 2/6 Booklets F1/34, 3/9 Booklets G1/9 and 5/– Booklets H1/16
SB56 Watermark upright   1·25   SB56a Watermark inverted   1·75

Booklet Cylinder Numbers

Panes of six (20-row cylinders)

Cyl. No.					No dot	Dot	Cyl. No.					No dot	Dot
J1 ..	..	..	..	..	2·00	2·00	J5 ..	..	..	..	..	2·00	2·00
J3 ..	..	..	..	..	2·00	2·00							

Cat. No.	S.G. No.	Shades	Unused	Used

1955 (SEPTEMBER 28). WATERMARK ST. EDWARD'S CROWN, TYPE W.23. TYPE I

S52   544   Carmine-red   10   5
  a. Imperf. between stamp and top   *d.* R flaw (Booklets R.1/1)   ..   1·25
    margin ..   ..   40·00   *e.* Frame retouch (Sideways coil,
  b. Watermark sideways (23.3.56)   20   12   Roll 7) ..   ..   1·00
  c. b for D in value (Cyl. 30.,   *f.* Cancelled two vert. black bars
    R.19/11)   ..   ..   ..   1·75   (P.O.T.S.)   8

Stamps with sideways watermark are from M coils with sideways delivery.

Listed Variety

S52c

For illustrations of No. S52d, see No. S51b and for S52e, see No. S50c.

Cylinder Numbers (Blocks of Six)

Perforation Type A

Cyl. No.					No dot	Dot	Cyl. No.					No dot	Dot
22 ..	..	..	..	..	75	75	39 ..	..	..	..	..	75	7 5
24 ..	..	..	..	..	75	—	40 ..	..	..	..	..	70	70
25 ..	..	..	..	..	75	75	42 ..	..	..	..	..	70	70
27 ..	..	..	..	..	75	75	43 ..	..	..	..	..	70	70
30 ..	..	..	..	..	75	75	44 ..	..	..	..	..	70	70
32 ..	..	..	..	..	75	75	45 ..	..	..	..	..	6·00	6·00
33 ..	..	..	..	..	75	75	Perforation Type E						
34 ..	..	..	..	..	†	90							
37 ..	..	..	..	..	75	75	32 ..	..	..	..	..	1·25	†
38 ..	..	..	..	..	75	75	37 ..	..	..	..	..	1·25	†

Minor Constant Sheet Flaws

Minimum price as singles: 75p

Multipositive flaws as for No. S50

Cylinder flaw
Cyl. 43 18/5 Red spot on Queen's lip (Th. D3)

Coils

Single pane cylinder L3 was used for the vertical delivery coils and L2 for the sideways delivery coils.

Printed in continuous reels

Code No.   Number in roll   Face value
(a) Vertical delivery. Watermark upright
F   960   £10
U   1920   £20
(b) Sideways delivery. Watermark sideways
M   480   £5

Sheet Markings

As for No. S50
In cylinder 42, both panes, the marginal arrows at the top and bottom were omitted at first, but added later.

59

Cat. No.	S.G. No.				Shades		Unused	Used

1957.† WATERMARK ST. EDWARD'S CROWN, TYPE W.23. TYPE II

S53   544b   Carmine-red   20   20

    a. Tête-bêche (horiz. pr.)   ..   40·00
    b. Imperf. pane* £130
    c. Part perf. pane*   ..   ..   45·00
    d. Imperf. between stamp and top
        margin ..   ..   40·00
    e. Watermark inverted (9.55)   ..   20   20

    f. "Swan's head" flaw (Booklets,
        R.1/1 or 2/1) ..   ..   ..   1·60
    g. Dotted R (Booklets, R.1/3 or
        2/3)   ..   ..   1·50

    *Booklet errors—see General Notes.

Listed Varieties

S53*f*, S55*e*
Top of figure 2 is
extended and curled (Cyl. J8)

S53*g*
Retouched on Crowns
wmk. (Cyl. J9)

Cylinder Numbers (Blocks of Six)

Perforation Type A

	Cyl. No.				No dot	Dot
	46 ..	..	..	..	1·50	1·50

Booklet Panes of Six

From 2/6 Booklets F34*b*/*c* and F35/61, 3/9 Booklets G9*a* and G10/21 and 5/– Booklets H17/36

SB57 Watermark upright   1·00   SB57*a* Watermark inverted   1·00

Booklet Cylinder Numbers

Panes of Six (J5 20-row cylinder, others 21-row cylinders)

Cyl. No.					No dot	Dot	Cyl. No.					No dot	Dot
J5 ..	..	..	..	..	2·00	2·00							
J6 ..	..	..	..	..	2·00	2·00	J6 T	..	..	..	..	2·00	2·00
J8 ..	..	..	..	..	1·60	1·60	J8 T	..	..	..	..	1·60	1·60
J9 ..	..	..	..	..	1·60	1·60	J9 T	..	..	..	..	1·60	1·60

Sheet Markings

As for No. S50.

1957 (NOVEMBER 19). WITH GRAPHITE LINES, TYPE S8. WMK. ST. EDWARD'S CROWN. TYPE II

S54   565   Carmine-red   40   35

    a. Coil join (horiz. pr.)   75

Cylinder Numbers (Blocks of Six)

Single pane cylinder

	Cyl. No.	Perf. Type	No dot
	49	B	.. 3·00
	49	C	.. 3·00

Coil

Made up from sheets with sheet margin joins. Horizontal delivery

	Code No.	Number in roll	Face value
	M	480	£5

Sheet Markings

Guide holes: Boxed opposite rows 14/15, at both sides and unboxed opposite rows 1 and 7/8 at both sides
Others: As given in General Notes except that there were no marginal arrows at sides

Quantity Issued   20,578,800

Cat. No.	S.G. No.		Shades	Unused	Used

1959 (SEPTEMBER 15).† WATERMARK CROWNS, TYPE W.24

A. Type II, Cream Paper

S55　　—　　　　　　　　　Carmine-red　　　　　8　　5
  a. Tête-bêche (horiz. pr.)　　..
  b. Imperf. strip of 3　..　　..
  c. Imperf. strip of 6　..　　..　　　　*e.* "Swan's head" flaw (Booklets,
  d. Watermark inverted (11.58) ..　35　　30　　　R.1/1 or 2/1) ..　　..　　..　4·50

B. Type I. Cream Paper (4 October 1961)

S56　　574b　　　　　　　Carmine-red　　　　　15　　15
  a. Watermark sideways (10.11.60)　12　　12
  ab. Frame retouch (Sideways coil,
　　Roll 7) ..　　..　　..　　..　1·00

C. Type I. Whiter Paper (30 October 1963)

S56b　　—　　　　　　　　Carmine-red　　　　　30　　15
  c. Watermark sideways (3.8.62)　10　　10
  d. Frame retouch (Sideways coil,
　　Roll 7) ..　　..　　..　　..　1·00

D. Type II. Whiter Paper (7 May 1962)

S57　　574　　　　　　　　Carmine-red　　　　　5　　5
  a. Watermark inverted (29.7.62)　15　　15　　*c.* Watermark Crown to right　..　20　　20
  b. Watermark Crown to left　　　　　　*d.* Watermark Crown to left (coil)
　　(1.7.64) ..　..　　..　　..　20　　20　　　(9.65) ..　　.. *Strip of three*　1·75

E. Type II. Chalky Paper Booklets only (15 July 1963)

S58　　574k　　　　　　　Carmine-red　　　　　10　　10
  a. Watermark inverted (15.7.63)　12　　12

No. S56b was only issued in F coils.

Imperf. stamps. No. S55b comes from a booklet with watermark upright and No. S55c is from an M coil with sideways watermark.

Sideways watermark. Nos. S56a, S56c and S57d came from M coils with sideways delivery and Nos. S57b/c are from 2/- Holiday Booklets No. NR2.

For illustration of Nos. S56ab and S56d, see No. S50c. No. S56d is known in a second state showing a vertical line adjoining the right-hand frame not filled in with colour.

Cylinder Numbers (Blocks of Six)

Type II. Cream Paper
Perforation Type A

Cyl. No.					No dot	Dot	Perforation Type B (no dot) and C (dot)						

Type II. Cream Paper — Perforation Type A

Cyl. No.	No dot	Dot
50	50	50
51	50	50
52	50	50
53	50	50
54	50	50

Perforation Type B (no dot) and C (dot)

Cyl. No.	No dot	Dot
50	70	70
51	70	70
52	60	60

Type I. Cream Paper
Perforation Type A

42	2·50	2·50

Type II. Whiter Paper
Perforation Type A

50	35	35
51	35	35
52	35	35
53	35	35
54	35	35
55	35	35
56	35	35

Perforation Type A

57	35	35
58	35	35
59	35	35

Perforation Type B (no dot) and C (dot)

51	50	50
52	45	45

Minor Constant Sheet Flaws

Minimum price as singles: 35p

Cyl. 42	1/4	Red spot over left of crown (Th. A3)
	12/4	Red spot in leaf of shamrock (Th. G1)
Cyl. 42.	4/1	Red and white dots in oval (Th. B2)
	5/8	Red dot in thistle (Th. G2)
	11/9	White spot in R of E R
	14/5	Slight retouch in forehead above Queen's right eye (Th. C2)
	16/3	White dot between thistle and leaf (Th. G2)
	17/2	Small white flaw on tail of R of E R
	18/10	Red dot between Queen's lip and nose (Th. D3). Later partially removed
	20/10	White flaw by oval at left (Th. D1–2)
Cyl. 50.	6/10	Background retouched behind P of POSTAGE and R of REVENUE
Cyl. 51.	7/5	Retouch to left of hair (Th. C2)
	9/6	White dot at bottom left of R of REVENUE

Booklet Panes of Six (Type II)

Cream or whiter paper
From 5/– Booklets H36*b*/*c*, *e* and H37/74 and 10/– Booklets X3/9

SB58 Watermark upright	25		SB58a Watermark inverted	60

Booklet Panes of Four (Type II)

Chalky paper
From 2/– Booklet NR1/1*a*

SB58b Watermark upright	30		SB58c Watermark inverted	35

Se-tenant Panes of Four from Holiday Booklets

For booklet panes of Nos. S57*b*/*c* *se-tenant* with ½d. value, see No. SB11 and for panes of No. S58 *se-tenant* with ½d., see No. SB10, where a variety is listed on the 2½d.

Booklet Cylinder Numbers

Panes of six (21-row cylinders)

Cream paper						Whiter paper					
Cyl. No				No dot	Dot	Cyl. No.				No dot	Dot
J6 ..	..	..	..	1·00	1·00	J13 ..	..	..	..	1·50	1·50
J6 T	..	..	..	1·00	1·00	J13 T	..	..	..	1·50	1·50
J8 ..	..	..	..	3·50	3·50	J14 ..	..	..	..	2·00	2·00
J8 T	..	..	..	3·50	3·50	J14 T	..	..	..	2·00	2·00
J9 ..	..	..	..	1·00	1·00						
J9 T	..	..	..	1·00	1·00						
J13 ..	..	..	..	1·00	1·00						
J13 T	..	..	..	1·00	1·00						

Se-tenant panes of four

For 2½d. Nos. S57*b*/*c*, cyl. J15, see after No. SB11. No cylinder numbers are known on No. S58.

Coils

Single pane cylinder L3 was used for the vertical delivery coils and cylinders L2 for sideways delivery Type I coils and L5 for Type II coils.

Printed in continuous reels

	Code No.	Number in roll	Face value	
	(a) Vertical delivery. Watermark upright			
	F	960	£10	Type I. Cream or whiter paper
	(b) Sideways delivery. Watermark sideways			
	M	480	£5	Type I. Cream or whiter paper
	M	480	£5	Type II. Whiter paper

Sheet Markings

Guide holes: Boxed opposite rows 14/15, at left (no dot) or right (dot)
Marginal arrows: In Type II these exist hand-engraved at left as well as photo-etched. Also sheets are known with the arrows omitted at bottom
Others: As given in General Notes

Cat. No.	S.G. No.	Shades	Unused	Used

1959 (JUNE 9). WITH GRAPHITE LINES, TYPE S8. WATERMARK CROWNS. TYPE II

S59   591   Carmine-red   1·00   1·00
   a. Watermark inverted (21.8.59)   4·25   4·25

Cylinder Numbers (Blocks of Six)

Single pane cylinder

Cyl. No.	Perf. Type	No dot
49	B ..	7·00
49	C ..	7·00

Booklet Panes of Six

From 5/– Booklets HG1/3
SB59 Watermark upright   5·00   SB59a Watermark inverted   22·00

Booklet Cylinder Numbers

Panes of six (21-row cylinders)

Cyl. No.				No dot	Dot	Cyl. No.				No dot	Dot
J6 ..	..	..	..	17·00	12·00	J9 ..	..	..	..	12·00	12·00
J6 T	..	..	..	12·00	12·00	J9 T	..	..	..	12·00	12·00

Sheet Markings

As for No. S54

Quantity Issued   10,022,800

1959 (NOVEMBER 18). PHOSPHOR-GRAPHITE ISSUE. WATERMARK CROWNS. TYPE II

This has two graphite lines (Type **S9**), on the back and two phosphor bands on the front, which react green under the lamp.

S60   606   Carmine-red   1·00   1·00

Cylinder Numbers (Blocks of Six)

Single pane cylinder

Cyl. No.	Perf. Type	No dot
49	B ..	7·00
49	C ..	7·00

Sheet Markings

As for No. S54

Quantity Issued   689,280

1960 (JUNE 22). TWO PHOSPHOR BANDS REACTING GREEN. WMK. CROWNS. TYPE II

The bands were applied in photogravure.

S61   —   Carmine-red   50   50
   a. Watermark inverted (9.60) .. 12·00   12·00

Cylinder Numbers (Blocks of Six)

Perforation Type B (no dot) and C (dot)

Cyl. No.				No dot	Dot
50 ..	..	.	..	3·50	3·50

Minor Constant Sheet Flaws

Minimum price as singles: £1

Cyl. 50.   6/10 Background retouch behind P of POSTAGE and R of REVENUE

Booklet Panes of Six

From 5/– Booklet HP1
SB60 Watermark upright   2·50   SB60a Watermark inverted   60·00

Booklet Cylinder Numbers

Panes of six (21-row cylinder)

Cyl. No.				No dot	Dot	Cyl. No.				No dot	Dot
J13 ..	..	..	..	12·00	12·00	J13 T	..	..	..	12·00	12·00

Sheet Markings

Guide holes: Boxed opposite rows 14/15, at left (no dot) or right (dot)
Black bar: This occurs by the marginal arrows opposite rows 10/11, at left (no dot) or right (dot)
Others: As given in General Notes

Cat. No.	S.G. No.	Shades	Unused	Used

1961 (JUNE 5). PHOSPHOR BANDS REACTING BLUE. WATERMARK CROWNS.
A. Two Bands (applied photo.). Type II. Cream Paper

S62 — Carmine-red
   a. Watermark inverted (3.61) .. 12·00   12·00   35   35

B. One Band at left (applied typo.). Type II. Cream Paper (4 October 1961)

S63   614*a*   Carmine-red
   a. Band applied photo. (3.11.61)   12   12   50   50
   b. Watermark inverted (3.62) ..   3·00   3·00

C. One Band at left (applied typo.). Type I. Cream Paper (7 November 1961)

S64   614*b*   Carmine-red
   a. One band at right .. ..   2·00   1·75   1·75
   b. Bands omitted, in pair with one
     band at right .. .. ..   2·50

D. One Band at left (applied typo.). Type II. Whiter paper (13 June 1962)

S65 — Carmine-red
   a. Band applied photo. (22.6.62)   20   20   75   75
   b. Watermark inverted (3.6.63)   3·00   3·00

E. Two Bands (applied photo.). Type II. Whiter Paper (20 September 1964)

S66   614   Carmine-red
   a. Bands applied typo   5   5

No. S66 was a reissue of No. S62 but from cylinder 57 and on whiter paper. The shade is slightly more carmine. It was first released in error in the S.E. London area in September 1964 and then put on sale in Birmingham in March 1965 as electronic sorting machines were not in use there at that time. To prepare for the alteration in postal rates on 17th May 1965 when the 2½d. ceased to be the second class mail rate, it was released in the phosphor areas on 3 May 1965 in place of the single band stamps. However, as there was no longer a postal need for this value it was not reprinted.

Cylinder Numbers (Blocks of Six)

Two bands. Type II. Cream paper. Perforation Type A

Cyl. No.				No dot	Dot		Cyl. No.		No dot	Do
50 ..	..	..	..	3·00	3·00					

One band. Type II. Cream paper
Perforation Type A   Perforation Type B (no dot) or C (dot)
   Applied typo.   Applied photo.

50 ..	..	..	..	..	5·00	5·00		50 ..	..	..	..	..	2·00	2·00
								53 ..	..	..	..	..	2·00	2·00

One band. Type I. Cream paper. Perforation Type A
42 .. .. 12·00 12·00

Type II. Whiter paper. Perforation Type A
   One band   Two bands
   Applied typo.

50 (applied photo.)		..	..	3·00	3·00						
51 ..	..	..	..	..	2·00	2·00					
52 ..	..	..	..	..	2·00	2·00					
54 ..	..	..	..	..	2·00	2·00					
56 ..	..	..	..	..	2·00	2·00					
57 ..	..	..	..	..	2·00	2·00		57 ..	..	..	..	..	60	60

Minor Constant Sheet Flaws

Minimum price as singles: 75p

As recorded for Nos. S55/7

Booklet Panes of Six (Type II)

Two bands. Cream paper. From 5/– Booklets HP2/5

SB61 Watermark upright	2·50	SB61a Watermark inverted	60·00

One band. Cream or whiter paper. From 5/– Booklets HP6/25

SB62 Watermark upright	25	SB62a Watermark inverted	13·00

Booklet Cylinder Numbers (Type II)

Panes of six (21-row cylinders)

Two bands. Cream paper

Cyl. No.				No dot	Dot	Cyl. No.				No dot	Dot
J13 ..	..	..	..	12·00	12·00	J13 T	..	..	..	12·00	12·00

One band. Cream or whiter paper

J13 ..	..	..	..	2·00	2·00	J13 T	..	..	..	2·00	2·00

One band. Whiter paper

J14 ..	..	..	..	2·00	2·00	J14 T	..	..	..	2·00	2·00

Sheet Markings

Guide holes: Boxed opposite rows 14/15, at left (no dot) or right (dot)
Others: As given in General Notes

1954–67. 3d. Deep lilac, Type S2

Variations in the Multipositives

There are similar variations in the tilt of the portrait in the multipositives used as occurred in the 2½d. value (see notes and illustration at the beginning of the 2½d. list).

The second multipositive, corresponding to Type B, was used for cylinders 25 to 33 and the third multipositive, corresponding to Type C, was employed for cylinders 36 and 37. A fourth multipositive, also Type C, was introduced for cylinders 41 onwards.

Cat. No.	S.G. No.	Shades	Unused	Used
1954 (JANUARY 18). WATERMARK TUDOR CROWN, TYPE W.22			15	5

S67	520	Deep lilac	

a. Imperf. between stamp and top
    margin .. .. 55·00

b. Coil join (horiz. pair) 35   *d.* Cancelled two vert. black bars

c. Coil join (vert. pair) 50   (P.O.T.S.) 10

Cylinder Numbers (Blocks of Six)

Perforation Type A						Perforation Type B (no dot) and C (dot)					
Cyl. No.				No dot	Dot	Cyl. No.				No dot	Dot
3 ..	..	..	..	1·25	1·25	3 ..	..	..	..	1·25	1·25

Minor Constant Sheet Flaws

Minimum price as singles: 50p

Multipositive flaws

No dot	1/3 White scratch to bottom right of R of large E R (Th. A–B6)
Dot	9/8 Dark patch to left of central cross of tiara (Th. B3)

Coils

Made up from sheets with sheet margin joins. Watermark upright

Code No.	Number in roll	Face value	
C	960	£12	Vertical delivery
S	480	£6	Sideways delivery

Sheet Markings

Guide holes: Boxed opposite rows 14/15, at left (no dot) or right (dot)
Others: As given in General Notes

Cat. No.	S.G. No.		Shades	Unused	Used

1956 (JULY 17).   WATERMARK ST. EDWARD'S CROWN, TYPE W.23

S68   545   Deep lilac   12   5
 a. Tête-bêche (horiz. pair)   .. 60·00
 b. Imperf. three sides (pair)   .. 45·00
 c. Imperf. between stamp and   *g.* Coil join (vert. pair)   50
       bottom margin   ..   .. 60·00   *h.* White   dot   on   laurel   leaf
 d. Watermark inverted (1.10.57)   20   15   (Booklet pane R.1/2 or 2/2) .. 1·00
 e. Watermark sideways (22.11.57)   75   60   *i.* Cancelled two vert. black bars
 f. Coil join (horiz. pair)   30   (P.O.T.S.)   10

Stamps with sideways watermark are from S coils with sideways delivery.

Listed Variety

S68*h*

Cylinder Numbers (Blocks of Six)

Perforation Type A

Cyl. No.					No dot	Dot	Cyl. No.					No dot	Dot
2 ..	..	..	..	..	1·00	1·00	10 ..	..	..	..	..	1·00	1·00
3 ..	..	..	..	..	1·00	1·00	15 ..	..	..	..	..	1·00	1·00
4 ..	..	..	..	..	1·00	1·00	16 ..	..	..	..	..	1·00	1·00
5 ..	..	..	..	..	1·00	1·00	17 ..	..	..	..	..	1·00	1·00
9 ..	..	..	..	..	1·00	1·00							

Perforation Type B (no dot) and C (dot)

2 ..	..	..	..	..	1·50	1·50	3 ..	..	..	..	..	1·50	1·50

Perforation Type F (L)

5 ..	..	..	..	..	4·00	†	

Minor Constant Sheet Flaws

Minimum price as singles: 50p

Multipositive flaws

No dot   1/3 White scratch to bottom right of R of large E R (Th. A–B6)
Dot   9/8 Dark patch to left of central cross of tiara (Th. B3)

Cylinder flaw

Cyl. 17   17/3 Coloured scratches through E of large E R (Th. A1)

Booklet Panes of Six

From 3/- Booklets M1/9, 4/6 Booklets L1/7 and 5/- Booklets H32/6
SB63 Watermark upright   60   SB63a Watermark inverted   1·00

Booklet Panes of Four

From 2/- Booklet N1
SB64 Watermark upright   40   SB64a Watermark inverted   60
   No cylinder numbers were used.

Booklet Cylinder Numbers

Panes of six (K8 20-row cylinder, others 21-row cylinders)

Cyl. No.					No dot	Dot	Cyl. No.					No dot	Dot
K1 ..	..	..	..	..	2·50	2·50	K7 ..	..	..	..	..	2·50	2·50
K1 T	..	..	..	..	2·50	2·50	K7 T	..	..	..	..	2·50	2·50
K2 ..	..	..	..	..	2·50	2·50	K8 ..	..	..	..	..	2.50	2·50
K2 T	..	..	..	..	2·50	2·50							

Coils

(a) Made up from sheets with sheet margin joins. Watermark upright

Code No.	Number in roll	Face value	
C	960	£12	Vertical delivery
S	480	£6	Sideways delivery

(b) Printed in continuous reels. Double pane cylinders M1 and M2 were used for the vertical delivery coils but the number for the sideways delivery coil is unknown

Code No.	Number in roll	Face value

(a) Vertical delivery. Watermark upright

C	960	£12
U	1920	£24

(b) Sideways delivery. Watermark sideways

S	480	£6

Sheet Markings

Guide holes:
  Perf. Types A, B and C, boxed opposite rows 14/15, at left (no dot) or right (dot)
  Perf. Type F (L), not known

Marginal arrows:
  " V " shaped, hand engraved at top and bottom
  " W " shaped, photo-etched at both sides
  Early printings from cylinder 2 no dot had the " V " shaped arrow omitted from the bottom of the sheet.
  (Price for positional block showing arrow omitted £4)

Marginal rule: These vary in width between 1½ and 2½ mm.

Others: As given in General Notes

Cat. No.	S.G. No.	Shades	Unused	Used

1957 (NOVEMBER 19). WITH GRAPHITE LINES, TYPE S8. WMK. ST. EDWARD'S CROWN

S69	566	3d. Deep lilac	35	10
a. Coil join (horiz. pair) ..	.. 1·25			

Cylinder Numbers (Blocks of Six)

Single pane cylinders

Cyl. No.	Perf. Type		No dot
7	B	..	2·50
7	C	..	2·50
11	B	..	2·50
11	C	..	2·50

Coils

Made up from sheets with sheet margin joins. Watermark upright

Code No.	Number in roll	Face value	
S	480	£6	Sideways delivery

Sheet Markings

Guide holes: Boxed opposite rows 14/15, at both sides and unboxed opposite rows 1 and 7/8, at both sides
Others: As given in General Notes

Quantities Issued   91,466,400

Cat. No.	S.G. No.		Shades	Unused	Used

1958 (DECEMBER 8).† WATERMARK CROWNS, TYPE W.24

A. Cream Paper

S70 — Deep lilac 8 5

a.	Imperf. pane**	.. .. ..	80·00	
b.	Part perf. pane**	.. ..	70·00	
c.	Imperf. between stamp and top margin	.. ..	60·00	
d.	Watermark Crown to left (Coils, 24.10.58 and booklets, 26.5.61)		15	15
e.	Watermark inverted (11.58) ..		15	12
f.	Watermark Crown to right (Booklets, 26.5.61)		20	20
g.	Spot on T of POSTAGE (Cyl. 37, R.19/11)		75	

h.	Phantom " R " (Cyl. 37, below R.20/12)	15·00	
i.	Do. Retouch	2·00	
j.	Phantom " R " (Cyl. 41, below R.20/12)	£130	
k.	Do. First retouch	1·75	
l.	Do. Second or third retouch ..	1·75	
m.	Cancelled two vert. black bars (P.O.T.S.)	10	

B. Whiter Paper (30 April 1962)

S71 575 Deep lilac 5 5

a.	Watermark Crown to left (Coils, 30.4.62 and booklets, 5.6.62)		10	15
b.	Watermark Crown to right (Booklets, 5.6.62)		15	15

c.	Watermark inverted (16.7.62)		8	5
d.	Experimental " T " watermark*	1·25		
e.	Flaw on E (R.14/11 on Cyls. 69. and others)		60	

**Booklet errors—See General Notes.

†In 1964 No. S71 was printed from Cylinder 70 no dot and dot on an experimental paper which is distinguished by an additional watermark letter "T" lying on its side, which occurs about four times in the sheet, usually in the side margins where it is easiest to see. It is difficult to see when it occurs on the stamps themselves. 48,000 sheets were issued. Price is for marginal block of 8.

See the notes at the beginning of the 3d. list about the variations in the tilt of the portrait on the different multipositives used.

Listed Varieties

S70g

S71e

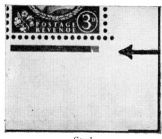

S70h

S70j, S74b   S70k

An incomplete marginal rule revealed an " R " on cyls. 37 and 41 no dot. It is more noticeable on the latter because of the wider marginal rule. The retouch on cyl. 37 is not easily identified. There is no trace of the " R " but the general appearance of that part of the marginal rule is uneven. However, the retouch can be confirmed in a positional block by the presence of the " Spot on T " variety on R.19/11, No. S70g.

The "R" on cyl. 41 was retouched three times, the first being as illustrated here (No. S70k) and traces of the "R" can still be seen in the others.

The rare variety, No. S70j, is best collected in a block of 4 or 6 with full margins in order to be sure that it is not No. S74b with phosphor lines removed.

Cylinder Numbers (Blocks of Six)

A. Cream paper
Perforation Type A

Cyl. No.					No dot	Dot	Cyl. No.					No dot	Dot
15	..	..	..	..	60	60	46	..	..	..	..	60	60
16	..	..	..	..	6·00	6·00	47	..	..	..	..	60	60
22	..	..	..	..	60	60	49	..	..	..	..	60	60
25	..	..	..	..	60	60	51	..	..	..	..	60	60
26	..	..	..	..	60	60	52	..	..	..	..	60	60
28	..	..	..	..	60	60	53	..	..	..	..	60	60
29	..	..	..	..	60	60	54	..	..	..	..	60	60
30	..	..	..	..	60	60	55	..	..	..	..	60	60
31	..	..	..	..	60	60	58	..	..	..	..	60	60
33	..	..	..	..	60	60	60	..	..	..	..	60	60
36	..	..	..	..	60	60	61	..	..	..	..	60	60
37	..	..	..	..	60	60	62	..	..	..	..	60	60
41	..	..	..	..	60	60							

Perforation Type B (no dot) and C (dot)

					No dot	Dot						No dot	Dot
28	..	..	..	..	1·00	1·00	52	..	..	..	..	1·00	1·00
41*	..	..	..	..	1·00	†	54	..	..	..	..	1·00	1·00
51	..	..	..	..	1·00	1·00							

Perforation Type H

					No dot	Dot						No dot	Dot
31	..	..	..	..	†	6·00	37	..	..	..	..	†	6·00
36	..	..	..	..	†	6·00	41	..	..	..	..	†	6·00

B. Whiter paper
Perforation Type A

					No dot	Dot						No dot	Dot
51	..	..	..	..	40	†	69	..	..	..	..	40	40
52	..	..	..	..	40	40	70	..	..	..	..	40	40
54	..	..	..	..	40	40	71	..	..	..	..	40	40
58	..	..	..	..	40	40	72	..	..	..	..	40	40
60	..	..	..	..	40	40	73	..	..	..	..	40	40
61	..	..	..	..	40	40	75	..	..	..	..	40	40
62	..	..	..	..	40	40	78	..	..	..	..	40	40
63	..	..	..	..	40	40	79	..	..	..	..	40	40
64	..	..	..	..	40	40	80	..	..	..	..	40	40
66	..	..	..	..	40	40	81	..	..	..	..	40	40
67	..	..	..	..	40	40	82	..	..	..	..	40	40
68	..	..	..	..	40	40							

*This has been seen Perf. Type B (no dot) and may be an example of No. S74 with phosphor bands omitted.

Minor Constant Sheet Flaws

Minimum price as singles: 45p

Multipositive flaws (Cyls. 15, 16 and 22 only)

| No dot | 1/3 | White scratch to bottom right of R of large E R (Th. A–B6) |
| Dot | 9/8 | Dark patch to left of central cross of tiara (Th. B3) |

Cylinder flaws

Cyl. 46. 20/2 White flaw on leaves of oval at left (Th. E–F1)
Cyl. 52 17/9 White spur to circle around 3d. by D (Th. G6)
Cyl. 52. 18/2 Coloured line from Queen's hair to top of oval (Th. B2)
Cyl. 60. 4/11 Coloured flaw on thistle leaf (Th. G2)
Cyl. 70. 10/4 White flaw above PO of POSTAGE (Th. G3)
   10/11 White flaw on daffodil stem giving appearance of thick stalk (Th. G–H2)
   19/8 Coloured scratch from tiara to oval (Th. C5)

Booklet Panes of Six

Cream or whiter paper
From 3/– Booklets M10/74, 4/6 Booklets L8/58, 5/– Booklets H36d/e and H37/74 and 10/– Booklets X1/14

SB65 Watermark upright	25	SB65a Watermark inverted	40

Booklet Panes of Four

Cream paper
From 2/– Booklets N2/3

SB66 Watermark upright	15	SB66a Watermark inverted	25

No cylinder numbers were used.

Cream or whiter paper. Sideways watermark
From 2/– Booklets N4/20 and NX1

SB67 Wmk. Crown to left	45	SB67a Wmk. Crown to right	45

Se-tenant Booklet Panes of Four

For booklet panes of Nos. S71a/b *se-tenant* with 1d. value, see No. SB29.

Booklet Cylinder Numbers

Panes of six (K13 and K15 20-row cylinders, others 21-row cylinders)

	Cream paper					Whiter paper			
Cyl. No.				No dot	Dot	Cyl. No.				No dot	Dot

Cyl. No.					No dot	Dot	Cyl. No.					No dot	Dot
K7 ..	..	..	..	..	1·25	1·25	K15 ..	..	..	..	..	1.50	1·50
K7 T	..	..	..	..	1·25	1·25	K16 ..	..	..	..	..	3·00	3·00
K13 ..	..	..	..	..	1·25	1·25	K18 ..	..	..	..	..	1·00	1·00
K15 ..	..	..	..	..	1·50	1·50	K18 T	..	..	..	..	1·00	1·00
K17 ..	..	..	..	..	1·25	1·25	K20 ..	..	..	..	..	1·00	1·00
K17 T	..	..	..	..	1·25	1·25	K20 T	..	..	..	..	1·00	1·00
K18 ..	..	..	..	..	1·25	1·25	K21 ..	..	..	..	..	1·00	1·00
K18 T	..	..	..	..	1·25	1·25	K21 T	..	..	..	..	1·00	1·00
K20 ..	..	..	..	..	1·25	1·25							
K20 T	..	..	..	..	1·25	1·25							

Panes of four

In the 2/- Booklets (N4/20 and NX1) the cylinder numbers were usually trimmed off.

Se-tenant panes of four

For 3d. Nos. S71a/b, cyl. K22, see after No. SB29

Coils

Printed in continuous reels. Double pane cylinder M2 was used for the vertical delivery coils and cylinders M9, M10 and M11 for the sideways delivery coils.

Code No.	Number in roll	Face value

(a) Vertical delivery. Watermark upright. Cream or whiter paper

C	960	£12
U	1920	£24
AC	480	£6
AD	960	£12

(b) Sideways delivery. Watermark sideways. Cream or whiter paper

| S | 480 | £6 |

Sheet Markings

Guide holes: Boxed opposite rows 14/15, at left (no dot) or right (dot). On the later cylinders there are single "S N" boxes for the guide holes

Marginal arrows: These vary from cylinder to cylinder. The following combinations are known:—
(a) All hand engraved. "V" shaped at top and bottom; "W" shaped at both sides
(b) "V" shaped, hand engraved at top and bottom; "W" shaped, photo-etched at both sides
(c) All photo-etched. "W" shaped at top and bottom and at both sides

Marginal rule: These vary in width from between 1½ and 2½ mm.

Others: As given in General Notes

Cat. No.	S.G. No.		Shades		Unused	Used

1958 (NOVEMBER 24).   WITH GRAPHITE LINES, TYPE S8. WATERMARK CROWNS

S72	592		Deep lilac		25	25

a. Watermark inverted (4.8.59)   30   30
b. Two lines at left (5.61)   .. 15·00
c. Three lines   30

d. One line   ..   ..   .. 3·00
e. Coil join (horiz. pair) ..   .. 1·50

The misplaced graphite lines (varieties *b/d*) came from sheets from cyls. 51 no dot and dot printed after the graphite line experiment had ended to use up residual stock of graphite-lined paper. (*Price for cylinder block, perf. Type A, £35.*)

Cylinder Numbers (Blocks of Six)

Single pane cylinder

Cyl. No.	Perf. Type	No dot
11	B	.. 2·00
11	C	.. 2·00

Booklet Panes of Six

From 3/- Booklets MG1/6, 4/6 Booklets LG1/5 and 5/- Booklets HG1/3
SB68 Watermark upright   1·25   SB68a Watermark inverted   1·50

Booklet Cylinder Numbers

Panes of 6 (K7 21-row cylinder, others 20-row cylinders)

Cyl. No.					No dot	Dot	Cyl. No.				No dot	Dot
K7 ..	..	..	..	..	2·50	2·50	K13 ..	..	..	..	5·00	5·00
K7 T	..	..	..	..	2·50	2·50	K15 ..	..	..	..	4·00	4·00

Coils

Printed in continuous reels. Double-pane cylinder M1 was used. Watermark upright.

Code No.	Number in roll	Face value	
C	960	£12	Vertical delivery

Made up from sheets with sheet margin joins. Watermark upright

S	480	£6	Sideways delivery

Sheet Markings

As for No. S69

Quantity Issued   57,222,960

Cat. No.	S.G. No.		Shades	Unused	Used

1959 (NOVEMBER 18).   PHOSPHOR-GRAPHITE ISSUE. WATERMARK CROWNS

This has two graphite lines, Type **S8**, on the back and two phosphor bands on the front, which react green under the lamp.

S73	607		Deep lilac	1·25	1·25

Cylinder Numbers (Blocks of Six)

Single pane cylinder

Cyl. No.	Perf. Type	No dot
11	B	.. 9·00
11	C	.. 9·00

Sheet Markings

As for No. S69

Quantity Issued   4,654,040

1960 (JUNE 22).   TWO PHOSPHOR BANDS REACTING GREEN. WMK. CROWNS

The bands were applied in photogravure.

S74	—	Deep Lilac	60	40

a. Watermark inverted (14.8.60)   75   75
b. Phantom "R" (Cyl. 41, below R.20/12) .. .. .. 6·00
For illustration of No. S74*b*, see No. S70*j*.

Cylinder Numbers (Blocks of Six)

Perforation Type B (no dot) and C (dot)

Cyl. No.				No dot	Dot
41 ..	..	..	..	5·00	5·00

Booklet Panes of Six

From 3/– Booklets MP1/3 and MP6, 4/6 Booklets LP1/2 and LP4 and 5/– Booklet HP1
SB69 Watermark upright   3·00   SB69a Watermark inverted   4·00

Booklet Cylinder Numbers

Panes of Six (21-row cylinders)

Cyl. No.					No dot	Dot	Cyl. No.				No dot	Dot
K17 ..	..	..	..	..	5·00	5·00	K17 T	..	..	..	6·00	6·00

Sheet Markings

Guide holes: Not known
Black bar: This occurs by the marginal arrows opposite rows 10/11, at left (no dot) or right (dot)
Others: As given in General Notes

Cat. No.	S.G. No.	Shades	Unused	Used

1961 (JUNE 5).† PHOSPHOR BANDS REACTING BLUE. WATERMARK CROWNS

The bands were all applied in photogravure.

A. Two Bands. Cream Paper

S75 — Deep lilac ... 12 10
  a. Watermark inverted (3.61) ... 25 15
  b. Watermark Crown to left
    (14.7.61) 40 40
      c. Watermark Crown to right .. 40 40
      d. One broad band in centre .. 1·25

B. Two Bands. Whiter Paper (24 October 1962)†

S76 615 Deep lilac ... 12 8
  a. Watermark Crown to left
    (15.8.62) 30 20
  b. Watermark Crown to right .. 30 20
      c. Watermark inverted (25.9.62) 20 12

C. One Side Band*. Whiter Paper (29 April 1965)

S77 — Deep lilac (band at left) 8 8
  a. Band at right .. 5 5
  b. Watermark Crown to left, band
    at left (16.8.65) 30 30
      d. Watermark Crown to right,
        band at left 30 30
  c. Watermark Crown to left, band
    at right 30 30
      e. Watermark Crown to right,
        band at right 30 30

*The one side band stamps were produced by an 8 mm. band applied down alternate vertical rows of the sheet over the perforations so that alternate stamps have the band at left (No. S77) or right (No. S77a). In theory the width of the band on a single stamp should be 4 mm. but this will vary if the bands have not been perfectly positioned.

Cylinder Numbers (Blocks of Six)

Two bands. Cream paper. Perforation Type B (no dot) and C (dot)

Cyl. No.	No dot	Dot	Cyl. No.	No dot	Dot
52	1·25	1·25	60	1·25	1·25

Whiter paper. Perforation Type A

Two bands			One side band		
60	90	90	67	90	90
61	90	90	68	90	90
62	90	90	72	90	90
64	90	90			
67	90	90			
71	90	90			

Minor Constant Sheet Flaws

Minimum price as singles: 60p

Cyl. 52 17/9 White spur to circle around 3d. by D (Th. G6)
Cyl. 52. 18/2 Coloured line from Queen's hair to top of oval (Th. B2)
Cyl. 60. 4/11 Coloured flaw on thistle leaf (Th. G2)

Booklet Panes of Six

Two bands. Cream or whiter paper.
From 3/- Booklets MP4/5, MP6a and MP7/38, 4/6 Booklets LP3 and LP4a/31 and 5/- Booklets HP2/25

SB70 Watermark upright 50   SB70a Watermark inverted 1·00

Booklet Panes of Four

Two bands. Cream or whiter paper. Sideways watermark
From 2/- Booklets NP1/13

SB71 Wmk. Crown to left 1·20   SB71a Wmk. Crown to right 1·20

Se-tenant Booklet Panes of Four

For booklet panes of Nos. S77b/e *se-tenant* with 1d. value, see No. SB34.

Booklet Cylinder Numbers

Panes of six (K15 20-row cylinder, others 21-row cylinders)
Two bands. Cream or whiter paper

Cyl. No.				No dot	Dot	Cyl. No.				No dot	Dot
K15 ..	..	..	..	1 75	1·75	K20 ..	..	..	..	1·75	1·75
K18 ..	..	..	..	1·50	1·50	K20 T	..	..	..	1·75	1·75
K18 T	..	..	..	1·50	1·50						

Panes of four (single pane cylinder)
   In the 2/– Booklets the cylinder numbers were usually trimmed off.

Se-tenant panes of four
   For 3d. Nos. S77b/e, cyl. K22, see after No. SB34.

Coils

Double pane cylinder M1 was used. Watermark upright.
Two bands. Vertical delivery in continuous reels. Cream or whiter paper

Code No.	Number in roll	Face value
U	1920	£24
AC	480	£6
AD	960	£12

One side band (left or right). Vertical delivery in continuous reels. Whiter paper

U	1920	£24
AC	480	£6
AD	960	£12

Sheet Markings

Guide holes: Boxed opposite rows 14/15, at left (no dot) or right (dot)
Marginal rules: These vary in width between 1 and 2½ mm.
Others: As given in General Notes

Cat. No.	S.G. No.	Shades	Unused	Used

1965 (AUGUST 13). PHOSPHOR BANDS REACTING VIOLET. WATERMARK CROWNS

The bands were all applied in photogravure.

A. One Side Band*

S78	615c	Deep lilac (band at left)	8	8

a. Band at right ..	..	..	8	8		
b. Watermark Crown to left, band at left (10.65)		..	30	30		
c. Watermark Crown to left, band at right ..	..	..	30	30		
d. Watermark Crown to right, band at left	..	..	30	30		

e. Watermark Crown to right, band at right ..	..	..	30	30
f. Watermark inverted (band at left) (2.67)†	..	..	75	75
g. Watermark inverted (band at right)†	..	..	35	35

B. One 4 mm. Centre Band (8 December 1966)

S79	615e	Deep Lilac	5	5

a. Watermark sideways (19.6.67)	15	8
b. Watermark inverted (8.67) ..	25	25

C. Two 9·5 mm. Bands. *Se-tenant* Booklets only (15 September 1967)

S80	—	Deep lilac (Watermark Crown to left)	20	20

a. Watermark Crown to right ..	20	20

*The one side band stamps were produced by an 8 mm. band applied down alternate vertical rows of the sheet over the perforations so that alternate stamps have the band at left (No. S78) or right (No. S78a). In theory the width of the band on a single stamp should be 4 mm. but this will vary if the bands have not been perfectly positioned. In addition, one side band stamps were produced by applying a 9·5 mm. band over the perforations but these only came in the October 1967 2/– Booklet (NP23a) *se-tenant* with the 1d. value as the result of an error. As it is not possible to distinguish these from the 8 mm. bands (Nos. S78b/e) *in singles*, the complete panes only are listed under No. SB38.
   †Nos. S78f/g only come from the 10/– Booklet of February 1967 (XP1/1a). Each pane comprises two stamps with band at left and four stamps with band at right.
   Sideways watermark. Nos. S78b/e come from 2/– Booklets NP15a, NP16a, NP17/23, No. S79a comes from S coils with sideways delivery and Nos. S80/a come from 2/– Booklets NP23a/6.

Cylinder Numbers (Blocks of Six)

Perforation Type A

Cyl. No.	One side band					No dot	Dot	Cyl. No.	One centre band					No dot	Dot
67 ..	..	..	..	..		40	40	78 ..	..	..	..	..	..	40	40
71 ..	..	..	..	..		40	40	79 ..	..	..	..	..	..	40	40
72 ..	..	..	..	..		40	40	81 ..	..	..	..	..	..	40	40
81 ..	..	..	..	..		40	40	82 ..	..	..	..	..	..	40	40
82 ..	..	..	..	..		40	40								

Booklet Panes of Six

One side band. From 10/– Booklet XP1/1a

SB72 Watermark upright　　　40　　　　SB72a Watermark inverted　　3·75

One centre band. From 10/– Booklets XP2/3

SB73 Watermark upright　　　25　　　　SB73a Watermark inverted　　1·25

Se-tenant Booklet Panes of Four

One side band. For booklet panes of Nos. S78b/e *se-tenant* with 1d. value, see No. SB36.
Two 9·5 mm. bands. For booklet panes of Nos. S80/a *se-tenant* with 1d. value, see No. SB38.

Booklet Cylinder Numbers

Panes of six (21-row cylinder)

Cyl. No.	One side band				No dot	Dot	Cyl. No.	One centre band				No dot	Dot
K18 ..	..	..	..	..	3·50	3·50	K18 ..	..	..	..	..	1·00	1·00
K18 T	..	..	..	..	3·50	3·50	K18 T	..	..	..	..	1·00	1 00

Se-tenant panes of four

For 3d. Nos. S78b/e and S80/a, cyl. K22, see after Nos. SB36 and SB38 respectively.

Coils

Double pane cylinder M2 was used for the vertical delivery coils and cylinder M11 for the sideways delivery coils.

(a) One side band. Vertical delivery printed in continuous reels with the watermark upright

Code No.	Number in roll	Face value
U	1920	£24
AC	480	£6
AD	960	£12

(b) One centre band. Printed in continuous reels

Code No.	Number in roll	Face value

(a) Vertical delivery. Watermark upright

AC	480	£6
AD	960	£12

(b) Sideways delivery. Watermark sideways

S	480	£6

Sheet Markings

Guide holes: Boxed opposite rows 14/15, at left (no dot) or right (dot). Later cylinders show single " S N " box

Marginal arrows: " W " shaped, photo-etched on all four sides

Marginal rules: These vary in width from cylinder to cylinder

Others: As given in General Notes

1953–67. 4d. Ultramarine, Type S3

Cat. No.	S.G. No.	Shades	Unused	Used

1953 (NOVEMBER 2). WATERMARK TUDOR CROWN, TYPE W.22

S81 521 Ultramarine 35 10
- *a.* Coil join (horiz. pr.) 80
- *b.* Dotted R (Cyl. 1, R.10/8) .. 6·00
- *c.* Cancelled two vert. black bars (P.O.T.S.) 15

Listed Variety

S81*b*, S82*c*

The blue dot is of varying size and was eventually touched out on the St. Edward's Crown watermark.

Cylinder Numbers (Blocks of Six)

Perforation Type A

Cyl. No.					No dot	Dot
1 ..	..	..	..	..	3·00	3·00

Perforation Type B (no dot) and C (dot)

Cyl. No.					No dot	Dot
1 ..	..	..	..	..	4·00	4·00

Minor Constant Sheet Flaws

Minimum price as singles: £1·25

Cyl. 1 1/4 Retouch on cheek left of ear (Th. D4)
16/9 Scar on neck. This was later the object of a major retouch (see No. S82*d*) but the original flaw is not available for illustrating and listing here

Coil

Made up from sheets with sheet margin joins. Sideways delivery with the watermark upright

Code No.	Number in roll	Face value
H	480	£8

Sheet Markings

Guide holes: Boxed opposite rows 14/15, at left (no dot) or right (dot)
Others: As given in General Notes

1955 (NOVEMBER 14). WATERMARK ST. EDWARD'S CROWN, TYPE W.23

S82 546 Ultramarine 50 8
- *a.* Coil join (vert. pr.) .. .. 1·50
- *b.* Coil join (horiz. pr.) .. .. 2·00
- *c.* Dotted R (Cyl. 1, R.10/8) .. 2·00
- *d.* Retouched neck (Cyl. 1, R.16/9) 1·50
- *e.* Cancelled two vert. black bars (P.O.T.S.) 15

For illustration of No. S82*c*, see No. S81*b*.

Listed Variety

S82*d*, S83*c*

This is the major retouch of the flaw described in this position on No. S81 and also under Minor Constant Sheet Flaws.

Cylinder Numbers (Blocks of Six)

Perforation Type A

Cyl. No.					No dot	Dot
1 ..	..	..	..	..	4·00	4·00
3 ..	..	..	..	..	5·00	5·00

Perforation Type B (no dot) and C (dot)

Cyl. No.					No dot	Dot
1 ..	..	..	..	..	4·00	4·00

Minor Constant Sheet Flaws

Minimum price as singles: £1

Cyl. 1   1/4 Retouch on cheek left of ear (Th. D4)
         16/9 Scar on neck before retouch as No. S82d

Coils

Made up from sheets with sheet margin joins with the watermark always upright

Code No.	Number in roll	Face value	
A	960	£16	Vertical delivery
H	480	£8	Sideways delivery

Sheet Markings

All as for No. S81

Cat. No.	S.G. No.	Shades	Unused	Used

1958 (OCTOBER 29).   WATERMARK CROWNS, TYPE W.24

A. Ultramarine. Cream Paper

S83   —   Ultramarine   35   10
  a. Coil join (vert. pair)   90
  b. Coil join (horiz. pair) ..   ..   1·00   *d.* Cancelled two vert. black bars
  c. Retouched neck (Cyl. 1, R.16/9) 1·00   (P.O.T.S.)   15

B. Ultramarine. Whiter Paper (18 October 1962)

S84   576   Ultramarine   30   8
  a. Coil join (vert. pair)   75
  b. Coil join (horiz. pair)   75

C. Deep Ultramarine†. Whiter Paper (28 April 1965)

S85   576a   Deep ultramarine   5   5
  a. Imperf. pane* ..   ..
  b. Imperf. between stamp and top
      margin ..   ..   45·00   *d.* Watermark inverted (21.6.65) 8   5
  c. Wmk. Crown to left (Coils,   *e.* Watermark Crown to right
      31.5.65 and booklets, 16.8.65)   8   8   (Booklets, 16.8.65)   8   8

†This "shade" was brought about by making more deeply etched cylinders from a new multipositive, resulting in apparent depth of colour in parts of the design but there is no difference in the colour of the ink. The change was made deliberately and coincided with the change in the first class letter rate from 3d. to 4d. on 17th May 1965.

*Booklet error—see General Notes.

For illustration of No. S83c, see No. S82d.

Cylinder Numbers (Blocks of Six)

Perforation Type A

(a) Ultramarine

	Cream Paper					
Cyl. No.					No dot	Dot
1 ..	..	..	..	..	2·40	2·40
6 ..	..	..	..	..	2·40	2·40
8 ..	..	..	..	..	2·40	2·40

	Whiter Paper					
Cyl. No.					No dot	Dot
8 ..	..	..	..	..	2·10	2·10

(b) Deep Ultramarine. Whiter Paper

Cyl. No.					No dot	Dot		Cyl. No.					No dot	Dot
12 ..	..	..	..	..	45	45		23 ..	..	..	..	..	45	45
13 ..	..	..	..	..	45	45		25 ..	..	..	..	..	45	45
16 ..	..	..	..	..	45	45		26 ..	..	..	..	..	45	45
18 ..	..	..	..	..	45	45		27 ..	..	..	..	..	45	45
20 ..	..	..	..	..	45	45								

Minor Constant Sheet Flaws

Minimum price as singles: 40p

Cyl. 1   1/4 Retouch on cheek left of ear (Th. D4)
           10/8 Darker shading to right of and below large R caused by retouching the dot variety
Cyl. 18 18/11 Two patches of retouching by frame at left (Th. C1)

Booklet Panes of Six

Deep ultramarine
From 4/6 Booklets L59/65, 6/– Booklets Q1/23 and 10/– Booklets X10/14

SB74 Watermark upright   25   SB74a Watermark inverted   40

Booklet Panes of Four

Deep ultramarine. Watermark sideways
From 2/– Booklets N21/27

SB75 Wmk. Crown to left   25   SB75a Wmk. Crown to right   25

Booklet Cylinder Numbers (Deep ultramarine)

Panes of six (21-row cylinders)

Cyl. No.					No dot	Dot	Cyl. No.					No dot	Dot
N1 ..	..	..	..	..	75	75	N1 T	..	..	..	..	75	75
N2 ..	..	..	..	..	75	75	N2 T	..	..	..	..	75	75
N3 ..	..	..	..	..	1·75	1·75	N3 T	..	..	..	..	1·75	1·75

Panes of four (20-row cylinder). Sideways watermark

N4 ..	..	..	..	..	1·00	1·00

Coils

(a) Ultramarine. Cream or whiter paper
Made up from sheets with sheet margin joins. Watermark upright

Code No.	Number in roll	Face value	
A	960	£16	Vertical delivery
H	480	£8	Sideways delivery

(b) Deep ultramarine
   Printed in continuous reels. It is believed that cylinder P1 was used for the vertical delivery coil and that it was a double pane cylinder but that cylinder P2 was used for the sideways delivery coil and that this was a single pane cylinder.

(a) Vertical delivery. Watermark upright

A	960	£16

(b) Sideways delivery. Watermark sideways

H	480	£8

Sheet Markings

Guide holes: Boxed opposite rows 14/15, at left (no dot) or right (dot)
   On the later cylinders there are double "S O N" boxes for the guide holes
Marginal rules: These vary in width and exist 1 mm., 2 mm. and 2½ mm. wide
Others: As given in General Notes

Cat. No.	S.G. No.		Shades	Unused	Used

1959 (APRIL 29). WITH GRAPHITE LINES, TYPE S9. WATERMARK CROWNS

S86	593		Ultramarine	1·25	1·25
a. Two lines at left	..	.. 90·00			

The misplaced graphite lines listed as No. S86*a* results in two lines at left (with the left line down the perforations) and traces of a third line down the opposite perforations.

Cylinder Numbers (Blocks of Six)

Perforation Type A

Cyl. No.					No dot	Dot
6 ..	..	..	..	..	9·00	9·00

Sheet Markings

   As for No. S83

Quantity Issued 6,891,600

Cat. No.	S.G. No.					Shades		Unused	Used

1959 (NOVEMBER 18). PHOSPHOR-GRAPHITE ISSUE. WATERMARK CROWNS

This has two graphite lines (Type **S8**), on the back and two phosphor bands on the front, which react green under the lamp.

S87	608		Ultramarine	1·25	1·25

Cylinder Numbers (Blocks of Six)

Perforation Type A

	Cyl. No.						No dot	Dot
	6 ..	..	..	..		..	9·00	9·00

Sheet Markings

As for No. S83

Quantity Issued   490,560

1960 (JUNE 22). TWO PHOSPHOR BANDS REACTING GREEN. WATERMARK CROWNS

The bands were applied in photogravure.   1·50 1·50

S88	—		Ultramarine	

Cylinder Numbers (Blocks of Six)

Perforation Type B (no dot) and C (dot)

	Cyl. No.						No dot	Dot
	8 ..	..	..	..		..	12·00	12·00

Sheet Markings

Guide holes: Boxed opposite rows 14/15, at left (no dot) or right (dot)
Black bar: This occurs by the marginal arrows opposite rows 10/11, at left (no dot) or right (dot)
Others: As given in General Notes

1961 (JUNE 5). TWO PHOSPHOR BANDS REACTING BLUE. WATERMARK CROWNS

The bands were applied in photogravure.

A. Ultramarine. Cream Paper

S89	616		Ultramarine	1·25	15
a. Broad band in centre ..	..	1·50			

B. Deep Ultramarine. Whiter Paper (15 April 1965)

S90	—		Deep ultramarine	15	12

a. Part perf. pane*   ..   ..
b. Watermark inverted (21.6.65)   30   30
c. Watermark Crown to left
(coils, 31.5.65 and booklets,
16.8.65)   20   20   *d.* Watermark Crown to right
(booklets, 16.8.65)   20   20

*Booklet error—see General Notes.

Cylinder Numbers (Blocks of Six)

(a) Ultramarine. Perforation Type B (no dot) and C (dot)

Cyl. No.					No dot	Dot	Cyl. No.			No dot	Dot
8 ..	..	..	..	..	10·00	10·00					

(b) Deep ultramarine. Perforation Type A

12 ..	..	..	..	..	1·25	1·25	18 ..	..	..	..	..	1·25	1·25
13 ..	..	..	..	..	1·25	1·25	20 ..	..	..	..	..	1·25	1·25

Minor Constant Sheet Flaws

Minimum price as singles: 75p

Cyl. 18 18/11 Two patches of retouching by frame at left (Th. C1)

Booklet Panes of Six

Deep ultramarine
From 4/6 Booklets LP32/3, LP34 and LP35, and 6/– Booklets QP1/8 without "a" numbers

SB76 Watermark upright	75	SB76a Watermark inverted	1·50

Booklet Panes of Four

Deep ultramarine. Watermark sideways
From 2/– Booklets NP14/15 and NP16

SB77 Wmk. Crown to left	75	SB77a Wmk. Crown to right	75

Booklet Cylinder Numbers (Deep Ultramarine)

Panes of six (21-row cylinder)

Cyl. No.					No dot	Dot	Cyl. No.				No dot	Dot
N1 ..	..	..	..	..	1·50	1·50	N1 T	..	..	..	1·50	1·50

Panes of four (20-row cylinder). Sideways watermark

N4 ..	..	..	..	..	1·50	1·75

Sheet Markings

As for Nos. S83/5

Cat. No.	S.G. No.	Shades	Unused	Used

1965 (AUGUST 13). TWO 8 mm. PHOSPHOR BANDS REACTING VIOLET. WMK. CROWNS

The bands were applied in photogravure only.

S91	—	Deep ultramarine	12	10
a. Watermark inverted (9.65) ..	25	25	
b. Wmk. Crown to left (10.65) ..	15	15	*c.* Wmk. Crown to right (10.65)..	15	15

Cylinder Numbers (Blocks of Six)

Perforation Type A

Cyl. No.					No dot	Dot	Cyl. No.				No dot	Dot
18 ..	..	..	..	..	80	80	20 ..	••	..	..	80	80

Minor Constant Sheet Flaws

Minimum price as singles: 60p

Cyl. 18 18/11 Two patches of retouching by frame at left (Th. C1)

Booklet Panes of Six

From 4/6 Booklets LP33a, LP34a and LP35a/38, 6/– Booklets QP4a, 5a, 6a, 7a, 8a and 9/20 and 10/– Booklet XP1

SB78 Watermark upright	60	SB78a Watermark inverted	1·25

Booklet Panes of Four

Watermark sideways. From 2/– Booklets NP15a, NP16a, NP17/23

SB79 Wmk. Crown to left	45	SB79a Wmk. Crown to right	45

Booklet Cylinder Numbers

Panes of six (21-row cylinders)

Cyl. No.					No dot	Dot	Cyl. No.				No dot	Dot
N1 ..	..	..	..	..	1·00	1·00	N1 T	..	..	..	1·00	1·00
N2 ..	..	..	..	..	1·00	1·00	N2 T	..	..	..	1·00	1·00
N3 ..	..	..	..	..	4·00	4·00	N3 T	..	..	..	4·00	4·00

Panes of four (20-row cylinder). Sideways watermark

N4 ..	..	..	..	..	1·50	1·50

Sheet Markings

As for Nos. S83/5

Cat. No.   S.G. No.   Shades   Unused Used

1967 (EARLY).   TWO 9·5 mm. PHOSPHOR BANDS REACTING VIOLET. WMK. CROWNS

The bands were applied in photogravure only.

S92	616a			Deep ultramarine	5	5
a.	Watermark inverted (2.67) ..	5	5			
b.	Wmk. Crown to left (Coils, 24.4.67 and booklets, 15.9.67)..	8	5	*c.* Wmk. Crown to right (Booklets, 15.9.67)	8	5

Cylinder Numbers (Blocks of Six)

Perforation Type A

Cyl. No.					No dot	Dot	Cyl. No.					No dot	Dot
16	..	..	..	..	40	40	26	..	..	..	..	40	40
18	..	..	..	..	40	40	27	..	..	..	..	40	40
23	..	..	..	..	40	40							

Minor Constant Sheet Flaws

Minimum price as singles: 50p

Cyl. 18 18/11 Two patches of retouching by frame at left (Th. C1)

Booklet Panes of Six

From 4/6 Booklets LP38a/44, 6/– Booklets QP21/27 and 10/– Booklets XP1a, XP2/3

SB80 Watermark upright	25	SB80a Watermark inverted	25

Booklet Panes of Four

Watermark sideways. From 2/– Booklets NP23a, NP24/6

SB81 Wmk. Crown to left	25	SB81a Wmk. Crown to right	25

Booklet Cylinder Numbers

Panes of six (21-row cylinders)

Cyl. No.					No dot	Dot	Cyl. No.					No dot	Do
N1	..	..	..	..	75	75	N1 T	..	..	..	..	75	75
N2	..	..	..	..	75	75	N2 T	..	..	..	..	75	75
N3	..	..	..	..	1·75	1·75	N3 T	..	..	..	..	1·75	1·75

Panes of four (20-row cylinder). Sideways watermark

N4	..	..	..	..	1·00

N4 ..   ..   1·00   1·00

Coil

Printed in continuous reels. It is believed that cylinder P2 was used and that it was a single pane cylinder.

Sideways delivery. Watermark sideways

Code No.	Number in roll	Face value
H	480	£8

Sheet Markings

As for Nos. S83/5

1959–66.   4½d. Chestnut, Type S3

1959 (FEBRUARY 9).   WATERMARK CROWNS, TYPE W.24

A. Cream Paper

S93	—		Chestnut	10 8
a.	Cancelled two vert. black bars (P.O.T.S.)	8		

B. Whiter Paper (29 May 1962)

S94	577		Chestnut	5 5
a.	Phantom frame (Cyl. 8, below R.20/12)	1·25		

Listed Variety

An incomplete marginal rule revealed a right-angled shaped frame-line on cylinder 8 no dot below R.20/12. Later retouched on No. S98.

S94*a*, S98*b*

Cylinder Numbers (Blocks of Six)
Perforation Type A

Cyl. No.					No dot	Dot	Cyl. No.					No dot	Dot
Cream paper							Whiter paper						
2 ..	..	..	..	..	1·25	1·25	7 ..	..	..	..	..	50	50
6 ..	..	..	..	..	1·00	1·00	8 ..	..	..	..	..	50	50
7 ..	..	..	..	..	80	80							

Minor Constant Sheet Flaws
Minimum price as singles: 50p

Multipositive flaw:
No dot   5/6   Pale top half of rose in bottom left corner (Th. F1–2)

Cylinder flaws

Cyl. 2   1/9   White spot on cheek level with mouth (Th. D3)
1/11   Break in bottom frame line at left corner
5/5   Three dots to right of curve in S of POSTAGE
10/8   White dot in laurel oval (Th. E6)
16/2   Dotted line in bottom right corner (Th. H6)
19/10   White dot on tail of R of E R
Cyl. 7   18/6   White flaw in thistle flower (Th. G2)

Sheet Markings
Guide holes: Boxed opposite rows 14/15, at left (no dot) or right (dot)
Others: As given in General Notes

Cat. No.	S.G. No.	Shades	Unused	Used

1959 (JUNE 3).   WITH GRAPHITE LINES, TYPE S8. WATERMARK CROWNS

| S95 | 594 | Chestnut | 1·10 | 1·10 |

Cylinder Numbers (Blocks of Six)
Perforation Type A

Cyl. No.					No dot	Dot
6 ..	..	..	..	..	7·50	7·50

Minor Constant Sheet Flaws
Minimum price as singles: £1·50

Cyl. 6   5/6   Pale top half of rose in bottom left corner (Th. F1–2)

Sheet Markings
As given for Nos. S93/4

Quantity Issued   5,388,480

Cat. No.   S.G. No.   Shades   Unused Used

1959 (NOVEMBER 18).   PHOSPHOR-GRAPHITE ISSUE. WATERMARK CROWNS

This has two graphite lines (Type **S8**), on the back and two phosphor bands on the front which react green under the lamp.

S96	609	Chestnut	7·00	5·00

Cylinder Numbers (Blocks of Six)

Perforation Type A

	No dot	Dot
Cyl. No.		
6	45·00	45·00

Minor Constant Sheet Flaws

Minimum price as singles: £9

Cyl. 6   5/6 Pale top half of rose in bottom left corner (Th. F1–2)

Sheet Markings

As given for Nos. S93/4

Quantity Issued   696,000

1961 (SEPTEMBER 13).   TWO PHOSPHOR BANDS REACTING BLUE. WATERMARK CROWNS

A. Cream Paper. Bands applied Typographically

S97	—	Chestnut	50	20

  a. Bands applied photo. (3.4.62).. 20 | 10

B. Whiter Paper. Bands applied in Photogravure (24 January 1963)

S98	616b	Chestnut	5	8

  a. Bands applied typo. (1966) ..   20   15
  b. Phantom frame (Cyl. 8, below
        R.20/12) ..   ..   ..   1·00

For illustration of No. S98*b*, see No. S94*a*.

Cylinder Numbers (Blocks of Six)

A. Cream Paper

Applied typo.			Applied photo.		
Perforation Type A			Perforation Type B (no dot) and C (dot)		
Cyl. No.	No dot	Dot	Cyl. No.	No dot	Dot
7	6·00	6·00	7	2·00	2·00

B. Whiter Paper

Applied photo.			Applied typo.		
Perforation Type A			Perforation Type A		
7	1·00	1·00	8	1·00	1·00
8	75	75			

Minor Constant Sheet Flaws

Minimum price as singles: 60p

Cyls. 7/8   5/6 Pale top half of rose in bottom left corner (Th. F1–2)
Cyl. 7   18/6 White flaw in thistle flower (Th. G2). Later retouched

Sheet Markings

As given for Nos. S93/4 except that the guide holes are in double boxes caused by the original box being inserted the wrong way and so another box was added on each pane, resulting in apparent double boxes

1953–67. 5d. Brown, Type S4

Cat. No.	S.G. No.		Shades			Unused	Used

1953 (JULY 6). WATERMARK TUDOR CROWN, TYPE W.22

S99   522   Brown   40   20

- *a.* Spot by E of POSTAGE (No dot, R.4/8) .. .. .. 1·50
- *b.* Spot on daffodil (No dot, R.10/12) .. .. 2·00
- *c.* Neck retouch (Cyl. 1., R.2/12) 1·50
- *d.* Cancelled two vert. black bars (P.O.T.S.) .. .. •• 8
- *e.* Overprinted "SCHOOL SPECIMEN" 15

Listed Varieties

S99/103*a*   S99/103*b*   S99/103*c*

These two varieties occur on
the multipositive

Cylinder Numbers (Blocks of Six)

Perforation Type A

Cyl. No.						No dot	Dot
1 ..	..	..	..	..		3·50	3·50

Sheet Markings

Guide holes: Boxed opposite rows 14/15, at left (no dot) or right (dot)
Others: As given in General Notes

1955 (SEPTEMBER 21). WATERMARK ST. EDWARD'S CROWN, TYPE W.23

S100   547   Brown   50   10

- *a.* Spot by E of POSTAGE (No dot, R.4/8) .. .. .. 1·25
- *b.* Spot on daffodil (No dot, R.10/12) .. .. .. 1·50
- *c.* Neck retouch (Cyl. 1., R.2/12) 1·00
- *d.* Cancelled two vert. black bars (P.O.T.S.) 8

For illustrations of Nos. S100*a/c*, see Nos. S99*a/c*.

Cylinder Numbers (Blocks of Six)

Perforation Type A

Cyl. No.						No dot	Dot
1 ..	..	..	..	..		3·50	3·50

Sheet Markings

All as for No. S99

Cat. No.	S.G. No.		Shades	Unused	Used

1958 (NOVEMBER 10).   WATERMARK CROWNS, TYPE W.24

A. Cream Paper

S101	—		Brown	12	8

   a. Spot by E of POSTAGE (No dot, R.4/8) .. .. .. 1·25

   b. Spot on daffodil (No dot, R.10/12) .. .. .. 1·25

   c. Neck retouch (Cyl. 1., R.2/12)   1·00

B. Whiter Paper (1 May 1963)

S102	578		Brown	8	5

   a. Spot by E of POSTAGE (No dot, R.4/8) .. .. .. 1·00

   b. Spot on daffodil (No dot, R.10/12) .. .. .. 1·00

   c. Neck retouch (Cyl. 1., R.2/12)   75

For illustrations of Nos. S101/2*a*, S101/2*b* and S101/2*c*, see Nos. S99*a*, S99*b* and S99*c* respectively.

Cylinder Numbers (Blocks of Six)

Cream Paper							Whiter Paper			

Perforation Type A

Cyl. No.					No dot	Dot
1	..	..	..	..	1·25	1·25
2	..	..	..	..	1·25	1·25

Perforation Type A

Cyl. No.					No dot	Dot
1	..	..	..	..	60	60

Perforation Type F(I.)*

1*	..	..	..	..

*This is probably No. S103 but with phosphor omitted.

Sheet Markings

All as for No. S99

1967 (JUNE 9).   TWO 9·5 mm. PHOSPHOR BANDS REACTING VIOLET. WMK. CROWNS

The bands were applied in photogravure.

S103	616c		Brown	5	8

   a. Spot by E of POSTAGE (No dot, R.4/8) .. .. .. 1·00

   c. Neck retouch (Cyl. 1., R.2/12)   75

   b. Spot on daffodil (No dot, R.10/12) .. .. .. 1·00

For illustrations of Nos. S103*a*/*c*, see Nos. S99*a*/*c*.

Cylinder Numbers (Blocks of Six)

Perforation Type A

Cyl. No.					No dot	Dot
1	..	..	..	..	60	60

Perforation Type F (L)*

Cyl. No.					No dot	Dot
1	..	..	..	..	60	60

Sheet Markings

Guide holes: Boxed, and also double-boxed, opposite rows 14/15 at left (no dot) or right (dot) but in the case of perforation Type F (L)* the double boxes remain in both panes but the holes are in single boxes at top and bottom of eighth vertical row in the no dot pane only

Others: As given in General Notes

1954-67. 6d. Purple, Type S4

Cat. No.	S.G. No.	Shades	Unused	Used

1954 (JANUARY 18). WATERMARK TUDOR CROWN, TYPE W.22

S104   523   Reddish purple   50   8
   a. Imperforate at top and sides
     (pair) .. ..
   b. Imperf. between stamp and
     bottom margin .. .. 45·00

   c. Coil join (vert. pr.) .. .. 1·25
   d. Cancelled two vert. black bars
     (P.O.T.S.) 10

Cylinder Numbers (Blocks of Six)

Single pane cylinder

Perforation Type B		Perforation Type C		Perforation Type F (L)	
Cyl. No.	No dot	Cyl. No.	No dot	Cyl. No.	No dot
1 ..	4·00	1 ..	4·00	1 ..	4·00

Minor Constant Sheet Flaws

Minimum price as singles: £1

Multipositive flaws used for cylinders 1, 2 and 3

   8/8 Small purple flaw joining C of PENCE to inner frame line
   19/6 Small dark flaw on daffodil stem (Th. G2)
   20/3 Coloured dot in top leaf of thistle (Th. A6)

Coil

Made up from sheets with sheet margin joins. Vertical delivery with the watermark upright

Code No.	Number in roll	Face value
J	480	£12

Sheet Markings

   Guide holes:
     Perf. Types B and C, opposite rows 1 and 7/8 at both sides and also boxed opposite rows 14/15 at both
     sides
     Perf. Type F (L), not known
   Others: As given in General Notes

1955 (DECEMBER 20). WATERMARK ST. EDWARD'S CROWN, TYPE W.23

A. Reddish Purple

S105   548   Reddish purple   1·00   8
   a. Imperforate three sides (pair)
   b. Coil join (vert. pair) .. .. 2·50
   c. Pink tinted paper†† .. .. 1·25

   d. Cancelled two vert. black bars
     (P.O.T.S.) 10

B. Deep Claret† (8 May 1958)

S106   548a   Deep claret   90   15
   a. Imperforate three sides (pair).. 85·00
   b. Coil join (vert. pr.) .. .. 2·00
    †This shade was a deliberate change of colour.
    ††This is known from cylinder 1 perforation Type C

Cylinder Numbers (Blocks of Six)

Single pane cylinders

Reddish Purple		Deep Claret	
Cyl. No.	No dot	Cyl. No.	No dot
Perforation Type B		Perforation Type B	
1	8·00	2	8·00
2	8 00	3	8·00
Perforation Type C		Perforation Type C	
1	7·00	2	7·00
2	7·00	3	7·00
		Perforation Type F (L)	
		3	9·00

Minor Constant Sheet Flaws

Minimum price as singles: £1·50

Multipositive flaws as shown for No. S104

Coils

Made up from sheets with sheet margin joins. Vertical delivery with the watermark upright

Code No.	Number in roll	Face value	
J	480	£12	Reddish purple
J	480	£12	Deep claret

Sheet Markings

All as for No. S104

Cat. No.	S.G. No.	Shades	Unused	Used

1958 (DECEMBER 23). WATERMARK CROWNS, TYPE W.24

A. Cream Paper

S107	—	Deep claret*	15	10
a. Imperforate three sides (pair)..				
b. Coil join (vert. pr.)	35			

B. Whiter Paper (29 June 1962)

S108	579	Deep claret*	8	5
a. Coil join (vert. pr.)	20			

*This colour is unstable and a range of shades exists which also vary according to the colour of the paper. One of the more marked variations is a purple-claret on the cream paper from cylinder 8.

Cylinder Numbers (Blocks of Six)

A. Cream Paper

Single pane cylinders

Perforation Type B							Perforation Type C					
Cyl. No.					No dot		Cyl. No.					No dot
2 ..	..	..	..	..	1·25		2 ..	..	..	..	..	1·25
3 ..	..	..	..	..	1·25		3 ..	..	..	..	..	1·25

Double pane cylinders

Perforation Type B (no dot) and C (dot)								Perforation Type A						
Cyl. No.					No dot	Dot		Cyl. No.					No dot	Dot
5 ..	..	..	..	..	2·50	2·50		7 ..	..	..	..	..	1·00	1·00
7 ..	..	..	..	..	1·00	1·00		8 ..	..	..	..	..	1·00	1·00

B. Whiter Paper

Perforation Type A								Perforation Type F (L)*					
8 ..	..	..	..	..	80	80							
10 ..	..	..	..	..	80	80		10 ..	..	..	..	80	8·00
11 ..	..	..	,.	..	5·00	5·00							

Minor Constant Sheet Flaws

Minimum price as singles: 70p

Multipositive flaws on cylinders 2 and 3 as shown for No. S104

A second multipositive was used for cylinder 5 and a third for cylinders 7 onwards.

Coils

(a) Made up from sheets with sheet margin joins. Vertical delivery with the watermark upright

Code No.	Number in roll	Face value	
J	480	£12	Cream paper
J	480	£12	Whiter paper

(b) Printed in continuous reels. Single pane cylinder Q1 was used. Vertical delivery. Watermark upright

J	480	£12	Whiter paper

Sheet Markings

Guide holes:
Single pane cylinders: Opposite rows 1 and 7/8 at both sides and also boxed opposite rows 14/15 at both sides
Double pane cylinders:
Perf. Types A, B and C, boxed opposite rows 14/15, at left (no dot) or right (dot)
Perf. Type F (L)*, not known
On cyl. 10 there are double boxes
Others: As given in General Notes
The marginal rule is damaged in most positions on cyl. 8

Cat. No.	S.G. No.	Shades	Unused	Used

1960 (JUNE 27). TWO PHOSPHOR BANDS REACTING GREEN. WATERMARK CROWNS

The bands were applied in photogravure.

S109	—	Deep claret	1·50	1·00

Cylinders Numbers (Blocks of Six)

Single pane cylinder

Perforation Type B		Perforation Type C	
Cyl. No.	No dot	Cyl. No.	No dot
2	10·00	2	10·00

Minor Constant Sheet Flaws

Minimum price as singles: £2

Multipositive flaws as shown for No. S104

Sheet Markings

Guide holes: As for Perf. Types B and C on No. S104
Black bar: This occurs by the marginal arrows opposite rows 10/11, at right
Others: As given in General Notes

1961 (JUNE 5). TWO PHOSPHOR BANDS REACTING BLUE. WATERMARK CROWNS

A. Cream Paper. Bands applied in Photogravure

S110	—	Deep claret	50	30

B. Whiter Paper. Bands applied in Photogravure (3 October 1963)

S111	—	Deep claret	15	10
a. Bands applied typo.		80	50	

Cylinder Numbers (Blocks of Six)

Perforation Type A

Bands applied photo.

Cream Paper				Whiter Paper			
Cyl. No.		No dot	Dot	Cyl. No.		No dot	Dot
7		4·00	4·00	8		1·25	1·25
				10		1·25	1·25
Bands applied typo.							
				8		6·00	6·00

Sheet Markings

Guide holes: Boxed opposite rows 14/15, at left (no dot) or right (dot) On cyl. 10 there are double boxes
Others: As given in General Notes
The marginal rule is damaged in most positions on cyl. 8

1965 (AUGUST 13). TWO 8 mm. PHOSPHOR BANDS REACTING VIOLET. WMK. CROWNS

The bands were originally applied by typography.

S112	—	Deep claret	60	40
a. Bands applied photo. (1968) ..		60	40	

Cylinder Numbers (Blocks of Six)

Perforation Type A

	Applied typo.						Applied photo.		

Cyl. No.					No dot	Dot	Cyl. No.						No dot	Dot
8 ..	..	..	..	..	4·50	4·50	10 ..	..	..	..	..	..	4·50	4·50

Sheet Markings

As for No. S111

Cat. No.	S.G. No.	Shades	Unused	Used

1967 (EARLY). TWO 9·5 mm. PHOSPHOR BANDS REACTING VIOLET. WMK. CROWNS

The bands were applied in photogravure only.

S113	617	Deep claret	5	5

Cylinder Numbers (Blocks of Six)

Perforation Type A | Perforation Type F (L)*

Cyl. No.					No dot	Dot	Cyl. No.						No dot	Dot
10 ..	..	..	..	..	90	90	10 ..	..	..	..	..	..	50	50
11 ..	..	..	..	..	50	50								

Coils

Printed in continuous reels. It is believed that cylinder Q1 was used and that it was a single pane cylinder.

Vertical delivery. Watermark upright

Code No.	Number in roll	Face value
J	480	£12

Sheet Markings

Guide holes: Boxed opposite rows 14/15 at left (no dot) or right (dot) but in the case of perforation Type F (L)* the boxes remain in both panes but the holes are in single boxes above and below the eighth vertical row in the no dot pane only

Others: As given in General Notes

1954-67. 7d. Bright green, Type S4

1954 (JANUARY 18). WATERMARK TUDOR CROWN, TYPE W.22

S114	524		Bright green	60	10
	a. Cancelled two vert. black bars				
	(P.O.T.S.)	10			

Cylinder Numbers (Blocks of Six)

Perforation Type A | Perforation Type B (no dot) and C (dot)

Cyl. No.					No dot	Dot	Cyl. No.						No dot	Dot
2 ..	..	..	..	..	4·50	4·50	2 ..	..	..	..	..	..	4·50	4·50

Sheet Markings

Guide holes: Double-boxed opposite rows 14/15, at left (no dot) or right (dot)

Others: As given in General Notes

1956 (APRIL 23). WATERMARK ST. EDWARD'S CROWN, TYPE W.23

S115	549		Bright green	2·50	8
	a. Cancelled two vert. black bars				
	(P.O.T.S.)	10			

Cylinder Numbers (Blocks of Six)

Perforation Type A

Cyl. No.					No dot	Dot
2 ..	..	..	..	..	15·00	15·00

Sheet Markings

As for No. S114

Cat. No.	S.G. No.	Shades	Unused	Used

1958 (NOVEMBER 26). WATERMARK CROWNS, TYPE W.24

A. Cream Paper

| S116 | — | Bright green | 15 | 8 |

B. Whiter Paper (3 July 1962)

| S117 | 580 | Bright green | 8 | 5 |

Cylinder Numbers (Blocks of Six)

<table>
<tr><td colspan="3">Cream Paper</td><td colspan="3">Whiter Paper</td></tr>
<tr><td colspan="3">Perforation Type A</td><td colspan="3">Perforation Type A</td></tr>
<tr><td>Cyl. No.</td><td>No dot</td><td>Dot</td><td>Cyl. No.</td><td>No dot</td><td>Dot</td></tr>
<tr><td>1 .. ..</td><td>1·25</td><td>1·25</td><td>1 .. ..</td><td>50</td><td>50</td></tr>
<tr><td>2 .. ..</td><td>1·25</td><td>1·25</td><td>2 .. ..</td><td>50</td><td>50</td></tr>
<tr><td colspan="3">Perforation Type B (no dot) and C (dot)</td><td colspan="3">Perforation Type F(L)*</td></tr>
<tr><td>2 .. ..</td><td>1·25</td><td>1·25</td><td colspan="3">1* .. ..</td></tr>
<tr><td colspan="3"></td><td colspan="3">*This is probably No. S118 but with phosphor omitted.</td></tr>
</table>

Sheet Markings

Guide holes: Double-boxed opposite rows 14/15, at left (no dot) or right (dot)
Marginal rule: At bottom of sheet (Cyl. 1, 1½ mm. wide; Cyl. 2, 2 mm. wide)
Others: As given in General Notes

1967 (FEBRUARY 15). TWO 9·5 mm. PHOSPHOR BANDS REACTING VIOLET. WMK. CROWNS

The bands were applied in photogravure.

| S118 | 617a | Bright green | 5 | 8 |

Cylinder Numbers (Blocks of Six)

<table>
<tr><td colspan="3">Perforation Type F (L)*</td><td colspan="3">Perforation Type A</td></tr>
<tr><td>Cyl. No.</td><td>No dot</td><td>Dot</td><td>Cyl. No.</td><td>No dot</td><td>Dot</td></tr>
<tr><td>1 .. ..</td><td>50</td><td>50</td><td>2 .. ..</td><td>50</td><td>50</td></tr>
</table>

Sheet Markings

Guide holes: Double-boxed opposite rows 14/15, at left (no dot) or right (dot) but in the case of perforation Type F (L)* the double boxes remain on both panes but the holes are unboxed above and below the eighth vertical row in the no dot pane only
Marginal rule: At bottom of sheet (Cyl. 1, 1½ mm. wide; Cyl. 2. 2 mm. wide)
Others: As given in General Notes

1953-67. 8d. Magenta, Type S5

1953 (JULY 6). WATERMARK TUDOR CROWN, TYPE W.22

| S119 | 525 | Magenta | 60 | 10 |
| | *a.* Overprinted "SCHOOL SPECI-MEN" .. .. | 20 | | |

Cylinder Numbers (Blocks of Six)

<table>
<tr><td colspan="3">Perforation Type A</td><td colspan="3">Perforation Type B (no dot) and C (dot)</td></tr>
<tr><td>Cyl. No.</td><td>No dot</td><td>Dot</td><td>Cyl. No.</td><td>No dot</td><td>Dot</td></tr>
<tr><td>3 .. ..</td><td>4·50</td><td>4·50</td><td>3 .. ..</td><td>4·50</td><td>4·50</td></tr>
</table>

Minor Constant Sheet Flaws

Minimum price as singles: 90p

Cyl. 3   20/1 Coloured dot between rose at top left and A of POSTAGE (Th. B2)

Sheet Markings

Guide holes: Double-boxed opposite rows 14/15, at left (no dot) or right (dot)
Others: As given in General Notes

Cat. No.	S.G. No.	Shades	Unused Used

1955 (DECEMBER 21). WATERMARK ST. EDWARD'S CROWN, TYPE W.23

S120   550   Magenta   85   15
   a. Cancelled two vert. black bars
     (P.O.T.S.)   10

Cylinder Numbers (Blocks of Six)
Perforation Type A

Cyl. No.					No dot	Dot
3 ..	..	..	..	..	6·00	6·00

Minor Constant Sheet Flaws
Minimum price as singles: £1·25

Cyl. 3   20/1 Coloured dot between rose at top left and A of POSTAGE (Th. B2). Later retouched

Sheet Markings
   As for No. S119

1960 (FEBRUARY 24). WATERMARK CROWNS, TYPE W.24

A. Cream Paper

S121   —   Magenta   12   8

B. Whiter Paper (6 July 1962)

S122   581   Magenta   8   5
   a. Diadem flaw (Cyl. 4 R.18/2)   1·50
   b. Extra pearl (Cyl. 4., R.16/2) ..   1·50

Listed Varieties

S122*a*, S123*a*
White flaw on diadem,
lower left of E of POSTAGE

S122*b*, S123*b*

Cylinder Numbers (Blocks of Six)

Cream Paper							Whiter Paper						

Cream Paper — Perforation Type A

Cyl. No.					No dot	Dot
3 ..	..	..	..	..	1·00	1·00

Whiter Paper — Perforation Type A

Cyl. No.					No dot	Dot
3 ..	..	..	..	..	50	50
4 ..	..	..	..	..	1·75*	50

Perforation Type F(L)*

1* ..	..	..	..	..	..

*This is probably No. S123 but
with the phosphor omitted.

Sheet Markings
   Guide holes: Unboxed opposite rows 1 and 7/8 and double-boxed opposite rows 14/15, at left (no dot) or
     right (dot); or double-boxed only opposite rows 14/15, at left (no dot) or right (dot)
   Marginal arrows:
     "V" shaped, hand engraved at top and bottom of sheet (Cyls. 3 and 4)
     "W" shaped, photo-etched at both sides (Cyl. 3) or photo-etched at left and hand engraved at right
     (Cyl. 4)
   Others: As given in General Notes

Cat. No.	S.G. No.	Shades	Unused	Used

1967 (JUNE 28). TWO 9·5 mm. PHOSPHOR BANDS REACTING VIOLET. WMK. CROWNS

The bands were applied in photogravure.

S123	617*b*	Magenta	5	8

  a. Diadem flaw (Cyl. 4, R.18/2) .. 1·50
  b. Extra pearl (Cyl. 4., R.16/2) .. 1·50

For illustrations of Nos. S123*a/b*, see Nos. S122*a/b*.

Cylinder Numbers (Blocks of Six)

Perforation Type A			Perforation Type F (L)*		
Cyl. No.	No dot	Dot	Cyl. No.	No dot	Dot
4	1·75*	50	4	1·75*	50

Sheet Markings

Guide holes: Double-boxed opposite rows 14/15, at left (no dot) or right (dot) but in the case of perforation Type F (L)* the double boxes remain on both panes but the holes are unboxed above and below the eighth vertical row in the no dot pane only

Marginal arrows:
  "V" shaped, hand engraved at top and bottom of sheet
  "W" shaped, photo-etched at left and hand engraved at right

Others: As given in General Notes

1954-66.   9d. Bronze-green, Type S5

1954 (FEBRUARY 8). WATERMARK TUDOR CROWN, TYPE W.22

S124	526	Bronze-green	1·75	20

  a. Frame break at upper right
    (Cyl. 1, R.8/6) .. .. .. 10·00
  b. Cancelled two vert. black bars
    (P.O.T.S.) 10

Listed Variety

S124*a*, S125*a*, S126*a*

Frame broken at upper right and shading below it missing. Later retouched on Crowns watermark. A very similar variety occurs on Cyl. 2, R.11/11; see Nos. S126*c*, etc.

Cylinder Numbers (Blocks of Six)

Perforation Type A			Perforation Type B (no dot) and C (dot)		
Cyl. No.	No dot	Dot	Cyl. No.	No dot	Dot
1	12·00	12·00	1	12·00	12·00

Sheet Markings

Guide holes: Boxed opposite rows 14/15, at left (no dot) or right (dot)
Others: As given in General Notes

Cat. No.   S.G. No.   Shades   Unused Used

1955 (DECEMBER 15). WATERMARK ST. EDWARD'S CROWN, W.23

S125   551   Bronze-green   1·60   15
   a. Frame break at upper right
      (R.8/6)   ..   ..   10·00
   b. Cancelled two vert. black bars
      (P.O.T.S.)   10
   For illustration of No. S125*a*, see No. S124*a*.

Cylinder Numbers (Blocks of Six)

Perforation Type A			Perforation Type B (no dot) and C (dot)		
Cyl. No.	No dot	Dot	Cyl. No.	No dot	Dot
1	9·00	9·00	1	9·00	9·00

Sheet Markings

   As for No. S124

1959 (MARCH 24). WATERMARK CROWNS, TYPE W.24

A. Cream Paper

S126   —   Bronze-green   15   8
   a. Frame break at upper right
      (Cyl. 1, R.8/6)   ..   ..   4·25
   b. Broken daffodil (Cyl. 2, R. 7/2)   2·25
   c. Frame break at upper right
      (Cyl. 2, R.11/11)   ..   ..   2·25   *d*. Frame flaw (Cyl. 2., R.12/5)   ..   1·50

B. Whiter Paper (4 June 1962)

S127   582   Bronze-green   8   5
   a. Broken daffodil (Cyl. 2, R.7/2) ..   1·75
   b. Frame break at upper right
      (Cyl. 2, R.11/11)   ..   ..   1·75   *c*. Frame flaw (Cyl. 2., R.12/5)   ..   1·25

Listed Varieties

   For illustration of No. S126*a*, see No. S124*a*.

S126*b*, S127*a*, S128*b*	S126*c*, S127*b*, S128*c*	S126*d*, S127*c*, S128*d*
Stem of daffodil is broken	A very similar variety to the one on Cyl. 1, R.8/6 but slightly more pronounced	Flaw on frame at lower left

Cylinder Numbers (Blocks of Six)

Cream Paper			Whiter Paper		
Perforation Type A			Perforation Type A		
Cyl. No.	No dot	Dot	Cyl. No.	No dot	Dot
1	1·25	1·25	2	90	90
2	1·25	1·25			

Sheet Markings

   Guide holes: Double-boxed opposite rows 14/15, at left (no dot) or right (dot)
   Others: As given in General Notes

Cat. No.	S.G. No.	Shades	Unused	Used

1966 (DECEMBER 29). TWO 9·5 mm. PHOSPHOR BANDS REACTING VIOLET. WMK. CROWNS

The bands were applied in photogravure.

S128	617c	Bronze-green	8	8

a. Imperf. between stamp and top margin .. ..   *c.* Frame break at upper right (Cyl. 2, R.11/11) .. .. 2·00

b. Broken daffodil (Cyl. 2, R.7/2)   1·75   *d.* Frame flaw (Cyl. 2., R.12/5) .. 1·50

For illustrations of Nos. S128b/d, see Nos. S126b/d.

Cylinder Numbers (Blocks of Six)

Perforation Type A

Cyl. No.					No dot	Dot
2 ..	..	..	..	..	90	90

Sheet Markings

As for Nos. S126/7

1954-66.   10d. Prussian blue, Type S5

1954 (FEBRUARY 8). WATERMARK TUDOR CROWN, TYPE W.22

S129	527	Prussian blue	1.25	20

a. Cancelled two vert. black bars (P.O.T.S.)   10

Cylinder Numbers (Blocks of Six)

Perforation Type A			Perforation Type B (no dot) and C (dot)		
Cyl. No.	No dot	Dot	Cyl. No.	No dot	Dot
1	9·00	9·00	1	9·00	9·00

Minor Constant Sheet Flaws

Minimum price as singles: £1·75

Cyl. 1   3/3 White spur on right fork of V of REVENUE
       10/12 White flaw on thistle shows as a cut into the left-hand side of the flower (Th. A6)
       13/10 White flaw on rim of diadem below emblems (Th. B4)

Sheet Markings

Guide holes: Boxed opposite rows 14/15, at left (no dot) or right (dot)
Others: As given in General Notes

1955 (SEPTEMBER 22). WATERMARK ST. EDWARD'S CROWN, TYPE W.23

S130	552	Prussian blue	1·90	15

a. Cancelled two vert. black bars (P.O.T.S.)   10

Cylinder Numbers (Blocks of Six)

Perforation Type A

Cyl. No.					No dot	Dot
1 ..	..	..	..	..	13·00	13·00

Minor Constant Sheet Flaws

Minimum price as singles: £2

Cyl. 1   3/3 White spur on right fork of V of REVENUE
       10/12 White flaw on thistle shows as a cut into the left-hand side of the flower (Th. A6)
       13/10 White flaw on rim of diadem below emblems (Th. B4). Later retouched

Sheet Markings

Guide holes: Boxed opposite rows 14/15, at left (no dot) or right (dot)
Others: As given in General Notes

Cat. No.	S.G. No.	Shades	Unused	Used

1958 (NOVEMBER 18). WATERMARK CROWNS, TYPE W.24

A. Cream Paper

| S131 | — | Prussian blue | 25 | 10 |

B. Whiter Paper (13 November 1962)

| S132 | 583 | Prussian blue | 10 | 5 |

Cylinder Blocks (Blocks of Six)

	Cream Paper					Whiter Paper		

Perforation Type A

Cyl. No.				No dot	Dot
1 ..	..	..	..	2·00	2·00

Perforation Type B (no dot) and C (dot)

1 ..	..	..	..	2·00	2·00

Perforation Type A

Cyl. No.				No dot	Dot
1 ..	..	..	..	80	80

Perforation Type F(L)*

1* ..	..	..	..	..	..

*This is probably No. S133 but with the phosphor omitted.

Minor Constant Sheet Flaws

Minimum price as singles: 50p

Cyl. 1   3/3 White spur on right fork of V of REVENUE. Later retouched
        10/12 White flaw on thistle shows as a cut into the left-hand side of the flower (Th. A6). Later retouched
        14/3 Retouch on Queen's nose (Th. D3)

Sheet Markings

Guide holes: Unboxed opposite rows 1 and 7/8 and boxed opposite rows 14/15, at left (no dot) or right (dot); or boxed only opposite rows 14/15, at left (no dot) or right (dot)

Others: As given in General Notes

1966 (DECEMBER 30). TWO 9·5 mm. PHOSPHOR BANDS REACTING VIOLET. WMK. CROWNS

The bands were applied in photogravure.

| S133 | 617d | Prussian blue | 8 | 8 |

Cylinder Numbers (Blocks of Six)

Perforation Type A

Cyl. No.				No dot	Dot
1 ..	..	..	..	80	80

Perforation Type F (L)*

Cyl. No.				No dot	Dot
1 ..	..	..	..	80	80

Minor Constant Sheet Flaws

Minimum price as singles: 50p

Cyl. 1   3/3 White spur on right fork of V of REVENUE. Later retouched
        14/3 Retouch on Queen's nose (Th. D3)

Sheet Markings

Guide holes: Boxed opposite rows 14/15, at left (no dot) or right (dot) but in the case of perforation Type F (L)* the boxes remain on both panes but the holes are unboxed above and below the eighth vertical row in the no dot pane only

Others: As given in General Notes

1954-55. 11d. Brown-purple, Type S5

1954 (FEBRUARY 8). WATERMARK TUDOR CROWN, TYPE W.22

| S134 | 528 | Brown-purple | 2·50 | 1·00 |

a. Cancelled two vert. black bars				
(P.O.T.S.) ..	..	..	30	

Cylinder Numbers (Blocks of Six)

Perforation Type B (no dot) and C (dot)

Cyl. No.				No dot	Dot
1 ..	..	..	..	15·00	15·00

Minor Constant Sheet Flaws

Minimum price as singles: £2·50

Cyl. 1   19/3 White flaw in frame pattern at left by O of POSTAGE (Th. D1)

Sheet Markings

Guide holes: Boxed opposite rows 14/15, at left (no dot) or right (dot)
Others: As given in General Notes

Cat. No.	S.G. No.	Shades	Unused	Used

1955 (OCTOBER 28).   WATERMARK ST. EDWARD'S CROWN, TYPE W.23

S135	553	Brown-purple	75	80

a. Cancelled two vert. black bars
(P.O.T.S.)   25

Cylinder Numbers (Blocks of Six)

Perforation Type A			Perforation Type B (no dot) and C (dot)		
Cyl. No.	No dot	Dot	Cyl. No.	No dot	Dot
1	2·75	2·75	1	2·75	2·75

Minor Constant Sheet Flaws

Minimum price as singles: £1·25

Cyl. 1   19/3 White flaw in frame pattern at left by O of POSTAGE (Th. D1)

Sheet Markings

Guide holes: Boxed opposite rows 14/15, at left (no dot) or right (dot)
Others: As given in General Notes

1953-67.   1s. Bistre-brown, Type S6

1953 (JULY 6).   WATERMARK TUDOR CROWN, TYPE W.22

S136	529	Bistre-brown	1·25	10

a. Overprinted "SCHOOL SPECI-
MEN"   25

Cylinder Numbers (Blocks of Six)

Perforation Type A			Perforation Type B (no dot) and C (dot)		
Cyl. No.	No dot	Dot	Cyl. No.	No dot	Dot
1	9·00	9·00	1	10·00	10·00
2	12·00	12·00			

Minor Constant Sheet Flaws

Minimum price as singles: £1·75

Cyl. 1.   3/10 Coloured flaw between left-hand leaves of thistle (Th. B6)
5/10 Coloured spur to top of lacing at right of value (Th. G5)

Cyl. 2.   3/10 As on Cyl. 1. (multipositive flaw)

Sheet Markings

Guide holes: Boxed opposite rows 14/15, at left (no dot) or right (dot)
Others: As given in General Notes

Cat. No.   S.G. No.   Shades   Unused Used

1955 (NOVEMBER 3). WATERMARK ST. EDWARD'S CROWN, TYPE W.23

S137   554   Bistre-brown   2·00   8
  a. Thistle flaw (Cyl. 3., R.4/5) ..   8·00
  b. Cancelled two vert. black bars
    (P.O.T.S.)   20

Listed Variety

S137*a*, S138*b*, S139*a*

Cylinder Numbers (Blocks of Six)

Perforation Type A

Cyl. No.					No dot	Dot	Cyl. No.					No dot	Dot
2	..	..	..	..	15·00	15·00	4	..	..	..	..	16·00	16·00
3	..	..	..	..	15·00	15·00							

Minor Constant Sheet Flaws

Minimum price as singles: £2·50

Cyl. 2.   3/10 Coloured flaw between left-hand leaves of thistle (Th. B6). Later retouched leaving a pale mark
Cyl. 3.   3/10 As on Cyl. 2. but flaw is retouched and appears much smaller (multipositive flaw)
Cyl. 4.   3/10 As for Cyl. 3.
         11/12 Coloured spur to foot of first E of REVENUE

Sheet Markings

  As for No. S136

1958 (OCTOBER 30). WATERMARK CROWNS, TYPE W.24

A. Cream Paper

S138   —   Bistre-brown   30   10
  a. Double impression   ..   ..   10·00
  b. Thistle flaw (Cyl. 3., R.4/5) ..   2·50

B. Whiter Paper (22 July 1962)

S139   584   Bistre-brown   15   5
  a. Thistle flaw (Cyl. 3., R.4/5) ..   2·00
  For illustration of Nos. S138*b* and S139*a*, see No. S137*a*.

Cylinder Numbers (Blocks of Six)

	Cream Paper						Whiter Paper					
Perforation Type A							Perforation Type A					
Cyl. No.					No dot	Dot	Cyl. No.				No dot	Dot
2	..	..	..	..	2·50	2·50	2	..	..	..	1·25	1·25
3	..	..	..	..	2·50	2·50	3	..	..	..	1·25	1·25
4	..	..	..	..	2·50	2·50	4	..	..	..	1·25	1·25

Minor Constant Sheet Flaws

Minimum price as singles: 60p

Multipositive flaw

Dot   3/10 Coloured flaw between left-hand leaves of thistle (Th. B6) now only exists retouched. Cyls. 2. and
         3. show as a smudge and Cyl. 4. as a much smaller flaw
Cyl. 4.   11/12 Coloured spur to foot of first E of REVENUE

Sheet Markings

  As for No. S136

Cat. No.	S.G. No.				Shades	Unused	Used

1967 (JUNE 28). TWO 9·5 mm. PHOSPHOR BANDS REACTING VIOLET. WMK. CROWNS

The bands were applied in photogravure.

| S140 | 617e | | | | Bistre-brown | 8 | 5 |

Cylinder Numbers (Blocks of Six)

Perforation Type F (L)*

	Cyl. No.					No dot	Dot
	4	..	..	..	..	80	80

Minor Constant Sheet Flaws

Minimum price as singles: 60p

Cyl. 4.   3/10 Coloured flaw between left-hand leaves of thistle (Th. B6) is now retouched leaving a much
smaller flaw
11/12 Coloured spur to foot of first E of REVENUE

Sheet Markings

Guide holes: Unboxed above and below the eighth vertical row in the no dot pane only. The usual boxes
opposite rows 14/15 remain
Others: As given in General Notes

1953-67.   1s.3d. Green, Type S7

1953 (NOVEMBER 2). WATERMARK TUDOR CROWN, TYPE W.22

S141	530		Green		1·50	15

a. White flaw in Queen's hair
(Dot, R.2/9)   ..   ..   ..   6·00
b. P flaw (Dot, R.6/10) ..   ..   6·00

c. Cancelled two vert. black bars
(P.O.T.S.)   20

Listed Varieties

S141a, S142a, S143a, S144a,
S145a, S146a, S147a

S141b, S142b, S143b, S144b,
S145b, S146b, S147b

Cylinder Numbers (Blocks of Six)

Perforation Type A

Cyl. No.					No dot	Dot
1	..	..	..	..	11·00	11·00

Perforation Type B (no dot) and C (dot

Cyl. No.					No dot	Dot
1	..	..	..	..	11·00	11·00

Sheet Markings

Guide holes: Boxed opposite rows 14/15, at left (no dot) or right (dot)
Others: As given in General Notes

Cat. No.	S.G. No.	Shades	Unused	Used

1956 (MARCH 27). WATERMARK ST. EDWARD'S CROWN, TYPE W.23

S142   555   Green   2·00   10
a. White flaw in Queen's hair
  (Dot, R.2/9) ..   ..   ..   5·00   *c.* Cancelled two vert. black bars
b. P flaw (Dot, R.6/10) ..   ..   5·00   (P.O.T.S.)   20

  For illustrations of Nos. S142*a*/*b*, see Nos. S141*a*/*b*.

Cylinder Numbers (Blocks of Six)

Perforation Type A

	Cyl. No.	No dot	Dot
	1	13·50	13·50

Sheet Markings

As for No. S141

1959 (JUNE 17). WATERMARK CROWNS, TYPE W.24

A. Cream Paper

S143   —   Green   25   10
a. White flaw in Queen's hair
  (Cyl. 1., R.2/9) ..   ..   2·50   *b.* P flaw (Cyl. 1., R.6/10) ..   2·50

B. Whiter Paper (29 August 1962)

S144   585   Green   10   5
a. White flaw in Queen's hair
  (Cyl. 1., R.2/9) ..   ..   ..   2·00   *b.* P flaw (Cyl. 1., R.6/10) ..   2·00

  For illustrations of Nos. S143*a*/*b* and S144*a*/*b*, see Nos. S141*a*/*b*.

Cylinder Numbers (Blocks of Six)

	Cream Paper				Whiter Paper		
Perforation Type A				Perforation Type A			
Cyl. No.		No dot	Dot	Cyl. No.		No dot	Dot
1		1·80	1·80	1		80	80
				2		80	80

Sheet Markings

As for No. S141

1960 (JUNE 22). TWO PHOSPHOR BANDS REACTING GREEN. WATERMARK CROWNS

The bands were applied in photogravure.

S145   —   Green   1·60   1·00
a. White flaw in Queen's hair
  (Dot, R.2/9) ..   ..   ..   6·00   *b.* P flaw (Dot, R.6/10) ..   ..   6·00

  For illustrations of Nos. S145*a*/*b*, See Nos. S141*a*/*b*.

Cylinder Numbers (Blocks of Six)

Perforation Type B (no dot) and C (dot)

	Cyl. No.	No dot	Dot
	1	12·00	12·00

Sheet Markings

Guide holes: Boxed opposite rows 14/15, at left (no dot) or right (dot)
Black bar: This occurs by the marginal arrows opposite rows 10/11, at left (no dot) or right (dot)
Others: As given in General Notes

Cat. No.	S.G. No.	Shades	Unused	Used

1961 (JUNE 5). TWO PHOSPHOR BANDS REACTING BLUE. WATERMARK CROWNS

The bands were applied in photogravure.

A. Cream Paper

S146 — Green 80 40

  a. White flaw in Queen's hair
  (Cyl. 1., R.2/9) .. .. .. 4·50   *b.* P flaw (Cyl. 1., R.6/10) .. 4·50

B. Whiter Paper (21 January 1963)

S147 — Green 35 20

  a. White flaw in Queen's hair
  (Cyl. 1., R.2/9) .. .. .. 4·00   *b.* P flaw (Cyl. 1., R.6/10) .. 4·00

For illustrations of Nos. S146a/b and S147a/b, see Nos. S141a/b.

Cylinder Numbers (Blocks of Six)

Cream Paper			Whiter Paper		
Perforation Type A			Perforation Type A		
Cyl. No.	No dot	Dot	Cyl. No.	No dot	Dot
1	6·00	6·00	1	2·50	2·50
			2	2·50	2·50

Sheet Markings

As for No. S141

1965 (AUGUST 13). TWO 8 mm. PHOSPHOR BANDS REACTING VIOLET. WMK. CROWNS

The bands were originally applied by typography.

S148 — Green 40 15

  a. Bands applied photo. (1966) .. 20 10

Cylinder Numbers (Blocks of Six)

Perforation Type A

Applied typo.			Applied photo.		
Cyl. No.	No dot	Dot	Cyl. No.	No dot	Dot
2	3·00	3·00	2	1·50	1·50

Sheet Markings

As for No. S141

1967 (EARLY). TWO 9·5 mm. PHOSPHOR BANDS REACTING VIOLET. WMK. CROWNS

The bands were applied in photogravure only.

S149 618 Green 10 8

Cylinder Numbers (Blocks of Six)

Perforation Type A

Cyl. No.	No dot	Dot
2	90	90

Sheet Markings

As for No. S141

1953-66.   1s.6d. Grey-blue, Type S6

Cat. No.	S.G. No.	Shades	Unused	Used

1953 (NOVEMBER 2).   WATERMARK TUDOR CROWN, TYPE W.22   2·00   15

S150   531   Grey-blue
a. White flaw in Queen's hair below
diadem (Dot, R.20/1) ..   ..   7·00
b. White flaw in Queen's hair
opposite N of REVENUE   *c.* Cancelled two vert. black bars
(Dot, R.20/2) ..   ..   ..   7·00   (P.O.T.S.)   20

Listed Varieties

S150*a*, S151*a*, S152*a*, S153*a*,
S154*a*

S150*b*, S151*b*, S152*b*, S153*b*
Later retouched on Crowns
Watermark

Cylinder Numbers (Blocks of Six)

Perforation Type A   Perforation Type B (no dot) and C (dot)
Cyl. No.   No dot Dot   Cyl. No.   No dot Dot
  1 ..   .. 15·00 20·00*   1 ..   .. 15·00 20·00*

Sheet Markings

Guide holes: Boxed opposite rows 14/15, at left (no dot) or right (dot)
Others: As given in General Notes

1956 (MARCH 27).   WATERMARK ST. EDWARD'S CROWN, TYPE W.23

S151   556   Grey-blue   2·25   15
a. White flaw in Queen's hair below
diadem (Dot, R.20/1) ..   ..   6·00
b. White flaw in Queen's hair
opposite N of REVENUE   *c.* Cancelled two vert. black bars
(Dot, R.20/2) ..   ..   ..   6·00   (P.O.T.S.)   20
For illustrations of Nos. S151*a*/*b*, see Nos. S150*a*/*b*.

Cylinder Numbers (Blocks of Six)

Perforation Type A   Perforation Type B (no dot) and C (dot)
Cyl. No.   No dot Dot   Cyl. No.   No dot Dot
  1 ..   .. 16·00 21·00*   1 ..   .. 16·00 21·00*

Sheet Markings

As for No. S150

Cat. No.	S.G. No.	Shades	Unused	Used

1958 (DECEMBER 16). WATERMARK CROWNS, TYPE W.24

A. Cream Paper

S152 — Grey-blue 40 12
   a. White flaw in Queen's hair below
     diadem (Cyl. 1., R.20/1)   ..   2·50
   b. White flaw in Queen's hair
     opposite N of REVENUE
     (Cyl. 1., R.20/2) ..   ..   ..   2·50

B. Whiter Paper (14 November 1962)

S153 586 Grey-blue 30 5
   a. White flaw in Queen's hair below
     diadem (Cyl. 1., R.20/1)   ..   1·75
   b. White flaw in Queen's hair
     opposite N of REVENUE
     (Cyl. 1., R.20/2)..   ..   ..   1·75

    For illustrations of Nos. S152*a/b* and S153*a/b*, see Nos. S150*a/b*.

Cylinder Numbers (Blocks of Six)

Cream Paper		Whiter Paper	

Perforation Type A

Cyl. No.   No dot Dot
1 ..   ..   3·00 7·00*
3 ..   ..   3·00 3·00

Perforation Type A

Cyl. No.   No dot Dot
1 ..   ..   2·10 5·00*

Perforation Type B (no dot) and C (dot)

1 ..   ..   3·00 7·00*
3 ..   ..   3·00 3·00

Sheet Markings

   As for No. S150

1966 (DECEMBER 12). TWO 9·5 mm. PHOSPHOR BANDS REACTING VIOLET. WMK. CROWNS

    The bands were applied in photogravure.

S154 618*a* Grey-blue 30 12
   a. White flaw in Queen's hair below
     diadem (Cyl. 1., R.20/1)   ..   1·75
    For illustration of No. S154*a*, see No. S150*a*.

Cylinder Numbers (Blocks of Six)

Perforation Type A   **Perforation Type F (L)***

Cyl. No.   No dot Dot   Cyl. No.   No dot Dot
1 ..   ..   2·10 2·25   8 ..   ..   2·25 2·25

Sheet Markings

   Guide holes: Boxed opposite rows 14/15, at left (no dot) or right (dot) but in the case of perforation Type F (L)* the boxes remain on both panes but the holes are unboxed above and below the eighth vertical row in the no dot pane only
   Others: As given in General Notes

Presentation Packs

SPP1 (issued 1960)   Eighteen values   12·00
    The issued pack contained one of each value. The 1½d. and 11d. were with St. Edward's Crown watermark (Nos. S26 and S135) and the remainder were Crowns watermark all on cream paper, ½d. (No. S4), 1d (S16), 2d. (S40), 2½d. (S55), 3d. (S70), 4d. (S83), 4½d. (S93), 5d. (S101), 6d. (S107), 7d. (S116), 8d. (S121), 9d. (S126), 10d. (S131), 1s. (S138), 1s.3d. (S144), 1s.6d. (S153).

SPP2 (issued 1960)   Sixteen values   30·00
    The issued pack contained two of each value of the Phosphor-Graphite experimental issue, ½d. (No. S8), 1d. (S19), 1½d. (S31), 2d (S43), 2½d. (S60), 3d (S73), 4d. (S87), 4½d. (S96). The ½d., 1d. and 1½d. were with St. Edward's Crown watermark and the remainder with Crowns watermark. Although the details printed on the pack erroneously describe the stamps as all having Crowns watermark, the packs usually bear a sticker inscribed "CORRECTION. The ½d, 1d, & 1½d stamps bear the St. Edward Crown Royal Cypher watermark".
    Two forms of the pack exist:
    (a) Inscribed "3s 8d" for sale in the U.K. and
    (b) Inscribed "50c" for sale in the U.S.A.

SECTION T

Dorothy Wilding Issues

1955–68. High Values. Recess-printed

General Notes

CROWNS WATERMARK. The Crowns are slightly smaller than in the low values.

PERFORATION. All stamps in this Section are comb perforated 11 × 12 and the sheet perforation is always Type A.

PLATE NUMBERS. All plates were made from the original Waterlow Die. All stamps were printed from double plates producing left and right panes which were guillotined to make Post Office sheets of 40 (4 × 10). Plate numbers were used both by Waterlow and De La Rue but they appeared between the panes and were trimmed off. The Bradbury, Wilkinson plate numbers appear below stamps 3/4 in the bottom margin, the whole numbers on the left pane and the "A" numbers on the right pane. All three printers used rotary sheet-fed machines.

Bradbury, Wilkinson Plate No.

DE LA RUE PLATE DOTS. De la Rue printed on paper with St. Edward's Crown watermark and with Crowns watermark and as a control to distinguish the two papers during the change-over period, dots were inserted in the bottom margin below the first stamp in the bottom row.

In the case of the 2s.6d. the first printings on St. Edward's Crown paper were without dot, but later a single dot appeared on this paper, whilst early printings of stamps on the Crowns paper had two dots.

In the 10s. the dots are 7 mm. from the design and 5 mm. apart and in the other values they are 6 mm. from the design and 2½ mm. apart.

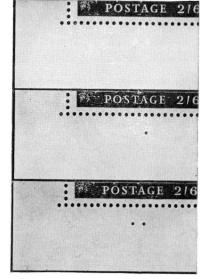

a. No dot
b. One dot
c. Two dots

The number of sheets printed with double dots were:—

2s.6d.	93,630	10s.	37,510
5s.	60,158	£1	18,660

DISTINGUISHING THE WORK OF THE THREE PRINTERS. Waterlow printed the stamps up to 31 December 1957 and then De La Rue held the contract until 31 December 1962, after which all printings were made by Bradbury, Wilkinson. The following characteristics will help to distinguish their work:—

Paper

Waterlow	De La Rue	Bradbury, Wilkinson
(a) Wmk. W.**23** Creamy	(a) Wmk. W.**23** Light cream	(a) Wmk. W.**24** Whiter
(b) Wmk. W.**23** Light cream	(b) Wmk. W.**24** Light cream	(b) Wmk. W.**24** Chalky
(From Feb., '57)	(c) Wmk. W.**24** Whiter	(2s.6d. only)
	(From 1962)	(c) No wmk. White

Shades

	Waterlow	De La Rue
2s.6d.	Blackish brown	More chocolate
5s.	Rose-carmine	Lighter red, less carmine
10s.	Ultramarine	More blue
£1	Black	Less intense

The shade variations result in part from the differences in paper.

Gutters. The width of gutters between the stamps varies, particularly the horizontal, as follows:—

Waterlow	De La Rue
3.8 to 4.0 mm.	3.4 to 3.8 mm.

Later De La Rue plates were less distinguishable in this respect.

Perforation. The vertical perforation of the Bradbury, Wilkinson is 11.9 to 12 as against 11.8 for the De La Rue.

Impression. The individual lines of the De La Rue impression are cleaner and devoid of the whiskers of colour of Waterlow's, and the whole impression is lighter and softer. The Bradbury, Wilkinson stamps are generally more deeply engraved than the De La Rue, showing more of the diadem detail and heavier lines on the Queen's face.

Waterlow Sheet Markings

Perforation Markings. As a check for the alignment of the perforations the following marks occur between the stamps in the Waterlow printings only:—

(a) 3 mm. cross in the centre of the sheet
(b) 2½ mm. vertical lines in centre at top and bottom of sheet
(c) 2½ mm. horizontal lines in centre at each side of sheet

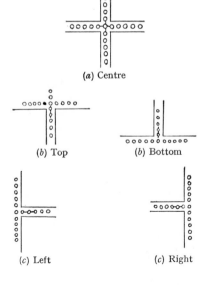

(a) Centre

(b) Top   (b) Bottom

(c) Left   (c) Right

103

Perforation Pin-holes. Coloured circles appear at left and right with a pin-hole through them opposite row six at left and right, although one is usually trimmed off.

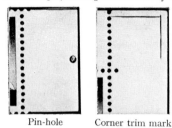

Pin-hole   Corner trim mark

Corner Trim Marks. These occur in the corners but naturally one or both sides may be trimmed off.

De La Rue Sheet Markings

Guide Marks. The only markings on De La Rue sheets are the guide marks which appear in the side margins between rows 5 and 6 which also serve to distinguish the left and right panes. Their position varies with each value and they differ again on the later plates used for the Crowns watermark. The circles or crosses also have pin-holes.

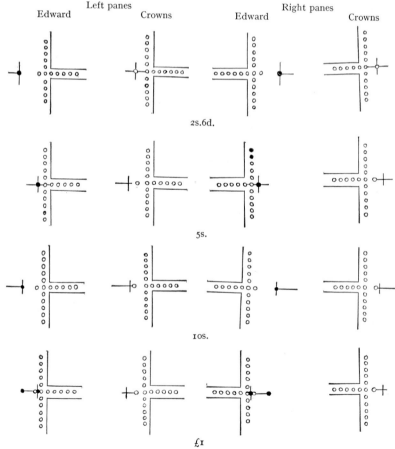

Bradbury, Wilkinson Sheet Markings

Guide Holes. These appear in a coloured circle opposite row 6, at left on left-hand panes and at right on right-hand panes.

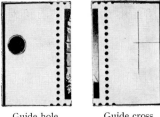

Guide hole   Guide cross

Guide Crosses. These occur between rows 5 and 6 at right on left-hand panes and at left on right-hand panes. However, these do not appear on all plates.

TINTED SHEET MARGINS. Some sheets show a background wash or tint of the colour in which the stamps are printed. This is an indication of a new state of a plate or a plate that has been rechromed. The explanation for this is that in wiping off the excess ink from the surface of the plate a small amount may be left at the edge of the plate and this will continue until the plate is sufficiently smooth for the surface to be thoroughly wiped clean of ink. These marginal tints stop short of the edge of the sheet as the extremities of the plate do not come into contact with the inking roller.

WITHDRAWAL DATES. It is known that the following went off sale at the Philatelic Bureau in the months shown:

Mar. 1968   £1 No. T24
Nov. 1968   2s.6d. No. T6
Nov. 1968   5s. No. T12
Jan. 1969   2s.6d. No. T5
Mar. 1970   10s. No. T18

The 2s.6d., 5s., 10s. and £1 no watermark, white paper (Nos. T7, T13, T19 and T25) were all withdrawn on 15th May 1970.

T1. Carrickfergus Castle.

T2.   Caernarvon Castle.

T3.   Edinburgh Castle.

T4.   Windsor Castle.

(Des. L. Lamb. Portrait by Dorothy Wilding, Ltd.)

CANCELLED
T5.

1955–68.   2s.6d., Type T1

Cat. No.	S.G. No.		Shades	Unused	Used

1955 (SEPTEMBER 23).   WATERMARK ST. EDWARD'S CROWN, TYPE W.23

(a) Waterlow Printings

T1	536		Black-brown	1·50	15

   a. Re-entry (R.2/2)   ..   ..   8·00
   b. Cancelled   vert.   black bars
      (P.O.T.S.)   50

(b) De La Rue Printings (17 July 1957)

T2	536a		Black-brown	4·00	30

   a. With one plate dot in bottom
      margin (R. 10/1)   ..   ..   10·00

Listed Variety

T1*a*

The doubling occurs down the left-hand margin

Cat. No.	S.G. No.	Shades	Unused	Used

1959 (JULY 22). WATERMARK CROWNS, TYPE W.24

(a) De La Rue Printings

A. Light Cream Paper

T3	—	Black-brown	2·00	30

a. With two plate dots in bottom
margin (R.10/1)   ..   ..   8·00

B. Whiter Paper (13 July 1962)

T4	595	Black-brown	1·50	20

(b) Bradbury, Wilkinson Printings

A. Whiter Paper (2 July 1963)

T5	595a	Black-brown	20	10

a. Watermark inverted   ..   40·00
b. Weak entry (Pl. 5A, R.5/4 or
6/4)   ..   ..   6·00

c. Re-entry (Pl. 9A, R.8/4)   ..   5·00
d. Re-entry (Pl. 9, R.10/2)   ..   5·00
s. "Cancelled", Type T**5** ..   ..   2·00

B. Chalky Paper (4 June 1968)

T6	595k	Black-brown	25	25

a. Re-entry (Pl. 9A, R.8/4)   ..   5·00

b. Re-entry (Pl. 9, R.10/2)   ..   5·00

Listed Varieties

<table>
<tr><td align="center">T5b</td><td align="center">T5c, T6a</td></tr>
<tr><td>Lines of shading weak or omitted at base of collar, on dress and at foot of background
Occurs on R.5/4 and 6/4 (the illustration is of R.6/4)</td><td>Re-entry shows in the form of brown dots over battlements
The re-entry on Nos. T5d and T6b occurs in the same place but is less marked</td></tr>
</table>

Plates Numbers (Blocks of Four)

Bradbury, Wilkinson Printings

Whiter Paper

Pl. No.		Pl. No.			Pl. No.		Pl. No.		
1	.. 10·00	1A	.. 10·00		6	.. 2·00	6A	.. 2·00
2	.. 10·00	2A	.. 10·00		7	.. 1·50	7A	.. 1·50
3	.. 10·00	3A	.. 10·00		8	.. 1·50	8A	.. 1·50
4	.. 35·00	4A	.. 35·00		9	.. 1·40	9A	.. 1·40
5	.. 2·50	5A	.. 2·50					

Chalky Paper

9	.. 1·50	9A	.. 1·50

Minor Constant Flaws

On Plate 9 there are a number of faint scratch marks in the top and bottom margins and these are particularly noticeable on the chalky paper. They occur in the top margin on R.10/3 and in the bottom margin on R.1/1, 1/2, 2/1, 3/3, 3/4, 7/2, 7/4 and 8/2.

Cat. No.	S.G. No.			Shades			Unused	Used

1968 (JULY 3). NO WATERMARK. WHITE PAPER

Bradbury, Wilkinson Printings

T7		759		Black-brown			20	15

Plate Numbers (Blocks of Four)

Pl. No.		Pl. No.			Pl. No.		Pl. No.		
10	.. 1·25	10A	.. 1·25		12	.. 1·10	12A	.. 1·10
11	.. 1·25	11A	.. 1·25		13	.. 1·10	13A	.. 1·10

1955–68. 5s., Type T2

Cat. No.	S.G. No.		Shades	Unused	Used

1955 (SEPTEMBER 23). WATERMARK ST. EDWARD'S CROWN, TYPE W.23

(a) Waterlow Printings

T8	537		Rose-carmine	3·50	40
a. Re-entry (R.8/1)	..	.. 10·00			
b. Cancelled vert. black bars (P.O.T.S.)	..	.. 50			

(b) De La Rue Printings (1 May 1958)

T9	537a		Rose-carmine	8·00	60

Listed Variety

T8*a*

Major re-entry showing doubling of vertical lines of background above the diadem, and in the diadem along the left edge of the frontal cross, both sides of the side cross and the diagonals

1959 (JUNE 15). WATERMARK CROWNS, TYPE W.24

(a) De La Rue Printings
A. Light Cream Paper

T10	—		Scarlet-vermilion	3·50	50
a. Watermark inverted	..	..			
b. With two plate dots in bottom margin (R.10/1)	..	.. 10·00			

B. Whiter Paper (7 May 1962)

T11	596		Scarlet-vermilion	2·50	40

(b) Bradbury, Wilkinson Printings
Whiter Paper (2 September 1963)

T12	596a		(1) Red	80	40
a. Watermark inverted	..	.. 50·00	(2) Brownish red		
b. Printed on the gummed side	..	90·00	(Plates 3, 4)	50	25

Plate Numbers (Blocks of Four)

Bradbury, Wilkinson Printings

Pl. No.			Pl. No.			Pl. No.			Pl. No.		
1	..	5·00	1A	..	5·00	3	..	2·50	3A	..	2·50
2	..	5·00	2A	..	5·00	4	..	3·00	4A	..	3·00

Cat. No.	S.G. No.	Shades	Unused	Used

1968 (APRIL 16). NO WATERMARK. WHITE PAPER

Bradbury, Wilkinson Printings

| T13 | 760 | Brownish red | 40 | 30 |

Plate Numbers (Blocks of Four)

Pl. No.		Pl. No.		Pl. No.		Pl. No.	
4	.. 1·75	4A	.. 1·75	5	.. 1·75	5A	.. 1·75
				6	.. 1·75	6A	.. 1·75

1955–68. 10s., Type T3

1955 (SEPTEMBER 1). WATERMARK ST. EDWARD'S CROWN, TYPE W.23

(a) Waterlow Printings

T14	538		(1) Ultramarine	10·00	90
a.	Weak entry (R.1/2) ..	.. 40·00 10·00	(2) Pale ultramarine	8·00	90
b.	Cancelled vert. black bars (P.O.T.S.) 50				

(b) De La Rue Printings (1 May 1958)

| T15 | 538a | Dull ultramarine | 20·00 | 1·50 |

Listed Variety

T14*a*

Weak entry to right of lower panel gives ragged appearance

Minor Sheet Flaws

In rows 8, 9 and 10 there are blue marks on the extremities of the white letters and figures of " POSTAGE " and value which are more marked on the bottom two rows. These may not be fully constant but could be helpful for purposes of identification.

1959 (JULY 21). WATERMARK CROWNS, TYPE W.24

(a) De La Rue Printings

A. Light Cream Paper

T16	—	Blue	7·00	90
a.	With two plate dots in bottom margin (R.10/1) .. .. 15·00			

B. Whiter Paper (30 April 1962)

T17	597	Blue	5·00	75
a.	Weak frame (R.4/1) .. .. 10·00			
s.	"Cancelled", Type T5 .. .. 2·00			

(b) Bradbury, Wilkinson Printings

Whiter Paper (1 November 1963)

T18	597a	Bright ultramarine	75	35
a.	Watermark inverted			

110

Listed Variety

Other weak frames
have been found on
this stamp in different
positions but always
on the right-hand side
of the stamp

T17a

Plate Numbers (Blocks of Four)

Bradbury, Wilkinson Printings

Pl. No.		Pl. No.			Pl. No.			Pl. No.	
1	.. 7·00	1A	.. 7·00		2	..	4·00	2A	.. 4·00

Cat. No.	S.G. No.	Shades	Unused	Used

1968 (APRIL 16). NO WATERMARK. WHITE PAPER
Bradbury, Wilkinson, Printings

T19	761	Bright ultramarine	**80**	40

Plate Numbers (Blocks of Four)

Pl. No.			Pl. No.		
2	..	3·50	2A	..	3·50

1955–67.   £1, Type T4

1955 (SEPTEMBER 1).   WATERMARK ST. EDWARD'S CROWN, TYPE W.23

(a) Waterlow Printings

T20	539			Black	17·00	2·00
a. Cancelled vert. black bars (P.O.T.S.)	..	..	.. 50			

(b) De La Rue Printings (1 May 1958)

T21	539a	Black	70·00	2·50

Minor Re-entries

Waterlow Printings

1/2 Slight doubling (Th. B1 and D–F1)
4/4 Slight doubling (Th. B1)
5/2 Slight doubling (Th. B1 and D–E1)
6/1 Slight doubling (Th. A–C13)
7/1 Slight doubling (Th. A–C13)

Other minute signs of doubling of left frame line occur on R.7/2 and of right frame line on R.1/1, 2/1, 3/3, 4/1, 4/2 and 9/2.

Cat. No.	S.G. No.	Shades	Unused	Used

1959 (JUNE 30).   WATERMARK CROWNS, TYPE W.24
(a) De La Rue Printings
A. Light Cream Paper

T22	—	Black	17·00	2·00

a. With two plate dots in bottom
   margin (R.10/1)   ..   .. 25·00

B. Whiter Paper (30 April 1962)

T23 ..	598	Black	13·00	1·50

a. Watermark inverted   ..   ..

(b) Bradbury, Wilkinson Printings
Whiter Paper (2 December 1963)

T24	598a	Black	2·00	75

Plate Numbers (Blocks of Four)
Bradbury, Wilkinson Printings

	Pl. No.			Pl. No.	
	1	.. 10·00		1A	.. 10·00

1967 (DECEMBER 6).   NO WATERMARK. WHITE PAPER
Bradbury, Wilkinson Printings

T25	762	Black	1·60	80

Plate Numbers (Blocks of Four)

	Pl. No.			Pl. No.	
	1	.. 7·00		1A	.. 8·00

Presentation Pack

TPP1 (issued 1960)	Four values	50·00

   The issued pack contained one of each value in the De La Rue printing with Crowns watermark on the light cream paper (Nos. T3, T10, T16 and T22).

SECTION U1

Machin Issues

1967-70. £.s.d. Low Values. Photogravure

General Notes

INTRODUCTION. On 5th June 1967 the first three values of the long-awaited Queen Elizabeth Machin series of definitives were placed on sale. The remaining values were issued in stages during the following thirteen months and the low value series was completed on 1st July 1968, although subsequent changes of stamp colours and variations in the number of phosphor bands on some values have introduced continual additions to the basic series.

The simple design, based on a plaster cast by Arnold Machin, is a complete contrast to the detailed designs of the previous Wilding definitives. The same basic design is used for all values, the only variation being in the figure of value which is placed either on the left or right of the portrait. Uniquely, this was the first definitive issue to be printed on paper without watermark, thus eliminating some of the factors which complicated the listings for previous issues.

The stamps were initially valid for use throughout the United Kingdom and at British Post Offices throughout the world. However, they ceased to be valid in Guernsey and Jersey from 1st October 1969 when these islands each established their own independent postal administrations and introduced their own stamps.

PRINTERS. To date all the low value Machin issues were printed in photogravure by Harrison & Sons. They were printed on continuous reels of paper "on the web" generally in double pane width, i.e. 480 stamps consisting of two panes (no dot and dot) each of 240 stamps arranged in twenty rows of twelve stamps, the panes being guillotined before issue. The 10d., 1s.6d., 1s.9d. and part of the 1s. printings were made from single cylinders printing sheets of 240 stamps (i.e. no dot panes only).

The phosphor bands were applied at the same operation. The bicoloured 1s.6d. and 1s.9d. were printed by the three-colour Halley machine and the remainder by the two-colour Timson machine. The multi-value coils and *se-tenant* panes from the £1 "Stamps for Cooks" booklet were printed by the five-colour Thrissell machine.

PAPER. Unwatermarked chalk-surfaced paper was used for all values. Exceptionally, all four panes from the £1 "Stamps for Cooks" booklet and the 10d. from sheets exist on uncoated paper. It does not respond to the chalky test (that is applying silver to see if it will produce a black line) and may be further distinguished from the normal chalk-surfaced paper by the fibres which clearly show on the surface, resulting in the printing impression being rougher, and by the screening dots which are not so evident.

Paper Thickness. Variation in the thickness of paper sometimes occurs in the making and is undetected where the finished reel conforms to the prescribed weight. Within the reel there may be sections where the paper is unusually thick or thin. A particular example is the 2s. booklet of March 1970 which is known with panes UB15 and UB18 on very thick paper. This has an effect on the thickness of the booklet and can cause jamming in the vending machine. Such varieties are not listed. Certain coil issues were on almost transparent paper, the design showing clearly on the back of the stamps.

GUM. Polyvinyl alcohol (PVA) was introduced by Harrison & Sons in place of gum arabic in 1968. It is almost invisible except that a small amount of pale yellowish colouring matter was introduced to make it possible to see that the stamps had been gummed. Although this can be distinguished from gum arabic in unused stamps there is, of course, no means of detecting it in used copies. Where the two forms of gum exist on the same stamp they are listed separately.

It should be further noted that gum arabic is shiny in appearance, and that, normally, PVA gum has a matt appearance. However, depending upon the qualities of the paper ingredients and the resultant absorption of the gum, occasionally, PVA gum has a shiny appearance. In such cases, especially in stamps from booklets, it is sometimes impossible to be absolutely sure which gum has been used except by testing the stamps with a very expensive infra-red spectrometer. Chemical tests unfortunately destroy the stamps. Therefore, whilst all gum arabic is shiny, it does not follow that all shiny gum is gum arabic. A few late printings of stamps originally issued on PVA were made on gum arabic paper, either in error or to use up stocks.

The term PVA is used because it is generally accepted but the official abbreviation is PVAl to distinguish it from PVAc, polyvinyl acetate, another adhesive which has not so far been used for stamps. De La Rue use PVOH, polyvinyl hydroxyl.

MACHIN HEADS. The master negative used for preparing the multipositives is in three parts for each value comprising (a) head and background, (b) value, and (c) frame. The portrait negative used for the initial releases had a three-dimensional effect only on the 10d.

and 1s. values where a light background was used. On the other values the darker background merged with the outline and much of the relief effect was lost.

Beginning with coils and booklets in March 1968 a new portrait negative was used giving greater contrast at those points where it had been lost. Thus there are two clearly different portraits; the original Head A with a flatter base, and Head B with a curved "shadow" below the bust. We consider that this difference is too small to warrant separate listing in this catalogue, but for those who wish to specialise to this extent we give a complete check list in combination with the different phosphor screens (see below) at the beginning of the catalogue list.

As a result of the tripartite nature of the master negative the position of the value in relation to the frame varies from one multipositive to another. Taking the 4d. for example, the distance to the left frame varies from 0·9 mm. on the early sheet cylinders to 1·2 mm. on the multi-value coils, while the spacing to the bottom is normally 0·9 mm. but decreases to 0·6 mm. in the £1 " Stamps for Cooks " booklet.

PHOSPHOR BANDS. See the General Notes for Section S for a detailed description of these. The Machin definitives were normally issued with " violet " phosphor bands only. Most values have appeared with the phosphor omitted in error and these are listed separately.

PHOSPHOR SCREENS. The phosphor bands were applied in photogravure, some of the cylinders having a 150-line screen and others a 250-line screen. The absence of a screen on parts of a printing is due to the cylinder becoming clogged.

The phosphor screen used for the single centre band on the 3d., 4d. sepia and 4d. vermilion booklet panes of six is unique in having a mixed screen. Continuous 21-row cylinders are produced from two pieces of carbon tissue, thus giving two joins. On this particular phosphor cylinder, the pieces of carbon tissue had different screens. Thus four types of booklet panes can be found—(1) 150 screen; (2) screen join 150/250; (3) 250 screen; (4) screen join 250/150. It is calculated that out of 100 panes the proportions are 67 150 screen, 14 250 screen and 19 screen joins.

It is not easy to distinguish the different screens and we therefore content ourselves by including them in the check list of the Machin Head types.

PERFORATION. Harrisons used the same 15 × 14 comb perforation as for the previous Wilding definitives. A number of different perforators were used for both sheets and booklets and these are described and illustrated in Appendix O. The cylinder numbers are listed and priced according to the type of perforator used.

BOOKLET ERRORS. Those listed as " Imperf. pane " show one row of perforations either at top or bottom of booklet pane. Those listed as " Part perf. pane " have one row of three stamps imperforate on three sides.

BOOKLET AND COIL VARIETIES. See the General Notes for Section S for detailed notes on these.

SHADES. There are numerous shades in these issues and we have restricted our listing to the most marked ones and related them to the cylinder number blocks where possible.

DATES OF ISSUE. The dates given are those announced by the Post Office, except in the case of dates for changes of gum or in the number of phosphor bands when we have quoted either the dates of release by the Philatelic Bureaux or the earliest dates known. As in Section S the dates given in bold type in the headings are those on which stamps first appeared in sheet form. Where a date is followed by a dagger it means that the stamp appeared earlier in coils or booklets as indicated in footnotes.

FIRST DAY COVERS. Prices for these are only quoted where there was a specific service provided by the Post Office. They are listed under the highest value of each group of stamps issued on a particular date.

PRESENTATION PACKS. See General Notes under Section W.

" UNPRINTED STAMPS ". Widely trimmed sheet margins often produce the effect of unprinted stamps as illustrated above. The blank paper often has the phosphor bands printed as on the normal stamps. In the Machin and Regional issues they come from either the left or right-hand margins; in the special issues they are known from the top of the sheet.

INVALIDATION. All £.s.d. stamps including Regionals and Special Issues are to be invalidated in February 1972.

SHEET MARKINGS. Reference should be made to the descriptions of sheet markings given in the General Notes for Section S, as most of these apply to this Section and the information given there is not repeated here. In the case of the 1s.6d. and 1s.9d. bicoloured Machin definitives reference should be made to the descriptions of sheet markings given in Section W as many of them also apply to these two values. Additional information to that provided in Sections S and W is given here.

Cylinder Numbers. In the Machin definitives ½d. to 1s. values they appear in the left-hand margin opposite Row 18 No. 1 in the style as illustrated in Section S. In the case of the 1s.6d. and 1s.9d. values the cylinder numbers appear boxed in the left-hand margin opposite Row 19 No. 1 in the style as illustrated in Section W.

Phosphor Cylinder Numbers. As with the Special issues in Section W, the phosphor cylinder number "Ph 1" was introduced during 1970 on the Machin issues. It only occurs on the dot panes and appears in the right-hand margin and therefore not on the cylinder block. Moreover it is not synchronised with the ink cylinders and so can appear anywhere in the margin, and the "1" is often trimmed off. Its existence is recorded under the sheet markings.

Varieties in Cylinder Blocks. Where a cylinder block contains a listed variety the price is adjusted accordingly and bears an asterisk.

Marginal Arrows. In the Machin definitives these are "W" shaped (photo-etched) at top, bottom and sides, unless otherwise stated.

"Traffic Light" type box

Perforation Guide Holes. A number of different styles of guide hole box have been used for the Machin definitives and these are fully illustrated as for Sections S and W.
In addition to guide hole boxes of one type or another opposite rows 14/15 (used for perforation Type A), most cylinders of nearly all the values from ½d. to 1s. also show a single "traffic light" type box above and below the eighth vertical row in the no dot panes. This latter type would only be used in conjunction with perforation Type F (L)* and it is illustrated here to explain its presence on the sheets. When Type F (L)* is used the circular central part of the box is either partly or completely removed.

Check List of Machin Heads and Phosphor Screens

For fuller explanations see General Notes.

Head A
Flatter Base

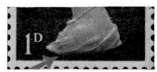

Head B
Curved Shadow

Abbreviations

Bands: 1C = one centre; 1L = one left side; 1R = one right side
Booklet panes: s/t = stamps *se-tenant*; s/t labels = stamps *se-tenant* with labels
Coils: MV = multi-value; S = sideways delivery; V = vertical delivery

Value	Cat. No.	Description	Bands	Gum	Head	Screen	Sheet Cylinders	Sources Booklet Panes	Coils
½d.	U 1		2	PVA	A	150	2, 3	—	
1d.	U 2		2	PVA	A	150	2	—	
	U 2		2	PVA	B	150	4, 6	6	V
	U 2		2	PVA	B	250	—	4 s/t, 6 s/t 15 s/t	—
	U 3		1C	PVA	B	250	—	6 s/t	
	U 4		1C	GA	B	250	—	—	MV
2d.	U 5	Type I	2	PVA	A	150	1	—	V
	U 6	Type II	2	PVA	B	150	5, 6	—	V
	U 6	,,	2	PVA	B	250	—	—	V, S
	U 7	,,	1C	GA	B	250	—	—	MV
3d.	U 8		1C	GA	A	150	1	—	V
	U 8		1C	GA	A	250	—	—	S
	U 8		1C	GA	B	250	—	—	MV
	U 9		1C	PVA	A	150	1, 3, 4	—	—
	U 9		1C	PVA	A	250	—	—	S
	U 9		1C	PVA	B	150	—	6	—
	U 9		1C	PVA	B	Join	—	6	—
	U 9		1C	PVA	B	250	—	6	—
	U10		2	PVA	A	150	3, 4	—	V
	U10		2	PVA	B	150	—	—	V
	U10		2	PVA	B	250	—	4 s/t	—
4d.	U11	Sepia	2	GA	A	150	4, 8	6	V
	U11	,,	2	GA	A	250	—	—	S
	U11	,,	2	GA	B	250	14	—	—
	U12	,,	2	PVA	A	150	4, 10, 12, 13	6	—
	U12	,,	2	PVA	B	250	14, 15	4	—
	U13	,,	1C	PVA	A	150	4, 12, 13	6	V
	U13	,,	1C	PVA	A	Join	—	6	—
	U13	,,	1C	PVA	A	250	—	6	S
	U13	,,	1C	PVA	B	250	14, 15	4, 4 s/t labels 6 s/t	—
	U14	Vermilion	1C	PVA	A	150	4, 10, 13	6	V
	U14	,,	1C	PVA	A	Join	—	6	—
	U14	,,	1C	PVA	A	250	—	6	S
	U14	,,	1C	PVA	B	150	—	6	—
	U14	,,	1C	PVA	B	Join	—	6	—
	U14	,,	1C	PVA	B	250	15, 16, 17	4, 4 s/t labels, 6, 15	S
	U15	,,	1C	GA	B	250	—	—	MV
	U15	,, Feb/Mar	⌈1C	GA	A	150	—	6	—
	U15	,, '69 6/- &	⎱1C	GA	A	Join	—	6	—
	U15	,, May '69 10/-	⌊1C	GA	A	250	—	6	—
	U16	,,	1L	PVA	B	250	—	6 s/t, 15 s/t,	
	U16a	,,	1R	PVA	B	250	—	15 s/t	
5d.	U17		2	PVA	A	150	1	—	—
	U17		2	PVA	B	150	7, 10, 13, 15	6	V
	U17		2	PVA	B	250	11	15, 15 s/t	S
6d.	U18		2	PVA	A	150	2, 3, 4, 5	—	V
	U18		2	PVA	B	150	—	—	V
	U18		2	PVA	B	250	—	—	V
7d.	U19		2	PVA	B	150	3, 4	—	—
8d.	U20	Vermilion	2	PVA	A	150	2	—	—
	U21	Turquoise-blue	2	PVA	B	150	3	—	—
9d.	U22		2	GA	A	150	2	—	—
	U23		2	PVA	A	150	2	—	—
10d.	U24		2	PVA	A	150	1	—	—
	U24		2	PVA	A	250	1	—	—
1s.	U25		2	GA	A	150	3, 11	—	—
	U26		2	PVA	A	150	11	—	—
	U26		2	PVA	A	250	11	—	—
1s.6d.	U27		2	GA	A	150	2A–2B, 3A–2B	—	—
	U27 (3)	"All-over" phos. omitted	—	GA	A	—	5A–2B	—	—
	U28		2	PVA	A	150	3A–2B, 5A–2B	—	—
	U28		2	PVA	A	250	3A–1B	—	—
	U29	"All-over" phos.	—	PVA	A	—	5A–2B	—	—
1s.9d.	U30		2	GA	A	150	1A–1B	—	—
	U31		2	PVA	A	250	1A–1B	—	—

PAPER AND WATERMARK

All the following issues are printed on chalk-surfaced paper without watermark, unless otherwise stated.

U1.
Value at left

Queen Elizabeth II

U2.
Value at right

(Des. after plaster cast by Arnold Machin)

½d., Type U1 (1968)

Cat. No.	S.G. No.			Shades		Unused	Used

1968 (FEBRUARY 5).　TWO 9·5 mm. PHOSPHOR BANDS. PVA GUM

U1	723			Orange-brown		5	5
a. Phosphor omitted	..	..	6·00				
b. Dot in 1 of ½ (Cyl. 3, R.20/2) ..	50						

Listed Variety

U1*b*

Cylinder Numbers (Blocks of Six)

Perforation Type A

Cyl. No.				No dot	Dot
2	..	..	..	50	50
3	..	..	..	80*	50

*Includes variety U1*b*.

Minor Constant Sheet Flaws

Minimum price as singles: 25p

Cyl. 2.　5/12 Small retouch at base of Queen's hair (Th. E4–5)
　　　　9/5 Dark horizontal strip of shading behind Queen's neck (Th. F5–6)

Cyl. 3　12/9 Dark patch below Queen's chin (Th. E2–3)

A number of stamps from cylinder 2 dot display irregularities of the background in the form of dark patches and lines. This is most prominent on R.9/5 recorded above; others occur on R.2/2, 7/6, 8/6, 9/11, 10/1, 13/2–5, 14/5, 17/4–5, and 18/1.

Sheet Markings

Guide holes: In double "S O N" box opposite rows 14/15, at left (no dot) or right (dot). In addition a single "traffic light" type box appears above and below the eighth vertical row in the no dot pane only. (These would only be used in conjunction with perforation Type F (L)*).

Others: As given in General Notes

Sold Out 10.2.70.

1d., Type U1 (1968-70)

Cat. No.	S.G. No.	Shades			Unused	Used

1968 (FEBRUARY 5).

A. Two 9·5 mm. Phosphor Bands. PVA Gum

U2   724

  a. Imperf (coil strip)* £120
  b. Uncoated paper ('70)**   ..
  c. Phosphor omitted   ..   50
  d. One side phosphor band   ..
  e. Neck retouches (Cyl. 4, R.20/3)   50

    (1) Light olive   5   5
    (2) Yellowish olive   5   5
    (3) Greenish olive   5   5

     f. Mole on neck (UB2, R.1/2)   ..   50
     s. Optd. "Specimen" (14 mm.)   ..

B. One 4 mm. Centre Phosphor Band. PVA Gum. *Se-tenant* Booklet pane only (16 September 1968)

U3   725   Yellowish olive   5   5

C. One 4 mm. Centre Phosphor Band. Gum Arabic. Multi-value coil only (27 August 1969)

U4   725Eg   Yellowish olive   5
  a. Dark vert. line (Roll 7 etc.)   ..   50

*No. U2a occurs in a vertical strip of four, top stamp perforated on three sides, bottom stamp imperf. three sides and the two middle stamps completely imperf.

**Uncoated paper. No. U2b comes from the *se-tenant* pane of 15 in the £1 "Stamps for Cooks" Booklet (see No. UB2a); see also General Notes.

No. U3 only comes from the 10/– Booklet of September 1968 (XP6). It also occurs with the phosphor omitted but since a single stamp would be indistinguishable from No. U2c it is only listed when in a complete *se-tenant* booklet pane (see No. UB3a).

No. U4 only comes from the multi-value coil strip which is listed as No. U32.

Listed Varieties

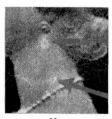

U2*e*   U2*f*

U4*a*
This is Roll 7 but a similar variety occurs on Roll 3 and it may occur on others.

Cylinder Numbers (Blocks of Six)

Two bands. Perforation Type A

Cyl. No.				No dot	Dot
2 (Shade 1)	..	..	..	2·50	2·50
4 (Shade 2)	..	..	..	50	50
6 (Shade 3)	..	..	..	50	50

Minor Constant Sheet Flaws

Minimum price as singles: 25p

Cyl. 2.   5/11 Small flaw at back of Queen's collar (Th. F5)
Cyl. 4   6/9 White flaw at top of Queen's hair (Th. B3)
Cyl. 6.   11/7 Horizontal line of coloured dots across Queen's shoulder (Th. F3–5)
               12/10 Vertical lines of coloured dots through Queen's forehead and cheek (Th. B2, C2–3 and D2)

1d. (contd.

Booklet Panes of Six

Two bands. From 4/6 Booklets LP45/59 and 10/– Booklets XP4/5

UB1 Pane of six	.. ..	30
a. Phosphor omitted ..	..	3·50

Se-tenant Booklet Pane with Recipe Label

Pane of fifteen comprising 6 × 1d. (two bands) with 3 × 4d. (No. U16), 3 × 4d. (No. U16a), 3 × 5d. (No. U17) and *se-tenant* recipe label

"BAKED STUFFED HADDOCK" recipe from £1 "Stamps for Cooks" Booklet ZP1

UB2 Pane of fifteen (stitched)	..	75	UB2c Pane of fifteen (stapled)	.. 3·00
a. Uncoated paper* ..	..	..		
b. Phosphor omitted ..	..	..		

*Uncoated paper—see General Notes.

Se-tenant Booklet Panes of Six

4 × 1d. (one centre band) with pair 4d. (one centre band, No. U13) from 10/– Booklet XP6

		Perf. Type	
		J	L
UB3 Pane of six	.. ..	75	1·50
a. Phosphor omitted	.. ..	2·50	3·00

4 × 1d. (two bands) with pair 4d. (one left side band, No. U16) from 10/– Booklets XP7/12

			Perf. Type L
UB4 Pane of six	.. ..	..	35
a. Phosphor omitted	.. ..	..	6·00

Se-tenant Booklet Panes of Four

Pair 1d. (two bands) with pair 3d. (two bands, No. U10) from 2/– Booklets NP27/9

	Perf. Type			Perf. Type	
	J	K		J	K
UB5 Pane of four with 1d. at left	.. 1·50	40	UB5a Pane of four with 1d. at right	.. 1·50	40

1d. (contd.)

Booklet Cylinder Numbers

Panes of six (21-row cylinders)

Cyl. No.					Perf. Type J No dot	Dot	Cyl. No.					Perf. Type J No dot	Dot
F1	..	..	..	..	3·00	3·00	F3	..	..	..	..	1·00	1·00
F1 T	..	..	..	..	3·00	3·00	F3 T	..	..	..	..	1·00	1·00

In the above and all other 21-row cylinders, which are printed continuously in the web, the perforated web is cut at every 20th row to make sheets of 480. Consequently on successive sheets the cylinder number appears one row lower and thus a pane can have it adjoining the top or bottom row. Where the cylinder number adjoins the top row of the pane it is designated by the letter " T ".

Se-tenant pane of fifteen and recipe label

In the £1 Booklet (ZP1) the cylinder numbers were always trimmed off, however, the cylinders known to have been used were F7 (1d.), N8 (4d.) and R5 (5d.).

Se-tenant pane of six (20-row cylinder)

	One centre band				Two bands		
Cyl. No.	Value	Perf. Type J No dot	L No dot	Cyl. No.	Value		Perf. Type L No dot
F4	1d. ..⎫			F4	1d. ..⎫		
N5	4d. ..⎭ 1·50		2·50	N5	4d. ..⎭		1·50

Se-tenant panes of four

In the 2/– Booklets (NP27/9) the cylinder numbers were always trimmed off.

Coils

Two bands. Vertical delivery printed in continuous reels

Code No.	Number in roll	Face value
E	480	£2
X	960	£4
Z	1920	£8

One centre band. Multi-value coil, see No. U32

Sheet Markings

Guide holes:
Cyls. 2 and 4, in single " S N " box opposite rows 14/15, at left (no dot) or right (dot)
Cyl. 6, in double " S O N " box opposite rows 14/15, at left (no dot) or right (dot)

Marginal arrows:
Cyls. 2 and 6, " W " shaped, photo-etched at top, bottom and sides
Cyl. 4, " W " shaped, hand engraved at top, bottom and sides

Marginal rule:
Cyl. 2, at bottom of sheet, 2 mm. wide
Cyls. 4 and 6, at bottom of sheet, 2½ mm. wide

Others: As given in General Notes

2d., Type U1 (1968-69)

Two Types

I   II

Type I. Value spaced away from left side of stamp (Cyls. 1 no dot and dot)
Type II. Value closer to left side from new multipositive (Cyls. 5 no dot and dot onwards). This results in the portrait appearing in the centre, thus conforming to the other values.

Cat. No.	S.G. No.	Shades		Unused	Used
1968 (FEBRUARY 5). TYPE I. TWO 9·5 mm. PHOSPHOR BANDS. PVA GUM					
U5	726	Lake-brown		5	5
a. Phosphor omitted		3·00			

Cylinder Numbers (Blocks of Six)

Perforation Type A

	Cyl. No.					No dot	Dot
	1	..	..	..	..	60	60

2d. (contd.)

Minor Constant Sheet Flaws

Minimum price as singles: 40p

Cyl.　1　3/11 Small white spot in band of diadem (Th. C5)
　　　　 8/8 Dark spot by emblems at rear of diadem (Th. B5)
　　　　 12/9 Retouching in Queen's hair just by ear (Th. C–D4)

Sheet Markings

　Guide holes: In double " S O N " box opposite rows 14/15, at left (no dot) or right (dot)
　Others: As given in General Notes

Cat. No.	S.G. No.	Shades	Unused	Used

1969 (FEBRUARY).†　CHANGE TO TYPE II

A. Two 9·5 mm. Phosphor Bands. PVA Gum

U6	727	Lake-brown	5	5
a. Phosphor omitted　.. 　.. 　25				

B. One 4 mm. Centre Phosphor Band. Gum Arabic. Multi-value coil only (27 August 1969)

U7	728	Lake-brown	5	5

　†No. U6 was issued on 4 April 1968 in sideways delivery coils, and on 19 March 1969 in vertical delivery coils.
　No. U7 only comes from the multi-value coil strip which is listed as No. U32.

Cylinder Numbers (Blocks of Six)

Two bands. Perforation Type A

Cyl. No.					No dot	Dot
5	..	..	..	..	30	30
6	..	..	..	..	30	30

Minor Constant Sheet Flaws

Minimum price as singles: 25p

Cyl.　5.　6/8 Dark area above 2 (Th. F1)
　　　　 8/1 Small flaw on Queen's shoulder (Th. F3)
　　　　 10/1 Coloured line through Queen's nose and upper lip (Th. C–D2)
　　　　 10/3 Dark spot below Queen's chin (Th. E2)
　　　　 19/5 Retouch to background to left of diadem (Th. A2–3). There are two states of this
Cyl.　6.　18/4 Small retouch at top of Queen's neck and vertical scratch extending to her dress (Th. E3–G3).
　　　　　 Several states exist

Coils

　Two bands. Printed in continuous reels.

Code No.	Number in roll	Face value	
T	480	£4	Sideways delivery
V	960	£8	Vertical delivery

　One centre band. Multi-value coil, see No. U32

Sheet Markings

　Phosphor cylinder number: "Ph 1" found on cyl. 6 dot, right margin (*Price* £1·50 *in block of 6)*
　Guide holes: In double " S O N " box opposite rows 14/15, at left (no dot) or right (dot). In addition a
　　single " traffic light " type box appears above and below the eighth vertical row in the no dot pane only.
　　(These would only be used in conjunction with perforation Type F (L)*).
　Others: As given in General Notes

3d., Type U1 (1967–69)

1967 (AUGUST 8).　ONE 4 mm. CENTRE PHOSPHOR BAND

A. Gum Arabic

U8	729		(1) Violet	5	5
a. Imperf (pair)　.. 　.. 　..	£325		(2) Bluish violet (horiz. coils)	10	10
b. Phosphor omitted　.. 　..	20				
c. Gash on diadem (Multi-value coil, Roll 1)　.. 　.. 　..	50				

B. PVA Gum (12 March 1968)

U9	729Ev		(1) Violet	5	
a. Phosphor omitted　.. 　..	25		(2) Bluish violet (horiz. coils)	50	
b. Spot on nose (Sideways coil, Roll 10)　.. 　.. 　.. 　..	50				

3d. (contd.)

No. U8 also comes from the multi-value coil strip and this is listed as No. U32. This differs in that it has Head B.

No. U8 is known pre-released on 7th August at Bournemouth, Hyde (Cheshire), in South London and at Torquay.

Listed Varieties

U8c

Occurs in sideways delivery multi-value GS and GL coils on every fifth 3d. stamp

U9b

From sideways delivery coils

Cylinder Numbers (Blocks of Six)

Gum Arabic

Perforation Type A

Cyl. No.					No dot	Dot
1	..	..	..	..	6·00	6·00

Perforation Type F (L)*

| 1 | .. | .. | .. | .. | 50 | 50 |

PVA Gum

Perforation Type A

Cyl. No.					No dot	Dot
1	..	..	..	..	50	50
3	..	..	..	..	50	50
4	..	..	..	..	1·50	1·50

There are two states of cyl. 1 no dot: (a) "1" is hatched, the bottom part lacks colour and the serifs are short; (b) "1" is solid and the serifs are long.

Cylinder blocks from the no dot pane of Cylinder 3 show a phantom "3", slightly smaller and just below and to the right of the normal cylinder number. This occurred on part of the printing.

Minor Constant Sheet Flaws

Minimum price as singles: 30p

Cyl. 1	1/9	Vertical scratch on Queen's neck (Th. E3–4)
	3/9	Pale patch in background around D of value
	7/1	Small white flaw inside cross of diadem (Th. B5)
Cyl. 1.	1/4	Small retouch on Queen's neck below ear (Th. D4). PVA only
	1/7	White scratch in Queen's hair below diadem at right (Th. C5). PVA only
	4/11	Small retouch on Queen's neck (Th. E3)
	12/4	Retouch at front of Queen's collar (Th. G3)
	19/6	Small retouch by Queen's mouth (Th. D3)
Cyl. 3.	8/3	Scratch on Queen's temple (Th. C3)
	12/7	Retouch on Queen's neck below necklace (Th. F4)
	16/4	Flaw on Queen's shoulder (Th. F4). Later retouched

Booklet Panes of Six

PVA Gum. From 10/- Booklets XP4/5

UB6 Pane of six	..	..	75
a. Phosphor omitted	..	..	2·00

Booklet Cylinder Numbers

Panes of six (21-row cylinder)

Cyl. No.				No dot	Dot	Cyl. No.					No dot	Dot
K2	..	..	..	5·00	5·00	K2 T	..	..	..	..	5·00	5·00

3d. (contd.)

Coils

Printed in continuous reels
Gum Arabic.

Code No.	Number in roll	Face value	
S	480	£6	Sideways delivery
AC	480	£6	Vertical delivery
AD	960	£12	do.
U	1920	£24	do.

PVA Gum

S*	480	£6	Sideways delivery

 *Stamps from this coil can be distinguished from all other PVA centre-band stamps in singles. The coil stamps have Machin Head Type A and 250-line phosphor screen. The sheet stamps have Head Type A and 150-line screen, whilst the booklet stamps have Head Type B.
For the multi-value coil, see No. U32

Sheet Markings

Guide holes:
   Perf. Type A, in double " S O N " box opposite rows 14/15, at left (no dot) or right (dot). In addition a single " traffic light " type box appears above and below the eighth vertical row in the no dot pane from cyl. 1 (latter only used in conjunction with perforation Type F (L)*).
   Perf. Type F (L)*, boxed above and below the eighth vertical row in the no dot pane only. The usual " S O N " boxes opposite rows 14/15 remain.

Others: As given in General Notes

Cat. No.	S.G. No.	Shades	Unused	Used

1969 (AUGUST 20).† CHANGE TO TWO 9·5 mm. PHOSPHOR BANDS. PVA GUM

U10	730	Violet	5	5

†Issued on 6.4.68 in 2/– Booklets dated May 1968, on 26 September 1968 in vertical delivery coils.

Cylinder Numbers (Blocks of Six)

Perforation Type A

Cyl. No.					No dot	Dot
3	..	..	..	..	50	50
4	..	..	..	..	1·50	1·50

   The note about the phantom "3" mentioned under No. U9 also applies here and the whole of the printing was affected.

Minor Constant Sheet Flaws

Minimum price as singles: 30p

Cyl. 3.   8/3 Scratch on Queen's temple (Th. C3)
   12/7 Retouch on Queen's neck below necklace (Th. F4)

Se-tenant Booklet Panes of Four

   For booklet panes of No. U10 *se-tenant* with 1d. value, see No. UB5.

Booklet Cylinder Numbers

Se-tenant panes of four
   In the 2/– Booklets (NP27/9) the cylinder numbers were always trimmed off.

Coil

   Vertical delivery printed in continuous reels

Code No.	Number in roll	Face value
AD	960	£12

Sheet Markings

Guide holes: In double " S O N " box opposite rows 14/15, at left (no dot) or right (dot)
Others: As given in General Notes

4d., Type U1 (1967-70)

Cat. No.	S.G. No.	Shades	Unused	Used

1967 (JUNE 5). TWO 9·5 mm. PHOSPHOR BANDS

A. Gum Arabic

U11	731/Ea	(1) Deep sepia	5	5
a. Part perf. pane*	.. ..	(2) Deep olive-brown	5	5
b. Phosphor omitted	 30			

B. PVA Gum (22 January 1968)

U12	731Eav	(2) Deep olive-brown	5	
a. One 9·5 mm. phosphor band ..	75	(3) Deep olive-sepia	8	5
b. Phosphor omitted	10	e. Dot on D (Booklet pane R.1/2)	50	
c. White patch (Cyl. 13, R.20/12)	50	f. Patch on cheek (Booklet pane		
d. Nick in hair (Cyl. 15., R.16/5) ..	50	R.1/2 or 2/2)	50	

*Booklet error—see General Notes.

No. U11 (1) in shades of washed out grey are colour changelings which we understand are caused by the concentrated solvents used in modern dry-cleaning methods.

No. U11 (1) is known pre-released on 25th May at Gravesend.

Listed Varieties

U12c, U13b, U14e
White patch over
eye and hair

U12d U13c, U14f
Reported as
being later retouched

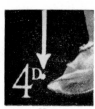

U12e
From 2s. booklet

U12f
From 10s. booklet

Cylinder Numbers (Blocks of Six)

Gum Arabic

Cyl. No.				No dot	Dot
Perforation Type F (L)*					
(a) Shade (1) Deep sepia					
4 ..	..	..	.. ..	2·50	2·50
8 ..	..	..	.. ..	1·50	1·50
(b) Shade (2) Deep olive-brown					
4 ..	..	..	.. ..	2·50	2·50
8 ..	..	..	.. ..	2·50	2·50
Perforation Type A					
14 ..	..	..	..	—	†

PVA Gum

Cyl. No.				No dot	Dot
(a) Shade (2) Deep olive-brown					
Perforation Type F (L)*					
4 ..	..	.. ..	..	5·00	5·00
Perforation Type A					
4 ..	..	..	..	2·50	2·50
10 ..	..	..	..	75	75
12 ..	..	..	..	75	75
13 ..	..	..	..	4·50	5·00
14 ..	..	..	..	50	50
15 ..	..	..	..	15·00	15·00
(b) Shade (3) Deep olive-sepia					
Perforation Type A					
14 ..	..	..	..	4·50	5·00
15 ..	..	..	..	15·00	15·00

Cylinder 15 has the number close to the stamp resulting in the dot often being removed by the perforations. The dot pane has a tiny dot on the horizontal rule below R.20/1 whilst in the no dot pane the marginal rule below R.20/1 is damaged and there is a line in the margin below R.20/2.

4*d.* **Brown (contd.)**

Minor Constant Sheet Flaws

Minimum price as singles: 40p

Cyl. 4. 2/9 Dark flaw in Queen's hair (Th. C4)
20/8 Scar on Queen's forehead (Th. C2–3)

Cyl. 8 18/12 Diagonal line through back of Queen's hair (Th. C5)

Cyl. 8. 9/9 White spot in band of diadem (Th. B3–4)
15/3 Diagonal coloured line on Queen's shoulder and dress (Th. F–G4)
15/5 Prominent retouch on Queen's neck just below jawline (Th. E3–4)

Cyl. 10 18/12 As Cyl. 8

Cyl. 10. 3/4 Coloured flaw on Queen's shoulder (Th. F3)
3/6 Two coloured flaws on Queen's shoulder (Th. F3)
10/8 Pale patch in background to left of Queen's throat (Th. E2)
11/7 Dark flaw at back of Queen's neck, just above necklace (Th. E4)
12/5 Dark flaw on Queen's shoulder, just below necklace (Th. F3)
15/3 As Cyl. 8
15/5 As Cyl. 8
19/2 Dark coloured vertical line in lower right-hand stamp margin (Th. G7)

Cyl. 12 18/12 As Cyl. 8

Cyl. 12. 15/3 As Cyl. 8
15/5 As Cyl. 8

Cyl. 13 9/12 Large area of retouching behind Queen's head (Th. C5–6 and D5–6)
18/12 As Cyl. 8

Cyl. 13. 15/3 As Cyl. 8
15/5 As Cyl. 8 but more prominent

Cyl. 14 6/11 Vertical white scratch on Queen's neck (Th. E–F4)
18/7 White flaw at back of Queen's dress (Th. F5)

Booklet Panes of Six

Gum Arabic

(a) Shade (1) Deep sepia. From 6/– Booklets QP28/32

UB7 Pane of six 50
  a. Phosphor omitted .. .. 2·00

(b) Shade (2) Deep olive-brown. From 6/– Booklets QP33/6

UB8 Pane of six 30
  a. Phosphor omitted .. .. 4·00

PVA Gum. From 4/6 Booklets LP45/6, 6/– Booklets QP37/40 and 10/– Booklets XP4/5

UB9 Pane of six 60
  a. Phosphor omitted .. .. 1·00
  b. One 9·5 mm. phosphor band ..

Booklet Panes of Four

PVA Gum. From 2/– Booklets NP27/31

	Perf. Type	
	J	K
UB10 Pane of four	1·50	50
a. Phosphor motted ..	2·50	1·00

Booklet Cylinder Numbers

Panes of six (21-row cylinders)

Gum Arabic			PVA Gum			
Cyl. No.	No dot	Dot	Cyl. No.		No dot	Dot
(a) Shade (1) Deep sepia						
N1	1·50	1·50				
N1 T	1·50	1·50				
(b) Shade (2) Deep olive-brown						
N1	1·50	1·50	N1	..	1·00	1·00
N1 T	1·50	1·00	N1 T	..	1·00	1·00
			N2	..	1·00	1·00
			N2 T	..	1·00	1·00

Panes of four

In the 2/– Booklets (NP27/31) the cylinder numbers were always trimmed off, however, the cylinder known to have been used was N3.

Coils

Printed in continuous reels

Gum Arabic. Shade (2) Deep olive-brown

Code No.	Number in roll	Face value	
H	480	£8	Sideways delivery
A	960	£16	Vertical delivery

4d. Brown (contd.)

Sheet Markings

Guide holes:
Perf. Type A, in double " S O N " box opposite rows 14/15, at left (no dot) or right (dot). In addition a single " traffic light " type box appears above and below the eighth vertical row in the no dot pane only (latter only used in conjunction with perforation Type F (L)*).
Perf. Type F (L)*, boxed above and below the eighth vertical row in the no dot pane only. The usual " S O N " boxes opposite rows 14/15 remain.
Others: As given in General Notes

Cat. No.	S.G. No.	Shades	Unused	Used

1968 (SEPTEMBER 16).   CHANGE TO ONE 4 mm. CENTRE PHOSPHOR BAND. PVA GUM

U13	732	(2) Deep olive-brown	5	5
a. Part perf. pane*	.. ..	(3) Deep olive-sepia	5	5
b. White patch (Cyl. 13, R.20/12)	50			
c. Nick in hair (Cyl. 15., R.16/5)	50			

*Booklet error—see General Notes.
For illustrations of Nos. U13*b/c* see Nos. U12*c/d*.
No. U13 also occurs with the phosphor omitted but since a single stamp would be indistinguishable from No. U12*b* it is only listed when in a complete *se-tenant* booklet pane (see No. UB3*a*).

Cylinder Numbers (Blocks of Six)

Perforation Type A

(a) Shade (2) Deep olive-brown

Cyl. No.						No dot	Dot
4	..	..	..	..	..	1·00	1·00
12	..	..	..	..	..	1·00	1·00
13	..	..	..	..	..	6·00	6·00
14	..	..	..	..	..	50	50
15	..	..	..	..	..	50	50

(b) Shade (3) Deep olive-sepia

Cyl. No.						No dot	Dot
14	..	..	..	..	..	75	75
15	..	..	..	..	..	75	75

The note about the cylinder number being close to the stamp on Cylinder 15 mentioned under No. U12 also applies here.

Minor Constant Sheet Flaws

Minimum price as singles: 40p

Cyl.	4.	2/9	Coloured flaw in Queen's hair (Th. C4)
		19/1	Flaw on lower rim of Queen's diadem shows as "missing pearls" (Th. C5)
		20/8	Scar on Queen's forehead (Th. C2–3)
Cyl.	12	18/12	Diagonal line through back of Queen's hair (Th. C5)
Cyl.	12.	15/3	Diagonal coloured line on Queen's shoulder and dress (Th. F–G4)
		15/5	Prominent retouch on Queen's neck just below jawline (Th. E3–4)
Cyl.	13	9/12	Large area of retouching behind Queen's head (Th. C5–6 and D5–6)
		18/12	As Cyl. 12
Cyl.	13.	15/3	As Cyl. 12
		15/5	As Cyl. 12, but more prominent
Cyl.	15.	5/12	Two small white dots on Queen's shoulder (Th. F–G4). Later retouched
		17/12	White scrath in background above value, extending to Queen's shoulder. Later retouched but flaw still shows on Queen's shoulder

Booklet Panes of Six

From 4/6 Booklets LP47/8, 6/– Booklets QP41/5 and 10/– Booklet XP6
UB11 Pane of six   30

The above also occurs with the phosphor omitted but since a single pane would be indistinguishable from No. UB9*a* it is only listed there.

Booklet Panes of Four

From 2/– Booklets NP31*a*/33

	Perf. Type		
	J	K	L
UB12 Pane of four ..	1·00	30	75

Phosphor omitted exists from these booklets but the panes are idenitical wth No. U10*a*.

4*d*. Brown (contd.)

Booklet Panes with Printed Labels

Panes of four comprising two stamps and two labels
"£4,315 FOR YOU AT AGE 55" (1st label) and "SEE OTHER PAGES" (2nd label) from
2/– Booklets NP30/3
UB13 Pane of four

	Perf. Type		
	J	K	L
UB13 Pane of four	50	20	75
a. Phosphor omitted ..	7·50	5·00	†

Se-tenant Booklet Panes of Six

For booklet pane of No. U13 *se-tenant* with 1d. value, see No. UB3.

Booklet Cylinder Numbers

Panes of six (21-row cylinders)

Cyl. No.				No dot	Dot	Cyl. No.					No dot	Dot
N1 ..	..	..	..	1·25	75	N2 ..	..	..	..	..	1·00	75
N1 T	..	..	..	1·25	75	N2 T	..	..	..	..	1·00	75

Panes of four (including panes of four comprising two stamps and two labels)
In the 2/– Booklets (NP30/3) the cylinder numbers were always trimmed off ,however
the cylinders known to have been used were N3 and N6.

Se-tenant panes of six

For 4d. No. U13, cyl. N5, see after No. UB5.

Coils

Printed in continuous reels

	Code No.	Number in roll	Face value	
	H	480	£8	Sideways delivery
	A	960	£16	Vertical delivery

Sheet Markings

Guide holes: As tor perf. Type A under Nos. U11/12
Others: As given in General Notes

Cat. No.	S.G. No.		Shades	Unused	Used

1969 (JANUARY 6).   CHANGE OF COLOUR. ONE 4 mm. CENTRE PHOSPHOR BAND

A. PVA Gum

U14	733		Bright vermilion	5	5

a. Tête-bêche (horiz. pair)   ..
b. Uncoated paper ('70)**   ..
c. Phosphor omitted   40
d. Red nick in D (Cyl. 4., R.1/4) ..   50
e. White patch (Cyl. 13., R.20/12)   50
f. Nick in hair (Cyl. 15., R.16/5) ..   50
g. Tail on 4 (Booklet pane UB16, R.1/4)   75
h. Spot over eye (Booklet pane UB17, R.2/2)   75
i. Damaged pearls in crown (Booklet pane UB18, R.1/2)   50
s. Optd. "Specimen" (14 mm.) ..

B. Gum Arabic. Multi-value coil only (27 August 1969)

U15	733Eg		Bright vermilion	5	

**Uncoated paper. No. U14*b* comes from the £1 "Stamps for Cooks" Booklet (see Nos.
UB16*a* and UB17*a*); see also General Notes.
Nos. U14 and U16/*a* from the £1 "Stamps for Cooks" Booklet (ZP1) show slight differences
compared with stamps from normal sheets and all other booklets. The main stem of the "4"
is thicker and it is only 0·6 mm. from its foot to the base of the design compared with 0·9
mm. on stamps from sheets and all other booklets. Also, the cross-bar of the "4", normally
opposite the point of the Queen's gown, is lower on the £1 booklet stamps. See under
"Machin Heads" in General Notes.
No. U15 comes from the multi-value coil strip which is listed as No. U32 and in the
February and part of March 1969 6/– Booklets (QP46/7) and also part of May 1969 10/–
Booklets (XP8).

4d. Vermilion (contd.)

Listed Varieties

For illustrations of Nos. U14e/f, see Nos. U12c/d.

U14d
Believed later retouched

U14g
From £1 booklet

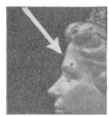

U14h
Later retouched on
UB17 and exists re-
touched only on UB16

U14i
From 2s. booklet

Cylinder Numbers (Blocks of Six)

Perforation Type A

Cyl. No.					No dot	Dot	Cyl. No.					No dot	Dot
4	..	..	..	..	50	50	15	..	..	..	..	.. 60	60
10	..	..	..	..	50	50	16	..	..	..	..	.. 60	60
13	..	..	..	..	50	50	17	..	..	..	..	.. 50	50

The note about the cylinder number being close to the stamp on Cylinder 15 mentioned under No. U12 also applies here.

Minor Constant Sheet Flaws

Minimum price as singles: 40p

Cyl. 4. 19/1 Flaw on lower rim of Queen's diadem shows as "missing pearls" (Th. C5)
20/8 Scar on Queen's forehead (Th. C2–3)

Cyl. 10 18/12 Diagonal line through back of Queen's hair (Th. C5)

Cyl. 10. 15/3 Diagonal coloured line on Queen's shoulder and dress (Th. F–G4)
15/5 Prominent retouch on Queen's neck just below jawline (Th. E3–4)

Cyl. 13 9/12 Large area of retouching behind Queen's head (Th. C5–6 and D5–6)
18/12 As Cyl. 10

Cyl. 13. 15/3 As Cyl. 10
15/5 As Cyl. 10., but more prominent

Cyl. 15. 17/12 Scratch on Queen's shoulder at left (Th. F3)

Cyl. 17   4/7 Small coloured spot in band of diadem (Th. B4)
7/3 Small retouch on Queen's shoulder (Th. F3)
18/4 Small flaw in band of diadem (Th. B4)

Cyl. 17. 19/10 White scratch at back of Queen's shoulder (Th. F5)

Booklet Panes of Six

PVA Gum. From 4/6 Booklets LP49/59, 6/– Booklets QP46/55 and 10/– Booklets XP7/12

UB14 Pane of six	..	..	30
a. Phosphor omitted	..	..	2·50
b. Gum arabic	..	..	1·50

4d. Vermilion (contd.)

Booklet Panes of Four

PVA Gum. From 2/– Booklets NP34/45

			Perf. Type	
			J	L
UB15 Pane of four	..	..	20	15
a. Phosphor omitted		..	1·75	1·75

Booklet Panes with Recipe Label

PVA Gum. Panes of fifteen *se-tenant* with recipe label

"STUFFED CUCUMBER" recipe and "METHOD" from £1 "Stamps for Cooks" Booklet ZP1

UB16 Pane of fifteen (stitched)	80		UB16c Pane of fifteen (stapled)	2·50
a. Uncoated paper ('70)* ..	..			
b. Phosphor omitted ..	..			

"METHOD" only for Braised Shoulder of Lamb from £1 "Stamps for Cooks" Booklet ZP1

UB17 Pane of fifteen (stitched)	80		UB17c Pane of fifteen (stapled)	2·50
a. Uncoated paper ('70)* ..	..			
b. Phosphor omitted ..	..			

  *Uncoated paper—See General Notes.

Booklet Panes with Printed Labels

PVA Gum. Panes of four comprising two stamps and two labels

"£4,315 FOR YOU AT AGE 55" (1st label) and "SEE OTHER PAGES" (2nd label) from 2/– Booklets NP34/45

			Perf. Type	
			J	L
UB18 Pane of four	..	..	25	15
a. Phosphor omitted	..	..	†	1·25

Booklet Cylinder Numbers

Panes of six (21-row cylinders)

Cyl. No.					No dot	Dot	Cyl. No.					No dot	Dot
N1 ..	..	..	..	..	75	75	N2 ..	..	..	..	..	60	60
N1 T	..	..	..	..	75	75	N2 T	..	..	..	..	60	60
N1 (gum arabic) ..	..	..	..	5·00	5·00	N7 ..	..	..	..	..	60	60
N1 T (gum arabic)..	..	..	..	5·00	5·00	N7 T	..	..	..	..	60	60

Panes of four (including panes of four comprising two stamps and two labels)

  In the 2/– Booklets (NP34/40) the cylinder numbers were always trimmed off, however, the cylinders known to have been used were N3 and N6.

Panes of fifteen *se-tenant* with recipe label

  In the £1 Booklet (ZP1) the cylinder number was always trimmed off, however, the cylinder known to have been used was N9.

Coils

  PVA Gum. Printed in continuous reels

Code No.	Number in roll	Face value	
H	480	£8	Sideways delivery
A	960	£16	Vertical delivery

  Gum Arabic. Multi-value coil, see No. U32.

Sheet Markings

  Guide holes: As for perf. Type A under Nos. U11/12
  Others: As given in General Notes

4d. Vermilion (contd.)

Cat. No.	S.G. No.	Shades	Unused	Used

1969 (JANUARY 6).   ONE SIDE PHOSPHOR BAND*. PVA GUM

These were only issued in booklets.

U16   734

Bright vermilion (band at left) 10 10

a. Band at right (1.12.69).. .. 15 10
b. Uncoated paper (band at left)
('70)** .. ..
c. Uncoated paper (band at right)
('70)** .. ..

d. One wide phosphor band .. 75
s. Optd. "Specimen" (14 mm.) ..
t. Do. Band at right ..

*The one side band stamps were produced by applying a 9·5 mm. band over the vertical perforations between the 4d. and its adjoining stamp in the booklet panes. In theory the width of the band on a single stamp should be 4¾ mm. but this will vary if the band has not been perfectly positioned.

**Uncoated paper. Nos. U16b/c come from the *se-tenant* pane of 15 in the £1 "Stamps for Cooks" Booklet (see No. UB2a); see also General Notes.

No. U16 comes from 10/– Booklets (XP7/12) and the £1 Booklet (ZP1) and No. U16a comes from the £1 Booklet (ZP1) only.

No. U16 also occurs with the phosphor omitted but since a single stamp would be indistinguishable from No. U14c it is only listed when in a complete *se-tenant* booklet pane (see No. UB4a).

See note after No. U15 *re* differences between 4d. stamps in the £1 Booklet (ZP1) and those in sheets and all other booklets.

Se-tenant Booklet Pane with Recipe Label

For booklet pane of Nos. U16/a *se-tenant* with 1d. and 5d. values, see No. UB2.

Se-tenant Booklet Panes of Six

For booklet pane of No. U16 *se-tenant* with 1d. value, see No. UB4.

Booklet Cylinder Numbers

Se-tenant pane of fifteen and recipe label

In the £1 Booklet (ZP1) the cylinder numbers were always trimmed off, however, the cylinders known to have been used were F7 (1d.), N8 (4d.) and R5 (5d.).

Se-tenant panes of six

For 4d. No. U16, cyl. N5, see after No. UB5.

5d., Type U1 (1968-70)

1968 (JULY 1).   TWO 9·5 mm. PHOSPHOR BANDS. PVA GUM

U17   735

(1) Royal blue   8   5
(2) Deep blue   5   5

a. Imperf. pane* £150
b. Part perf. pane* .. ..
c. Imperforate (pair)† .. ..
d. Uncoated paper ('70)** .. 15·00
e. Phosphor omitted 30
f. One phosphor band 10
g. Neck retouch (Cyls. 7, 10, 11, 13
  no dot, R.18/1 and cyl. 15, R.19/1   50

h. Scratch severing neck (Cyl. 13.,
  R.19/4) 50
i. White flaw on diadem (Booklet
  pane UB19, R.1/2 or 2/2) .. 50
j. White flaw below collar (Booklet
  pane UB20, R.1/2) 50
s. Optd. "Specimen" (14 mm.) ..

*Booklet errors—see General Notes.

†No. U17c comes from the original state of cylinder 15 which is identifiable by the screening dots in the gutters (see note after cylinder number list). This must not be confused with imperforate stamps from cylinder 10, a large quantity of which was stolen from the printers early in 1970.

**Uncoated paper. No. U17d comes from the £1 "Stamps for Cooks" Booklet (see Nos. UB2a and UB20a); see also General Notes.

No. U17 from the £1 "Stamps for Cooks" Booklet (ZP1) and cylinders 7, 10 and 11 (no dot and dot panes) show slight differences compared with stamps from cylinder 1 (no dot and dot) and all other booklet panes. The "5D" is slightly thicker and is positioned fractionally lower than on stamps from cylinder 1 and all other booklet panes. See under "Machin Heads" in the General Notes.

No. U17 is known postmarked at Trafalgar Square (London) on 29th June and at Dorking and Guildford on 30th June.

5d. (contd.)

Listed variety

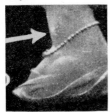

This variety is due to damage on the multipositive. Cyl. 1 is normal and the most marked retouch is on cyl. 11. Cyl. 15 was formed by moving up one row of the multipositive (which is 28 rows by 31 columns) and the variety occurs on 19/1.

U17g

U17h

U17i

U17j

Cylinder Numbers (Blocks of Six)

Perforation Type A

Cyl. No.				No dot	Dot	Cyl. No.				No dot	Dot
1 (Shade 1)	..	..	..	50	50	11 (Shade 2)	..	..	..	1·00*	50
7 (Shade 2)	..	..	..	1·00*	50	13 (Shade 2)	..	..	..	10·00*	10·00
10 (Shade 2)	..	..	..	1·00*	50	15 (Shade 2)	..	..	..	1·50*	60

Cyl. 15 dot has a smudge so that it looks like "151".

Original printings of cylinder 15 (no dot and dot) had screening dots extending through the gutters of the stamps and into the margins of the sheet. Later the cylinder was cleaned and re-chromed.

Minor Constant Sheet Flaws

Minimum price as singles: 40p

Cyl. 1	7/1 Coloured spot in band of diadem (Th. C5)
	7/5 Short white flaw in Queen's hair (Th. C4)
	12/2 White flaw in band of diadem (Th. B4)
Cyl. 1.	1/11 Pale patch in background below top bar of 5 (Th. G1)
	20/4 White spot in band of diadem (Th. C5)
Cyl. 7	18/2 Scratch on Queen's shoulder (Th. F4)
Cyl. 7.	1/10 White flaw on Queen's forehead (Th. C3)
	14/12 Small retouch on Queen's shoulder (Th. G4)
Cyl. 10	15/8 Coloured flaw below Queen's earring (Th. D4)
	18/2 Scratch on Queen's shoulder (Th. F4)
	20/5 Two diagonal scratches on Queen's neck (Th. E3-4, F4 and G4)
	20/6 Retouch on Queen's neck (Th. E4)
Cyl. 15	16/8 Coloured flaw below Queen's earring (Th. D4)
	19/2 Scratch on Queen's shoulder (Th. F4)
Cyl. 15.	1/10 Scratch on Queen's nose (Th. C2)

Booklet Panes of Six

From 5/- Booklets HP26/38 and 10/- Booklets XP6/12

| UB19 Pane of six | .. | .. | 50 |
| *a.* Phosphor omitted | .. | .. | 2·00 |

Booklet Pane with Recipe Label

Pane of fifteen *se-tenant* with recipe label

" METHOD " only for Cream of Potato Soup from £1 " Stamps for Cooks " Booklet ZP1

UB20 Pane of fifteen (stitched)	80	UB20c Pane of fifteen (stapled)	2·50
a. Uncoated paper*	.. ..	
b. Phosphor and recipe omitted		*d.* Uncoated paper*	.. ..

*Uncoated paper—see General Notes.

5d. (contd.)

Se-tenant Booklet Pane with Recipe Label

For booklet pane of No. U17 *se-tenant* with 1d. and 4d. values, see No. UB2.

Booklet Cylinder Numbers

Panes of six (21-row cylinders)

Cyl. No.					No dot	Dot	Cyl. No.					No dot	Dot
R2	..	..	..	..	75	75	R3 ..	.	..	..	..	75	75
R2 T	..	..	..	..	75	75	R3 T	.	..	..	..	75	75

Panes of fifteen *se-tenant* with recipe label and *se-tenant* pane of fifteen and recipe label

In the £1 Booklet (ZP1) the cylinder numbers were always trimmed off, however, the cylinders known to have been used were R6 (pane of fifteen) and F7 (1d.), N8 (4d.) and R5 (5d.) (*se-tenant* pane).

Coils

Printed in continuous reels

Code No.	Number in roll	Face value	
AF	480	£10	Sideways delivery
AE	960	£20	Vertical delivery

Sheet Markings

Phosphor cylinder number: "Ph 1" found on cyl. 15 dot, right margin *(Price £1·25, block of 6)*.

Guide holes: In double "S O N" box (or "S O" box, cyl. 10) opposite rows 14/15, at left (no dot) or right (dot). In addition a single "traffic light" type box appears above and below the eighth vertical row in the no dot pane only. (These would only be used in conjunction with perforation Type F (L)*).

Others: As given in General Notes.

6d., Type U1 (1968)

Cat. No.	S.G. No.	Shades		Unused	Used

1968 (FEBRUARY 5).   TWO 9·5 mm. PHOSPHOR BANDS.   PVA GUM

U18	736					

a. Phosphor omitted   ..   ..   2·00
b. Hair flaws (Cyl. 2, R.18/1)   ..   75
c. Background retouch (Cyl. 2,
   R.11/1)   75
d. Diadem flaw (Cyl. 3, R.2/3)   ..   60

U1, U2, U5 and U18

(1) Bright reddish purple (*shades*)   15   10
(2) Bright magenta   12   10
(3) Claret   5   5

   e. Two spots in front of neck (Vert.
     coil, Roll 12)   50

First Day Cover   †   25

Listed Varieties

U18*b*
Two coloured lines
crossing base of
diadem, one extending
in curves through
the hair

U18*c*
Large circular
retouch above
value

U18*d*
Coloured flaw
in band of
diadem

6d. (contd.)

U18e
Two spots in front of neck

Cylinder Numbers (Blocks of Six)
Perforation Type A

(a) Shade (1) Bright reddish purple

Cyl. No.					No dot	Dot
2	..	..	..	..	1·50*	50
3	..	..	..	..	40	40
4	..	..	..	..	4·00	4·00
5	..	..	..	..	40	40

(b) Shade (2) Bright magenta

Cyl. No.					No dot	Dot
3	..	..	..	..	2·50	2·50

(c) Shade (3) Claret

5	..	..	..	..	50	50

Minor Constant Sheet Flaws
Minimum price as singles: 50p

Cyl. 2. 2/4 White flaw in band of diadem (Th. B4)
       4/4 Coloured line in band of diadem (Th. B3–4)
       4/11 Small retouch on Queen's collar (Th. G4)
       10/11 Vertical flaws in Queen's hair and in band of diadem (Th. B–C4)
Cyl. 3 13/5 Two small white flaws on Queen's neck above necklace (Th. F3)
       19/9 Small coloured dot in band of diadem (Th. B3)
Cyl. 3. 5/3 Line of white dashes on Queen's collar (Th. G3–4)
       11/5 Small retouch on Queen's collar (Th. G4)
Cyl. 4 11/10 Small background retouch left of Queen's forehead (Th. B2)
Cyl. 5 18/1 White tail below "D"

Coil
Vertical delivery printed in contiuous reels

Code No.	Number in roll	Face value
J	480	£12

Sheet Markings
Phospher cylinder number: "Ph. 1" found on cyl. 5 dot, right margin (*Price £2 block of 6*)

Guide holes: In double "S O N" box opposite rows 14/15, at left (no dot) or right (dot). In addition a single "traffic light" type box appears above and below the eighth vertical row in the no dot pane only. (These would only be used in conjunction with perforation Type F (L)*.)

Others: As given in General Notes

7d., Type U2 (1968)

Cat. No.	S.G. No.	Shades	Unused	Used

1968 (JULY 1). TWO 9·5 mm. PHOSPHOR BANDS. PVA GUM

U19	737	Bright emerald	5	5
a. Phosphor omitted	..	..	7·50	

No. U19 is known postmarked at Dorking and at Guildford on 30th June.

Cylinder Numbers (Blocks of Six)
Perforation Type A

Cyl. No.					No dot	Dot
3	..	..	..	..	50	50
4	..	..	..	..	2·50	2·50

7d. (contd.)

Minor Constant Sheet Flaws

Minimum price as singles: 50p

Cyl. 3   8/6 Flaw in background by Queen's collar (Th. F5)
         12/6 Dark flaw on jewel in band of diadem (Th. C5)

Sheet Markings

Phosphor cylinder number: "Ph 1" found on cyl. 4 dot, right margin (*Price £2·50, block of 6*)
Guide holes: In single hand engraved box opposite rows 14/15, at left (no dot) or right (dot)
Marginal arrows: " W " shaped, hand engraved at top, bottom and sides on cyl. 3, photo-etched on cyl.4
Others: As given in General Notes

8d., Type U2 (1968-69)

Cat. No.	S.G. No.	Shades	Unused	Used

1968 (JULY 1). TWO 9·5 mm. PHOSPHOR BANDS. PVA GUM

U20	738	Bright vermilion	8	8
a. Phosphor omitted	.. .. 20·00			

No. U20 is known postmarked at Dorking and at Guildford on 30th June.

Cylinder Numbers (Blocks of Six)

Perforation Type A

Cyl. No.					No dot	Dot
2	..	..	..	..	75	75

Sheet Markings

Guide holes: In double "S O N" box opposite rows 14/15, at left (no dot) or right (dot). In addition a single "traffic light" type box appears above and below the eighth vertical row in the no dot pane only. (These would only be used in conjunction with perforation Type F (L)*.)
Others: As given in General Notes

1969 (JANUARY 6). CHANGE OF COLOUR. TWO 9·5 mm. PHOSPHOR BANDS. PVA GUM

U21	739	Light turquoise-blue	5	5
a. Phosphor omitted	.. .. 15·00			
b. Missing pearls (Cyl. 3, R.19/2) ..	75			

Listed Variety

U21*b*

Cylinder Numbers (Blocks of Six)

Perforation Type A

Cyl. No.					No dot	Dot
3	..	..	..	..	1·00*	50

Minor Constant Sheet Flaw

Minimum price as single: 50p

Cyl. 3.   19/2 White flaw by Queen's mouth (Th. D2)

8d. Turquoise-blue (contd.)

Sheet Markings

Guide holes: In single " S N " box opposite rows 14/15, at left (no dot) or right (dot). In addition a single " traffic light " type box appears above and below the eighth vertical row in the no dot pane only. (These would only be used in conjunction with perforation Type F (L)*.

Others: As given in General Notes.

9d., Type U2 (1967-68)

Cat. No.	S.G. No.	Shades	Unused	Used

1967 (AUGUST 8). TWO 9·5 mm. PHOSPHOR BANDS

A. Gum Arabic

U22	740	Myrtle-green	5	5
a. Phosphor omitted	.. .. 2·50			

B. PVA Gum (29 November 1968)

U23	740Ev	Myrtle-green	5
a. Phosphor omitted	.. .. 1 50		

No. U22 is known pre-released on 7th August at Bournemouth and Torquay.

Cylinder Numbers (Blocks of Six)

Gum Arabic				PVA Gum			
Cyl. No.		No dot	Dot	Cyl. No.		No dot	Dot
Perforation Type F (L)*				Perforation Type A			
2		50	50	2		60	60
Perforation Type A							
2		4·00	4·00				

Cylinder 2 has the number close to the stamp resulting in the dot often being removed by the perforations. The no dot cylinder can be distinguished by a horizontal line below R.20/2, although this may be trimmed off if the margin is narrow.

Minor Constant Sheet Flaws

Minimum price as singles: 50p

Cyl. 2   2/7 Coloured line in gutter above stamp (Th. above A4–6)
         3/12 Retouch on Queen's shoulder (Th. F4)
         6/2 Pale area on Queen's shoulder (Th. F4). Retouched on PVA
         6/7 Dark patches on Queen's neck (Th. E–F3). Less noticeable on PVA
         7/3 Dark spot over D of value (Th. F6)

Cyl. 2. 6/10 Coloured line across Queen's shoulder and dress (Th. F–G4)
         8/11 Retouch on Queen's forehead (Th. B–C2)
         10/4 Coloured spot at rear of diadem (Th. C5)
         14/8 Two white flaws on Queen's neck by hair (Th. D–E4). Retouched on PVA
         14/11 Retouch on Queen's neck by necklace (Th. E4)
         15/11 Retouch on Queen's dress at front (Th. G3)
         19/10 Retouch on Queen's shoulder (Th. F4)

Sheet Markings

Phoshor cylinder number: "Ph. 1" found on cyl. 2 dot, right margin (*Price, £2·50 block of 6*)

Guide holes:
Perforation Type A, in double " S O N¦" box opposite rows 14/15, at left (no dot) or right (dot). In addition a single " traffic light " type box appears above and below the eighth vertical row in the no dot pane only (latter only used in conjunction with perforation Type F (L)*).
Perforation Type F (L)*, boxed above and below the eighth vertical row in the no dot pane only. The usual " S O N " boxes opposite rows 14/15 remain

Others: As given in General Notes

10d., Type U1 (1968)

Cat. No.	S.G. No.		Shades	Unused	Used

1968 (JULY 1). TWO 9·5 mm. PHOSPHOR BANDS. PVA GUM

U24	741		Drab	8	5
a. Uncoated paper ('69)* ..	.. 12·00				
b. Phosphor omitted ..	.. 25·00		*c.* Neck flaw (Cyl 1, R.2/12) ..	50	
U17, U19, U20 and U24			First Day Cover	†	30

*Uncoated paper—see General Notes.

No. U24 is known postmarked at Dorking and at Guildford on 30th June.

Listed Variety

Flaw comprises dark spots surrounded by white "halo" caused by lack of screening dots

U24c

Cylinder Number (Block of Six)

Single pane cylinder

Perforation Type F (L)

	Cyl. No.				No dot
	1	..	..	..	.. 75

Minor Constant Sheet Flaw

Minimum price as single: 50p

Cyl. 1 20/5 Coloured flaw in Queen's hair (Th. B3)

Sheet Markings

Guide holes: Through marginal arrow above vertical rows 6/7 and below vertical row 10

Others: As given in General Notes

1s., Type U1 (1967-68)

1967 (JUNE 5). TWO 9·5 mm. PHOSPHOR BANDS

A. Gum Arabic

U25	742/E*a*	(1) Light bluish violet	8	5
a. Phosphor omitted ..	.. 20·00	(2) Pale bluish violet	20	5
b. Background retouches (Cyl. 3,				
R.20/5)	75			

B. PVA Gum (26 April 1968)

U26	742Ea*v*	Pale bluish violet	8
a. Phosphor omitted ..	.. 1·00		

No. U25(1) is known pre-released on 25th May at Gravesend.

136

1s. (contd.)

Listed Variety

Retouching extends from behind the Queen's neck to the base of the design where it is most noticeable. There are also minor retouches on the Queen's shoulder and on her dress

U25*b*

Cylinder Numbers (Blocks of Six)

Gum Arabic
Double pane cylinder
Perforation Type F (L)*
Shade (1) Light bluish violet

Cyl. No.				No dot	Dot
3	..	..	..	..	1·50	1·50

Single pane cylinder
Perforation Type F (L)
Shade (2) Pale bluish violet

Cyl. No.				No dot
11	..	..	..	..	1·50

PVA Gum
Single pane cylinder
Perforation Type F (L)

Cyl. No.				No dot
11	..	..	..	..	75

Minor Constant Sheet Flaws

Minimum price as singles: 50p

Cyl. 3 1/10 Retouch in background above diadem (Th. A5)
2/2 Light diagonal line extending from lowest point of Queen's hair to bottom right-hand corner (E5 through to G6)
2/3 White spot in background left of Queen's shoulder (Th. G2)
9/12 White spot in background to right of Queen's necklace (Th. E5)
11/11 Coloured spot in band of diadem (Th. B4)
17/2 As 11/11 but Th. B3
18/12 Coloured spot in hyphen of value
19/10 Coloured scratch through Queen's neck and background below portrait
20/4 Horizontal scratch through Queen's neck and into background at right

Cyl. 3. 1/8 White spot in background at top of stamp (Th. A4)
7/8 Coloured flaw in Queen's hair to right of earring (Th. D4)
8/4 Coloured flaw in Queen's hair (Th. B3)
9/7 Retouch to background to right of Queen's ear (Th. D5)
19/8 Coloured spot in background above diadem emblems (Th. B5)

Cyl. 11 7/8 Coloured spot by band of diadem, also small spot in background at rear of diadem (Th. B4 and C5)
7/9 Diagonal coloured line in background behind Queen's neck (Th. F5)
15/4 Disturbed area in background at rear of diadem (Th. C–D5)
16/9 Diagonal coloured scratches extending the depth of the stamp behind the Queen's portrait
18/7 Diagonal coloured scratch about 10 mm. long at left of Queen's portrait
19/2 White flaw in Queen's hair to right of ear (Th. D4)

Sheet Markings

Guide holes:
Perforation Type F (L)*, boxed above and below the eighth vertical row in the no dot pane only. In addition double "S O N" box appears opposite rows 14/15, at left (no dot) or right (dot). (These would only be used in conjunction with perforation Type A.)
Perforation Type F (L), through marginal arrow above vertical rows 6/7 and below vertical row 10
Others: As given in General Notes

1s.6d., Type U1 (1967-69)

Cat. No.   S.G. No.   Shades   Unused Used

1967 (AUGUST 8).   TWO 9·5 mm. PHOSPHOR BANDS

A. Gum Arabic

U27	743		(1) Greenish blue and deep blue	10	5
a. Greenish blue omitted ..	..	25·00	(2) Pale blue and deep blue	10	5
b. Phosphor omitted	..	1·00	(3) Prussian blue and indigo (all-		
c. Retouch on dress (Cyl. 2A,			over phosphor omitted)	1·00	1·00
R.7/12)	75		e. Neck retouch (Cyl. 2A, R.20/3)	75	
d. Neck retouch (Cyl. 2A, R.19/4)	75				

B. PVA Gum (28 August 1968)

U28	743Ev		(2) Pale blue and deep blue	10	5
a. Pale blue omitted	..	25·00	(3) Prussian blue and indigo	10	5
b. Imperf. top margin	..	..			
c. Phosphor omitted	..	1·00	d. One wide phosphor band	..	75

U8, U22 and U27   First Day Cover   †   50

No. U27 is known pre-released on 7th August at Bournemouth and Torquay.

No. U27(3) occurred during the printing of No. U29.

Listed Varieties

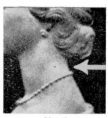

U27c   U27d   U27e

Cylinder Numbers (Blocks of Four)

Single pane cylinders.

Cyl. Nos. (No dot)

	Perforation Type A	
	Gum Arabic	PVA Gum
2A (deep blue)—2B (greenish blue)	2·00	†
3A (deep blue)—2B (pale blue)	1·75	1·00
3A (indigo)—1B (Prussian blue)	†	1·25
5A (indigo)—2B (Prussian blue)	15·00	1·00

Minor Constant Sheet Flaws

Minimum price as singles: 60p

Cyls. 2A–2B	3/12 Coloured spot in band of diadem (Th. B4)
	7/8 Coloured spots on Queen's collar (Th. G3)
	14/1 Coloured spot on Queen's shoulder (Th. F4–5)
	17/3 Coloured spot on Queen's temple (Th. C3)
	18/4 Coloured spot on Queen's shoulder (Th. F5)
	20/2 Pale patch on Queen's neck (Th. E3–4)
	20/7 Retouch on Queen's neck (Th. E4)
Cyls. 3A–2B	3/12 As for cyls. 2A–2B
Cyls. 5A–2B	19/1 Retouch on Queen's shoulder (Th. F5)

Sheet Markings

Cylinder numbers: Boxed, opposite R.19/1
Guide holes: In single " traffic light " type box opposite rows 14/15, at both sides
Colour register marks: Opposite rows 3/4 and 17/18, at both sides
Autotron marks (solid): Deep blue and greenish blue opposite rows 7/8, left margin
Colour designations: "G1" (greenish blue) opposite rows 7/8 an d"G2" (deep blue) opposite rows 5/6 both
   reading up in right margin
Traffic lights (boxed): Deep blue and greenish blue opposite row 19, right margin
Others: As given in General Notes

1s.6d. (contd.)

Cat. No.	S.G. No.	Shades	Unused	Used

1969 (DECEMBER 10). CHANGE TO " ALL-OVER " PHOSPHOR. PVA GUM

U29	743b	Prussian blue and indigo	10	5
a. Prussian blue omitted ..	..			

No. U29 was an experimental issue and the small printing represented approximately three months normal issue. After the supply was exhausted No. U28 again became the normal issue.

No. U29 is also known with phosphor omitted but on *gum arabic* and this is listed under No. U27 (3).

Cylinder Numbers (Block of Four)

Single pane cylinders.

Cyl. Nos. (No dot)	Perf. Type A
5A (indigo)—2B (Prussian blue)	1·00

Minor Constant Sheet Flaws

Minimum price as singles: 60p

Cyls. 5A–2B   12/5 Two white spots on Queen's dress (Th. G3)
19/1 Retouch on Queen's shoulder (Th. F5)

Sheet Markings

All the same as for Nos. U27/8

1s.9d., Type U1 (1967-70)

1967 (JUNE 5). TWO 9·5 mm. PHOSPHOR BANDS

A. Gum Arabic

U30	744	(1) Dull orange and black	12	5
a. Phosphor omitted .. .. 5·00		(2) Bright orange and black	12	5

B. PVA Gum (16 November 1970)

U31	744Ev	Bright orange and black	12	
U11, U25 and U30		First Day Cover	†	50

No. U30 is known pre-released on 25th May at Gravesend.

The bright orange shade occurs on whiter paper and may be due to this.

Cylinder Numbers (Blocks of Four)

Single pane cylinders

	Perforation Type A	
Cyl. Nos. (No dot)	Gum Arabic	PVA Gum
1A (black)—1B (dull orange)	1·00	†
1A (black)—1B (bright orange)	1·00	2·50

Minor Constant Sheet Flaws

Minimum price as singles: 60p

Cyls. 1A–1B   4/6 White spot in Queen's ear (Th. D4)
5/7 Coloured spots on Queen's upper lip (Th. D2)
5/10 White patch in Queen's hair (Th. B4)
8/1 Coloured flaw on Queen's neck (Th. E4)
13/1 Retouch on Queen's shoulder (Th. F3–4)
20/1 Pale patch in Queen's hair (Th. C4)

Sheet Markings

Cylinder numbers: Boxed, opposite R.19/1
Guide holes: In single " traffic light " type box opposite rows 14/15, at both sides
Colour register marks: Opposite rows 3/4 and 17/18, at both sides
Autotron marks (solid): Black and orange opposite rows 7/8, left margin
Colour designations: "G1 " (orange) opposite rows 7/8 and "G2 " (black) opposite rows 5/6 both reading up in right margin
Traffic lights (boxed): Black and orange opposite row 19, right margin
Others: As given in General Notes

Multi-value Coil Strip (1969)

Cat. No.	S.G. No.		Shades	Unused Used

1969 (AUGUST 27). STRIP OF FIVE (2d.+2d.+3d.+1d.+4d. SE-TENANT) EACH WITH ONE 4 mm. CENTRE PHOSPHOR BAND. GUM ARABIC

| U32 | 725m | | 1d. Light olive (No. U4), 2d. lake-brown (No. U7 × 2), 3d. violet (No. U8) and 4d. bright vermilion (No. U15) .. | 12 |

No. U31 was issued in strips from stamp vending machines taking a shilling or a five new pence piece. Complete coils only were available from the Philatelic Bureau at Edinburgh.

For listed variety on 3d. value, see No. U8c.

A new type of perforation was adopted for these coils. The paper was drawn over a cylinder containing short points pushing up pimples from the undersurface which were then shaved off.

It is understood that gum arabic was used for these coils, as also for the decimal multi-value coils, because it is more brittle than PVA and facilitates the clean removal of the perforations.

Coils

Sideways delivery printed in continuous reels

Code No.	Number in roll	Face value
GS	1500 (300 strips)	£15
GL	3000 (600 strips)	£30

Presentation Pack

UPP1 (issued 5 March 1969)	Fourteen values	1·00
a. With German text		

The issued Pack contained one each of the low value definitive stamps (½d. to 1s.9d.). The 4d. and 8d. were in the changed colours (Nos. U14 and U21 respectively).

SECTION U2

Machin Issues

1969. £ s. d. High Values. Recess-printed

General Notes

INTRODUCTION. The four high values, in similar design to the low values, were issued on 5th March, 1969 thus completing the Machin definitive series.

PRINTERS. The Machin high values were recess-printed by Bradbury, Wilkinson & Co. Ltd. on rotary sheet-fed machines.

PAPER. Unwatermarked lightly coated paper was used for all values. Several types of coated paper appear to have been used and generally there is only a slight response to the chalky test. Variations in the thickness of the paper also exist. Shades are known but it is probable that they are due to the variations in the coating and thickness of the paper rather than to the use of different inks.

GUM. Only PVA gum has been used for the Machin high values.

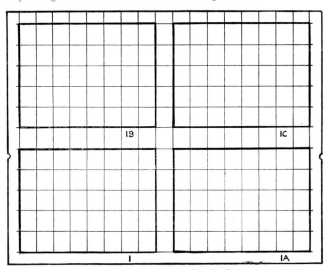

Diagram showing the printer's sheet
comprising four Post Office panes, the
method of perforation, and the positions of the
plate numbers and perforation guide holes

SHEET DETAILS. The printer's sheets comprised 160 stamps in four panes of 40 each arranged in five rows of eight stamps (see diagram above), the sheet being guillotined into four before issue.

Perforation. All values are comb perforated 12. The printer's sheet was perforated as a complete sheet with perforation Type A*; therefore, the characteristics of each individual pane are different as is clearly shown in the diagram above. Perforator Type A* is described in Appendix O.

Plate Numbers. See the General Notes for Section T for an illustration of these. Each printer's sheet produces four plate numbers comprising a "whole number" and "A", "B" and "C" numbered panes and these appear below stamp 7 in the bottom row of each pane, as shown in the diagram above. The arrangement of the panes is the same for all plates of all the values.

Perforation Guide Holes. See the General Notes for Section T for an illustration of these. In the Machin high values they appear opposite the first row of stamps, in the left margin of the "whole number" pane and in the right margin of the "A" pane, as shown in the diagram above. They are usually heavily rimmed with colour and may be either partly or completely trimmed off.

U3. Queen Elizabeth II

(Des. after plaster cast by Arnold Machin)

1969. Type U3

Cat. No.	S.G. No.	Shades	Unused	Used

1969 (MARCH 5). 2s.6d. BROWN

U33	787	Brown	20	15

Plate Numbers (Blocks of Four)

Pl. No.				Pl. No.				Pl. No.			
2	..	..	1·50	3	..	..	1·50	6	..	..	2·00
2A	..	..	1·50	3A	..	..	1·50	6A	..	..	2·00
2B	..	..	1·50	3B	..	..	1·50	6B	..	..	2·00
2C	..	..	2·50	3C	..	..	1·50	6C	..	..	3·50

Minor Constant Flaw

Minimum price as single: 75p

Pl. 3A 8/5 Dot to right of Queen's eye (Th. D–E4)

1969 (MARCH 5). 5s. CRIMSON-LAKE

U34	788	Crimson-lake	35	25

Plate Numbers (Blocks of Four)

Pl. No.				Pl. No.			
2	..	..	2·50	3	..	..	2·00
2A	..	..	2·50	3A	..	..	2·00
2B	..	..	2·50	3B	..	..	2·00
2C	..	..	2·50	3C	..	..	2·00

1969 (MARCH 5). 10s. DEEP ULTRAMARINE

U35	789	Deep ultramarine	75	45

Plate Numbers (Blocks of Four)

Pl. No.				Pl. No.			
1	..	..	4·00	1B	..	..	4·00
1A	..	..	4·00	1C	..	..	4·00

Cat. No.	S.G. No.	Shades	Unused	Used

1969 (MARCH 5). £1 BLUISH BLACK

| U36 | 790 | Bluish black | 1·50 | 75 |
| U33/6 | | First Day Cover | † | 4·00 |

Plate Numbers (Blocks of Four)

Pl. No..				Pl. No.			
3	..	..	7·50	4	..	..	7·50
3A	..	..	8·50	4A	..	..	7·50
3B	..	..	7·50	4B	..	..	7·50
(3C)*	..	..	†	4C	..	..	7·50

*This plate number block is not known as there was a fault on the plate and only the left half of this pane was issued.

Plate blocks of four showing Plates 3 or 4 together with part of the "TOTAL SHEET VALUE" inscription in the right margin come from the decimal issue and are listed in Section U4.

Presentation Pack

UPP2 (issued 5 March 1969)	Four values	3·00

   a. With German text   ..   ..

The issued Pack contained one each of Nos. U33/6.

Machin Decimal Issues

1971. Low Values. Photogravure

General Notes

PRINTERS. All the low value Machin decimal issues were printed in photogravure by Harrison & Sons. They were printed on continuous reels of paper "on the web" in double pane widths, i.e. 400 stamps consisting of two panes (no dot and dot) each of 200 stamps arranged in twenty rows of ten stamps, the panes being guillotined before issue.

PAPER. Unwatermarked chalk-surfaced paper was used for all values.

GUM. Polyvinyl alcohol (PVA) gum was used for all values but as with the £.s.d. issue, the multi-value coil has gum arabic.

PERFORATION. Harrisons used the same 15 × 14 comb perforation as before and all sheets are perforated Type A as illustrated in Appendix O. Several perforation types were used for the booklets, also illustrated in Appendix O.

MACHIN HEAD. Type B as illustrated in the General Notes to Section U1 was used for all values except the ½, 2½, 3½, 5, 6 and 7½p which are in light colours and bear relief head Type A.

PHOSPHOR BANDS. See the General Notes for Section S for a detailed description of these. In this issue the "violet" phosphor was used throughout and the bands were applied in photogravure in the same operation as the printing. In sheet form the screen is 250-line for all values except the 2½p which is 150-line. All booklets have 150-line screen as does the 2½p CL coil and the multi-value coil, the remaining coils having the 250-line screen.

PHOSPHOR CYLINDER NUMBERS. The phosphor cylinder numbers appear in the left-hand margin on both panes and are found in various states as follows:—

Cyl. 1.
State 1. Small 1 unsynchronised so that it can appear anywhere in the margin.
State 2. Large 1 always synchronised so that it appears close to the ink cylinder number.

Cyl. 2.
State 1. Small 2 which is 1½ mm. high on no dot panes and 2 mm. high on dot panes. Unsynchronised.
State 2. An additional large 4 mm. 2 was engraved on the cylinder approximately 41 mm. below the small 2, but still unsynchronised. The large 2 on the dot pane was later re-engraved but inadvertently this was done upside-down so that it appears as an inverted 2.
State 3. As state 2 but synchronised.

Cyl. 3. This has not been seen.

Cyl. 4.
State 1. Small 4 about 2 mm. high on both panes and unsynchronised.
State 2. Large 4 about 4 mm. superimposed over the small 4 and always synchronised.

Cyl. 5.
Large 5 always synchronised and so far only used for the single band 2½p value.

It thus becomes necessary to list cylinder blocks so as to show the ink cylinder numbers in conjunction with the phosphor cylinder numbers. Cylinder blocks which do not include a phosphor number are indicated by a dash in the phosphor cylinder number column. These can come from sheets with unsynchronised phosphor cylinders 1S, 2S or 4S. The letters S and L for phosphor cylinders denote Small and Large.

Prices are also indicated for blocks of six of unsynchronised phosphor cylinder numbers 1, 2 or 4 which fall outside the ink cylinder blocks and for ink cylinder blocks of ten which include the large and small phosphor cylinder 2.

BOOKLET CYLINDER NUMBERS. These all have the prefix letter "B" but this is often trimmed off. Phosphor cylinder numbers were also used but they are placed outside the ink cylinder number and are invariably trimmed off.

BOOKLET AND COIL VARIETIES. See the General Notes for Section S for detailed notes on these.

DATE OF ISSUE. A country-wide postal strike had been in operation before 15th February and did not end until 10th March 1971. All but a few Crown post offices were closed but most sub-offices remained open. However, distribution of supplies of the decimal issues had started before the strike and we understand that it was possible to purchase all issues, including booklets and coils, at some places on the 15th February. Special arrangements were made to cater for first day covers as explained in the notes at the end of this Section.

SHEET MARKINGS. All values have the same sheet markings except that the 9p value has additional features appropriate to a bicoloured stamp. Illustrations of the markings will be found in the General Notes to the Sections indicated in brackets.

Cylinder Number

Cylinder Numbers. These are now boxed in the manner shown above and occur opposite R.18/1. In the 9p the black number appears in the box and the orange below it.

Varieties in Cylinder Blocks. Where a cylinder block contains a listed variety the price is adjusted accordingly and bears an asterisk.

Marginal Arrows. These are "W" shaped (photo-etched) and occur above and below vertical rows 5/6 and at sides opposite rows 10/11 (Section W).

Perforation Guide Holes. In double "S O N" box (Type (a) Section W) opposite rows 14/15, at left on no dot panes and at right on dot panes.

Marginal Rules. Wide co-extensive rule below the bottom row (Section S).

Total Sheet Values. These occur four times on each pane opposite rows 5/7 and 15/17 reading up at left and down at right (Section W).

Colour Register Marks. 9p only. Opposite rows 1/2 and 17/18 at left on no dot panes and at right on dot panes (Section W).

Autotron Marks. 9p only. Photo-etched solid below vertical rows 2/4 in dot pane only (Section W).

Colour Dabs. 9p only. These are shown as squares in a box opposite R.19/10.

PAPER AND WATERMARK

All the following issues are printed on chalk-surfaced paper without watermark, unless otherwise stated.

U4. Queen Elizabeth II
(Des. after plaster cast by Arnold Machin)

1971. Type U4

Cat. No.	S.G. No.	Shades	Unused	Used

1971 (FEBRUARY 15). ½p. TWO 9·5 mm. PHOSPHOR BANDS

A. PVA Gum

U37   841   Turquoise-blue   5   5
  a. Phosphor omitted 35   *c.* Deformed base to 2 (Cyl. 2.,
  b. One broad band 25   R.20/9) 25

B. Gum Arabic. Multi-value coil only

U38   841Eg   Turquoise-blue   5

Listed Variety

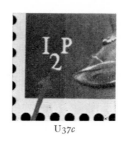

U37*c*

Cylinder Numbers (Blocks of Six)

Perforation Type A

Cyl. No.	Phos. No.			No dot	Dot
2	—	..	..	8	8
2	2L*	..	..	8	8
2	4L	..	..	8	8

*Block of ten with small phosphor 2, *price* 15p, and block of six with small 2 only, *price* 15p.

Minor Constant Sheet Flaws

Minimum price as singles: 20p

Cyl. 2. 8/5 Diagonal scratch from Queen's collar to hair (Th. G3–4E)

½p (contd.)

Se-tenant Booklet Panes of Four
Pair ½p with pair 2p from 10p Booklets

		Perf. Type	
		J	L
UB21 *Se-tenant* vertically		30	10
b. One broad band		1·50	1·00
c. Se-tenant horiz. (14.7.71) ..		30	10

Booklet Panes with Printed Labels
Panes of six comprising five stamps and one label "B. ALAN LTD." etc. from 25p Booklets

	Perf. Types		
	K	L	M
UB22 Pane of six	40	10	40

Panes of six comprising five stamps and one label "LICK battery failure with the amazing new ESSO VOLTPAK" from 50p Booklets

	Perf. Types		
	K	L	M
UB23 Pane of six	40	10	40
a. Phosphor omitted ..	—	1·50	—

Booklet Cylinder Numbers
Panes of six

Pane	Cyl. No.			Perf. Type K
UB22	B8	..	..	60
UB23	B3	..	..	60

Se-tenant panes of four

    These are 24-row single pane cylinders bearing numbers B6 (½p) and B2 (2p) but they are always trimmed off.

Cat. No.	S.G. No.	Shades	Unused	Used

1971 (FEBRUARY 15). 1p. TWO 9·5 PHOSPHOR BANDS
A. PVA Gum

			Shades	Unused	Used
U39	842		Crimson	5	5
a. Phosphor omitted	25				

B. Gum Arabic. Multi-value coil only

			Shades	Unused	Used
U40	842Eg		Crimson	5	5
b. Malformed P (Roll 10)	25				

1p (contd.)

Listed Variety

Occurs on the left-hand 1p in every fifth position on the coil.

U40b

Cylinder Numbers (Blocks of Six)

Perforation Type A

Cyl. No	Phos. No.			No dot	Dot	Cyl. No.	Phos. No.			No dot	Dot
1	—	..	..	8	8	3	—	..	..	8	8
1	2S	..	..	8	8	3	1S	..	..	8	8
1	2L*	..	..	8	8	3	1L	..	..	8	8

*Block of ten with small phosphor 2, *price* 15p and block of six with small 2 only, *price* 8p. Also block of six with small phosphor 1 only, *price* 8p.

Minor Constant Sheet Flaws

Minimum price as singles: 20p

Cyl. 1   2/10 Hoirzontal scratch on Queen's shoulder close to collar (Th. F3)
6/4 White flaw on Queen's hair (Th. C4)
18/4 White dot on Queen's nose (Th. D2)

Se-tenant Booklet Panes of Four

Pair 1p with pair 1½p from 10p Booklets

	Perf. Type	
	J	L
UB24 *Se-tenant* vertically	30	10
c. Se-tenant horiz. (14.7.71)	30	10

Booklet Cylinder Numbers

The *se-tenant* booklet panes are from 24-row single pane cylinders bearing numbers B1 (1p) and B2 (1½p) but they are always trimmed off.

Coils

Vertical delivery printed in continuous reels. Cylinder R4 was used.

Code No.	Number in roll	Face value
EL	1000	£10

Cat. No.	S.G. No.		Shades		Unused	Used

1971 (FEBRUARY 15) 1½p. TWO 9·5 mm. PHOSPHOR BANDS. PVA GUM

U41	843		Black		5	5
a. Phosphor omitted	..	..	75			
b. Malformed 2 (Cyl. 1, R.14/9) ..			25			

1½p. (contd.)

Listed Variety

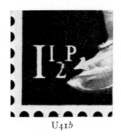

U41*b*

Cylinder Numbers (Blocks of Six)

Perforation Type A

Cyl. No.	Phos. No.			No dot	Dot
I	—	..	..	12	12
I	2S	..	..	12	12
I	2L*	..	..	12	12

*Block of ten with small phosphor 2, *price* 15p and block of six with small 2 only, *price* 8p.

Se-tenant Booklet Panes of Four

For booklet pane of No. U41 *se-tenant* with ½p value, see No. UB21.

Cat. No.	S.G. No.			Shades	Unused	Used
1971 (FEBRUARY 15). 2p. TWO 9·5 mm. PHOSPHOR BANDS						
A. PVA Gum						
U42	844			Myrtle-green	5	5
a. Phosphor omitted		..	..	75		
b. One broad band		..	..	30		

B. Gum Arabic. Multi-value coil only

U43	844Eg			Myrtle-green	5	

Cylinder Numbers (Blocks of Six)

Perforation Type A

Cyl. No.	Phos. No.			No dot	Dot
4	2L*	..	..	15	15
5	2L*	..	..	15	15

*Block of ten with small phosphor 2, *price* 25p. Block of six with large and small phosphor 2 only (*state* 2), *price* £1.

Minor Constant Sheet Flaws

Minimum price as singles: 20p.

Cyl. 4　8/7 Dark spot in band of crown (Th. B4)

Se-tenant Booklet Panes of Four

For booklet pane of No. U42 *se-tenant* with 1p value, see No. UB24.

1971 (FEBRUARY 15). 2½p. PVA GUM

A. One 4 mm. Centre Phosphor Band

U44	845			Magenta	5	5

a. Phosphor omitted　..　..　15

b. Screen damage (Vert. coil, Roll 11)　..　..　..　..　30

c. Two parallel lines (Horiz. coil, Roll 6)　..　..　..　..　30

B. One 4 mm. Left Side Phosphor Band (50p Booklets)

U45	846			Magenta	5	5

149

2½p (contd.)

Listed Varieties

U44*b*   U44*c*

Cylinder Numbers (Blocks of Six)
Perforation Type A

Cyl. No.	Phos. No.			No dot	Dot
5	5	..	..	20	20
7	5	..	..	20	20
8	5	..	..	20	20

Minor Constant Sheet Flaws
Minimum price as singles: 20p.

Cyl. 5. 10/5 Coloured dots in base bar of 2 of fraction
Cyl. 7 3/5 Missing serif on 2 of fraction
       6/7 Dark spot in band of crown (Th. B3)

UB25

Se-tenant Booklet Panes of Six
Pair of 2½p (band at left) with block of four of 3p from 50p Booklets

	Perf. Type		
	K	L	M
UB25 Pane of six	1·00	30	1·00

Booklet Panes with Printed Labels
Panes of six comprising five stamps (centre band) and one label "STICK FIRMLY to Esso The Action Station" from 25p Booklets

	Perf. Type		
	K	L	M
UB26 Pane of six	75	20	75

150

2½p (contd.)

Panes of six comprising four stamps (centre band) and two labels "UNIFLO STAMPS out needless engine wear" and "STICK FIRMLY on the road with Esso E110 Tyres" from 25p Booklets

	Perf. Type		
	K	L	M
UB27 Pane of six	60	15	60

Panes of six comprising five stamps (centre band) with one label "TEAR OFF to ESSO for Action-packed petrols" from 50p Booklets

	Perf. Type		
	K	L	M
UB28 Pane of six	75	20	75

Booklet Cylinder Numbers

Se-tenant pane of six

Value	Cyl. No.			Perf Type K
2½p	B2	⎱	.. ..	1·20
3p	B9	⎰		

Panes of six with labels

Pane	Cyl. No.			Perf. Type K
UB26	B6	..	..	1·00
UB27	B4	..	..	80
UB28	B1	..	..	1·00

Coils

Centre band. Printed in continuous reels. Cylinder R1 was used for vertical delivery coils and cylinders R2 and R4 for sideways delivery coils.

Code No.	Number in roll	Face value	
AS	500	£12·50	Sideways delivery
CL	1000	£25·00	Vertical delivery

Cat. No.	S.G. No.		Shades		Unused	Used

1971 (FEBRUARY 15). 3p. TWO 9·5 mm. PHOSPHOR BANDS. PVA GUM

U46	847			Ultramarine		**5**	5
a. Imperf. coil strip of 5	..	..					
b. Phosphor omitted	..	..	15				

Cylinder Numbers (Blocks of Six)

Perforation Type A

Cyl. No.	Phos. No.			No dot	Dot
2	2L*	..	..	20	20
2	4L	..	..	20	20
4	2L*	..	..	20	20
4	4S	..	..	20	20
4	4L	..	..	20	20

*Block of ten with small phosphor 2, *price* 35p. Block of six with small phosphor 4 only, *price* 20p.

Minor Constant Sheet Flaws

Minimum price as singles: 25p

Cyl. 4.   2/1   White flaw in crown left of diadem (Th. B4)

Booklet Panes of Six

From 50p Booklets

	Perf. Type		
	K	L	M
UB29 Pane of six	1·00	30	1·00

Se-tenant Booklet Panes of Six

For booklet pane of No. U46 *se-tenant* with 2½p value, see No. UB25.

Booklet Panes with Printed Labels

Panes of six comprising five stamps and one label "£4,315 FOR YOU AT AGE 55 Send Coupon" from 30p Booklets

		Perf. Type		
	J	K	L	M
UB30 Pane of six	1·50	80	30	80
a. Phosphor omitted	..			
b. Label imperf. in				
binding margin	†	80	25	80

3p (contd.)

Booklet Cylinder Numbers

Panes of six

Pane	Cyl. No.			Perf. Type	
				J	K
UB29	B6	..	..	†	1·00
UB30	B1	..	..	1·00	1·00
UB30b	B1	..	..	†	1·00

Coils

Printed in continuous reels. Cylinder R10 was used for vertical delivery coils and Cylinder R4 for sideways delivery coils.

Code No.	Number in roll	Face value	
BS	500	£15	Sideways delivery
DL	1000	£30	Vertical delivery

Cat. No.	S.G. No.	Shades	Unused	Used

1971 (FEBRUARY 15). 3½p. TWO 9·5 mm. PHOSPHOR BANDS. PVA GUM

U47	848		Pale olive-grey	5	5
a. Phosphor omitted	..	.. 1·75			

Cylinder Numbers (Blocks of Six)

Perforation Type A

Cyl. No.	Phos. No.			No dot	Dot
1	2L*	..	..	35	35
4	4L	..	..	35	35

*Block of ten with small phosphor *2, price* 60p.

Minor Constant Sheet Flaws

Minimum price as singles: 30p.

Cyl. 1 19/2 Retouch on Queen's neck below jawline (Th. at point of intersection of D3–4 and E3–4)
20/2 Dotted line from back of crown to edge of design (Th. C6)

1971 (FEBRUARY 15). 4p. TWO 9·5 mm. PHOSPHOR BANDS. PVA GUM

U48	849		Ochre-brown	5	5
a. Phosphor omitted	..	.. 60			

Cylinder Numbers (Blocks of Six)

Perforation Type A

Cyl. No.	Phos. No.				No dot	Dot
5	—	..	..	..	40	40
5	2S	..	..	..	40	40
5	2L*	..	..	..	40	40
5	4L	..	..	..	40	40

*Block of ten with small phosphor *2, price* 65p and block of six with small *2* only, *price* £1·50. Block of six with large and small phosphor *2* only (*state 2*), *price* £1·50.

Minor Constant Sheet Flaws

Minimum price as singles: 30p.

Cyl. 5 1/4 Front loop of P omitted

1971 (FEBRUARY 15). 5p. TWO 9·5 mm. PHOSPHOR BANDS. PVA GUM

U49	850		Pale violet	8	5
a. Phosphor omitted	..	.. 50			

Cylinder Numbers (Blocks of Six)

Perforation Type A

Cyl. No.	Phos. No.			No dot	Dot
2	2L*	..	..	50	50
2	4L	..	..	50	50

*Block of ten with small phosphor *2, price* 90p.

5p (contd.)

Minor Constant Sheet Flaws

Minimum price as singles: 30p.

Cyl. 2 14/5 Diagonal scratch through value (Th. G1–F2)

Cat. No.	S.G. No.	Shades	Unused	Used

1971 (FEBRUARY 15). 6p. TWO 9·5 mm. PHOSPHOR BANDS. PVA GUM

U50	851	Light emerald	10	5
a. Phosphor omitted	..	..		

Cylinder Numbers (Blocks of Six)

Perforation Type A

Cyl. No.	Phos. No.			No dot	Dot
1	—	..	..	60	60
1	2L*	..	..	60	60
1	4L	..	..	60	60

*Block of ten with small phosphor 2, *price* £1·10 and block of six with small 2 only, *price* 60p.

Minor Constant Sheet Flaws

Minimum price as singles: 35p.

Cyl. 1 20/9 White flaw on bottom jewel at back of crown (Th. C6)

1971 (FEBRUARY 15). 7½p. TWO 9·5 mm. PHOSPHOR BANDS. PVA GUM

U51	852	Pale chestnut	10	5
a. Phosphor omitted	..	..	35	

Cylinder Numbers (Blocks of Six)

Perforation Type A

Cyl. No.	Phos. No.			No dot	Dot
1	—	..	..	70	70
1	2S	..	..	70	70
1	2L*	..	..	70	70

*Block of ten with small phosphor 2, *price* £1·20 and block of six with small 2 only, *price* 70p. Also block of six with small phosphor 2 only, *price* 70p.

Minor Constant Sheet Flaws

Minimum price as singles: 40p.

Cyl. 1 6/8 White scratch on Queen's forehead (Th. C2)

1971 (FEBRUARY 15). 9p. TWO 9·5 mm. PHOSPHOR BANDS. PVA GUM

U52	853	Orange-yellow and black	12	5
a. Phosphor omitted	..	..	..	

Cylinder Numbers (Blocks of Six)

Perforation Type A

Cyl. Nos.	Phos. No.		No dot	Dot
3A (black)–2B (yellow)	—	..	1·00	1·00
3A (black)–3B (yellow)	—	..	1·00	1·00
3A (black)–2B (yellow)	1S	..	1·00	1·00
3A (black)–3B (yellow)	1L	..	1·00	1·00

Block of six with small phosphor 1 only, *price* £1.

10p. This value was due to be issued on 11 August 1971 after this went to press.

9p (contd.)

Minor Constant Sheet Flaws

Minimum price as singles: 40p.

Cyl. 3A–2B   9/1 Blotch on Queen's jawline (Th. D2–3)
             9/2 Rectangular flaw on Queen's jaw (Th. D3)
Cyl. 3A.–2B. 4/8 Vertical scratch down back of crown (Th. B–C5)
             11/7 Black dotted line diagonally through 9 P. Also on cyls. 3A–3B

Multi-value Coil Strip (1971)

Cat. No.	S.G. No.	Description	Unused	Used

1971 (FEBRUARY 15). STRIP OF FIVE (2p+½p+½p+1p+1p SE-TENANT) EACH WITH TWO 9·5 mm. PHOSPHOR BANDS. GUM ARABIC

| U53 | 841n | ½p turquoise-blue (No. U38), 1p crimson (No. U31) and 2p myrtle-green (No. U43) | 10 | |

No. U53 was issued in strips from stamp vending machines taking five new pence. For listed variety on the 1p, see No. U40b.

Coils

Sideways delivery printed in continuous reels. Cylinders used were ½p R1 and R2, 1p R1 and 2p R1 and R2.

Code No.	Number in roll	Face value
G1	1500 (300 strips)	£15
G2	3000 (600 strips)	£30

The notes after No. U32 concerning the method of perforation also apply here.

Presentation Pack

UPP3 (issued 15 February 1971)	Twelve values	75
a. "Scandinavia 71" Edition (15.4.71) .. .. 1·00		

The issued packs contained one each of the low value definitive stamps (½p to 9p) with PVA gum, the 2½p having one centre band and the rest two phosphor bands.

There was also a cellophane packet of each low value plus an extra 2p and 2½p sold for 50p with a white card reading both sides: "This packet contains a complete set of the new DECIMAL LOW VALUE DEFINITIVE STAMPS issued by the British Post Office. Two additional stamps have been added to bring the value to a round 50p (10s.0d.)."

The "Scandinavia 71" is a special pack produced for sale during a visit to six cities in Denmark, Sweden and Norway by a mobile display unit between 15th April and 20th May 1971. The pack gives details of this tour and also lists the other stamps which were due to be issued in 1971, the text being in English. A separate insert gives translations in Danish, Swedish and Norwegian. The pack was also available at the Philatelic Bureau, Edinburgh. A special cover showing the royal coat of arms and listing the cities visited was also issued.

154

First Day Cover

| With commemorative postmark | Twelve values | † | 80 |

The Post Office issued special covers for use on the first day of issue and announced that mail posted on the 15th February 1971 at post offices where special first day posting boxes are provided would be postmarked "First Day of Issue—15 February 1971".

In the event there was a country-wide postal strike at this time and the Post Office then stated that the postmark would be applied to mail posted in the special boxes on the fourth and fifth days following the resumption of work. The postal service was resumed on 10th March and this policy was put into effect for covers posted on the 13th and 14th March which bore a distinguishing cachet "POSTING DELAYED BY THE POST OFFICE STRIKE 1971" or others with similar wording. Our quotation is for a cover containing the set of twelve values posted on one of these days.

Meanwhile it had been possible for some people to purchase stamps on the 15th February at some of the 23,000 sub-offices and the few Crown offices that were open and to get these stamps used on mail in a few scattered areas where local deliveries were still operating. Generally these did not have the special postmark.

SECTION U4

Machin Decimal Issues

1970. High Values. Recess-printed

General Notes

INTRODUCTION. The four high values were issued on 17th June 1970 in advance of decimalisation which was introduced on 15th February 1971. These values were brought into use early to accustom the public to the changeover and followed the introduction of the 10p and 50p coins. The £1 value does not differ from its predecessor except that it was printed in sheets of 100.

PRINTERS. As with the £.s.d. Machin high values the decimal equivalents were recess-printed by Bradbury, Wilkinson & Co. on rotary sheet-fed machines. They were issued in sheets of 100 arranged in ten rows of ten stamps.

PAPER. Unwatermarked lightly coated paper was used giving only slight response to the chalky test and no response at all for the 10p value which has all-over phosphor.

GUM. Only PVA gum has been used.

PERFORATION. All values are comb perforated 12 with perforation Type N which is described in Appendix O. There are no perforation guide holes, or if there were they have been trimmed off before issue.

SHEET MARKINGS. The only sheet markings are the Plate Numbers and "Total Sheet Values" which occur for all values.

Plate Numbers. In bottom margin below R.10/9.

Total Sheet Values. As an aid to clerks in stocktaking and selling stamps by the sheet, the "TOTAL SHEET VALUE" and amount was printed in the margins and this is the first time they have appeared on high values. They occur four times opposite rows 2/4 and 7/9 reading up at left and down at right.

U5. Queen Elizabeth II
(Des. after plaster cast by Arnold Machin)

1970.   Type U5

Cat. No.	S.G. No.	Shades	Unused	Used

1970 (JUNE 17). 10p. CERISE. "ALL-OVER" PHOSPHOR

U71	829	Cerise	15	8

Plate Numbers (Blocks of Four)

Pl. No.			Pl. No.			Pl. No.		
3	..	.. 75	7	..	.. 75	11	..	.. 75
4	..	.. 75	8	..	.. 75	12	..	.. 75
5	..	.. 75	9	..	.. 75	13	..	.. 75
6	..	.. 75	10	..	.. 75			

1970 (JUNE 17). 20p. OLIVE-GREEN

U72	830	Olive-green	30	15
a. Uncoated paper*	.. ..			

*This does not respond to the chalky test, and may be further distinguished from the normal paper by the fibres which clearly show on the surface.

Plate Numbers (Blocks of Four)

Pl. No.			Pl. No.			Pl. No.		
3	..	.. 1·25	8	..	.. 1·25	13	..	.. 1·25
4	..	.. 1·25	9	..	.. 1·25	14	..	.. 1·25
5	..	.. 1·25	10	..	.. 1·25	15	..	.. 1·25
6	..	.. 1·25	11	..	.. 1·25	16	..	.. 1·25
7	..	: 1·25	12	..	.. 1·25			

1970 (JUNE 17). 50p. ULTRAMARINE

U73	831	Deep ultramarine	75	35

Plate Numbers (Blocks of Four)

Pl. No.			Pl. No.			Pl. No.		
4	..	.. 3·00	7	..	.. 3·00	10	..	.. 3·00
5	..	.. 3·00	8	..	.. 3·00	11	..	.. 3·00
6	..	.. 3·00	9	..	.. 3·00			

Presentation Pack

UPP4	Three values	1·75

A slip-in wallet bearing the Royal Arms and inscribed "BRITISH POST OFFICE" containing a set of the twelve low values and four high values was on sale at the G.P.O. Stand at the NABA Philatelic Exhibition held at Basle in June 1971.

First Day Cover

With commemorative postmark   Three values   † 1·75

£1 BLUISH BLACK

   This was also issued but it does not differ from No. U36 in singles. However, it was issued in sheets of 100 like the others and we therefore list the plate numbers. In the case of Plates 3 and 4 they can be differentiated from these plates used for No. U36 when in blocks of four as part of the "Total Sheet Value" inscription appears in the margin opposite R. 9/10.

Plate Numbers (Blocks of Four)

Pl. No.			Pl. No.			Pl. No.		
2	..	..	5·50	3	..	..	5·50	4	..	..	5·50

SECTION W
Special Issues

General Notes

SPECIAL ISSUES. Until 1966 it had been the policy of the Post Office to restrict commemorative issues to celebrating particular events, such as anniversaries or exhibitions, conferences and festivals, etc. The introduction of the Landscape series in May 1966 heralded a new departure as this was followed by pictorial sets showing British Birds, Paintings, Bridges, Cathedrals, etc. and Technological Achievements. These cannot be described as being commemorative stamps, yet it is obviously convenient and logical for them to be listed in the same Section as the commemoratives and so we have headed this Section Special Issues.

PRINTERS. To date all the special issues were printed in photogravure by Harrison & Sons with the exception of the 1964 2s. 6d. Shakespeare and 1966 2s. 6d. Westminster Abbey which were recess-printed by Bradbury, Wilkinson & Co. and the 1969 Post Office Technology and 1970 Commonwealth Games issues which were printed by De La Rue & Co. by lithography.

Generally, the double-sized stamps were printed on continuous reels of paper "on the web" in double pane width, i.e. 240 stamps consisting of two panes (no dot and dot) each of 120 stamps arranged in twenty rows of six stamps, the panes being guillotined before issue. However, the higher values were often printed in single panes, either on reel or sheet-fed machines. After the listing of each issue we give the sheet arrangement and state whether printed in the reel or in sheets.

QUEEN'S PORTRAIT. Up to the 1966 Westminster Abbey issue the portrait from the photograph by Dorothy Wilding Ltd. was used and thereafter the silhouette profile from the coinage design of Mrs. Mary Gillick adapted by David Gentleman.

PAPER. The same type of paper as for the definitive issues was used up to the 1960 General Letter Office issue and thereafter chalk-surfaced paper was used except for the 2s.6d. Westminster Abbey stamp.

SCREEN. The 200–line screen as used for the Wilding definitives was employed up to the 1960 Europa issue but thereafter Harrisons used a finer 250-line screen.

WATERMARKS. These are illustrated in Section S and were used as follows:

Tudor Crown	1953 Coronation issue
St. Edward's Crown	1957 World Scout Jubilee and Inter-Parliamentary Union and 1958 Commonwealth Games
Crowns	All later issues until 1967 Wild Flowers and British Discovery and Invention
No watermark	1967 Paintings and Sir Francis Chichester and all issues from 1967 Christmas onwards

The watermark normally appears sideways on upright designs. On certain stamps, the 2½d. and 3d. 1962 Productivity Year, and the 1963 Freedom from Hunger and Paris Postal Conference issues, the watermark is normally inverted. These stamps were printed "on the web" and for technical reasons the paper had to be re-reeled and, to save time and expense, it was decided to print on the paper wound in the reverse direction to normal, thus resulting in the watermark being inverted. Other inverted watermark varieties on commemorative issues are from sheet-printed issues where the paper has been accidentally fed the wrong way and these are often quite scarce.

GUM. The distinction between gum arabic and PVA gum is explained in the General Notes relating to Section U1. It is sufficient to state here that gum arabic was used for all commemorative stamps up to the 1967 Christmas issue and thereafter Harrisons and De La Rue only used PVA gum.

PERFORATION. Harrisons used the same 15 × 14 comb perforation as for the Wilding definitives but some of the upright designs are perforated 14 × 15. The 1964 2s.6d. Shakespeare and 1966 2s.6d. Westminster Abbey were comb perforated 11 × 12 by Bradbury, Wilkinson and the 1969 Post Office Technology and 1970 Commonwealth Games issues were comb perforated 13½ × 14 by De La Rue. Harrisons have used a number of different perforators in the commemorative issues and these are illustrated and described in Appendix O. The cylinder numbers are listed and priced according to the type of perforator used.

PHOSPHOR BANDS. See the General Notes for Section S for a detailed description of these. In the special issues they were applied as follows:

"Blue": From 1962 N.P.Y. to 1965 Salvation Army and 1965 I.T.U. Generally 8 mm. but occasionally 9·5 mm. bands.
"Violet" 8 mm. bands: Other 1965 issues to 1966 Christmas.
"Violet" 9·5 mm. bands: 1967 E.F.T.A. to date.

From 1962 until the 1967 Wild Flowers set the special issues appeared both with and without phosphor bands. From the 1967 British Paintings set onwards it was intended that all special issues should appear only with phosphor bands. However, it is quite common practice for sheets to be issued with the phosphor accidentally omitted and these are listed as varieties.

Method of Application. Issues prior to the 1965 Churchill stamps had the bands applied by typography, flexography or photogravure but from the Churchill set onwards only photogravure has been employed. We have, therefore, indicated whether they were applied by typography or in photogravure for all issues prior to the Churchill set. As with the Wilding definitives we have not indicated issues where it is believed that flexography was used as this is merely a form of typography and it is difficult to be quite sure in all cases in distinguishing between the two from a close examination of the stamps; these are accordingly described as being typographed.

Another characteristic of the typographed phosphors is that generally the bands along the side margins are 6 mm. wide instead of the normal 8 mm. and on the 9d. and 1s.3d. Botanical stamps the side margin bands are only 4 mm. wide. In most of the typographed phosphors the bands are split, i.e. each band has a narrow gap through the centre.

Phosphor Cylinder Numbers. Starting with the 1970 Anniversaries issue cylinder numbers were introduced on the phosphor cylinders as an additional check on tracing errors in applying the bands.

Flaws on Phosphor Issues. In the recorded lists of flaws on stamps which come both ordinary and phosphor, "O" means that the flaw occurs only on the ordinary stamp, "P" phosphor only and "OP" on ordinary and phosphor.

PRESENTATION PACKS. Special Packs comprising slip-in cards with printed commemorative inscriptions and descriptive notes on the back and with protective covering, were introduced in 1964 with the Shakespeare issue. These are listed and priced.

Issues of 1968–69 (British Paintings to the Prince of Wales Investiture) were also issued in packs with text in German for sale through the Post Office's German Agency and these are also listed. Subsequently, however, the packs sold in Germany were identical with the normal English version with the addition of a separate printed card with German text. These, as also English packs with Japanese printed cards for sale through the Japanese Agency, are not recorded.

"SPECIMEN" AND "CANCELLED" STAMPS. The former practice of distributing these ceased during the reign of King George VI but occasionally such overprints were applied to Elizabethan Special Issues for advance publicity or exhibition purposes and these are listed.

Issues of 1970 are known with "CANCELLED" applied with a violet *rubber* handstamp (26 × 3½ mm.), generally across a corner of the stamps. This practice was introduced in an attempt to defeat the postal use of the stamps prior to their first day of issue and which could be obtained from advance publicity material distributed to shops supplied by the Post Office Agency in West Germany. When it was realised that the use of the rubber handstamp created material of a collectable nature the practice was discontinued. These items are not listed.

WITHDRAWAL DATES. The earlier commemorative issues were left on sale until exhaustion and definite withdrawal dates are not always known, but starting with 1963 Red Cross issue the Post Office announced a standard practice to keep commemorative stamps on sale at the Philatelic Bureau for twelve months from date of issue unless sold out before.

QUANTITIES. Up to the end of the 1962 issues (N.P.Y.) it is believed that stamps were sold to exhaustion except where a definite withdrawal date was announced, and so the printing figures are quoted as being the *quantities sold*. Starting with the 1963 Freedom from Hunger issue the quantities are stated as being the number *sold, issued* or *printed*. These are defined as follows:

Sold	Actual quantities sold after accounting for undistributed stocks and unsold stocks returned to stores for destruction.
Issued	Quantities issued from Post Office Stores Department to post offices, including the Philatelic Bureau. These figures are given for the 1965 issues (Churchill to I.T.U.) and for which we do not have actual sales figures. Some may have been withdrawn and destroyed.
Printed	Quantities actually supplied by the printers. These often differ from advance announcements of quantities ordered, owing to spoilage, etc. and for this reason we do not quote quantities ordered for the latest issues.

We also quote figures for sales of Presentation Packs and these were only made available after the total quantities sold, etc., had been announced The quantities for Packs are not additional as they have already been included in the figures for the numbers sold, issued or printed.

We have noticed slight variations in the figures given for quantities sold, etc., stated in other publications and would point out that the figures we have given are those furnished to us by the Post Office. However, the differences are insignificant.

SHEET MARKINGS. Reference should be made to the descriptions of sheet markings given in the General Notes for Section S, as most of these apply to this section and the information given there is not repeated here. In the commemorative issues the markings are most interesting as they begin with the same basic markings as for the definitives for the first monocoloured issues but as more colours were introduced other markings began to appear. They are described here in the order of their appearance.

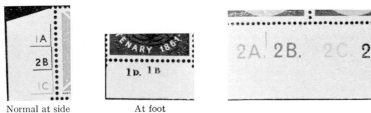

Normal at side   At foot

Harrison   De La Rue

Cylinder Numbers

Cylinder Numbers. These are described in Section S but we show above how they occur on stamps printed in more than one colour. In the listing of cylinder number blocks for stamps printed in more than one colour we give the colour of each cylinder number in order, reading downwards. The information is sometimes helpful in connection with varieties and flaws where more than one cylinder has been used for the same colour in combination with others.

Varieties in Cylinder Blocks. Where a cylinder block contains a listed variety the price is adjusted accordingly and bears an asterisk.

Plate Numbers. The Plate Numbers used by Bradbury, Wilkinson for the 2s.6d. Shakespeare and the 2s.6d. Westminster Abbey are as shown in our notes on the sheet markings for Section T. It should be stated that some of the sheet-fed commemorative stamps were printed by Harrisons on a Linotype and Machinery No. 4 press which uses curved plates and on these the "cylinder numbers" are, strictly speaking, plate numbers. However, as they appear just like the cylinder numbers they are referred to as such.

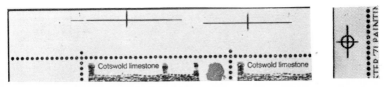

Colour Register Marks. These are coloured crosses of very fine lines, one for each colour superimposed, as illustrated. They appear on all sheets of stamps printed in more than one colour, starting with the 1960 Europa issue.

The circle over cross type was introduced in 1971 with the Ulster Paintings issue. Sometimes all the colours are shown in one marking or they may be split over two markings depending upon the number of colours.

Photo-etched Solid

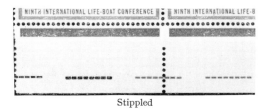

Stippled

Autotron Marks. Coloured bars which may be photo-etched solid or stippled (dotted lines). They serve as an electronic control on colour registration and were first used on the 1961 C.E.P.T. issue.

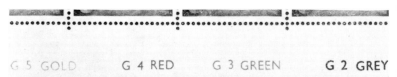

G 5 GOLD   G 4 RED   G 3 GREEN   **G 2 GREY**

Colour Designations. These consist of colour names usually preceded by a figure and the letter "G" which stands for "Gear". They are usually trimmed off but sometimes appear on extra wide right-hand margins on double and single pane reel-fed printings. They are to indicate which side the cylinder should be fitted and aligned with the colour gear in the press. They are not always shown in the colour indicated. They began to be used on the 1961 C.E.P.T. issue.

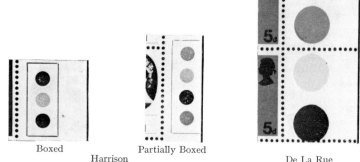

Boxed   Partially Boxed

Harrison

De La Rue

"Traffic Lights". This term is used to denote coloured check dots which were first introduced on the 1963 N.P.Y. issue. They are intended as a means of checking sheets for missing colours before delivery to the Post Office. They may be fully boxed or partially boxed as shown but we have not distinguished between these. We quote the colours in the order of their appearance reading downwards. Sometimes they are in the same order as the cylinder numbers in which case we state this to save space. Rather larger dots were used by De La Rue.

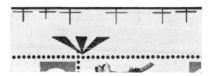

Coloured Crosses. These are most usually found on sheet-fed printings and they serve as an additional check on colour registration. They are often trimmed off. They first appeared on the 1s.3d. 1964 Botanical stamp.

162

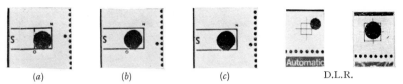

(a)   (b)   (c)   D.L.R.

Perforation Guide Holes. At first the styles as shown in the General Notes for Section S were used but the types illustrated above were introduced as follows:—

(a) Double "S O N" box for the 6d. 1965 Parliament
(b) Single "S O N" box for the 4d. 1966 Landscapes
(c) Single "S N" box for the 4d. 1966 World Football Cup

The letters stand for " Selvedge ", " Off-side " and " Near-side " and they appear in the reverse order on the other side of the sheet. The " S " or " S O " and part of the box are liable to be trimmed off. We also show the styles used by De La Rue for the 1969 Post Office Technology set and 1970 Commonwealth Games issue respectively.

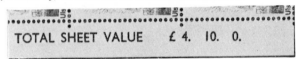

TOTAL SHEET VALUE   £ 4.   10.   0.

Total Sheet Values. As an aid to counter clerks in stocktaking and in selling stamps by the sheet, the "TOTAL SHEET VALUE" and amount was printed in the margin. This practice was introduced with the 1969 Anniversaries issue and this was presumably found to be necessary with the introduction of stamps of unusual size and sheet make-up.

Embossed Head. Starting with the 1968 British Paintings set the Queen's head was sometimes embossed over the gold printing. This gives rise to missing embossing varieties which are listed, although we do not list misplaced embossing. Provision is also made for an embossed dot in the traffic lights.

*PRICES FOR CYLINDER BLOCKS WITH ASTERISKS

These denote cylinder blocks containing a listed variety and the price includes the variety.

W1
(Des. E. G. Fuller)

W2
(Des. M. Goaman)

W3
(Des. E. Dulac)

W4
(Des. M. C. Farrar-Bell)

(Portrait by Dorothy Wilding Ltd (except 1s.3d.))

1953 (JUNE 3). CORONATION OF QUEEN ELIZABETH II

Celebrating the Coronation of Queen Elizabeth II

Cat. No.	S.G. No.	Type	Wmk.	Description	Unused	Used
W1	532	**W1**	**W.22**	2½d. Carmine-red	12	5
a. Missing pearl (Cyl. 3., R.1/4) ..12·00						
b. Pearls retouched	..	.. 6·00				
W2	533	**W2**	**W.22**	4d. Ultramarine	30	45
a. Daffodil leaf flaw						
(Cyl. 1, R.19/1)	..	.. 2·50				
W3	534	**W3**	**W.22**	1s.3d. Deep yellow-green	1·25	1·40
a. Clover leaf flaw						
(Cyl. 2, R.20/1)	..	.. 5·00				
W4	535	**W4**	**W.22**	1s.6d. Deep grey-blue	1·50	1·60
a. Mis-shapen emblems						
(Cyl. 1., R.1/6) ..	..	.. 5·00		b. Thistle flaw (Cyl. 1., R.16/5)	4·50	
W1/4				First Day Cover	†	8·00

Listed Varieties

W1a   W1b

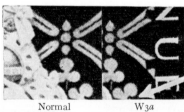

Normal   W3a

W2a

W4a

W4b

Cylinder Numbers (Blocks of six)

Perforation Type A

	Cyl. No.			Cyl. No.			Cyl. No.			Cyl. No.		
2½d.	1	..	1·25	1.	..	1·25	4d.	1	..	4·25*	1.	..	2·50
	2	..	1·00	2.	..	1·00	1s.3d.	2	..	12·00*	2.	..	10·00
	3	..	1·00	3.	..	1·00	1s.6d.	1	..	12·00	1.	..	12·00
	4	..	1·00	4.	..	1·00							

Minor Constant Flaws

Minimum prices as singles: 2½d. £1; 4d. £1·75; 1s.3d. £2·50; 1s.6d. £3

2½d. Cyl. 1 no dot
19/2 Spur to top of A of POSTAGE

2½d. Cyl. 3 dot
13/2 Bulge on left-hand fraction bar

2½d. Cyl. 4 no dot
1/3 White flaw in diadem (Th. A7)
1/4 White spur on left-hand crown (Th. B2)
7/1 Red spot behind hair level with ear-ring (Th. D8–9)
14/2 Red spot on face level with ear-ring (Th. D7)
17/1 White spot on branch below left-hand crown (Th. C3)

4d. Cyl. 1 dot
1/4 Retouched stem of daffodil (Th. F2–3)

1s.3d. Cyl. 2 dot
2/6 Retouch behind upper part of E of E R and white flaw at top of sceptre (Th. B4)

1s.6d. Cyl. 1 no dot
18/2 Malformed foot to R of REVENUE

1s.6d. Cyl. 1 dot
19/1 White flaw on wreath below R of REVENUE (Th. B9)

Sheet Details

Sheet size: 120 (6 × 20). Double pane reel-fed
Sheet markings:
  Cylinder numbers: Opposite R.18/1
  Guide holes: Boxed opposite rows 14/15, at left (no dot) or right (dot
  Marginal arrows:
    "V" shaped, hand engraved at top and bottom of sheet
    "W" shaped, photo-etched at both sides
  Marginal rule: At bottom of sheet

Quantities Sold

2½d. 415,034,000; 4d. 19,816,000; 1s.3d. 8,012,000; 1s.6d. 5,987,200

W5. Scout Badge and
"Rolling Hitch"
(Des. Mary Adshead)

W6. "Scouts coming
to Britain"
(Des. Pat Keely)

W7. Globe within a Compass
(Des. W. H. Brown)

1957 (AUGUST 1). WORLD SCOUT JUBILEE JAMBOREE

Commemorating the 50th Anniversary of the founding of the Boy Scout Movement. The Jubilee Jamboree was held at Sutton Coldfield

Cat. No.	S.G. No.	Type	Wmk.	Description	Unused	Used
W5	557	**W5**	**W.23**	2½d. Carmine-red	5	5
a. Broken rope strand				b. Neck retouch		
(Cyl. 4., R.1/1)	..	.. 2·00		(Cyl. 5, R.11/5)	..	.. 2·00
W6	558	**W6**	**W.23**	4d. Ultramarine	25	20
a. Solid pearl at right						
(Cyl. 1, R.14/5) ..	..	.. 3·50				
W7	559	**W7**	**W.23**	1s.3d. Green	1·00	90
a. Major retouch						
(Cyl. 1., R.2/4) ..	..	.. 5·00				
W5/7				First Day Cover	†	3·00

Listed Varieties

W5a

W5b

W6a

W7a

Cylinder Numbers (Blocks of six)

Perforation Type A

	Cyl. No.			Cyl. No.				Cyl. No.				Cyl. No.		
2½d.	4	..	60	4.	..	60	4d.	1	..	1·75	1.	..	1·75
	5	..	60	5.	..	60	1s.3d.	1	..	7·00	1.	..	7·00

Perforation Type B | Perforation Type C

	Cyl. No.			Cyl. No.				Cyl. No.			Cyl. No.		
4d.	1	..	2·50	1.	..	2·50	4d.	1	..	†	1.	..	2·50

Minor Constant Flaws

Minimum prices as singles: 2½d. £1; 4d. £1·50; 1s.3d. £2·50

2½d. Cyl. 4 dot
  11/2 Red spot over Queen's left eyebrow, later retouched (Th. C9)
  14/1 Red spot in rope between L E (Th. G5)
  16/5 White spot in rope at junction with fifth line at left (Th. C1)
  17/3 Red spot in large 2 just left of curve
  19/2 White dot after small 2
  20/4 White stop after M

2½d. Cyl. 5 dot
  13/4 Red spot in top of A

1s.3d. Cyl. 1 dot
  18/2 Green spot in compass point above badge (Th. E2)

Coils

Special rolls were prepared of this issue for servicing first day covers mechanically. They were produced from different cylinders and printed on continuous reels of paper. The cylinders bore 126 impressions in 21 rows of six. The cylinders were numbered J1 for the 2½d. and 4d. and J2 for the 1s.3d. The reels were cut so as to provide single rolls of 4800 stamps, numbered 1 to 6. Some very minor flaws have been noted on these coil stamps.

The rolls were put on sale at the London Chief Office but as the quantities were too large for stamp collectors, some were rewound into smaller rolls of 480 for the 2½d. and 4d. and 240 for the 1s.3d. and put on sale there on 2nd September.

Sheet Details

Sheet size: 120 (6 × 20). Double pane reel-fed

Sheet markings:
Cylinder numbers: Opposite R.18/1
Guide holes: Opposite rows 14/15, at left (no dot) or right dot)
Marginal arrows:
  "V" shaped, hand engraved at top and bottom of sheet
  "W" shaped, hand engraved on both sides
Marginal rule: At bottom of sheet

Quantities Sold

Sheets and coils: 2½d. 137,235,286; 4d. 9,318,477; 1s.3d. 3,820,478
Coils:

Value	Size	Printed	Sold	Size	Printed	Sold
2½d.	4800	487	23	480	100	49
4d.	4800	480	21	480	100	37
1s.3d.	4800	482	20	240	100	33

Total number of coil stamps sold or used on covers:
  2½d. 133,920; 4d. 118,560; 1s.3d. 103,920

Only 60,632 covers were serviced and 14 large rolls of each value were used for this purpose.

Withdrawn 11.9.57

W8
(Des. M. C. Farrar-Bell with added lettering)

1957 (SEPTEMBER 12).   46th INTER-PARLIAMENTARY UNION CONFERENCE

To mark the 46th Conference held at Church House, Westminster. The Union was founded in 1889

Cat. No.	S.G. No.	Type	Wmk.	Description	Unused	Used
W8	560	**W8**	**W.23**	4d. Ultramarine	50	65
a. Broken wreath (R.2/6)		..	3·75	c. Partial double frame line	..	
b. Broken frame (R.12/5)		..	1·75	(R.17/3, 17/6 and 18/6)	..	2·00
W8				First Day Cover	†	1·25

Listed Varieties

W8*a*   W8*b*   W8*c*

Cylinder Numbers (Blocks of six)

	Cyl. No.	Perf. Type B	Perf. Type C
4d.	2 ..	4·00	4·00

Minor Constant Flaws

Minimum price as singles: £1·25

4d. Cyl. 2 no dot

1/5 Blue blob in frame over last N of CONFERENCE (Th. E6)
1/6 Outline of left-hand jewel of diadem incomplete (Th. A/B3)
2/1 Line joining shamrock leaf to bottom frame (Th. G–H1)
3/2 Blue scratch on right frame near bottom (Th. H6)
8/7 Small break in frame opposite last E in CONFERENCE
14/6 Fine scratch from ear right across neck (Th. E4)
15/8 Blue blob in bottom right corner (Th. H6)
18/1 Blue spot below A of POSTAGE

Sheet Details

Sheet size: 240 (12 × 20). Single pane reel-fed
Sheet markings:
 Cylinder number: Opposite R.18/1
 Guide holes: Six. Opposite rows 1 and 7/8 at both sides and also boxed opposite rows 14/15 at both side
 Marginal arrows:
  "V" shaped, hand engraved at top and bottom of sheet
  "W" shaped, etched in photogravure at both sides
 Marginal rule: At bottom of sheet

Quantity Sold 10,472,160

Withdrawn 13.10.57

W9. Welsh Dragon
(Des. Reynolds Stone)

W10. Flag and Games Emblem
(Des. W. H. Brown)

W11. Welsh Dragon
(Des. Pat Keely)

SPECIMEN

A

1958 (JULY 18). SIXTH BRITISH EMPIRE AND COMMONWEALTH GAMES

The 1958 Empire and Commonwealth Games were held at Cardiff

Cat. No.	S.G. No.	Type	Wmk.	Description		Unused	Used
W9	567	**W9**	**W.23**	3d. Deep lilac		8	5
a. Short scale (Cyl. 2., R.1/1)	..		1·50	e. Body flaw. State III ..	..	1·50	
b. Shoulder flaw (Cyl. 2., R.12/2) ..	..	..	2·25	f. Retouched face (Cyl. 7., R.10/6)		1·25	
c. Shoulder flaw retouched		..	1·25	g. "H" flaw (Cyl. 7., R.11/2)	..	3·00	
d. Body flaw. State II (Cyl. 2., R.20/3)..	..	..	2·00	h. "H" flaw retouched ..	..	1·25	
				s. "Specimen", Type A ..	..	5·00	
W10	568	**W10**	**W.23**	6d. Reddish purple		25	25
s. "Specimen", Type A ..	..		5·00				
W11	569	**W11**	**W.23**	1s.3d. Green		65	75
s. "Specimen", Type A ..	..		5·00				
W9/11				First Day Cover		†	3·00

Listed Varieties

Normal   W9a

Part of the shading is missing on the scale near M of EMPIRE.

W9b   W9c

White flaw on shading of dragon's body above shoulder. Later re-touched with an irregular pattern of dots.

W9d   W9e

W9f

Flaw on body above second E of EMPIRE. This is a progressive flaw. Initially normal, the first stage showed the faintest outline of a flaw. State II shows the flaw solid and state III with a dark outline and pale centre.

The retouches across the Queen's cheek and below the chin are quite marked on Cyl. 7 dot, R.10/6 but there are other minor retouches in this position in stamp No. 6 in rows 2 to 13.

W9g

White flaw crossing line behind dragon's left foreleg shows as a letter "H". After retouching there is a light vertical line across the flaw.

Cylinder Numbers (Blocks of six)

Perforation Type A

	Cyl. No.			Cyl. No.				Cyl. No.				Cyl. No.		
3d.	2	..	60	2.	..	60	6d.	6	..	2·00	6.	..	2·00
	7	..	60	7.	..	60	1s.3d.	3	..	4·50	3.	..	4·50

Minor Constant Flaws

Minimum prices as singles: 3d. 60p; 6d. £1; 1s.3d. £1·50

3d. Cyl. 2 no dot
    13/1 Dark diagonal line across last two fins of dragon's tail; later the upper line was touched out (Th.F–G9)
    19/3 Dots to left of right stroke of H in BRITISH (Th. D2)

3d. Cyl. 7 dot
    3/4 White flaw on fin of dragon's tail above E of COMMONWEALTH (Th. F8)
    4/5 Break in left frame by top of 3 (Th. E1)
    20/3 White flaw on dragon's ankle above N of COMMONWEALTH (Th. F7)

6d. Cyl. 6 no dot
    18/6 Dot between O and N of COMMONWEALTH (Th. A6)

6d. Cyl. 6 dot
    10/1 BRI thicker than normal and retouch under left corner of flag (Th. G3)
    11/1 IRE thicker than normal
    16/1 IR thicker than normal
    20/3 Dent in bottom frame below Queen (Th. H10–11)

1s.3d. Cyl. 3 no dot
    12/3 Retouched background above RE of EMPIRE (Th. G5)

1s.3d. Cyl. 3 dot
    16–19/5 Vertical scratch of varying length in left-hand margin, petering out in rows 18/19

Sheet Details

Sheet size: 120 (6 × 20). Double pane reel-fed

Sheet markings:
    Cylinder numbers: Opposite R.18/1
    Guide holes: Boxed opposite rows 14/15, at left (no dot) or right (dot)
    Marginal arrows:
        "V" shaped, hand engraved at top and bottom of sheet
        "W" shaped, photo-etched at both sides
        In the early printings of the 6d. the arrow was omitted in the right margin on the no dot pane, and in the left margin on the dot pane. Later they were inserted by hand engraving and appear quite rough

    Price for block of twelve (rows 10/11) with marginal arrows on one side only £10
    Marginal rule: At bottom of sheet

Quantities Sold 3d. 320,400,000; 6d. 28,595,880; 1s.3d. 9,870,000

CROWNS WATERMARK

The Multiple Crowns watermark, Type **W.24,** was used for all the following special issues up to the 1967 Wild Flowers issue.

W12.   Postboy of 1660
(Des. Reynolds Stone)

W13.   Posthorn of 1660
(Des. Faith Jaques)

1960 (JULY 7). TERCENTENARY OF ESTABLISHMENT OF "GENERAL LETTER OFFICE"

Charles II Act of 1660 establishing the G.P.O. "legally settled" the Post Office and was the first of a long series of laws for the regulation of postal matters

The watermark is sideways on the 1s.3d.

Cat. No.	S.G. No.	Type	Description	Unused	Used
W12	619	**W12**	3d. Deep lilac	12	5
a. Broken mane (Cyl. 1,			b. Face scratch (Cyl. 1,		
R.17/2) ..	..	.. 1·50	R.17/3) ..	..	.. 1·25
W13	620	**W13**	1s.3d. Green	1·40	1·40
W12/3			First Day Cover	†	2·00

Part of the printing of the 3d. was on chalk-surfaced paper.

Listed Varieties

Normal

W12a

W12b

Scratch extends from eye to hair

Cylinder Numbers (Blocks of six)

Perforation Type A

		Cyl. No.			Cyl. No.	
3d.		1 ..	90		1. ..	90

		Cyl. No.	Perf. Type B	Perf. Type C	
1s.3d.		1 .. 10·00		1 .. 10·00	

The 1s.3d. is with sheet orientated showing head to right.

Minor Constant Flaws

Minimum prices as singles: 3d. 75p; 1s.3d. £2

3d. Cyl. 1 no dot
    1/2 White dot in bottom of large C (Th. B1)
    10/5 White notch in bottom frame below r of Letter (Th. H7)
    13/1 r of Letter weak (Th. G7)
    15/6 White patch on left foreleg of horse (Th. E5)
3d. Cyl. 1 dot
    11/6 White dot in hair near top of ear (Th. D12)
    20/5 White nick in back of boy (Th. D4)
1s.3d. Cyl. 1 no dot
    1/18 White bulge inside o of 1960 (Th. E7)
    2/20 White bulge on stem of acorn under horn (Th. L3)
    5/19 White spot in centre of leaf on right of portrait (Th. G6)
    6/5 White dot at junction of two acorns under Queen's shoulder (Th. G5)

Sheet Details

Sheet sizes:
    3d. 120 (6 × 20). Double pane reel-fed; 1s.3d. 120 (20 × 6). Single pane reel-fed
Sheet markings:
    Cylinder numbers: 3d. opposite R.18/1; 1s.3d. opposite R.4/1
    Guide holes:
        3d. opposite rows 14/15, at left (no dot) or right (dot)
        1s.3d. Six. Above and below vertical rows 1, 7/8 and boxed above and below 14/15
    Marginal arrows (hand engraved):
        3d. "V" shaped at top and bottom of sheet; "W" shaped on both sides
        1s.3d. "V" shaped on both sides: "W" shaped at top and bottom of sheet.
    Marginal rule: 3d. at bottom of sheet and 1s.3d. at right-hand side

Quantities Printed 3d. 143,390,520; 1s.3d. 6,090,840

Withdrawn 31.12.60

CHALKY PAPER

All the following special issues are on chalk-surfaced paper, unless otherwise stated.

W14.   Conference Emblem
(Des. P. Rahikainen and Reynolds Stone)

Miniature Sheets

On the occasion of the EUROSTAMP—1962 London Stamp Exhibition, organised with the help of the Council of Europe, a miniature sheet, size 114 × 124 mm., was produced comprising three each of Nos. W14/15 *se-tenant* in a block of six (2 × 3) printed in grey-blue, imperforate and surrounded by a brown frame and inscriptions in black on white unwatermarked gummed paper. The stamps were printed by Harrison & Sons in photogravure and the rest of the sheet was printed by Wm. Clowes & Sons by letterpress. The sheet had no franking value.

A similar sheet exists, size 110 × 125 mm., but with the stamps printed in black and surrounded by a green frame and inscription giving details of the issue in red. The Stamps were printed in photogravure and the rest of the sheet by letterpress by Harrison & Sons. The sheet had no franking value.

1960 (SEPTEMBER 19).   FIRST ANNIVERSARY OF EUROPEAN POSTAL AND TELE-COMMUNICATIONS CONFERENCE

Celebrating the first Anniversary of the Conference of European Postal and Tele-communications Administrations

Cat. No.	S.G. No.	Type		Description	Unused	Used
W14	621	**W14**		6d. Bronze-green and purple	45	45
a. Broken diadem (R.1/2) ..		.. 3·00		*b.* Blurred E (R.13/5) ..	.. 3·00	
W15	622	**W14**		1s.6d. Brown and blue	1·00	1·00
a. Broken diadem (R.1/2)		.. 4·00		*c.* Blurred E (R.13/5) ..	.. 4·00	
b. Major retouch (R.9/2)		.. 3·50				
W14/5				First Day Cover	†	2·00

Listed Varieties

W14*b*, W15*c*

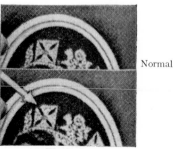

Normal

W14/15*a*

W15*b*

Cylinder Numbers (Blocks of four)

	Cyl. Nos. (No dot)				Perf. Type B	Perf. Type C
6d.	1 (purple)–1A (green)	..	..	..	3·00	3·00
1s.6d.	2 (blue)–1A (brown)	..	..	..	5·00	5·00

The same cylinder 1A was used for both values.

Minor Constant Flaws

Minimum prices as singles: 6d. £2; 1s.6d. £2·50

6d. Cyls. 1–1A no dot
    1/4 Pale purple spots in bottom of oval and below bottom frame (Th. G9–10 and H10)
    6/2 Two short lines in scroll above T of TELECOMMUNICATIONS (Th. E2)
    9/3 Small coloured line in scroll above E of EUROPEAN (Th. B1)
    12/2 Dot in M of ADMINISTRATION
    19/1 Vertical scratch left of scroll containing EUROPEAN (Th. B–D1)
    20/5 Two scratches in scroll left of C of CONFERENCE (Th. A1–2)

1s.6d. Cyls. 2–1A no dot
    10/4 Retouch to spine of P of EUROPA
    12/2 Dot in M of ADMINISTRATION
    17/4 Dotted retouch above CO (Th. F4)
    18/5 Retouch in background above first M of TELECOMMUNICATIONS

Sheet Details

Sheet size: 120 (6 × 20). Single pane reel-fed
Sheet markings:
    Cylinder numbers: Bottom margin below R.20/5
    Guide holes: Opposite rows 1 and 7/8, at both sides and boxed opposite rows 14/15, at both sides
    Marginal arrows (hand engraved):
        "V" shaped at top and bottom and "W" shaped at both sides
    Marginal rule: At bottom of sheet
    Colour register marks: Opposite rows 2 and 19 at both sides

Quantities Printed 6d. 16,990,320; 1s.6d. 7,682,520

Withdrawn 31.12.60

W16. "Growth of Savings"
(Des. M. Goaman)

W15. Thrift Plant
(Des. P. Gauld)

W17. Thrift Plant
(Des. M. Goaman)

1961 (AUGUST 28). POST OFFICE SAVINGS BANK CENTENARY

To mark the centenary of the establishment of the P.O. Savings Bank
The watermark is sideways on the 2½d.

Cat. No.	S.G. No.	Type	Description	Unused	Used

A. "TIMSON" Machine

2½d. Cyls. 1E–1 F no dot. Deeply shaded portrait (dull black)
3d. Cyls. 3D–3 E no dot. Clear, well-defined portrait with deep shadows and bright high-lights

W16	623I	**W15**	2½d. Dull black and red	12	10
W17	624I	**W16**	3d. Orange-brown and violet	10	8
a. Orange-brown omitted					
b. Perf. through side sheet margin	9·00				
c. Do. and orange-brown omitted			*d.* Nick in S (R.9/3)	10·00	
			e. Nick retouched	2·50	
W18	625	**W17**	1s.6d. Red and blue	75	75
W16/8			First Day Cover	†	1·60

B. "THRISSELL" Machine

2½d. Cyls. 1D–1 B no dot or dot. Lighter portrait (grey-black)
3d. Cyls. 3C–3B no dot or dot. Dull portrait, lacking in contrast

W19	623II	**W15**	2½d. Grey-black and red	75	75
W20	624II	**W16**	3d. Orange-brown and violet	20	8
a. Orange-brown omitted ..					
b. Notch in flower (No dot, R.7/1)	1·25		*c.* Notch in leaf (No dot, R.14/4)..	1·25	

A very small quantity of all values was pre-released at the Chorley, Lancs., P.O. on 21st August, 1961.

Listed Varieties

W17d
Nick in S

W17e
Nick filled in but centre of S is narrower

W20b

W20c

Cylinder Numbers (Blocks of four)

A. "Timson" printings. Single pane cylinders only (no dot).

Cyl. Nos.		Perforation Types	
	B	C	D
2½d. 1E (black)–1F (red)*	75	75	†
3d. 3D (violet)–3E (brown)	65	65	20·00
1s.6d. 2E (blue)–2C (red)	4·50	4·50	†

*The black number is superimposed over the red.

B. "Thrissell" printings. Double pane cylinders.

Cyl. Nos.	Perforation Type A	
	No dot	Dot
2½d. 1D (black)–1B (red)†	4·50	4·50
3d. 3C (violet)–3B (brown)††	6·00	2·00

†In the 2½d. dot pane the dot was omitted in error after 1B.
††In the 3d. no dot pane "3E" was wrongly inserted and the "C" was engraved over the "E".
Two blocks of four are needed to show both cylinders in the 3d. "Thrissell" printing.
The 2½d. is with sheet orientated showing head to right.

Minor Constant Flaws

Minimum prices as singles: 2½d. 75p; 3d. 60p; 1s.6d. £1·50

2½d. Cyls. 1E–1F no dot
  1/13 Two white dots on right curve below last S of SAVINGS
  1/16 Two black dots right of Queen's left eye (Th. D4)
  1/17 State I. Dark red patch left of top thrift flower (Th. H3)
     State II. Later printings show whitish patch
  2/3 White horizontal line from Queen's hair to OF of OFFICE (Th. C3)
  4/19 Retouch to flaw in forehead above Queen's right eye (Th. C3)
  5/3 White spot on top of right arm of V of SAVINGS

3d. Cyls. 3D–3E no dot
  8/1 Diagonal retouch across Queen's cheek from right of her left eye to nose (Th. D9–10)
  11/5 Brown spot on squirrel's neck (Th. D5)
  17/1 Retouch on Queen's chin (Th. E9)
  17/2 Retouch on neck (Th. E10)
  19/2 Retouch above necklace (Th. E–F10)
  20/1 Vertical violet line on branch in bottom right corner (Th. F–G13

3d. Cyls. 3C–3B no dot
  1/4 Additional serif at top of K of BANK
  3/3 Notch in upper right leaf on lowest right-hand branch of tree (Th. E7)
  4/2 Retouch on neck below ear-ring (Th. E10)
  4/6 Dot in B of BANK
  7/3 Retouch above necklace (Th. E10)

Sheet Details

	Timson	Thrissell
Sheet sizes:		
2½d. 120 (20 × 6)	Single pane reel-fed	Double pane reel-fed
3d. 120 (6 × 20)	Single pane reel-fed	Double pane reel-fed
1s.6d. 120 (6 × 20)	Single pane reel-fed	
Sheet markings:		
Cylinder numbers:		
2½d.	Bottom margin below R.6/19	Bottom margin below R.6/19
3d.	Bottom margin below R.20/5	Bottom margin below R.20/2
1s.6d.	As 3d.	and R.20/5
Guide holes:		
2½d.	Above and below vertical rows 1, 7/8 and (boxed) 14/15	Below vertical rows 14/15 (no dot) or above (dot), boxed
3d.	Opposite rows 1, 7/8 and (boxed) 14/15, both sides	Opposite rows 14/15, at left (no dot) or right (dot), boxed
1s.6d.	As 3d.	
Marginal arrows (hand engraved):		
2½d.	"V" shaped on both sides; "W" shaped at top and bottom	As Timson
3d.	"V" shaped, all round	"V" shaped, at top and bottom; "W" shaped at both sides
1s.6d.	"V" shaped, at top and bottom; "W" shaped, at both sides	
Marginal rule:		
2½d.	At right-hand side	As Timson
3d.	At bottom	As Timson
1s.6d.	At bottom	
Colour register marks:		
2½d.	Above and below vertical rows 2/3 and 17/18	Below vertical rows 2/3 and 17/18 (no dot) or above (dot)
3d.	Opposite rows 3/4 and 17/18 at both sides	Opposite rows 3/4 and 17/18 at left (no dot) or right (dot)
1s.6d.	Opposite rows 2/3 and 18/19 at left (no dot) or right (dot)	
Colour designations (usually trimmed off):		
1s.6d.	" RED " opposite row 15 and " BLUE " opposite row 16, right margin	
Others	None	

In the case of marginal copies the differences in sheet markings, in conjunction with the different types of perforators used, provide helpful clues for identifying the printing machine used.

Quantities Sold 2½d. 24,720,000; 3d. 114,360,000; 1s.6d. 7,560,000

W18. C.E.P.T. Emblem

W19. Doves and Emblem

W20. Doves and Emblem

(All values des. M. Goaman, doves by T. Kurperschoek)

1961 (SEPTEMBER 18). EUROPEAN POSTAL AND TELECOMMUNICATIONS (C.E.P.T.) CONFERENCE

Representatives of nineteen countries met at Torquay on 11th September for the Conference of the European Postal and Telecommunication Administrations

These were the first stamps of Great Britain to be printed in three colours

Cat. No.	S.G. No.	Type	Description	Unused	Used
W21	626	**W18**	2d. Orange, pink and brown	5	5
a. White ear (Dot, R.11/2)		.. 1·00			
W22	627	**W19**	4d. Buff, mauve and ultramarine	10	10
W23	628	**W20**	10d. Turquoise, pale green and Prussian blue	20	20
a. Green omitted ..	..	..			
b. Turquoise omitted	..	..			
W21/3			First Day Cover	†	1·00

Listed Variety

W21*a*

Cylinder Numbers (Blocks of four)

	Cyl. Nos.	Perforation Type A	
		No dot	Dot
2d.	1A (brown)—1B (orange)—1C (pink) ..	30	30
4d.	2E (ultramarine)—2B (buff)—2C (mauve)	50	50
10d.	3G (Prussian blue)—3D (green)—3A (turq.)	1·00	1·00

In this issue the panes were transposed, the dot being on the left and the no dot on the right.

Minor Constant Flaws

Minimum prices as singles: 2d. 50p; 4d. 50p; 10d. 75p

2d. Cyls. 1A–1B–1C dot
  6/4 Small white dot to left of P
  18/6 Hairline from right-hand frame to sheet margin (Th. E13–14)

2d. Cyls. 1A–1B–1C no dot
  6/4 Pale spot on neck below necklace (Th. F10)
  17/4 Dot in lower right pink horn (Th. F12)
  18/1 Diagonal dark brown patch across Queen's cheek. Later retouched (Th. E10)

4d. Cyls. 2E–2B–2C dot
  5/3 Flaw at top right of E
  12/6 Dark patch above diadem (Th. A8)
  15/3 Flaw down Queen's forehead and nose (Th. C–D6)
  17/6 Pale patch on cheek (Th. D7)

10d. Cyls. 3G–3D–3A dot
  4/3 Break in loop of posthorn around P (Th. C7)
  4/6 Notch in frame at top right (Th. A13)
  14/2 Dark patch to right of lower right posthorn (Th. C8)

10d. Cyls. 3G–3D–3A no dot
  4/6 White patch above Queen's right eye (Th. C10)
  6/1 Pale patch to right of Queen's neck (Th. E12–13 F12–13)
  10/3 White patch on Queen's forehead (Th. C10). Started during the run gradually becoming more prominent
  15/5 Small white patch at top centre of Queen's forehead (Th. C10)

Sheet Details

Sheet size: 120 (6 × 20). Double pane reel-fed

Sheet markings:
  Cylinder numbers: Bottom margin below R. 20/5
  Guide holes: Opposite rows 14/15, at left (dot) or right (no dot), boxed
  Marginal arrow (hand engraved):
    "V" shaped at top and bottom; "W" shaped at both sides
  Marginal rule: At bottom of sheet
  Colour register marks:
    2d. Opposite rows 2/3 and 17/18 at left (dot) or right (no dot)
    4d. Opposite rows 2/3 and 18/19 at left (dot) or right (no dot)
    10d. None
  Autotron marks (solid):
    2d. Respectively brown, pink and orange opposite rows 18/20, at left (dot) or right (no dot)
    4d. Respectively ultramarine and mauve opposite rows 18/19, at left (dot) or right (no dot)
    10d. Respectively Prussian blue, green and turquoise opposite rows 18/20, at left (dot) or right (no dot)
  Colour designations:
    2d. "BROWN" in right margin reading upwards opposite rows 14/13 (no dot)
    4d. "YELLOW", "MAUVE", "BLUE" respectively in right margin opposite rows 11/12, 12/13 and 13 (no dot)
    10d. None

Quantities Sold 2d. 47,530,920; 4d. 7,614,480; 10d. 5,427,780

W21. Hammer Beam Roof, Westminster Hall

W22. Palace of Westminster

(Des. Faith Jaques)

1961 (SEPTEMBER 25). SEVENTH COMMONWEALTH PARLIAMENTARY CONFERENCE

The "Empire Parliamentary Association" was formed at the Coronation of King George V and in 1948 its name was changed to its present form

The watermark is sideways on the 1s.3d.

Cat. No.	S.G. No.	Type	Description	Unused	Used
W24	629	**W21**	6d. Purple and gold	20	12
a. Gold omitted £150					
W25	630	**W22**	1s.3d. Green and blue	75	75
a. Blue (Queen's head) omitted ..					
W24/5			First Day Cover	†	2·00

Cylinder Numbers (Blocks of four)

Cyl. Nos. (No dot)				Perforation Types	
				Type B	Type C
6d. 1B (gold)—1D (purple)	..	..	..	1·00	1·00
1s.3d. 2A (green)—2B (blue)	..	..	..	4·00	4·00

The 1s.3d. is with sheet orientated showing head to right.

Minor Constant Flaws

Minimum prices as singles: 6d. 60p;   1s.3d. £1·50

6d. Cyls. 1B–1D no dot
    3/4 Dot in middle bar of second E in CONFERENCE
    5/5 Enlarged white patch in Queen's hair (Th. C7)
    6/3 Two small retouches in neck above necklace (Th. F7–8)
    10/3 Patch of retouching below crossed maces (Th. G5–6)

1s.3d. Cyls. 2A–2B no dot
    5/4 White patch on Queen's forehead (Th. D4)
    6/2 Small white vertical line on Queen's forehead (Th. C–D4)

Sheet Details

Sheet sizes: 6d. 120 (6×20); 1s.3d. 120 (20×6). Single pane reel-fed
Sheet markings:
    Cylinder numbers: Bottom margin below R. 20/5 (6d.) or 6/19 (1s.3d.)
    Guide holes:
      6d. opposite rows 1 and 7/8, at both sides and boxed opposite rows 14/15, at both sides
      1s.3d. above and below vertical rows 1 and 7/8 and boxed above and below vertical rows 14/15
    Marginal arrows (hand engraved):
      6d. "V" shaped at top and bottom and "W" shaped at both sides
      1s.3d. "V" shaped at both sides and "W" shaped at top and bottom
    Marginal rule: 6d. at bottom of sheet; 1s.3d. at right side
    Colour register marks:
      6d. Opposite both sides of rows 2/3 and 18/19
      1s.3d. Above and below vertical rows 2/3 and 18/19

Quantities Sold 6d. 16,680,000; 1s.3d. 5,760,000

W23.   "Units of Productivity"

W24.   "National Productivity"

W25.   "Unified Productivity"
(Des. D. Gentleman)

The National Productivity Year issue was the first commemorative series to appear with phosphor bands and presents a number of other interesting facets:

The watermark on the 2½d. and 3d. is inverted for the reason explained in the General Notes to this section.

There were several printings on the low values which are characterised by their distinct shades and confirmed by different states of some of the flaws and varieties. It is believed that the second printing of the 2½d. comes from sheets numbered between about 439,000 and 450,000. Only the third printing was used for the phosphor stamps. There was considerable variation in the carmine-red during the printing and carmine-rose shades are quite common.

2½d. During the first printing both green cylinders were seriously damaged, hence the major repairs in the later printings.

3d. There were several printings of this value which fall into two shade groups. The violet cylinder 2A provided a number of minor flaws and was quickly replaced. It is believed that stamps from this cylinder were supplied only to Canterbury and Chelmsford.

1962 (NOVEMBER 14). NATIONAL PRODUCTIVITY YEAR

The stamps emphasised the need for greater productivity as an essential element in the continuing prosperity of Great Britain.

The watermark is inverted on the 2½d. and 3d.

Cat. No.	S.G. No.	Type	Description	Unused	Used

A. Ordinary

W26 631 **W23**   2½d.

		Unused	Used
a. Emblem and arrows retouch (No dot, R. 3/3) (2)	4·00	(1) Myrtle-green and carmine-red	8	5
b. Ditto (3) ..	1·75	(2) Deep green and bright car-mine-red	10	8
c. Arrow head retouch (No dot, R.4/4) (2) ..	3·00	(3) Blackish olive and car-mine-red	12	8
d. Ditto (3) ..	1·50			
e. Retouches, arrows 2 and 6 (No dot, R. 4/5) (2) ..	3·00	k. Smudged red centre cube (Dot R. 18/3) (2)	3·00	
f. Ditto (3) ..	1·50	l. Ditto (3)	1·25	
g. White nose (Dot, R. 2/6) (1) ..	1·25	m. Arrow head retouch (Dot, R. 19/3) (2)	3·00	
h. Neck retouch (Dot, R. 15/4) (1)	1·50	n. Ditto (3)	1·25	
i. Ditto (2) ..	4·50			
j. Ditto (3)	2·50			

W27 632 **W24**   3d.

		Unused	Used
a. Light blue (Queen's head) omitted	£350	(1) Light blue and violet	15	8
b. Lake in Scotland (Cyls. 2A–2B dot, R. 1/3)	3·00	(2) Light blue and deep bluish purple	20	10
c. "Kent" omitted (Cyls. 2C–2B, R. 18/2) ..	2·50			
d. Lake in Yorkshire (Cyls. 2C–2B dot, R. 19/1) ..	2·00	f. Ditto, removed	1·25	
e. Forehead line (Cyls. 2D–2B, R. 17/6) ..	1·50	g. Ditto, retouched	1·00	

W28	633	**W25**	1s.3d. Carmine, light blue and deep green	75	75
a. Light blue (Queen's head) omitted	£500				
			First Day Cover	†	1·50

W26/8

B. Phosphor

2½d. has one band at left; others have three bands, all applied typo.

		Unused	Used
WP26 631p **W23**		2½d. Blackish olive and car-mine-red	20	12
a. Emblem and arrows retouch (No dot, R. 3/3)	2·00			
b. Arrow head retouch (No dot, R. 4/4)	1·75	e. Smudged red centre cube (Dot, R. 18/3)	1·50	
c. Retouches, arrows 2 and 6 (No dot, R. 4/5)	1·60	f. Arrow head retouch (Dot, R. 19/6)	1·75	
d. Neck retouch (Dot, R. 15/4) ..	1·75			
WP27 632p **W24**		3d. Light blue and violet	30	20
a. Forehead line (Cyls. 2D–2B, R. 17/6)	1·60	b. Forehead line removed ..	1·50	
WP28 633p **W25**		1s.3d. Carmine, light blue and deep green	3·00	2·25
WP26/8		First Day Cover	†	3·75

About 60 2½d., 350 3d. and 20 1s.3d. were pre-released at a Lewisham post office, London, on 16th and 17th October, 1962.

Listed Varieties

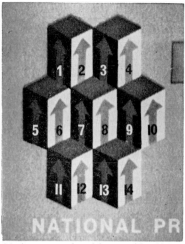

2½d. Arrows numbered for easy identification of varieties and flaws

W26a/b, WP26a
N and arrow head of emblem strongly shaded with diagonal cuts and dashes, also arrows 4, 10 and 14

In W26c/d, WP26b the arrow head alone is retouched with diagonal lines and in W26m/n, WP26f with irregular dots
Less marked retouches occur in the same area on dot cyl., R. 19/2 and 19/4

W26e/f, WP26c

W26g

W26h/j, WP26d

W26k/l, WP26e
This may not be fully constant

W27b   W27c   W27d

W27e, WP27a   W27f, WP27b   W27g

The original variety was a horizontal line from Queen's left eye to hair which was later removed, leaving a white gap and this was finally partly filled in by retouching

Cylinder Numbers (Blocks of four)

(a) Ordinary

	Cyl. Nos.			Perforation Type A	
				No dot	Dot
2½d.	1D (red)–1B (green) (shade 1)	..	..	50	50
	1D (red)–1B (green) (shade 2)	..	..	2·50	4·50*
	1D (red)–1B (green) (shade 3)	..	..	60	1·50*
3d.	2A (violet)–2B (blue)	..	..	8·00	8·00
	2C (violet)–2B (blue)	..	..	75	75
	2D (violet)–2B (blue)	..	..	1·00	1·00
1s.3d.	3C (carmine)–3B (blue)–3E (green)		..	3·75	†

			No dot	
			Type B	Type C
1s.3d.	3C (carmine)–3B (blue)–3E (green)	..	7·00	7·00

(b) Phosphor

				Perforation Type A	
				No dot	Dot
2½d.	1D (red)–1B (green) (shade 3)	..	..	1·00	1·50
3d.	2D (violet)–2B (blue)	..	..	2·00	2·00
1s.3d.	3C (carmine)–3B (blue)–3E (green)	..	..	15·00	†

Minor Constant Flaws

Minimum prices as singles:

	Ordinary	Phosphor			Ordinary	Phosphor
2½d. (shade 1)	50	†	3d. (either shade)	..	1·00	1·10
2½d. (shade 2)	2·00	†	1s.3d.	..	1·25	4·00
2½d. (shade 3)	60	1·00				

2½d. Cyls. 1D–1B no dot
  1/2 Two small green dots right of arrow 2 (Th. B–C4) all shades, OP
  3/2 Scratch through top of bottom right cube (Th. F–E4) all shades, OP
  3/4 Minor retouches to face around mouth (Th. D–E10) shades 2/3, OP
  5/1 White scratch below Queen's nose and through mouth (Th. D–E10) all shades, OP
  17/5 Small retouch to cheek to right of mouth (Th. D10–11) all shades, OP

3d. Cyls. 2C–2B no dot
  1/4 Retouch in Scotland (Th. C3), O
  6/5 Dark patch above R of PRODUCTIVITY (Th. G6), O
  13/5 Line of retouching above blue sea of Ireland (Th. C2), O

3d. Cyls. 2C–2B dot
  7/1 Purple line across Solway Firth (Th. D3), O
  15/6 Row of dots from Queen's left eye to hair (Th. C11), O

3d. Cyls. 2D–2B no dot
  13/5 Lines of retouching above blue sea of Ireland (Th. C2), OI

3d. Cyls. 2D–2B dot
  1/3 Retouch in Yorkshire (Th. D4), OP

181

1s.3d. Cyls. 3C–3B–3E no dot
 3/4 White flaw at back of Queen's hair (Th. D12), OP
 6/2 Retouch on tail of large blue arrow (Th. D2), OP
 13/4 White flaw left of ear-ring (Th. E11), OP

Sheet Details

Sheet size: 120 (6 × 20)
 2½d. Double pane reel-fed on a Timson machine
  1s.3d. Single pane reel-fed on a new Thrissell machine capable of using five colours
Sheet markings:
 Cylinder numbers: Bottom row below R. 20/5
 Guide holes:
  2½d. and 3d. Opposite rows 14/15 (boxed), at left (no dot) or right (dot)
  1s.3d. Opposite rows 1 and 7/8, at both sides and boxed opposite rows 14/15, at both sides
 Marginal arrows (photo-etched): "W" shaped at top, bottom and sides
 Marginal rule: At bottom of sheet
 Colour register marks:
  2½d. and 3d. Opposite rows 2/3 and 18/19, at left (no dot) or right (dot)
  1s.3d. Opposite rows 2/3 and 18/19, at both sides
 Autotron marks (stippled):
  2½d. and 3d. Bottom margin in various positions
  1s.3d. Respectively red, green, blue, green, red below vertical rows 4/6
 Colour designations (usually trimmed off):
  2½d. "G GREY" (not green) opposite rows 8/9 and "G RED" opposite row 13, right margin on the dot
   cylinder
  3d. "G BLUE" opposite rows 8/9 and "G MAUVE" opposite row 13, right margin on the dot cylinder
  1s.3d. "G BLUE" opposite row 9 and "G GREEN" opposite rows 12/3, left margin
 Traffic lights (boxed):
  2½d. Green, red opposite R. 20/6 dot pane
  3d. Blue, violet opposite R. 20/6 dot pane
  1s.3d. Blue, red, green boxed opposite R. 20/6

Quantities Sold

	Ordinary	Phosphor
2½d.	99,240,000	7,320,090
3d.	182,580,000	13,320,000
1s.3d.	8,832,000	1,132,000

Of the 2½d. ordinary it is estimated that about 62 million came from the first printing, 2½ million from the second printing and 32 million from the third printing

W26. Campaign Emblem and Family   **W27.** Children of Three Races
(Des. M. Goaman)

1963 (21 MARCH). FREEDOM FROM HUNGER

The stamps were part of a world-wide co-operative effort to focus attention on the problem of hunger and malnutrition

The watermark is inverted

Cat. No.	S.G. No.	Type		Description	Unused	Used
A. Ordinary						
W29	634	**W26**		2½d. Crimson and pink	8	8
a. Line through MPA (Cyls. 1D.–1H. R. 7/2)			1·10	*b.* Broken R in FREEDOM (Cyls. 1D–1H, R. 16/2)	1·50	
W30	635	**W27**		1s.3d. Bistre-brown and yellow	75	75
W29/30				First Day Cover	†	1·25
B. Phosphor (applied typo.)						
WP29	634p	**W26**		2½d. One band	25	15
a. Line through MPA (Cyls. 1D.–1H., R. 7/2)			1·40	*b.* Broken R in FREEDOM (Cyls. 1D–1H, R. 16/2)	1·75	
WP30	635p	**W27**		1s.3d. Three bands	3·25	2·50
WP29/30				First Day Cover	†	3·50

Listed Varieties

C A M P A I G N

W29a, WP29a
An unsuccessful attempt was
made to touch this out

W29b, WP29b

Cylinder Numbers (Blocks of four)

(a) Ordinary

	Cyl. Nos.				Perforation Types		
					A		E
					No dot	Dot	No dot
2½d.	1D (pink)–1G (crimson)	..	..	..	12·00	12·00	†
	1D (pink)–1H (crimson)	..	..	..	1·00	1·00	†
1s.3d.	2E (yellow)–2G (brown)	..	..	..	4·00	4·00	—

(b) Phosphor

2½d.	1D (pink)–1H (crimson)	..	..	..	2·00	2·00	†
1s.3d.	2E (yellow)–2G (brown)	..	..	..	15·00	15·00	15·00

In the 1s.3d. the panes are reversed, the dot pane being on the left and the no dot pane on the right.

Minor Constant Flaws

Minimum prices as singles:

2½d. ordinary 75p; phosphor £1; 1s.3d. ordinary £1·50; phosphor £4

2½d. Cyls. 1D–1H no dot
9/6 Dot in upper part of second A of CAMPAIGN, OP
15/2 Retouch from base of portrait to M of CAMPAIGN (Th. E11 and F12–13), OP

2½d. Cyls. 1D–1H dot
8/1 and 7/1 Hairline extends from under GN on 8/1 to CAMPAIGN on 7/1, OP
19/1 Retouch on left cheek and jawbone (Th. D10), OP

1s.3d. Cyls. 2E–2G no dot
1/2 Small white line in extreme right wheatsheaf (Th. C6), OP

Sheet Details

Sheet size: 120 (6 × 20). Double pane reel-fed

Sheet markings:
  Cylinder numbers: Bottom row below R. 20/5
  Guide holes:
    2½d. Opposite rows 14/15 (boxed), at left (no dot) or right (dot)
    1s.3d. Opposite rows 14/15 (boxed), at left (dot) or right (no dot)
  Marginal arrows (photo-etched): "W" shaped at top, bottom and sides
  Marginal rule: At bottom of sheet
  Colour register marks:
    2½d. Opposite rows 2/3 and 18/19, at left (no dot) or right (dot)
    1s.3d. Opposite rows 2/3 and 18/19, at left (dot) or right (no dot)
  Autotron marks (stippled):
    2½d. Below vertical rows 2/3, no dot pane
    1s.3d. Below vertical rows 2/3, dot pane
  Colour designation:
    1s.3d. "G2" in brown opposite row 7 at right, no dot, on wide cut margins
  Traffic lights (boxed):
    2½d. Red, pink opposite R. 20/6, dot pane
    1s.3d. Brown, yellow opposite R. 20/6, no dot pane

Quantities Sold

	Ordinary	Phosphor
2½d.	97,050,000	2,784,920
1s.3d.	9,009,000	624,960

W28. "Paris Conference"
(Des. Reynolds Stone)

1963 (MAY 7). PARIS POSTAL CONFERENCE CENTENARY

A postal conference was held in Paris to commemorate the centenary of the first international meeting of postal authorities held in 1863

The watermark is inverted

Cat. No.	S.G. No.	Type	Description	Unused	Used

A. Ordinary

W31	636	**W28**	6d. Green and mauve	20	20
a. Green omitted £375			*b.* White spot in frame line (No dot, R. 19/3)	1·25	
W31			First Day Cover	†	65

B. Phosphor, applied typo.

WP31	636p	**W28**	6d. Three bands	80	80
a. Pair, with and without phosphor 8·00			*b.* White spot in frame line (No dot, R. 19/3)	2·00	
WP31			First Day Cover	†	1·50

Listed Variety

W31*b*, WP31*b*

Cylinder Numbers (Blocks of four)

	Cyl. Nos.		Perforation Type A	
			No dot	Dot
6d.	2A (mauve)–1B (green) Ordinary		1·00	1·00
6d.	2A (mauve)–1B (green) Phosphor ..		4·00	4·00

The panes were reversed, the dot being on the left and the no dot on the right.

Minor Constant Flaws

Minimum prices as singles: Ordinary 50p; phosphor £1·50

6d. Cyls. 2A–1B no dot
1/1 Flaw in oval frame at 11 o'clock (Th. B9) and lack of definition in top right rose (Th. B13), OP
14/6 First N of CONFERENCE appears white, OP
19/5 Dot under R of CENTENARY, OP
20/5 White spot on ivy stem below first E of CONFERENCE and coloured dot in right frame near top (Th. A13), OP

6d. Cyls. 2A–1B dot
14/2 White spot in R of CONFERENCE, OP

Sheet Details

Sheet size: 120 (6 × 20). Double pane reel-fed

Sheet markings:
Cylinder numbers: Below R. 20/5
Guide holes: Opposite row 15 (boxed), at left (dot) or right (no dot)
Marginal arrows (photo-etched): "W" shaped at top, bottom and sides
Marginal rule: At bottom of sheet
Colour register marks: Opposite rows 2/3 and 18/19, at left (dot) or right (no dot)
Autotron marks (stippled): Bottom margin, dot pane
Traffic lights (boxed): Green, mauve opposite R. 20/6, no dot pane

Quantities Sold Ordinary 18,536,400; phosphor 1,430,800

W29. Posy of Flowers
(Des. S. Scott)

W30. Woodland Life
(Des. M. Goaman)

1963 (MAY 16). NATIONAL NATURE WEEK

The Council for Nature organised a Nature Week from 18th–25th May in order to draw attention to the natural history movement and the importance of wild life conservation

The 4½d. value was the first stamp of Great Britain to be printed in five colours

Cat. No.	S.G. No.	Type		Description	Unused	Used
A. Ordinary						
W32	637	**W29**		3d. Yellow, green, brown and		
a. "Caterpillar" flaw (Dot, R. 3/2)			1·75	black	8	5
W33	638	**W30**		4½d. Black, blue, yellow,		
a. Nose retouch (Cyl. 2E, R. 14/4)			2·25	magenta and brown-red	20	20
W32/3				First Day Cover	†	65
B. Phosphor						
WP32	637p	**W29**		3d. Three bands, applied photo.	20	15
a. "Caterpillar" flaw (Dot, R. 3/2)			2·00			
WP33	638p	**W30**		4½d. Three bands, applied typo.	60	60
a. Nose retouch (Cyl. 2E, R. 14/4)			2·50			
WP32/3				First Day Cover	†	1·75

Listed Varieties

W32a, WP32a
Several states exist,
later retouched

W33a, WP33a

185

Cylinder Numbers (Blocks of six)

(a) Ordinary

	Cyl. Nos.	Perforation Type A	
		No dot	Dot
3d.	1A (black)–3B (brown)–1C (green)–1D (yellow)	50	50

		No dot	
		Rows 12/13	Rows 18/19
4½d.	1A (brown-red)–1B (yellow)–1C (magenta)– 1D (blue)–2E (black)	1·40	2·00
	1A (brown-red)–1B (yellow)–1C (magenta)– 1D (blue)–3E (black)	1·75	2·25

b) Phosphor

		No dot	Dot
3d.	1A (black)–3B (brown)–1C (green)–1D (yellow)	1·40	1·40

		No dot	
		Rows 12/13	Rows 18/19
4½d.	1A (brown-red)–1B (yellow)–1C (magenta)– 1D (blue)–2E (black)	4·20	5·00
	1A (brown-red)–1B (yellow)–1C (magenta)– 1D–(blue)–3E (black)	5·20	6·00

In the 3d. the panes were reversed, the dot being on the left and the no dot on the right.

In the 4½d. there are two sets of cylinder numbers in the left-hand margin opposite rows 12/13 and 18/19. In position 18/19 the "1D" is in grey-blue superimposed over an additional "1C" in magenta. Also in position 12/13 the black "2" is superimposed over a black "1". The cylinder numbers are engraved more boldly in position 12/13 and are boxed, the others being without boxes.

Minor Constant Flaws

Minimum prices as singles:

3d. ordinary 50p; phosphor 50p; 4½d. ordinary 75p; phosphor £1

3d. Cyls. 1A–3B–1C–1D no dot
  2/1 Retouch to Queen's left jaw (Th. D–E11), OP
  2/5 Dot between top of A and T of NATURE, OP
  2/6 White line through top of 3 of value, OP
  4/4 Green flaw at bottom right foot of I of NATIONAL, OP
  5/4 First N of NATIONAL blurred at top left, OP
  6/5 Diagonal green line crosses petals of left-hand daisy (Th. B–C3), OP
  7/1 Retouch on Queen's left cheek (Th. D11), OP
  9/1 Green dot near centre of N of NATURE, OP
  9/2 White flaw at top of left-hand buttercup (Th. B2), OP
  10/1 Patch of white to left of Queen's right eye (Th. C10), OP
  10/4 Green dot at top right of 2, OP
  12/6 White patch just above NA of NATIONAL, OP
  13/6 Green spot above EK of WEEK, OP
  14/1 White spot above 3 of value (Th. E8), OP
  16/6 Dark spot to right of Queen's mouth (Th. E11–12), OP
  18/3 Retouch above second A of NATIONAL, later retouched, appearing as a whitish blob (Th. F5), OP
  18/5 White flaw under top left buttercup, at right (Th. C2), OP
  19/3 Brown flaw to bottom right of T of NATURE, later retouched, OP
  19/5 Large green blob above second A of NATIONAL, later touched out, OP
  20/4 White dot between top of 3 of value and leaf (Th. E7–8), OP

3d. Cyls. 1A–3B–1C–1D dot
  2/3 White dot just left of top of 3 of value, OP
  6/6 Retouch under jaw extending to bottom of ear (Th. E10–11), OP
  8/1 Brown dot under right leg of last A of NATIONAL, OP
  8/3 Retouch by L of NATIONAL (Th. G6), OP
  9/6 Brown dot under right leg of second N of NATIONAL, OP
  14/1 Retouch above first E of WEEK, OP
  14/4 Retouch left of 3 of value (Th. F7–8), OP
  15/4 White flaw at bottom of oblique stroke in first N of NATIONAL, OP
  15/5 Greyish smear over dot of value, OP
  16/5 Retouch from mouth to ear (Th. D11), OP
  18/4 Green dot above upper lip (Th. D10), OP
  19/6 Small white retouch between 63 of 1963 and dark hairline between 3 of value and leaf (Th. F8), OP

4½d. Cyls. 1A–1B–1C–1D–2E no dot and 1A–1B–1C–1D–3E no dot
  3/3 Dark spot under fawn (Th. G10), OP
  7/1 Yellow patch above fawn's right ear (Th. E11), OP
  14/1 Brown spot in second upper leaf from butterfly (Th. B3), OP
  19/3 Retouch in background behind woodpecker (Th. E9), OP

Sheet Details

Sheet size: 120 (6 × 20). 3d. double pane reel-fed; 4½d. single pane reel-fed

Sheet markings:
  Cylinder numbers: Both values left margin opposite rows 18/19; in addition the 4½d. has boxed cylinder numbers opposite rows 12/13
  Guide holes:
    3d. Opposite rows 14/15 (boxed), at left (dot) or right (no dot)
    4½d. Opposite rows 14/15 (boxed), at both sides
  Marginal arrows (photo-etched): "W" shaped at top, bottom and sides
  Marginal rule: At bottom of sheet
  Colour register marks:
    3d. Opposite rows 2/3 and 17/19, at left (dot) or right (no dot)
    4½d. Opposite rows 3/4 and 17/18, at left (no dot) or right (dot)
  Autotron marks (stippled):
    3d. Between panes vertically, opposite rows 6/9 (seen either in right or left margin)
    4½d. Below vertical rows 1/3 and 4/6 but omitted from rows 1/3 in the first printing
  Colour designations (usually trimmed off):
    3d. "G BROWN" (rows 4/5), "G GREEN" (rows 6/7), "G YELLOW" (rows 8/9), "G ORANGE" (row 13), left margin dot pane reading downwards
    4½d. "G1 BROWN G2 YELLOW G3 RED G4 BLUE G5 BLACK" in left margin reading downwards opposite rows 5/9
  Traffic lights (boxed):
    3d. Yellow, black, green, brown opposite R. 20/6, no dot pane
    4½d. Black, blue, magenta, yellow, brown-red opposite rows 19/20 at right

Quantities Sold

	Ordinary	Phosphor
3d.	148,560,000	8,640,000
4½d.	12,480,000	1,140,000

W31. Rescue at Sea

W32. 19th-century Lifeboat

W33. Lifeboatmen
(Des. D. Gentleman)

1963 (MAY 31). NINTH INTERNATIONAL LIFEBOAT CONFERENCE

The International Lifeboat Conferences are held every four years. In 1963 the Conference was held at Edinburgh from 3rd to 5th June

Cat No.	S.G. No.	Type		Description	Unused	Used
A. Ordinary						
W34	639	**W31**		2½d. Blue, black and red	10	5
a. Missing neckline (No dot, col. 1)			1·00	*b.* Shaded diadem (Dot, R. 20/6)	1·00	
W35	640	**W32**		4d. Red, yellow, brown, black and blue	20	15
a. Spot on boom (R. 6/6) ..		..	1·50			
b. Spot under I (R. 13/3) ..		..	1·25			
W36	641	**W33**		1s.6d. Sepia, yellow and grey-blue	75	85
W34/6				First Day Cover	†	1·90

Cat. No.	S.G. No.	Type	Description	Unused	Used

B. Phosphor (applied typo.)

WP34	639p	**W31**	2½d. One band	25	10
a. Missing neckline (No dot, col. 1)	1·25		*b.* Shaded diadem (Dot, R. 20/6)..	1·50	
WP35	640p	**W32**	4d. Three bands	35	30
a. Spot on boom (R. 6/6) ..	..	2·50	*b.* Spot under I (R. 13/3) ..	.. 2·00	
WP36	641p	**W33**	1s.6d. Three bands	3·25	2·75
WP34/6			First Day Cover	†	3·75

In the 1s.6d. the grey-blue is lighter on the phosphor stamps, presumably in order to show the phosphor more clearly.

All values are known pre-released on 30th May.

Listed Varieties

W34*a*, WP34*a*

Occurs on all stamps in
first vertical row in
varying degrees

W34*b*, WP34*b*

Occurred during the
course of printing

W35*a*, WP35*a*

W35*b*, WP35*b*

Cylinder Numbers (Blocks of six)

(a) Ordinary

	Cyl. Nos.	Perforation Type A			
		No dot		Dot	
		Row 12	Row 19	Row 12	Row 19
2½d.	3A (red)–3B (black)–1C (blue)..	75	1·00	75	1·00
4d.	1A (blue–1B (black)–1C (red)–1D (brown)–1E (yellow)	1·50	1·75	†	†
			Row 18		
1s.6d.	3A (blue)–1B (sepia)–1C (yellow)	5·25	6·00		†

(b) Phosphor

			Row 19		
2½d.	3A (red)–3B (black)–1C (blue)..	2·00	2·50	2·00	2·50
4d.	1A (blue–1B (black)–1C (red)–1D (brown)–1E (yellow)	3·50	4·00	†	†
			Row 18		
1s.6d.	3A (blue)–1B (sepia)–1C (yellow)	22·00	24·00	†	†

In the 2½d. the cylinder numbers in row 12 are shown as A (red)–B (black)–1C (blue) in left margin of left pane and the same in the right margin of right pane but without dot after C.

In the 1s.6d. the 1C is shown twice opposite row 18.

Minor Constant Flaws

Minimum prices as singles:

	Ordinary	Phosphor
2½d.	50	60
4d.	75	90
1s.6d.	1·00	4·50

2½d. Cyls. 3A–3B–1C no dot
 7/5 Scratch down Queen's face from hair to chin (Th. C–D11), OP
 8/5 Scratch continues from hair to shoulder (Th. C–D11), OP
 9/1 White scratch on dress above ENC (Th. F12), OP
 11/1 Scratch from hair to ear (Th. C–D12), OP
 14/3 Black dot below lower lip (Th. D10), OP

2½d. Cyls. 3A–3B–1C dot
 3/4 Retouch left of Queen's ear (Th. C11), OP
 9/6 Retouch on Queen's forehead (Th. C10), OP
 19/6 Pale grey patch over back of shoulder, normal in State I (Th. F12–13), OP

4d. Cyls. 1A–1B–1C–1D–1E no dot
 1/6 Retouch on Queen's nose (Th. B–C10), OP
 3/5 Vertical line of retouching on Queen's face down to shoulder (Th. C–E11), OP
 4/2 Vertical black line through shoulder to just above EN (Th. E–F12), OP
 13/1 Pale blue streak across top frame line at apex of sail (Th. A5), OP
 13/2 Yellow scratch across main sail from mast to rigging (Th. D6), OP
 18/2 Black dot over Queen's left eye (Th. C10), OP
 20/2 Blue dot on Queen's neck (Th. E11), OP
 20/3 Vertical red line down first N of CONFERENCE, OP

1s.6d. Cyls. 3A–1B–1C no dot
 6/5 Length of retouching on Queen's collar (Th. E11–12), OP
 15/6 Retouch over Queen's right eye (Th. B10), OP

Sheet Details

Sheet size: 120 (6 × 20). 2½d. double pane reel-fed; others single pane reel-fed

Sheet markings:

Cylinder numbers:
 2½d. Boxed opposite R. 12/1 (no dot pane) or R. 12/6 (dot pane)
  Also opposite R. 19/1 on both panes without box
 4d. Boxed opposite R. 12/1 and without box in left margin opposite rows 17/20
 1s.6d. Boxed opposite rows 11/12, left margin and unboxed opposite R. 18/1

Guide holes:
 2½d. Opposite rows 14/15 (boxed), at left (no dot) or right (dot)
 4d. and 1s.6d. Opposite rows 14/15 (boxed), at both sides

Marginal arrows (photo etched): "W" shaped, at top, bottom and sides

Marginal rule: At bottom of sheet

Colour register marks:
 2½d. Opposite rows 3/4 and 18/19. at left (no dot) or right (dot)
 4d. Opposite rows 2/3 and 17/18, at both sides
 1s.6d. Opposite rows 2/4 and 18/19, at both sides

Autotron marks (stippled):
 2½d. Blue, black, red below vertical rows 4/6 on dot pane
 4d. Yellow, brown, black, red, blue below vertical rows 4/6
 1s.6d. Yellow, sepia, blue below vertical rows 4/6

Colour designations (usually trimmed off):
 2½d. "G RED G BLACK G BLUE" opposite rows 6, 7 and 9 respectively reading upwards at left (no dot) or right (dot)
 4d. "G YELLOW G BROWN G BLACK G RED G BLUE" in right margin reading upwards opposite rows 14/10
 1s.6d. "G BLUE G BROWN G YELLOW" in left margin reading downwards opposite rows 6/9

Traffic lights (boxed):
 2½d. Blue, black, red opposite R. 20/6, dot pane
 4d. Yellow, brown, black, red, blue opposite R. 20/6
 1s.6d. Yellow, sepia, blue opposite R. 20/6

Quantities Sold

	Ordinary	Phosphor
2½d.	81,405,000	4,239,000
4d.	7,475,040	840,000
1s.6d.	7,484,780	886,000

W34. Red Cross

W35. Red Cross

W36. Red Cross
(Des. H. Bartram)

1963 (AUGUST 15). RED CROSS CENTENARY CONGRESS

The Congress which opened in Geneva on 2nd September marked the Centenary of the establishment of the Red Cross organisation

Cat. No.	S.G. No.	Type	Description	Unused	Used
A. Ordinary					
W37	642	**W34**	3d. Red and deep lilac	8	5
a. Red omitted		£350			
b. Repaired cross (Cyls. 2A–2B, R. 5/6)		1·50			
W38	643	**W35**	1s.3d. Red, blue and grey	50	50
W39	644	**W36**	1s.6d. Red, blue and bistre	65	65
a. Retouch in C of Cross (R. 14/4)		2·00			
b. Retouch over 1 of 1/6 (R. 16/4)		2·00			
W37/9			First Day Cover	†	1·40
B. Phosphor (applied typo.)					
WP37	642p	**W34**	3d. Three bands	25	8
a. Red omitted					
WP38	643p	**W35**	1s.3d. Three bands	1·60	1·50
WP39	644p	**W36**	1s.6d. Three bands	1·90	1·75
a. Retouch in C of Cross (R. 14/4)		4·00			
b. Retouch over 1 of 1/6 (R. 16/4)		4·00			
WP37/9			First Day Cover	†	3·75

Listed Varieties

W37*b*

W39*a*, WP39*a*

W39*b*, WP39*b*

Cylinder Numbers (Blocks of four)

(a) Ordinary

Cyl. Nos.							Perforation Types		
							A No dot	A Dot	E Dot
3d. 2A (lilac)–2B (red)	..	..	..	..	..	..	50	50	1·75
3A (lilac)–2B (red)	..	..	..	..	..	..	50	50	†
3A (lilac)–3B (red)	..	..	..	..	..	..	50	50	†
1s.3d. 1A (grey)–3B (blue)–1C (red)	..	..	..	..	..	..	3·00	†	†
1s.6d. 1A (blue)–1B (red)–1C (bistre)	..	..	..	..	..	..	3·50	†	†

(b) Phosphor

3d. 3A (lilac)–2B (red)	..	..	..	..	..	..	1·50	1·50	†
3A (lilac)–3B (red)	..	..	..	..	..	..	1·50	1·50	†
1s.3d. 1A (grey)–3B (blue)–1C (red)	..	..	..	..	..	..	10·00	†	†
1s.6d. 1A (blue)–1B (red)–1C (bistre)	..	..	..	..	..	..	12·00	†	†

Minor Constant Flaws

Minimum prices as singles:

	Ordinary	Phosphor
3d.	50	75
1s.3d.	1·00	2·50
1s.6d.	1·25	3·00

3d. Cyl. 3A no dot in combination with red cyls. 2B or 3B no dot
2/3 Lilac coloured spot above t of Centenary. Retouched with cyl. 3B (Th. F10–11), OP

3d. Cyl. 2B no dot in combination with lilac cyls. 2A or 3A no dot
4/1 Red retouch in top left centre of cross (Th. D4), OP
7/3 Pale centre to cross (with cyl. 3A only), OP

3d. Cyl. 3A dot in combination with red cyls. 2B or 3B dot
4/3 Coloured spur on C of Congress (Th. G9), OP
15/2 Scratch above 3D. Retouched with cyl. 3B (Th. B8–C9), OP
17/5 Retouching in and around D of 3D (Th. D9), OP

3d. Cyl. 2B dot in combination with lilac cyls. 2A or 3A dot
16/1 Red retouches in left arm and top left centre of cross (Th. D3–4), OP
19/1 Red retouch in lower arm of cross (Th. E4), OP

1s.3d. Cyls. 1A–3B–1C no dot
11/4 Diagonal scratch from Queen's nose to jaw (Th. D7), OP
12/1 White spot to left of Queen's ear-ring (Th. D8), OP
12/5 Dark patch to right of Queen's left eye (Th. C7), OP
15/3 Line through words Red Cross, OP
18/4 Large retouch on Queen's neck (Th. E7), OP

1s.6d. Cyls. 1A–1B–1C no dot
15/3 Large retouch in right arm of cross (Th. C–D8), OP

Sheet Details

Sheet size: 120 (6 × 20). 3d. double pane reel-fed; others single pane reel-fed
Sheet markings:
    Cylinder numbers: Opposite R. 19/1, boxed
    Guide holes:
        3d. Opposite rows 14/15 (boxed), at left (no dot) or right (dot)
        1s.3d. and 1s.6d. Opposite rows 14/15 (boxed), at both sides
    Marginal arrows (photo-etched): "W" shaped, at top, bottom and sides
    Marginal rule: At bottom of sheet
    Colour register marks:
        3d. Opposite rows 2/3 and 18/19, at left (no dot) or right (dot)
        1s.3d. and 1s.6d. Opposite rows 17/19, at both sides
    Autotron marks (stippled):
        3d. Lilac, red below vertical rows 2/3 on no dot panes
        1s.3d. Grey, blue, red below vertical rows 1/3
        1s.6d. Blue, red, bistre below vertical rows 1/3 and 4/6
    Colour designations (usually trimmed off):
        3d. "G RED" in right margin opposite rows 5/6 (Cyls. 3A–3B dot)
        1s.3d. "G1 GREY G2 BLUE G3 YELLOW" in right margin reading downwards opposite rows 9/4
        1s.6d. None
    Traffic lights (boxed):
        3d. Lilac, red opposite R. 19/6
        1s.3d. Grey, blue, red opposite R. 19/6
        1s.6d. Blue, red, bistre opposite R. 19/6

Quantities Sold

	Ordinary	Phosphor
3d.	157,277,800	10,349,280
1s.3d.	7,278,120	929,040
1s.6d.	6,995,160	1,038,840

Withdrawn 1.9.64

CANCELLED

W37. "Commonwealth Cable"   B
(Des. P. Gauld)

1963 (DECEMBER 3). OPENING OF "COMPAC"

The Trans-Pacific Cable (COMPAC) was the first telephone cable to be laid across the Pacific Ocean. It links Canada with Australia and New Zealand by way of Hawaii and Fiji

Cat. No.	S.G. No.	Type	Description	Unused	Used

A. Ordinary

W40	645	**W37**	1s.6d. Blue and black	85	75
a. Black omitted £300					
s. "Cancelled", Type B, in red .. 1·50					
W40			First Day Cover	†	90

B. Phosphor (applied typo.)

WP40	645p	**W37**	1s.6d. Three bands	2·00	2·00
a. Left band omitted .. .. 4·00					
WP40			First Day Cover	†	2·50

The stamp handstamped "CANCELLED" was applied to Philatelic Bulletin No. 3 (November 1963) so that it only exists unused stuck down.

Cylinder Numbers (Blocks of four)

	Cyl. Nos.		Perforation Type F. No dot	
			Ordinary	Phosphor
1s.6d. 1A (blue)–1B (black)			4·00	12·00

Minor Constant Flaws

Minimum prices as singles: ordinary £1·25; phosphor £3

1s.6d. Cyls. 1A–1B no dot
    17/6 Bulge at top of figure 1 of value (Th. F10), OP
    19/1 Extra white dot on Queen's right eye (Th. C10), OP

Sheet Details

Sheet size: 120 (6 × 20). Single pane reel-fed
Sheet markings:
    Cylinder numbers: Opposite R. 19/1, boxed
    Guide holes: at top above R. 1/2 and at bottom below R. 20/4, cutting marginal arrow
    Marginal arrows (photo-etched): "W" shaped, at top, bottom and sides
    Marginal rule: At bottom of sheet
    Colour register marks: Opposite rows 1/2 and 17/8, at both sides
    Autotron marks (stippled): Below vertical rows 2/3
    Colour designations: "G1 BLUE" (row 9), "G2 BLACK" (row 12), left margin
    Traffic lights: Black, blue (boxed), opposite R. 19/6

Quantities Sold   Ordinary 8,015,880; phosphor 824,280

Withdrawn   1.9.64

W38. Puck and Bottom
(*A Midsummer Night's Dream*)

W39. Feste
(*Twelfth Night*)

W40. Balcony Scene
(*Romeo and Juliet*)

W41. "Eve of Agincourt"
(*Henry V*)

(All the above des. D. Gentleman)

W42. Hamlet contemplating Yorick's Skull
(*Hamlet*)

(Des. C. and R. Ironside. Recess printed, Bradbury, Wilkinson)

CANCELLED
C

1964 (APRIL 23). SHAKESPEARE FESTIVAL

Issued on the occasion of the 400th Anniversary of the Birth of William Shakespeare. An additional feature of this issue was the introduction of Presentation Packs by the G.P.O. The packs include one set of stamps and details of the designs, the designer and the stamp printer. They were issued for this and almost all later commemorative issues.

The 2s.6d. is perf. 11 × 12, comb.

Cat. No.	S.G. No.	Type		Description	Unused	Used
A. Ordinary						
W41	646	**W38**		3d.		
a. Black dots across Puck's head (Dot, R. 7/6)			1·50	(1) Yellow-bistre, black and deep violet-blue	5	5
				(2) Bistre-brown, black and deep violet-blue	10	5
W42	647	**W39**		6d.		
a. Broken H (No dot, R. 12/3) ..			2·00	(1) Yellow, orange, black and yellow-olive	15	15
b. Missing floorboards (No dot, R. 20/1 and 20/2)			1·50	(2) Yellow, orange, black and olive-green	20	15
W43	648	**W40**		1s.3d.		
a. Large pearl (Dot, R. 13/2) ..			2·00	(1) Cerise, blue-green, black and sepia	10·00	
				(2) Cerise, turquoise, black and sepia	25	25

Cat. No.	S.G. No.	Type	Description	Unused	Used
W44	649	**W41**	1s.6d.		
a. Watermark inverted ..	..		(1) Violet, turquoise, black and blue	40	40
			(2) Pale violet, turquoise, black and blue	80	80
W45	650	**W42**	2s.6d.		
a. Watermark inverted .	.. 55·00		(1) Deep slate-purple	60	60
s. "Cancelled", Type C ..	..		(2) Blackish brown	1·00	1·00
W41/5			First Day Cover	†	3·00
W41/5			Presentation Pack	2·25	

B. Phosphor (Three bands) (3d. applied photo.; others typo.)

WP41	646p	**W38**	3d.		
a. Black dots across Puck's head (Dot, R. 7/6) .. .. .. 2·00			(1) Yellow-bistre, black and deep violet-blue	10	5
			(2) Bistre-brown, black and deep violet-blue	15	5
WP42	647p	**W39**	6d. Yellow, orange, black and yellow-olive	25	25
a. Broken H (no dot, R. 12/3) .. 6·00					
b. Missing floorboards (No dot, R. 20/1 and 20/2) .. .. 1·75					
WP43	648p	**W40**	1s.3d. Cerise, turquoise, black and sepia	1·00	1·00
a. Watermark inverted .. .. 55·00					
b. Large pearl (Dot. R. 13/2) .. 2·75					
WP44	649p	**W41**	1s.6d. Violet, turquoise, black and blue	1·00	1·00
WP41/4			First Day Cover	†	3·00

Shades. The listed shades of the 6d. to 2s.6d. result from different printings. The 3d. and 6d. shades are quite distinct, the blue-green shade of the 1s.3d. comes from the scarce first printing from cylinder 1B, and although the pale violet in the 1s.6d. may only be due to under-inking, it came from part of the second printing. There were three printings of the 2s.6d. which produced a number of shades, but they fall into the two groups listed. In addition a jet-black shade is said to exist and to be rare. We have never seen one which corresponds to this description and if some do exist it has been suggested that they may have come from a proof sheet issued in error.

The 3d. is known with yellow-bistre missing on the top two-thirds of the figures of Puck and Bottom. This occurred on the top row only of a sheet.

Listed Varieties

W41*a*, WP41*a*

SHAKESPE

W42*a*, WP42*a*
Also grey patch on Shakespeare's right cheek. Both later retouched

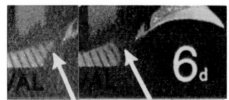

Normal   W42*b*, WP42*b*
Other less prominent states of missing floorboards also occur on R. 19/1, 19/2, 19/6 and 20/6

W43*a*, WP43*b*

Cylinder Numbers (Blocks of four)

(a) Ordinary

	Cyl. Nos.	Perforation Type A	
		No dot	Dot
3d.	1A (violet-blue)–1B (black)–1C (bistre)	40	40
6d.	1A (olive-green)–1B (orange)–1C (yellow)–1D (black) ..	2·00*	†

		Perforation Type A(T)	
		No dot	Dot
1s.3d.	3A (sepia)–1B (turquoise)–1C (cerise)–1D (black)	15·00	15·00
	3A (sepia)–2B (blue-green)–1C (cerise)–1D (black)	1·25	1·25
1s.6d.	1A (blue)–1B (violet)–1C (black)–1D (turquoise)	2·00	2·00

(b) Phosphor

		Perforation Type A	
		No dot	Dot
3d.	1A (violet-blue)–1B (black)–1C (bistre)	60	60
6d.	1A (olive-green)–1B (orange)-1C (yellow)–1D (black) ..	2·75*	†

		Perforation Type A(T)	
		No dot	Dot
1s.3d.	3A (sepia)–2B (blue-green)–1C (cerise)–1D (black) ..	6·00	6·00
1s.6d.	1A (blue)–1B (violet)–1C (black)–1D (turquoise)	6·00	6·00

The 3d. no dot cylinders exist with a false dot after the 1B but this was later removed. In the dot cylinders of the 1s.6d. the dots appear to the left of 1C and 1D.

Plate Numbers (Blocks of four)

	Perforation Type A
2s.6d. Plate 1	3·00
Plate 1A	3·00

Minor Constant Flaws

Minimum prices as singles:

	Ordinary	Phosphor		Ordinary	Phosphor
3d.	50	60	1s.3d.	50	1·50
6d.	60	75	1s.6d.	75	1·50

3d. Cyls. 1A–1B–1C no dot
  9/5 White scratch on boards above AL (Th. 9/5), OP
  19/1 White line in floorboard division above S of FESTIVAL (Th. G8), OP
  20/1 White patch on Queen's collar, later retouched (Th. E12), OP

3d. Cyls. 1A–1B–1C dot
  2/5 White patch on floorboards above F (Th. G7), OP
  7/5 Retouches on Queen's left cheek, later partly retouched (Th. D11), OP
  11/5 Retouch below Queen's left eye (Th. C11), OP
  16/2 White spur to bottom arc of 3, OP
  20/1 Dark flaw in stage above VA, later retouched (Th. G9), OP

1s.3d. Cyls. 3A–2B–1C–1D no dot
  18/2 Outline of Shakespeare's nose cut short, later corrected (Th. C3), OP

1s.6d. Cyls. 1A–1B–1C–1D no dot
  1/6 White flaw on stage above EAR (Th. F4–G5), OP
  18/1 Black flaw at base of tent over last A of SHAKESPEARE, (Th. F5), OP
  20/2 Vertical scratches on Queen's face (Th. B–D11), OP

1s.6d. Cyls. 1A–1B–1C–1D dot
  13/3 Flaw on stage above EA (Th. G4), OP

Sheet Details

Sheet sizes:
  3d. 120 (6 × 20). Double pane reel-fed
  6d. 120 (6 × 20). Single pane reel-fed
  1s.3d., 1s.6d. 120 (6 × 20). Double panes sheet-fed
  2s.6d. 40 (4 × 10). Double pane sheet-fed

The 1s.3d. and 1s.6d. were printed by the Linotype and Machinery No. 4 machine, a rotary sheet-fed double pane machine.

Sheet markings:
  Cylinder numbers: Opposite R. 19/1, boxed
  Plate numbers (2s.6d.): Bottom margin below vertical rows 5/6
  Guide holes:
  3d. Opposite rows 14/15 (boxed), at left (no dot) or right (dot)
  6d. Opposite row 13 (boxed), at both sides
  1s.3d. Opposite rows 15/16 (boxes only, no holes), at left (no dot) or right (dot)
  1s.6d. Opposite rows 14/15 (boxes only, no holes), at left (no dot) or right (dot)
  2s.6d. Opposite row 6 (unboxed), at left (Plate 1) or right (Plate 1A)
  False boxes appear in both margins opposite rows 14/15 in the 6d. value and these are deleted by a diagonal black line.

Marginal arrows (photo-etched): "W" shaped, at top, bottom and sides (none on 2s.6d.)
Marginal rule: At bottom of sheet (except 2s.6d.)
Colour register marks:
   3d. Opposite rows 2 and 17/18, at left (no dot) or right (dot)
   6d. Opposite rows 1/3 and 17/18, at both sides (usually trimmed off)
   Others, none
Autotron marks:
   6d. Below vertical rows 1/3: black (stippled), olive (solid), orange (stippled), yellow (solid)
   Others, none
Colour designations (usually trimmed):
   3d. "G BLUE" (rows 13/12), "G BLACK" (rows 9/8), "G YELLOW" (rows 5/4) reading upwards,
   right margin dot pane
   Others, none
Traffic lights (boxed): All R. 19/6
   3d. Violet-blue, black, bistre
   6d. Black, yellow, orange, olive
                        1s.3d. Black, cerise, turquoise, sepia
                        1s.6d. Turquoise, black, violet, blue

Quantities Sold

	Ordinary	Phosphor		Ordinary	Phosphor
3d.	133,670,000	10,427,880	1s.6d.	6,910,120	657,120
6d.	19,238,200	1,318,560	2s.6d.	3,664,920	—
1s.3d.	7,067,200	727,800	Pack	93,434	—

W43. Flats near Richmond Park ("Urban Development")

W44. Shipbuilding Yards, Belfast ("Industrial Activity")

W45. Beddgelert Forest Park, Snowdonia ("Forestry")

W46. Nuclear Reactor, Dounreay ("Technological Development")

(All des. D. Bailey)

1964 (JULY 1). 20TH INTERNATIONAL GEOGRAPHICAL CONGRESS

The first International Geographical Congress was held in 1871; since then one has normally been held at four-yearly intervals. London was chosen in 1964 and the Congress lasted from 20th to 28th July

Cat. No.	S.G. No.	Type		Description	Unused	Used

A. Ordinary

W46	651	**W43**		2½d. Black, olive-yellow, olive-grey and turquoise-blue	8	5

   a. Short line under 2½d. (various)..   50
   b. Line repaired (No dot, R. 18/5)   1·75
   c. Retouched lawn (No dot, R. 11/1 and 11/6)   75

W47	652	**W44**		4d. Orange-brown, red-brown, rose, black and violet	12	10

   a. Violet omitted £130
   b. Red-brown omitted   .. £200
   c. Violet and red-brown omitted.. 60·00
   d. Watermark inverted   ..
   e. Scarred neck (R. 20/3) ..   .. 1·25

W48	653	**W45**		8d. Yellow-brown, emerald, green and black	30	25

   a. Green (lawn) omitted ..
   b. Watermark inverted   .. 30·00

W49	654	**W46**		1s.6d. Yellow-brown, pale pink, black and brown	60	50

   a. Watermark inverted   .. 12·00
   b. Neck flaw (R. 8/4)   .. 1·00

W46/9   First Day Cover   † 1·60
W46/9   Presentation Pack   4·50

Cat. No	S.G. No.	Type	Description	Unused	Used
B. Phosphor (2½d. applied photo.; others typo.)					
WP46	651p	**W43**	2½d. One band	15	10
a. Short line under 2½d. (various)		1·10			
b. Line repaired (No dot, R. 18/5)		1·90			
c. Retouched lawn (No dot, R. 11/1 and 11/6)		1·00			
WP47	652p	**W44**	4d. Three bands	30	20
a. Scarred neck (R. 20/3)		2·25			
WP48	653p	**W45**	8d. Three bands	1·60	1·60
WP49	654p	**W46**	1s.6d. Three bands	1·50	1·50
a. Neck flaw (R. 8/4)		2·00			
WP46/9			First Day Cover	†	4·00

Listed Varieties

2¼d
W46*a*, WP46*a*

The short lower line occurs on no dot R. 5/5, 9/5 (most marked) and 10/2 and on dot R. 3/4, 4/5 and 7/5 (short at left).
In No. W46*b* and WP46*b* the line has been repaired but there remains a short gap unfilled.

W46*c*, WP46*c*

The illustration shows the retouch on R. 11/1. On 11/6 it starts further over the line and is less extensive.

W47*e*, WP47*a*

W49*b*, WP49*a*
Later retouched

Cylinder Numbers (Blocks of four)

(a) Ordinary

	Cyl. Nos.	A(T) No dot	A(T) Dot	F No dot
		Perforation Types		
2½d.	3D (black)–1C (yellow)–1B (grey)–1A (blue)	50	50	†
4d.	1E (orange-brown)–1D (red-brown)–1C (rose)–1B (black)–1A (violet)	†	†	75
8d.	1D (brown)–1C (green)–1B (emerald)–1A (black)	5·00	†	2·00
1s.6d.	1D (yellow-brown)–1C (pink)–1B (black)–1A (brown)	3·50	†	†

(b) Phosphor

		A(T) No dot	A(T) Dot	F No dot
2½d.	3D (black)–1C (yellow)–1B (grey)–1A (blue)	1·25	1·25	†
4d.	1E (orange-brown)–1D (red-brown)–1C (rose)–1B (black)–1A (violet)	†	†	2·00
8d.	1D (brown)–1C (green)–1B (emerald)–1A (black)	†	†	8·00
1s.6d.	1D (yellow-brown)–1C (pink)–1B (black)–1A (brown)	†	†	8·00

Minor Constant Flaws

Minimum prices as singles:

	Ordinary	Phosphor		Ordinary	Phosphor
2½d.	50	60	8d.	75	2·50
4d.	60	75	1s.6d.	75	2·25

2½d. Cyls. 3D–1C–1B–1A no dot
  2/4 Black line from Queen's left eye to base of back of diadem, later retouched and showing as faint white line (Th. C12–13), O
  4/1 Blue spot on Queen's collar, later retouched (Th. E12), OP
  12/3 Green spot at foot of hills above second N of INTERNATIONAL (Th. F5), OP
  15/2 Blue dot left of oval and above left end of upper value bar, later retouched (Th. E10), OP
  19/3 Green blob above 2 of 20th (Th. E1), OP
  20/3 White dot in portrait oval above right corner of central cross of crown (Th. A12), OP
  20/5 White flaw in hair below central cross of crown (Th. B11), OP

2½d. Cyls. 3D–1C–1B–1A dot
    7/5 Small retouch to right of Queen's nostril (Th. C11), OP
    9/3 Retouch by Queen's left eye, later retouched on phosphor only (Th. B–C12), OP
    12/3 White flaw in h of 20th, OP
    12/5 Blue dot by grey panel opposite value (Th. G10), OP
    13/5 Blue scratch on Queen's left cheek (Th. C11), OP
    15/2 Two diagonal white lines above central cross of crown (Th. A12), OP
    15/4 Blue patch in hills above black arrow (Th. D8) and slight retouch to right of L of GEOGRAPHICAL,
         OP
    15/5 White flaw in hair above Queen's left eye (Th. B12), OP
    17/4 Retouch on Queen's neck above collar (Th. E12), OP

4d. Cyls. 1E–1D–1C–1B–1A no dot
    1/1 Horizontal black line joining centre of 2 to left frame line, OP
    1/2 Black spur on frame line below last S in CONGRESS, OP
    1/5 White dot in panel to right of rear cross of crown (Th. B13), OP
    1/6 Small flaw under right arm of N of CONGRESS (Th. H2), OP
    3/6 White spike projecting from back on neck (Th. D12), OP
    6/1 Several small black dots on collar (Th. E11–12), OP
    7/1 Horizontal line between Queen's lips and ear (Th. C11–12), OP
    7/2 Similar retouch but lower down (Th. D11–12), OP
    8/1 Violet dot to right of d in value (Th. G12), OP
    14/2 Horizontal grey line through NATION, OP
    16/5 Broken R in GEOGRAPHICAL, OP
    18/1 Break in vertical lines above AT of INTERNATIONAL and small black dot to left of break (Th. E3),
         OP
    20/2 Black dot above Queen's nostril (Th. D11), and break in vertical frame line to left of value, OP
    20/5 Corner break in frame line left of value (Th. H9), OP
         Numerous other minor frame breaks are known

8d. Cyls. 1D–1C–1B–1A no dot
    1/1 Extensive retouching to back of Queen's collar (Th. E12–13), OP
    4/2 Dark patch in front of Queen's neck (Th. D–E11), OP
    4/6 Nick in final A of GEOGRAPHICAL, OP
    6/6 Retouch at back of Queen's collar (Th. E13), OP
    7/6 Shading on Queen's forehead, later retouched appearing as white patch (Th. B11–12), OP
    16/4–6 Green line runs through emerald field below brown area, OP
    17/5 Horizontal white line across Queen's face (Th. C11–12), OP
    18/5 Two horizontal white lines across face and chin (Th. C–D–11–12), OP

1s.6d. Cyls. 1D–1C–1B–1A no dot
    1/1 Dark flaw in front of Queen's collar (Th. E11), OP
    2/2 White scratch across necklace (Th. D12), OP
    13/3 White dot in panel below rear cross in crown (Th. B13), OP
    20/6 Dark spot below Queen's nose (Th. C12), OP

Sheet Details

Sheet size: 120 (6 × 20). 2½d. double pane reel-fed; others single pane sheet-fed

Sheet markings:
    Cylinder numbers: Opposite rows 19/20 at left, boxed
    Guide holes:
        2½d. Opposite rows 14/15 (boxed), at left (no dot) or right (dot)
        Others: Usually trimmed off
    Marginal arrows (photo-etched): "W" shaped, at top, bottom and sides
    Marginal rule: At bottom of sheet
    Colour register marks:
        2½d. Opposite rows 2/3 and 18/19, at left (no dot) or right (dot)
        Others: Above and below vertical rows 1 and 5/6
    Autotron marks (stippled):
        2½d. Black, blue, yellow, grey opposite rows 6/8, at right (no dot) or left (dot)
        Others: Trimmed off
    Colour designations (usually trimmed):
        2½d. "G1 GREY G2 DARK GREEN G3 YELLOW G4 BLACK" reading upwards, right margin dot pane
        Others: Trimmed off
    Traffic lights (boxed): All opposite rows 19/20 at right
        2½d. Black, yellow, blue, grey
        4d. Orange-brown, red-brown, rose, black, violet
        8d. Brown, green, black, emerald
        1s.6d. Order not known

Quantities Sold

	Ordinary	Phosphor		Ordinary	Phosphor
2½d.	109,768,120	3,377,520	1s.6d.	10,154,040	519,000
4d.	15,241,680	577,800	Pack	20,105	—
8d.	8,226,800	465,720			

W47. Spring Gentian

W48. Dog-Rose

W49. Honeysuckle

W50. Fringed Water Lily

(All des. M. and Sylvia Goaman)

1964 (AUGUST 5). TENTH INTERNATIONAL BOTANICAL CONGRESS

Botanical Congresses are held every five years each alternate one taking place in Europe. The King of Sweden was Hon. President of the 1964 Congress, which took place in Edinburgh

Cat. No.	S.G. No.	Type		Description	Unused	Used
A. Ordinary						
W50	655	**W47**		3d. Violet, blue and sage-green	8	5
a. Blue omitted	..	..				
b. Broken petal (Cyls. 3A–1B–1C						
dot, R. 1/2)	..	.. ..	3·00	s. "Cancelled", Type B	75	
W51	656	**W48**		6d. Apple-green, rose, scarlet	15	15
a. Inverted watermark	..	..	75	and green		
b. Rose hip flaw (No dot, R. 2/2)				s. "Cancelled", Type B	75	
W52	657	**W49**		9d. Lemon, green, lake and	30	30
a. Green (leaves) omitted..	..			rose-red		
b. Watermark inverted	..	..				
c. Line through INTER (R. 1/1)		2·50		s. "Cancelled", Type B	75	
W53	658	**W50**		1s.3d. Yellow, emerald, reddish	50	50
a. Watermark inverted	..	..	65·00	violet and grey-green		
b. Fruit flaw (R. 14/2)	..	..	2·25	s. "Cancelled", Type B	75	
W50/3				First Day Cover	†	1·50
W50/3				Presentation Pack	4·50	
B. Phosphor (applied typo.)						
WP50	655p	**W47**		3d. Three bands	12	10
a. Right band omitted	..	..				
b. Broken petal (Cyls. 3A–1B–1C						
dot, R. 1/2)	..	.. ..	3·75			
WP51	656p	**W48**		6d. Three bands	35	35
a. Rose hip flaw (No dot, R. 2/2)..		1·25				
b. Four bands	..	.. ..				
WP52	657p	**W49**		9d. Three bands	1·40	1·40
a. Line through INTER (R. 1/1)..		3·75				
WP53	658p	**W50**		1s.3d. Three bands	1·40	1·40
a. Fruit flaw (R. 14/2)	..	..	3·50			
WP50/3				First Day Cover	†	3·75

Nos. W50s/53s have the "CANCELLED" handstamp as used on No. W40 applied in black spread over two values. It was used on sample first day covers distributed by the Post Office with the notice announcing the service.

All values were accidentally released before the official date of issue at several post offices and by the Philatelic Bureau. The earliest known date is 27th July.

The 1s.3d. exists with the yellow partly omitted, due to a paper fold.

Listed Varieties

Normal　　　　W50b, WP50b
Petal is broken where the violet overlaps
the blue

W51b, WP51a
White flaw in rose hip

W52c, WP52a

W53b, WP53a
Grey-green overlaps centre of fruit

Cylinder Numbers (Blocks of four)

(a) Ordinary

	Cyl. Nos.		A(T) No dot	A(T) Dot	F No dot
3d.	2A (violet)–1B (blue)–1C (sage-green)		50	50	†
	3A (violet)–1B (blue)–1C (sage-green)		50	50	†
6d.	1D (apple-green)–1C (rose)–1B (scarlet)–1A (green)		90	90	†
9d.	2D (lemon)–2C (green)–2B (lake)–2A (rose-red) ..		†	†	1·60
1s.3d.	1D (yellow)–1C (emerald)–1B (reddish violet)– 1A (grey-green)		†	†	1·50

(b) Phosphor

3d.	3A (violet)–1B (blue)–1C (sage–green)		75	75	†
6d.	1D (apple-green)–1C (rose)–1B (scarlet)–1A (green)		3·00	1·50	†
9d.	2D (lemon)–2C (green)–2B (lake)–2A (rose-red) ..		†	†	7·00
1s.3d.	1D (yellow)–1C (emerald)–1B (reddish violet)– 1A (grey-green)		†	†	8·00

Minor Constant Flaws

Minimum prices as singles:

	Ordinary	Phosphor		Ordinary	Phosphor
3d.	50	60	9d.	75	2·00
6d.	50	75	1s.3d.	1·00	2·00

3d. Cyls. 2A–1B–1C and 3A–1B–1C no dot
　1/4 White dot between 3rd and 4th fruits below portrait (Th. E12), OP
　2/4 Curved white line across right petal of left Gentian (Th. C3), OP
　6/1 Small white vertical line on same petal as above (Th. C–D3), OP

3d. Cyl. 3A no dot
　2/5 Retouch on upper lip, OP
　7/5 Blue dash on small leaf pointing left below first flower (Th. F2), OP
　10/5 White dot below first S of CONGRESS, OP
　12/5 Line of damage extends from Queen's upper lip to base of ear (Th. C10–12), OP
　12/6 Line of damage extends from Queen's right cheek across nose to ear (Th. C10–12), OP
　13/1 Clear line of white dots joins SS of CONGRESS, OP
　19/3 White flaw at edge of petal under 3 (Th. C1), OP
　20/2 Retouch from Queen's left eye to ear (Th. B11–C12), OP

3d. Cyls. 2A–1B–1C and 3A–1B–1C dot
　1/4 Small patch of white on Queen's forehead (Th. B10), OP
　5/6 White dot in pod above R of CONGRESS (Th. F12), OP
　15/5 Green dots in leaves above OT of BOTANICAL (Th. E–F7), OP
　17/1 Retouch under necklace below ear-ring (Th. D12), O but almost completely repaired on 3A phosphor
　19/1 White dot on right petal of partly opened bud (Th. B8), OP
　19/2 Retouch between Queen's left eyebrow and hair (Th. B11), OP

3d. Cyl. 2A dot
  10/6 Coloured line across Queen's neck (Th. D11), O
3d. Cyl. 3A dot
  6/4 Violet dot in Queen's forehead (Th. B10), OP
  12/5 Flaw in Queen's left eye, OP
  13/3 Thin white line from leaf to R of INTER (Th. G2), OP
  13/6 Small white dash above O of BOTANICAL and violet spot above middle of collar (Th. D12), OP
  19/6 Diagonal white line above ES of CONGRESS, and retouch from centre of cheek to ear-ring (Th. C11–12), OP
  20/1 Light patch in background above 2nd N in INTERNATIONAL, OP
6d. Cyls. 1D–1C–1B–1A no dot
  2/6 Green flaws in T of INTER, OP
  5/4 Green spot between eyebrows (Th. B10), OP
  6/4 Retouch above necklace (Th. D11) and green dot on lower petal of flower nearest to portrait (Th. C–D9), OP
  10/1 White spot in hair below flowers of crown (Th. B12), OP
  11/1 Retouch in Queen's collar (Th. D12), OP
  17/2 Small retouch in front of Queen's ear (Th. C11), OP
  18/2 Green indent in left side of seed pod (Th. F10), OP
  20/1 Green spot in lowest leaf above TE of INTER (Th. F2), OP
  20/4 Retouch on Queen's left cheek (Th. C11–12), OP
6d. Cyls. 1D–1C–1B–1A dot
  2/6 Green flaws in T of INTER and line of yellow dots on middle leaf at left (Th. D1), OP
  4/4 Three scarlet dots to right of Queen's left eye (Th. B11), OP
  20/4 Retouch on Queen's left cheek (Th. C11–12), OP
  20/5 Two green spots on seed pod (Th. F10), OP
9d. Cyls. 2D–2C–2B–2A no dot
  4/4 ON of INTERNATIONAL joined by white line, OP
  7/1 Red spot under jewel of necklace (Th. E11), OP
  13/2 White dot between two left stamens of lower bloom (Th. F3), OP
  14/2 Green dot above Queen's upper lip (Th. C11), OP
  14/3 Red dot above Queen's right eye (Th. B10–11), OP
1s.3d. Cyls. 1D–1C–1B–1A no dot
  5/1 White line through NI and above C of BOTANICAL, OP
  8/3 Grey-green flaw at base of E of CONGRESS, OP
  11/1 Retouch on Queen's jaw line and neck (Th. C11), OP
  12/6 Horizontal dark line on left-hand bud (Th. B–C1–2), OP
  13/2 Green spot on stem of largest bloom (Th. C5), OP
  15/6 Pale patch in background adjoining Queen's lips (Th. C10), OP
  18/3 Three dark horizontal dots above L of INTERNATIONAL (Th. G5–6), OP
  19/1 Dark spot in leaf below left-hand flower (Th. D–E2), OP
  20/1 Tops of IN of INTER joined, OP
  20/6 White scratch through seed extending from above C of BOTANICAL to R of CONGRESS (Th. G8–12), OP

Sheet Details

Sheet size: 120 (6 × 20)
  3d., 6d. double pane reel-fed
  9d., 1s.3d. single pane sheet-fed
Sheet markings:
  Cylinder numbers: Boxed, opposite R. 20/1 3d., 19–20/1 others
  Guide holes:
    3d., 6d. Opposite rows 14/15 (boxed), at left (no dot) or right (dot)
    9d., 1s.3d. None
  Marginal arrows (photo-etched): "W" shaped, at top, bottom and sides
  Marginal rule: At bottom of sheet
  Colour register marks:
    3d., 6d. None
    9d., 1s.3d. Above and below vertical rows 1 and 6
  Autotron marks:
    3d. Solid, violet blue, sage-green opposite rows 4/5 and 15/16 at right (no dot) or left (dot)
    6d. Stippled, green, scarlet, rose, apple-green opposite rows 4/6 at right (no dot) or left (dot) and again apple-green, rose, scarlet opposite rows 14/15 at right (no dot) or left (dot)
    9d., 1s.3d. None
  Coloured crosses (partly trimmed):
    1s.3d. Above and below vertical rows 1/2
    Others: None
  Traffic lights (boxed):
    3d. Violet, blue, sage-green, opposite R. 20/6
    6d. Apple-green, rose, scarlet, green opposite R. 19–20/6
    9d. Lemon, green, lake, rose-red opposite R. 19–20/6
    1s.3d. Yellow, emerald, reddish violet grey-green opposite R. 19–20/6

Quantities Sold

	Ordinary	Phosphor		Ordinary	Phosphor
3d.	166,491,720	6,764,880	1s.3d.	15,664,600	650,920
6d.	23,361,120	996,720	Pack	15,895	—
9d.	11,896,060	498,460			

W51.   Forth Road Bridge   **W52.**   Forth Road and
                                              Railway Bridges

(Des. A. Restall)

1964 (SEPTEMBER 4).   OPENING OF FORTH ROAD BRIDGE

At that time the largest suspension bridge in Europe and the fourth largest in the world.
Opened by Her Majesty The Queen

Cat. No.	S.G. No.	Type	Description	Unused	Used
A. Ordinary					
W54	659	**W51**	3d. Black, blue and reddish violet	8	5
a. Imperforate between stamp and top margin		70·00			
b. Dotted 3 (Cyl. 2A., R. 15/1) . .		75			
W55	660	**W52**	6d. Black, light blue and carmine-red	25	20
a. Light blue omitted		£450 £450			
b. Watermark inverted		1·00			
W54/5			First Day Cover	†	50
W54/5			Presentation Pack	12·00	
B. Phosphor (3d. applied photo., 6d. typo.)					
WP54	659p	**W51**	3d. Three bands	20	12
a. Dotted 3 (Cyl. 2A., R. 15/1) . .		1·00			
WP55	660p	**W52**	6d. Three bands	80	80
a. Watermark inverted		12·00			
WP54/5			First Day Cover	†	1·75

Listed Variety

W54*b*, WP54*a*

Cylinder Numbers (Blocks of four)

(a) Ordinary

	Cyl. Nos.	Perforation Type A	
		No dot	Dot
3d.	1C (blue)–1B (black)–2A (violet)	50	50
	1C (blue)–1B (black)–3A (violet)	4·00	4·00
	1C (blue)–1B (black)–4A (violet)	1·00	1·00
	2C (blue)–1B (black)–4A (violet)	1·00	1·00
6d.	1C (blue)–2B (black)–2A (red)*	1·50	1·50

		Perforation Type A(T)	
		No dot	Dot
6d.	1C (blue)–2B (black)–2A (red)*	2·00	2·00

(b) Phosphor

		Perforation Type A	
		No dot	Dot
3d.	1C (blue)–1B (black)–2A (violet)	1·25	1·25
	1C (blue)–1B (black)–4A (violet)	12·00	12·00

		Perforation Type A(T)	
		No dot	Dot
6d.	1C (blue)–2B (black)–2A (red)*	4·00	4·00

*In the 6d. no dot pane the cylinder numbers are expressed in error th is: "1C–2.B.–2A

Minor Constant Flaws

Minimum prices as singles:

   3d. ordinary 40p; phosphor 50p; 6d. ordinary 75p; phosphor £1·50

3d. Cyl. 1C no dot in combination with cyls. 1B–2A or 1B–4A no dot
   4/2 Blue spot to left and above B of BRIDGE, OP
   8/1 Blue spot below B of BRIDGE, OP
   13/6 Blue spot in sky S.W. of moon (Th. B1), O

3d. Cyl. 1C dot in combination with cyls. 1B–2A, 1B–3A or 1B–4A dot
   18/6 Blue dash to left of 3d. (Th. F–G11); also blue spot to left of tanker (Th. G3), latter coincident with
      a similar violet spot on cyl. 2A

3d. Cyl. 1B no dot in combination with cyls. 1C–2A, 1C–3A, 1C–4A, or 2C–4A no dot
   1/3 Detail at rear of diadem is weak (Th. B–C10), OP
   2/3 Scratch on necklace and collar (Th. E9), OP
   4/4 Lack of detail at rear of diadem (Th. B–C10), OP
   8/4 Black flaw on Queen's neck above large jewel (Th. E9), OP
   9/2 White spot on Queen's nose (Th. D8), OP
   9/4 Black scratch on Queen's forehead (Th. C8–9), OP
   14/4 Black spot below Queen's left nostril (Th. D8), OP
   16/4 Loss of detail at back of Queen's neck and collar. Almost normal with cyl. 3A (Th. E10–F10–11),
      OP
   18/1 Black spots under G of BRIDGE (Th. A10), OP

3d. Cyl. 1B dot in combination with cyls. 1C–2A, 1C–3A, 1C–4A or 2C–4A dot
   2/2 White flaw in sea appears as extra wave (Th. G8), OP
   13/2 Weak top to O of FORTH, OP
   18/4 Small white flaw in hair above Queen's left eye (Th. B9), OP

3d. Cyls. 2A, 3A and 4A no dot (multipositive flaws)
   17/4 White patch at left side of moon (Th. B2), OP. Less pronounced on cyl. 3A
   19/4 Large retouch in sky left of bridge (Th. D1), OP. Most marked on cyl. 4A
   20/1 White tower on hill above funnel (Th. F3), OP. Retouched on cyls. 3A and 4A
   20/4 Large retouch in sky left of moon (Th. A–B1), OP. Most pronounced on cyls. 3A and 4A

3d. Cyls. 1C–1B–2A no dot
   10/6 Violet retouches below 1 and 4 of 1964 (Th. B11 and B13), OP
   18/5 White arc at top left of moon (Th. A–B2), OP

3d. Cyl. 4A no dot in combination with cyls. 1C–1B or 2C–1B no dot
   12/6 Faint acute accent over d of 3d (Th. F13), OP
   14/4 Small nick in left edge of value panel (Th. D11), OP
   16/2 Retouch in sky above funnel (Th. E–F3), OP

3d. Cyl. 4A dot in combination with cyls. 1C–1B or 2C–1B dot
   14/2 Violet coloured flaw in sky at left of pylon (Th. E2), OP

3d. Cyls. 2C–1B–4A dot
   17/3 Dark patch on skyline under bridge (Th. F5), O

6d. Cyls. 1C–2B–2A no dot
   5/1 Small nick in top of 9 of 1964, OP
   5/5 Red scratch over D of BRIDGE, OP
   7/1 Red scratch over 6 of 6d, OP
   7/3 Two small breaks in bridge below portrait (Th. G8), OP
   8/2 Black spot on Queen's collar (Th. E10), OP
   15/6 Dark red patch below 4 of 1964 (Th. B13), OP
   16/1 Black dot in front of D of ROAD, OP
   16/5 Mottled portrait, OP
   17/6 Mottled portrait, OP
   18/4 Black spot in water between left-hand towers of bridge (Th. F1), OP

6d. Cyls. 1C–2B–2A dot
   1/4 White scratch on Queen's cheek (Th. D9), OP
   15/5 Two small coloured flaws on Queen's forehead (Th. C9); also two small red spots below portrait by
      bridge (Th. G9), OP
   17/2 Diagonal red stroke by value panel (Th. D11), OP
   19/1 Queen's face is a mass of white dots (State I) OP; later appears normal (State II), O only. Other
      stamps in the sheet show a similar appearance but this is the most marked

Sheet Details

Sheet size: 120 (6 × 20). 3d. double pane reel-fed; 6d. double pane sheet-fed

Sheet markings:

   Cylinder numbers: Opposite R. 19/1, boxed

   Guide holes:
      3d. Opposite rows 14/15 (boxed), at left (no dot) or right (dot)
      6d. None

   Marginal arrows (photo-etched): "W" shape, at top, bottom and sides

   Marginal rule: At bottom of sheet

   Colour register marks:
      3d. Opposite rows 2/3 and 17/18, at left (no dot) or right (dot)
      6d. Opposite rows 1/2 and 17/18, at left (no dot) or right (dot)

Autotron marks (solid):
    3d. Black, blue, violet opposite rows 4/6 and violet, blue, black opposite rows 13/15 at right (no dot) or
      left (dot)
    6d. None
Colour designations (usually trimmed off):
    3d. "G MAUVE G BLUE G BLACK" in right margin reading upwards opposite rows 8/4 on dot panes
      only
    6d. None
Traffic lights (boxed):
    3d. Violet, blue, black opposite R. 19/6
    6d. Blue, red, black opposite R. 19/6

Quantities Sold

	Ordinary	Phosphor
3d.	108,098,480	8,020,920
6d.	12,055,960	1,240,800
Pack	10,453	—

PHOSPHOR BANDS.   From the Churchill issue onwards all phosphor bands were applied in
photogravure.

W53.   Sir Winston Churchill   **W54.**   Sir Winston Churchill
(Des. D. Gentleman and Rosalind Dease, from photograph by Karsh)

1965 (JULY 8). CHURCHILL COMMEMORATION

Cat. No.	S.G. No.	Type	Description	Unused	Used

I. "REMBRANDT" Machine

Cyls. 1A–1B dot and no dot. Lack of shading detail on Churchill's portrait. Queen's
portrait appears dull and coarse

A. Ordinary

W56	661	**W53**		4d. Black and olive-brown	8	5
a. Watermark inverted	..	..	75			
b. Vertical scratch (Dot, R. 20/3)		1·00				

B. Phosphor

WP56	661p	**W53**		4d. Three bands	20	12
a. Left band omitted	..	..	3·00			
b. Vertical scratch (Dot, R. 20/3)..		1·00				

II. "TIMSON" Machine

Cyls. 5A–6B no dot. More detail on Churchill's portrait—furrow on forehead, his left
eye-brow fully drawn and more shading on cheek. Queen's portrait lighter and sharper

Ordinary only

W57	661a	**W53**	4d. Black and pale olive-brown	10	5

III. "LINOTYPE AND MACHINERY NO. 4" Machine

A. Ordinary

W58	662	**W54**		1s.3d. Black and grey	20	20
a. Watermark inverted	..	..	20·00			
W56 and W58				First Day Cover	†	60
W56 and W58				Presentation Pack	1·50	

B. Phosphor

WP58	662p	**W54**		1s.3d. Black and grey	60	60
a. Phosphor back and front	..	5·00				
WP56 and WP58				First Day Cover	†	1·50

These are known postmarked 7th July.
Two copies of the 4d. value exist with the Queen's head omitted, one due to something
adhering to the cylinder and the other due to a paper fold. The stamp also exists with
Churchill's head omitted, also due to a paper fold

Listed Variety

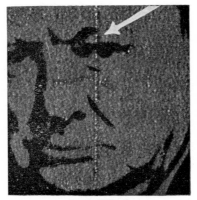

W56*b*, WP56*b*

Cylinder Numbers (Blocks of four)

(a) Ordinary

Cyl. Nos.				A(T) No dot	A(T) Dot	F No dot
4d. 1A (olive-brown)–1B (black) ..	..	..	..	40	40	†
4d. 5A (olive-brown)–6B (black) ..	..	..	..	†	†	60
1s.3d. 1A (black)–1B (grey) ..	..	..	..	†	†	1·50

(b) Phosphor

4d. 1A (olive-brown)–1B (black) ..	..	..	..	1·00	1·00	†
1s.3d. 1A (black)–1B (grey) ..	..	..	..	†	†	3·00

Minor Constant Flaws

Minimum prices as singles:
4d. ordinary 40p; phosphor 50p; 1s.3d. ordinary 75p; phosphor £1

4d. Cyls. 1A–1B no dot
   1/1 Background retouch left of Churchill's right eye (Th. D2), scratch from Churchill's ear to Queen's chin
      (Th. D8–11), small background retouch to right of Churchill's left ear (Th. C9), OP
   6/6 Queen's face mottled with white streaks (Th. B–D10–12), OP
   14/1 Dark patch above Queen's left eye (Th. B11), OP

4d. Cyls. 1A–1B dot
   1/6 Vertical line of white dots near hair above Churchill's right eye (Th. A–C3), OP
   4/3 Disturbance under Churchill's left eye (Th. D6), OP
   7/1 Queen's face mottled with white specks (Th. B–D10–12), OP
   7/2 Queen's face mottled with white specks (Th. B–D10–12), OP
   20/5 Brown diagonal line on bridge of Queen's nose (Th. C11), OP

    The mottled face of the Queen varieties on no dot R. 6/6 and dot R. 7/1 and 7/2 are very
marked and occur on ordinary and phosphor but only on some sheets. Many other stamps on
this cylinder show signs of mottling

4d. Cyls. 5A–6B no dot (ordinary only)
   4/2 Retouch in background between portraits (Th. B9)
   6/4 Retouch at top of Churchill's nose (Th. D5)
   10/4 Two spots in vertical white line level with Churchill's shoulder (Th. E10)
   12/3 Small white flaw by Churchill's right eye (Th. C10)
   14/5 Background retouch just above Churchill's right shoulder (Th. E–F2) and brown flaw in margin below
      Churchill's chin (Th. H5)
   15/5 Brown flaw left of Churchill's head (Th. A2)

1s.3d. Cyls. 1A–1B no dot
   1/4 Line of white dots in Queen's hair (Th. C12), OP
   7/1 Small white dot over Queen's left eyelid (Th. C11), OP
   15/4 White flaw at base of Queen's neck (Th. D2), OP
   19/4 Spur on top jewel of emblems in diadem (Th. A12), OP

205

Sheet Details

Sheet size: 120 (6 × 20)
  4d. Rembrandt double pane sheet-fed
    Timson single pane reel-fed
  1s.3d. L. & M. No. 4 single pane sheet-fed
Sheet markings:
  Cylinder numbers: Opposite R. 19/1, boxed
  Guide holes:
    4d. Timson above vertical row 2 (boxed) and below vertical rows 3/4 (unboxed and over arrow)
    Others: None
  Marginal arrows (photo etched): "W" shaped, at top, bottom and sides; Rembrandt very small at bottom,
    others normal
  Marginal rule: At bottom of sheet
  Colour register marks:
    4d. Rembrandt, none
    4d. Timson, opposite rows 1/2 and 17/18, at both sides
    1s.3d. Above and below vertical rows 1/2 and 6
  Autotron marks (solid):
    4d. Timson: Brown, black above R. 1/2 and 1/3
    Others: None
  Colour designations: None
  Traffic lights (boxed): All R. 19/6
    4d. Black, brown; 1s.3d. Grey, black

Quantities Issued

	Ordinary	Phosphor		Ordinary	Phosphor
4d. Rembrandt	103,217,520	10,322,760	1s.3d.	7,893,480	864,960
4d. Timson	32,040,000	—	Pack	40,946	—

Withdrawn   4d. phosphor sold out Dec. 1965, remainder withdrawn 28.2.66

W55.   Simon de Montfort's Seal

(Des. S. R. Black)

W56.   Parliament Buildings
(after engraving by Hollar, 1647)
(Des. Prof. R. Guyatt)

1965 (JULY 19). 700th ANNIVERSARY OF SIMON DE MONTFORT'S PARLIAMENT

Simon de Montfort summoned the first parliament representing many cities and shires and it met in various buildings at Westminster in January 1265

Cat. No.	S.G. No.	Type	Description	Unused	Used
A.	**Ordinary**				
W59	663	**W55**	6d. Olive-green	10	10
a. Imperforate between stamp and top margin .. .. .. 80·00					
W60	664	**W56**	2s.6d. Black and pale drab	35	45
a. Watermark inverted .. .. 4·50					
W59/60			First Day Cover	†	75
W59/60			Presentation Pack	2·50	
B.	**Phosphor**				
WP59	663p	**W55**	6d. Three bands	25	25
WP59			First Day Cover	†	60

Both values were accidentally released in several post offices in the London area on 8th July, the date of issue of the Churchill stamps. Covers are also known with both values, bearing the "First Day" cancellation of the Philatelic Bureau dated 8th July

206

Cylinder Numbers (Blocks of four)

	Cyl. Nos.					Perforation Type A	
						No dot	Dot
6d. 2 (olive-green). Ordinary	..	..	..	..	..	60	60
6d. 2 (olive-green). Phosphor	..	..	..	..	.. 1·25	1·25

The 2s.6d. sheets had no cylinder numbers. Perforation is Type A(T).

Minor Constant Flaws

Minimum prices as singles: 6d. ordinary 50p; 6d. phosphor 50p; 2s.6d. 65p

6d. Cyl. 2 no dot
    1/1 Background scratch behind right cross of diadem (Th. C11–12), OP
    5/3 Small background blemish above jewels in diadem (Th. B11), OP
    9/4 Retouch at rear of horse's belly (Th. E4), OP
    15/2 Dot below e of Anniversary, OP
    17/3 Cut in m of Parliament, OP
    17/5 Background retouch to right of diadem, (Th. C11), OP

6d. Cyl. 2 dot
    10/6 Spur to m of Parliament, OP
    14/5 White flaw on Queen's necklace (Th. E10), OP

2s.6d. No numbers
    4/1 Vertical line running through river wall and building in centre of stamp Th. (E–F9)
    4/6 Vertical line from left of steps at centre through Thames to frame line (Th. G–H7)
    6/3 Blemish between 5th and 6th windows of building in front of Westminster Hall (Th. E10)
    8/1 White scratches above V of ANNIVERSARY
    10/1 Nick in S of ANNIVERSARY

Sheet Details

Sheet sizes:
    6d. 120 (6 × 20). Double pane reel-fed
    2s.6d. 80 (8 × 10). Single pane sheet-fed
Sheet markings:
    Cylinder numbers: 6d. opposite R. 19/1, boxed; 2s.6d. none
    Guide holes:
        6d. In double photo-etched box opposite rows 14/15, at left (no dot) or right (dot). In the left margin the
        boxes are lettered "S O N", the "S" being in left box (usually trimmed off), the "O" below centre line
        and the "N" above right line. In the right margin the sequence is reversed. The letters are very small
        and denote respectively selvedge, off-side and near-side
        2s.6d. None
    Marginal arrows (photo-etched): "W" shaped, at top, bottom and sides
    Marginal rule: At bottom of sheet
    Colour register marks, Autotron marks, colour designations: None
    Traffic lights (boxed):
        6d. None
        2s.6d. Grey, drab and black opposite R. 9/8, boxed
This shows that the stamp was printed in three colours and accounts for misplacement of the Queen's head downwards in some badly registered sheets

Quantities Issued

	Ordinary	Phosphor
6d.	12,973,800	1,537,920
2s.6d.	4,055,120	—
Pack	24,427	—

Withdrawn   28.2.66

W57. Bandsmen and Banner
(Des. M. C. Farrar Bell)

W58. Three Salvationists
(Des. G. Trenaman)

1965 (AUGUST 9). SALVATION ARMY CENTENARY

A religious militant movement, the Salvation Army was founded in 1865 by William Booth who became its General in 1880

Cat. No.	S.G. No.	Type		Description	Unused	Used
A. Ordinary						
W61	665	**W57**		3d. Indigo, grey-blue, cerise, yellow and brown	8	8
a. Diadem flaw (R. 16/6) ..		..	1·00			
W62	666	**W58**		1s.6d. Red, blue, yellow and brown	40	30
a. Extra pearl (R. 17/1) ..		..	1·50			
W61/2				First Day Cover	†	60
B. Phosphor						
WP61	665p	**W57**		3d. One band	20	10
a. Diadem flaw (R. 16/6) ..		..	1·50			
WP62	666p	**W58**		1s.6d. Three bands	1.40	1·40
a. Extra pearl (R. 17/1) ..		..	3·00			
WP61/2				First Day Cover	†	2·25

Listed Varieties

W61*a*, WP61*a*

W62*a*, WP62*a*

Cylinder Numbers (Blocks of six)

(a) Ordinary

	Cyl. Nos. (No dot)	Perforation Type A
3d.	2A (blue)–2B (indigo)–1C (brown)–1D (cerise)–1E (yellow) ..	50
1s.6d.	1A (red)–1B (brown)–1C (blue)–1D (yellow)	2·80

(b) Phosphor

3d	2A (blue)–2B (indigo)–1C (brown)–1D (cerise)–1E (yellow) ..	1·75
1s.6d.	1A (red)–1B (brown)–1C (blue)–1D (yellow)	12·00

Minor Constant Flaws

Minimum prices as singles:

   3d. ordinary 40p; phosphor 60p; 1s.6d. ordinary £1; phosphor £2·50

3d. Cyls. 2A–2B–1C–1D–1E no dot
   1/6 Pale area below D of 3D (Th. G13), OP
   2/1 Dark spot on Queen's chin (Th. D11), OP
   3/6 Vertical scratch below flag-bearer's collar (Th. D–E4), OP
   8/1 Spur at foot of T of SALVATION at bottom of stamp, OP
   11/2 Blue scratch in white vertical dividing line to left of Queen's lips (Th. D10); also blue spot to left of flag-bearer's lips (Th. D4), both OP
   15/6 Grey flaw protruding from collar under Queen's chin (Th. E11), OP
   16/1 Due to faulty registration on the multipositive, the cerise colour is positioned slightly to the right resulting in a white line at left of flag in sky, also cerise colour overlaps ear and face below ear (Th. B–C3 and C4), OP. *Note*—This variety is not an ordinary colour shift and is therefore best collected in a positional block. A similar variety, although much less marked, is found on R. 14/1, also OP
   17/4 White spot in lower part of V of SALVATION at bottom of stamp, OP
   19/3 Retouched left arm of V of SALVATION at bottom of stamp. Appears enlarged and fuzzy, OP

1s.6d. Cyls. 1A–1B–1C–1D no dot
   1/1 Retouch on right arm of left-hand man (Th. D1–2), OP
   1/4 White flaw on Queen's hair behind ear (Th. D12), OP
   15/6 Retouch on right leg of left-hand man (Th. G2), OP
   19/3 Diagonal scratch across Queen's forehead and nose (Th. B–C10), OP
   20/1 White flaw on Queen's neck by necklace (Th. E11), OP
   20/3 Small red flaw at back of Queen's hair (Th. D12), OP
   20/5 A whispy line of blue dots by left leg of right-hand man (Th. F7), OP

Sheet Details

Sheet size: 120 (6 × 20). Single pane reel-fed

Sheet markings:

Cylinder numbers:
   3d. Opposite rows 18/19 at left, boxed
   1s.6d. Opposite row 19 at left, boxed

Guide holes: Opposite rows 14/15 (boxed), at both sides

Marginal arrows (photo-etched): "W" shaped, at top, bottom and sides

Marginal rule: At bottom of sheet

Colour register marks:
   Opposite rows 1/2 and 17/18, at both sides

Autotron marks (solid):
   3d. Blue, indigo, brown, cerise, yellow below vertical rows 1/3
   1s. 6d. Red, brown, blue, yellow below vertical rows 1/3

Colour designations:
   3d. "G1 YELLOW G2 RED G3 BROWN G4 BLUE BLACK G5 BLUE" in right margin reading up-
      wards opposite rows 9/3 ("G1 YELLOW" is very faint on some sheets)
   1s.6d. "G1 YELLOW G2 BLUE G3 BROWN G4 RED" in right margin reading upwards opposite
      rows 9/3

Traffic lights (boxed):
   3d. Blue, indigo, brown, cerise, yellow opposite rows 18/19 at right
   1s.6d. Red, brown, blue, yellow opposite rows 18/19 at right

Quantities Issued

	Ordinary	Phosphor
3d.	54,312,000	4,261,200
1s.6d.	5,244,120	652,320

Withdrawn   28.2.66 (3d. ordinary sold out Dec. 1965)

W59.   Lister's Carbolic Spray
(Des. P. Gauld)

W60.   Lister and Chemical Symbols
(Des. F. Ariss)

**1965 (SEPTEMBER 1). CENTENARY OF JOSEPH LISTER'S DISCOVERY OF
ANTISEPTIC SURGERY**

Cat. No.	S.G. No.	Typ		Description	Unused	Used
A. Ordinary						
W63	667	**W59**		4d. Indigo, brown-red and grey-	5	5
a. Brown-red (tube) omitted		..	75·00	black		
b. Indigo omitted ..		..	£100			
c. Corner scratch (No dot, R.17/1)			1·00			
d. Face retouch (No dot, R.18/1)			75	e. Filled e (No dot, R. 20/4) ..	75	
W64	668	**W60**		1s. Black, purple and new blue	25	20
a. Watermark inverted ..		..	35·00			
W63/4				First Day Cover	†	40
B. Phosphor						
WP63	667p	**W59**		4d. Three bands	12	8
a. Brown-red (tube) omitted		..				
b. Corner scratch (No dot, R. 17/1)			1·10	c. Face retouch (No dot, R. 18/1)..	1·00	
WP64	668p	**W60**		1s. Three bands	60	60
a. Watermark inver		..	.. 30·00			
WP63/4				First Day Cover	†	1·10

These are known postmarked 31st August

Listed Varieties

W63c, WP63b	W63e	W63d, WP63c
	e of Antiseptic nearly filled by white flaw (later touched out)	Large grey retouch outlines face

Cylinder Numbers (Blocks of four)

Cyl. Nos.

Perforation Types

	A No dot	A Dot	F No dot
4d. 4A (black)–1B (blue)–1C (red). Ordinary	1·00*	40	†
4A (black)–1B (blue)–1C (red). Phosphor	1·25*	75	†
1s. 1A (black)–1B (purple)–1C (blue). Ordinary	†	†	1·50
1A (black)–1B (purple)–1C (blue). Phosphor	†	†	3·00

Minor Constant Flaws

Minimum prices as singles:
   4d. ordinary 40p; phosphor 50p; 1s. ordinary 75p; phosphor £1

4d. Cyls. 4A–1B–1C no dot
   4/1 Line of white dots under apparatus (Th. H3–4), OP
   4/4 Two dark flaws to lower right of apparatus (Th. G5–6), OP
   5/6 Prominent retouch in front of Queen's dress (Th. E–F10), OP
   6/6 Grey flaw hanging from rear jewel of tiara (Th. B12), OP
   10/3 Grey flaw on Queen's forehead (Th. B10), OP
   11/4 to 12/4 Grey line under g of Surgery extending across gutter joining frames, OP
   11/6 Diagonal grey line from top left corner to apparatus (Th. A1–B2), OP
   16/5 Retouch on Queen's forehead (Th. B10), OP
   17/2 White flaw in loop of d of value, OP
   19/6 Grey spots on Queen's forehead (Th. B10–11), OP
   19/6 and 20/6 Grey line extends down right-hand margin, OP
   20/3 Vertical grey line from lower left corner of stamp to gutter (Th. H1), OP
   20/6 Base of 4 joined to tube by dark line (Th. B7), OP

4d. Cyls. 4A–1B–1C dot
   1/4 Blue spot between p and t of antiseptic, OP
   8/2 Retouch on Queen's collar (Th. E12), OP
   10/2 Diagonal grey line above te of Lister and in front of Queen's collar (Th. F8–E10), OP
   13/3 Retouch behind Queen's necklace (Th. D12), OP
   18/1 Retouch on Queen's jaw close to ear (Th. D11), OP
   19/2 White scratch above ur of Surgery, OP
   20/1 Two dark spots at right of Queen's mouth (Th. D11), OP
   20/6 Retouch in front of Queen's neck (Th. E10), OP

1s. Cyls. 1A–1B–1C no dot
   1/5 Large black spot at rear of Queen's collar (Th. E13), OP
   3/1 Retouch along Lister's right shoulder (Th. D3–C4), OP
   3/2 Broken frame line behind Queen's portrait was retouched by dots (Th. C13), OP
   6/1 Missing portions of jewels left of large cross on diadem heavily retouched (Th. A10), OP
   8/1 White retouch on Queen's throat (Th. D11), OP
   11/2 Extra pearl half way up necklace (Th. D11), OP
   11/3 Small retouch on Queen's left cheek (Th. D11), OP
   14/2 Retouch on Queen's collar (Th. E12), OP
   15/6 Line from Queen's left eyebrow into hair (Th. B11), OP
   16/4 Retouch on back of Queen's collar (Th. E13), OP
   17/6 Blue spot normally found by Lister's right wrist is missing (Th. E6), OP
   19/1 Dark spot under Queen's nose (Th. C10), OP
   20/3 Retouch below Queen's necklace (Th. D12), OP

Sheet Details

Sheet size: 120 (6 × 20). 4d. double pane reel-fed; 1s. single pane sheet-fed
Sheet markings:
   Cylinder numbers: Opposite R. 19/1, boxed
   Guide holes: Opposite rows 14/15 (boxed), at left (no dot) or right (dot)
   Marginal arrows (photo-etched): "W" shaped, at top, bottom and sides
   Marginal rule: At bottom of sheet
   Colour register marks:
      4d. Opposite rows 2/3 and 16/17, at left (no dot)
      1s. Above and below vertical rows 1/2 and 5/6

Autotron marks (solid):
    4d. Black, indigo, brown-red opposite rows 3/5, at right (no dot) or left (dot)
    1s. None
Colour designations: None
Traffic lights (boxed):
    4d. Black, indigo, brown-red opposite R. 19/6
    1s. Black, purple, blue opposite R. 20/6

Quantities Issued

	Ordinary	Phosphor
4d.	92,167,440	10,732,800
1s.	8,368,800	1,452,360

Withdrawn 15.4.66

W61. Trinidad Carnival Dancers   **W62.** Canadian Folk-dancers
(Des. D. Gentleman and Rosalind Dease)

1965 (SEPTEMBER 1). COMMONWEALTH ARTS FESTIVAL

The Festival was aimed at promoting the cultural traditions of Commonwealth countries and was held in London and other centres between 16th September and 2nd October

Cat. No.	S.G. No.	Type	Description	Unused	Used
A. Ordinary					
W65	669	W61	6d. Black and orange	8	5
W66	670	W62	1s.6d. Black and light reddish violet	30	25
W65/6			First Day Cover	†	60
B. Phosphor					
WP65	669p	W61	6d. Three bands	25	25
a. Phosphor back and front	..	6·00			
WP66	670p	W62	1s.6d. Three bands	60	60
WP65/6			First Day Cover	†	1·50

Cylinder Numbers (Blocks of four)

	Cyl. Nos.					Perforation Type F(L)
						No dot
6d.	1A (orange)–1B (black). Ordinary	..	..	..	..	50
	1A (orange)–1B (black). Phosphor	..	..	..	..	1·50
1s.6d.	1A (violet)–1B (black). Ordinary	..	..	..	..	1·80
	1A (violet)–1B (black). Phosphor	..	..	..	••	3·00

Minor Constant Flaws

Minimum prices as singles:
    6d. ordinary 50p; phosphor 60p; 1s.6d. ordinary 75p; phosphor £1

6d. Cyls. 1A–1B (no dot)
  1/2 Damaged right arm of v of Festival, OP
  1/6 Black spot at back of Queen's neck under hair (Th. C12), OP
  11/6 S shaped line of white dots on Queen's neck (Th. D–E11), OP
  17/1 Pale area in background by right sleeve of central figure (Th. D3–4), OP

1s.6d. Cyls. 1A–1B no dot
  2/3 White flaw under n of Commonwealth, OP
  3/4 Vertical scratch from Queen's ear to neck (Th. C–D12), OP
  5/6 Vertical line from diadem to neck (Th. B–D11), OP
  7/5 Pale area below C of Commonwealth, OP
  15/1 Diagonal scratch to right of C of Commonwealth (Th. G1–2), OP
  13/6 White spot between emblems and rear cross of diadem (Th. B12), OP
  20/6 Two dots to right of Queen's left eyebrow (Th. C11), OP

Sheet Details

Sheet size: 120 (6 × 20). Single pane reel-fed

Sheet markings:

Cylinder numbers: Opposite R. 19/1, boxed

Guide holes: Above vertical rows 3/4 and below vertical row 5, unboxed

Marginal arrows (photo-etched): "W" shaped, at top, bottom and sides

Marginal rule: At bottom of sheet

Colour register marks:
6d. Opposite rows 1/2 and 18/19, at both sides and opposite rows 10/11 (orange only), at left
1s.6d. Opposite rows 1/2, at both sides, rows 9/10 (violet only), at left and rows 18/19, at left and 17/18, at right

Autotron marks (solid):
6d. Orange, black above and below vertical rows 3/4
1s.6d. Violet, black above and below vertical rows 3/4

Colour designations:
6d. "G ORANGE G BLACK" reading upwards opposite rows 14/12, right margin
1s.6d. "G MAUVE G BLACK" reading upwards opposite rows 15/13, right margin

Traffic lights (boxed):
6d. Black, orange opposite R. 19/6
1s.6d. Black, violet opposite R. 19/6

Quantities Issued

	Ordinary	Phosphor
6d.	12,264,840	1,621,080
1s.6d.	5,003,000	788,880

Withdrawn 15.4.66

W63. Flight of Spitfires

W64. Pilot in Hurricane

W65. Wing-tips of Spitfire and Messerschmitt "ME-109"

W66. Spitfires attacking Heinkel "HE-111" Bomber

W67. Spitfires attacking Stuka Dive-bomber

W68. Hurricanes over Wreck of Dornier "DO-17z2" Bomber

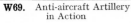

W69.   Anti-aircraft Artillery
in Action

W70.   Air-battle over St. Paul's
Cathedral

(4d. × 6 and 1s.3d. des. D. Gentleman and Rosalind Dease. 9d. des. A. Restall)

1965 (SEPTEMBER 13).   25th ANNIVERSARY OF BATTLE OF BRITAIN

The "Battle of Britain" was the first major campaign in world history to be fought entirely between opposing air forces

The 4d. values were issued together *se-tenant* in blocks of six (3 × 2) within the sheet

Cat. No.	S.G. No.	Type		Description	Unused	Used
A. Ordinary						
W67	671	**W63**		4d. Yellow-olive and black	8	5
W68	672	**W64**		4d. Yellow-olive, olive-grey and black	8	5
W69 *a.* Damaged wing (Cyl. 3D., R. 19/3)	673	**W65**	60	4d. Red, new blue, yellow-olive, olive-grey and black	8	5
W70	674	**W66**		4d. Olive-grey, yellow-olive and black	8	5
W71 *a.* Stuka retouch (Cyl. 1E, R. 2/2)	675	**W67**	50	4d. Olive-grey, yellow-olive and black	8	5
W72 *b.* New blue omitted .. .. *b.* Damaged tailplane (Cyl. 3D., R. 20/3)	676	**W68**	— £100 60	4d. Olive-grey, yellow-olive, new blue and black	8	5
W73 *a.* Watermark inverted	677	**W69**	11·00	9d. Bluish violet, orange and slate-purple	20	15
W74 *a.* Watermark inverted	678	**W70**	4·50	1s.3d. Light and deep grey, black and light and bright blue	25	20
W67/74				First Day Cover	†	1·00
W67/74				Presentation Pack	2·50	
B. Phosphor						
WP67	671p	**W63**		4d. Three bands	10	5
WP68	672p	**W64**		4d. Three bands	10	5
WP69 *a.* Damaged wing (Cyl. 3D., R. 19/3)	673p	**W65**	75	4d. Three bands	10	5
WP70	674p	**W66**		4d. Three bands	10	5
WP71 *a.* Stuka retouch (Cyl. 1E, R. 2/2)	675p	**W67**	65	4d. Three bands	10	5
WP72 *a.* Damaged tailplane (Cyl. 3D., R. 20/3)	676p	**W68**	75	4d. Three bands	10	5
WP73	677p	**W69**		9d. Three bands	30	25
WP74 *a.* Watermark inverted	678p	**W70**	65	1s.3d. Three bands	60	50
WP67/74				First Day Cover	†	1·75

Listed Varieties

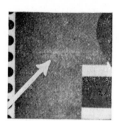

W69a, WP69a

W71a, WP71a

This variety only occurs in combination with cyls. 3A–1B–1C–3D. With cyls. 2A–1B–1C–3D it is normal

W72b WP72a

Cylinder Numbers (Blocks of twelve (3 × 4) (4d.), four (9d.), six (1s.3d.))

(a) Ordinary

Cyl. Nos.		Perforation Types		
		A No dot	A Dot	F No dot
4d. 2A (black)–1B (blue)–1C (red)–3D (olive-grey)–1E (yellow-olive)		1·00	1·00	†
3A (black)–1B (blue)–1C (red)–3D (olive-grey)–1E (yellow-olive)		1·00	1·75*	†
9d. 1A (slate-purple)–1B (violet)–1C (orange)		†	†	1·00
1s.3d. 1A (black)–1B (light blue)–1C (light grey)–1D (deep grey)–1E (bright blue)		†	†	1·50

(b) Phosphor

4d. 3A (black)–1B (blue)–1C (red)–3D (olive-grey)–1E (yellow-olive)		2·00	3·00*	†
9d. 1A (slate-purple)–1B (violet)–1C (orange)		†	†	1·50
1s.3d. 1A (black)–1B (light blue)–1C (light grey)–1D (deep grey)–1E (bright blue)		†	†	5·00

Minor Constant Flaws

Minimum prices as singles:

	Ordinary	Phosphor
4d.	40	50
9d.	50	75
1s.3d.	75	1·00

4d. Cyls. 1B–1C–3D–1E no dot in combination with black cyls. 2A or 3A no dot
1/3 Horizontal scratch retouch under right of cross (Th. F5–7), OP
1/6 Similar retouch under centre of cross (Th. F3–6), OP
15/2 Nick in centre line of fuselage at left (Th. D1), OP
20/1 Small dark area on left wing of bomber (Th. D2), OP

4d. Cyl. 3A no dot
1/4 Nick in lower curve of B in BRITAIN, OP
7/2 Black spot in front of Queen's ear (Th. C12), OP
12/3 White scar across Queen's left cheek (Th. C12), OP
13/2 Fine vertical line on Queen's left cheek (Th. C12), OP
18/3 Extra white dot in Queen's hair behind ear-ring (Th. C13), OP

4d. Cyls. 1B–1C–3D–1E dot in combination with black cyls. 2A or 3A dot
5/3 Dark horizontal line below right arm of cross (Th. F5–6), OP
8/1 Dark spot at left end of bomber's wing (Th. C1), OP
11/2 Line of white dots on pilot's right shoulder (Th. E8–F10), OP
16/1 Dark spot at right end of bomber's wing (Th. B9), OP
16/3 Notch in bomber's tail under B of Battle (Th. A4), OP

9d. Cyls. 1A–1B–1C no dot
11/2 Line across Queen's face under eyes (Th. C10–11), OP
12/3 Retouch in sky behind hat of man with flag (Th. C1), OP
20/5 White patch below where vapour trails cross (Th. C5–6), OP

1s.3d. Cyls. 1A–1B–1C–1D–1E no dot
  4/4 Scratch below 1 of 1940 (Th. H5), OP
  5/3 Horizontal bright blue line above building at right (Th. F8–10), OP
  5/4 Dark line between Br of Britain (Th. G–H5), OP
  9/5 Retouches in sky at lower right (Th. D–E9–10), OP
  14/4 Blue dot in front of Queen's ear (Th. C12), OP
  20/3 Line under value is shorter at right, OP

Sheet Details
Sheet size: 120 (6 × 20)
  4d. In *se-tenant* blocks of six, double pane reel-fed
  9d. and 1s.3d. Single pane sheet-fed
Sheet markings:
  Cylinder numbers:
    4d. and 1s.3d. Opposite rows 18/19 at left, boxed
    9d. Opposite R. 19/1, boxed
  Guide holes:
    4d. In double "S O N" box opposite rows 14/15, at left (no dot) or right (dot)
    Others: None
  Marginal arrows (photo-etched): "W" shaped, at top, bottom and sides
  Marginal rule: At bottom of sheet
  Colour register marks:
    4d. None
    9d. Above and below vertical rows 1/2 and 6
    1s.3d. Above and below vertical rows 1/2 and 5/6
      There is a large violet blob of colour under vertical rows 1/2 in the 9d. value
  Autotron marks (solid):
    4d. Black, red, blue, olive-grey, yellow-olive opposite rows 3/7, at right (no dot) or left (dot)
    Others: None
  Colour designations: None
  Traffic lights (boxed):
    4d. Olive-grey, red, black, blue, yellow-olive opposite rows 18/19 at right
    9d. Violet, orange, slate-purple opposite R. 19/6
    1s.3d. Deep grey, light blue, light grey, black, bright blue opposite rows 18/19 at right

Quantities Issued

	Ordinary	Phosphor
4d.	103,417,440	11,560,440
9d.	6,195,960	1,143,120
1s.3d.	6,469,440	1,239,840
Pack	28,374	—

Withdrawn 31.5.66

W71.   Post Office Tower and
  Georgian Buildings

W72.   Post Office Tower and
  "Nash" Terrace, Regent's Park

(Des. C. Abbott)

1965 (OCTOBER 8). OPENING OF POST OFFICE TOWER
The tallest building in London the Post Office Tower is 620 feet high and helps to provide more long distance telephone circuits and more television channels. An additional feature of this issue was the inclusion of the names of both the designer and printers at the foot of the stamps and this became the practice for many later issues

Watermark sideways on 3d.

Cat. No.	S.G. No.	Type	Description	Unused	Used
A. Ordinary					
W75	679	**W71**	3d. Olive-yellow, new blue		
a. Olive-yellow (tower) omitted..			and bronze-green	5	5
b. Extra window (Dot. R. 4/18) ..		65			

Cat. No.	S.G. No.	Type			Shades	Unused	Used
W76	680	**W72**			1s.3d. Bronze-green, yellow-		
a. Watermark inverted	..	..	14·00		green and blue	20	15
W75/6					First Day Cover	†	40
W75/6					Presentation Pack	35	

B. Phosphor

WP75	679p	**W71**			3d. One band (at left or right)	5	5
a. Extra window (Dot, R. 4/18)	..		75				
WP76	680p	**W72**			1s.3d. Three bands	15	15
a. Watermark inverted	..	..	15·00				
WP75/6					First Day Cover	†	90
WP75/6					Presentation Pack*	30	

*See note under "Withdrawn" at end of listing

The above are known pre-released on 4th October at Aish, South Brent (Devon).

Listed Variety

W75*b*, WP75*a*

Cylinder Numbers (Blocks of four)

(a) Ordinary

	Cyl. Nos.		Perforation Types		
			A	A	F
			No dot	Dot	No dot
3d.	1A (blue)–1B (green)–1C yellow)*	.. ..	40	40	†
1s.3d.	1A (yellow-green)–1B (bronze-green)–1C (blue)	..	†	†	1·25

(b) Phosphor

3d.	1A (blue)–1B (green)–1C (yellow)*	.. ..	60	60	†
1s.3d.	1A (yellow-green)–1B (bronze-green)–1C (blue)	..	†	†	1·80

*In the 3d. dot pane the dot after "1C" is omitted in error

The 3d. is with sheet orientated showing head to left

Minor Constant Flaws

Minimum prices as singles:

   3d. ordinary 40p; phosphor 50p; 1s.3d. ordinary 75p; phosphor £1

3d. Cyls. 1A–1B–1C dot

  1/20 White spot at base of tower (Th. L3), OP
  2/19 Olive-yellow spot below second ground floor window of building at base of tower at right (Th. M4), OP
  2/20 Blue spot below SO of HARRISON, OP
  5/2 White spot in O of OFFICE, OP
  5/8 Blue spot surrounded by pale area below T of TOWER, OP
  5/16 Pale spot in blue panel to left of 3d (Th. J4), OP

1s.3d. Cyls. 1A–1B–1C no dot

  1/5 Pale area around lower tip of 3 of 1/3, OP
  3/1 Small retouch below T of TOWER (Th. C–D1), OP
  4/1 Horizontal line of retouching below 1/3 (Th. D11–12), OP
  6/2 Scratch in sky above roof of left-hand terrace (Th. E2), OP
  10/3 Dark spot to left of Queen's nose (Th. C8), OP
  10/4 Retouch to background at top right of 1 of 1/3, OP
  15/4 White scratch through E and over R of TOWER, OP

Sheet Details

Sheet sizes:
  3d. 120 (20 × 6). Double pane reel-fed
  1s.3d. 120 (6 × 20). Single pane sheet-fed

Sheet markings:
  Cylinder numbers:
    3d. Above vertical row 2, boxed
    1s.3d. Opposite R. 19/1, boxed
  Guide holes:
    3d. In double "S O N" box above vertical rows 6/7 (no dot) or below (dot)
    1s.3d. None
  Marginal arrows (photo-etched): "W" shaped, at top, bottom and sides
  Marginal rule: 3d. At left of sheet; 1s.3d. At bottom of sheet

Colour register marks:
    3d. None
    1s.3d. Above and below vertical rows 1/2 and 5/6
Autotron marks (solid):
    3d Yellow, green, blue below vertical rows 15/17 (no dot) or above (dot)
    1s.3d. None
Colour designations: None
Traffic lights (boxed):
    3d. Yellow, green, blue, reading left to right below vertical row 2
    1s.3d. Yellow-green, bronze-green, blue opposite R. 19/6

Quantities Issued

	Ordinary	Phosphor
3d.	51,291,120	4,274,880
1s.3d.	5,722,320	1,107,480

Withdrawn 30.6.66

When the Post Office Tower was opened on 19th May 1966 these stamps were issued from automatic machines giving a block of four of the 3d. and a pair of the 1s.3d. dispensed in envelopes, and packs were also issued from a machine. These continued to be available after the stamps had been withdrawn everywhere else and early in 1968 the ordinary stamps were replaced by phosphor stamps and packs. At the time of going to press these were still available. The above figures for quantities issued are presumed to include reserve stocks for sale at the tower.

W73. U.N. Emblem   **W74.** I.C.Y. Emblem
(Des. J. Matthews)

1965 (OCTOBER 25). 20th ANNIVERSARY OF THE UNITED NATIONS

Commemorating the 20th Anniversary of the formation of the United Nations in 1945. 1965 was also designated International Co-operation Year and the symbol of clasped hands is shown on the 1s.6d. value

Cat. No.	S.G. No.	Type		Description	Unused	Used
A. Ordinary						
W77	681	**W73**		3d. Black, yellow-orange and	5	5
a. Broken circle (Dot, R. 11/4) ..		75		light blue		
b. Lake in Russia (Dot, R. 19/3)..		75				
W78	682	**W74**		1s.6d. Black, bright purple and	30	30
a. Watermark inverted				light blue		
W77/8				First Day Cover	†	40
B. Phosphor						
WP77	681p	**W73**		3d. One Centre Band	10	10
a. Band at left		50		d. "Flying saucer" flaw (Dot, R.		
b. Broken circle (Dot, R. 11/4) ..		1·25		18/3)		
c. Lake in Russia (Dot, R. 19/3)..		1·25		e. Retouched		
WP78	682p	**W74**		1s.6d. Three bands	50	60
WP77/8				First Day Cover	†	1·40

Listed Varieties

W77a, WP77b   W77b WP77c   WP77d   WP77e
Stroke over S of   Retouched.
ANNIVERSARY   Smudge
and smudge   removed

Cylinder Numbers (Blocks of four)

(a) Ordinary

	Cyl. Nos.		Perforation Types		
			A	A	F
			No dot	Dot	No dot
3d.	1A (black)–1B (blue)–1C (orange)* ..	.. ..	40	40	†
1s.6d.	1A (black)–1B (blue)–1C (purple) ..	.	†	†	1·50

(b) Phosphor

3d.	1A (black)–1B (blue)–1C (orange)* ..	. ..	50	50	†
1s.6d.	1A (black)–1B (blue)–1C (purple) .	.. ..	†	†	4·00

*In the 3d. dot pane the dot is before instead of after the "1C"

Minor Constant Flaws

Minimum prices as singles:

3d. ordinary 40p; phosphor 50p; 1s.6d. ordinary 75p; phosphor £1·50

3d. Cyls. 1A–1B–1C no dot

1/1 Diagonal scratch across Queen's face (Th. C11–12), OP
1/4 Round pale grey flaw by Queen's left eye (Th. C11–12), OP
2/2 Pale patch on Queen's neck (Th. E12), OP
8/5 Dotted white scratch on right side of o of large 20 (Th. D8–9) ,OP
9/2 Black flaw in lower loop of 3, OP
10/4 Small break in middle of S of ANNIVERSARY, OP
13/1 Curved white scratch in bottom right-hand corner of blue panel (Th. H9–10), OP
14/4 Scratch on Queen's neck by necklace (Th. E12), OP
15/6 Black spot on Queen's forehead (Th. C11), OP
19/4 Horizontal white scratch over VERSARY, OP
20/6 Black flaws between laurel leaves over middle of large 2 (Th. D3), OP

3d. Cyls. 1A–1B–1C dot

20/1 White scratch through ARY U, OP

1s.6d. Cyls. 1A–1B–1C no dot

2/1 White scratch behind Queen's neck (Th. D12–E12), OP
5/1 Small patch of white dots to right of Queen's head (Th. B13), OP
6/2 Pale patch to left of top of large U (Th. B1), OP
10/1 Pale patch in background to left of Queen's mouth (Th. D10), OP
11/2 Pink spot central below large N (Th. F7), OP
15/1 White scratch in base of large U, (Th. E2), OP
20/1 Vertical white scratch in background behind Queen's head (Th. C–D13), OP
20/5 Retouch to background within upper thumb of symbol (Th. B5), OP

Sheet Details

Sheet size: 120 (6 × 20). 3d. double pane reel-fed; 1s.6d. single pane sheet-fed
Sheet markings:
  Cylinder numbers: Opposite R. 19/1, boxed
  Guide holes:
    3d. In double " S O N " box opposite rows 14/15, at left (no dot) or right (dot). An unusual feature of this
      stamp is that there is an additional single box printed in orange beneath the double box which is in
      black
    1s.6d. None
  Marginal arrows (photo-etched): "W" shaped, at top, bottom and sides
  Marginal rule: At bottom of sheet
  Colour register marks:
    3d. None
    1s.6d. Above and below vertical rows 1 and 6
  Autotron marks (solid):
    3d. Black, blue, orange opposite rows 5/6 at right (no dot) or left (dot)
    1s.6d. None
  Colour designations (usually trimmed off):
    3d. "G1 BROWN G2 BLUE G3 BLACK" in right margin reading upwards opposite rows 8/5 on dot panes
    1s.6d. None
  Traffic lights (boxed):
    3d. Black, blue, orange opposite R. 19/6
    1s.6d. Black, blue, purple opposite R. 19/6

Quantities Issued

	Ordinary	Phosphor
3d.	50,598,720	4,488,240
1s.6d.	5,476,800	1,018,560

Withdrawn 30.6.66

W75. Telecommunications Network   **W76.** Radio Waves and Switchboard
(Des. A. Restall)

1965 (NOVEMBER 15). I.T.U. CENTENARY

The aims of the Union created in 1865, then known as the International Telegraph Union, are to promote, maintain and extend international co-operation in telecommunication

Cat. No.	S.G. No.	Type		Description	Unused	Used
A. Ordinary						
W79	683	**W75**		9d. Red, ultramarine, deep slate-violet, black and pink	10	8
a. Watermark inverted			2·25			
W80	684	**W76**		1s.6d. Red, greenish blue, indigo, black and light pink	25	25
a. Pink omitted			£150			
b. Retouched arm (R. 1/4)			1·00			
W79/80				First Day Cover	†	50
B. Phosphor						
WP79	683p	**W75**		9d. Three bands	25	25
a. Watermark inverted			25·00			
WP80	684p	**W76**		1s.6d. Three bands	1·25	1·25
a. Two bands			2·00			
b. Red pin with arm (R. 1/4)			2·00			
				c. Retouched		
WP79/80				First Day Cover	†	1·75

Originally scheduled for issue on 17th May 1965, supplies from the Philatelic Bureau were sent in error to reach a dealer on that date and another dealer received his supply on 27th May.

Listed Varieties

WP80a. This variety was caused by a misplacement of the phosphor bands

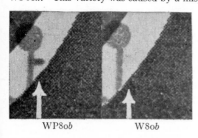

On the phosphor printing the red pin has a projecting arm at right; this was later retouched leaving faint traces of red on the pink background and it is only known in the retouched state on the ordinary printing.

WP80b   W80b

Cylinder Numbers (Blocks of six)

(a) Ordinary

	Cyl. Nos. (No dot)	Perforation Type F
9d.	1A (ultram.)–1B (red)–1C (violet)–1D (pink)–2E (black) ..	60
1s.6d.	2A (blue)–1B (indigo)–1C (pink)–1D (red)–2E (black) ..	1·60

(b) Phosphor

9d.	1A (ultram.)–1B (red)–1C (violet)– 1D (pink)–2E (black)	2·00
1s.6d.	2A (blue)–1B (indigo)–1C (pink)–1D (red)–2E (black) ..	10·00

The same black cylinder was used for both values.

Minor Constant Flaws

Minimum prices as singles:
    9d ordinary 60p; phosphor 75p; 1s.6d. ordinary 75p; phosphor £1·75

9d. and 1s.6d. Cyl. 2E
  2/4 Small white curl in hair behind Queen's ear (Th. C12), OP
  5/2 Small nick in diagonal stroke of first N of UNION, OP

9d. Cyls. 1A–1B–1C–1D–2E
  6/5 Small break in diagonal blue network line at right (Th. B8), OP
  9/5 Diagonal white scratch in blue background above ATIO of INTERNATIONAL (Th. E3), OP
  10/5 Damaged lower half of 1 of 1865, shows as white nick and white scratch, OP
  17/6 Small nick in right-hand stroke of first M of TELECOMMUNICATION, OP
  20/5 Wavy scratch in background over OMMUNI of TELECOMMUNICATION (Th. E7–9), OP

1s.6d. Cyls. 2A–1B–1C–1D–1E
  3/3 Retouches to background above first C of TELECOMMUNICATION, P

Sheet Details

Sheet size: 120 (6 × 20). Single pane sheet-fed
Sheet markings:
  Cylinder numbers: Opposite rows 18/19 at left, boxed
  Guide holes: None
  Marginal arrows (photo-etched): "W" shaped, at top, bottom and sides
  Marginal rule: At bottom of sheet
  Colour register marks: Above and below vertical rows 1/2 and 5/6
  Autotron marks: None
  Colour designations: None
  Traffic lights (boxed):
    9d. Ultramarine, red, violet, pink, black opposite rows 18/19 at right
    1s.6d. Blue, indigo, pink, red, black opposite rows 18/19 at right

Quantities Issued

	Ordinary	Phosphor
9d.	5,321,880	556,080
1s.6d.	5,287,920	589,800

Withdrawn   30.6.66 (1s.6d. phosphor sold out December 1965)

W77. Robert Burns (after Skirving chalk drawing)

W78. Robert Burns (after Nasmyth portrait)

(Des. G. F. Huntly)

1966 (JANUARY 25). BURNS COMMEMORATION

Robert Burns (1759–1796), Scotland's celebrated national poet, was born in Alloway, near Ayr

Cat. No.	S.G. No.	Type	Description	Unused	Used
A. Ordinary					
W81	685	**W77**	4d. Black, deep violet-blue and new blue	5	5
W82	686	**W78**	1s.3d. Black, slate-blue and yellow-orange	20	15
W81/2			First Day Cover	†	35
W81/2			Presentation Pack	1·50	
B. Phosphor					
WP81	685p	**W77**	4d. Three bands	10	8
WP82	686p	**W78**	1s.3d. Three bands	50	65
WP81/2			First Day Cover	†	1·25

These are known postmarked 24th January

220

Cylinder Numbers (Blocks of four)

(a) Ordinary

Cyl. Nos.		Perforation Types		
		A No dot	A Dot	F No dot
4d.	1A (violet–blue)–1B (black)–1C (new blue) ..	40	40	†
	1A (violet–blue)–2B (black)–1C (new blue) ..	40	40	†
1s.3d.	2A (slate-blue)–1B (black)–1C (orange) ..	†	†	1·25

(b) Phosphor

4d.	1A (violet–blue)–1B (black)–1C (new blue) ..	50	50	†
1s.3d.	2A (slate-blue)–1B (black)–1C (orange) ..	†	†	3·00

Minor Constant Flaws

Minimum prices as singles:

4d. ordinary 40p; phosphor 50p; 1s.3d. ordinary 60p; phosphor £1

4d. Cyls. 1A–2B–1C dot
  9/4 Small white flaw at front of diadem (Th. A10), OP
  15/1 White spot at back of Burns's hair by parting (Th. A5), O
  18/1 Coloured spot above Queen's upper lip (Th. C10), OP
  19/3 White flaw on Queen's neck above centre of collar (Th. E11), OP

1s.3d. Cyls. 2A–1B–1C no dot
  2/6 Pale background flaw in front of Queen's neck (Th. D9), OP
  3/6 Grey spot on Burns's nose near his right eye (Th. C5), OP
  4/6 Grey diagonal line through white line to panel at lower right (Th. E8–G9), OP
  6/5 White patch to right of Queen's left eyebrow (Th. B11), OP
  9/4 Large dark retouch in Burns's hair left of parting (Th. B4), OP
  19/1 Flaw on Burns's right cheek (Th. D4),OP
  19/5 Dark flaw on Burns's shirt touching left lapel (Th. F5), OP

Sheet Details

Sheet size: 120 (6×20). 4d. double pane reel-fed; 1s.3d. single pane sheet-fed

Sheet marking:
  Cylinder numbers: R. 19/1, boxed
  Guide holes:
    4d. In double "S O N" box opposite rows 14/15, at left (no dot) or right (dot)
    1s.3d. None
  Marginal arrows (photo-etched): "W" shaped, at top, bottom and sides
  Marginal rule: At bottom of sheet
  Colour register marks:
    4d. None
    1s.3d. Above and below vertical rows 1 and 6
  Coloured crosses:
    4d. None
    1s.3d. Above and below vertical row 2
  Autotron marks (solid):
    4d. Violet-blue, black, new blue opposite rows 5/6, at right (no dot) or left (dot)
    1s.3d. None
  Colour designations: None
  Traffic lights (boxed):
    4d. New blue, black, violet-blue opposite R. 19/6
    1s.3d. Orange, black, slate-blue opposite R. 19/6

Quantities Sold

	Ordinary	Phosphor
4d.	77,905,176	8,738,520
1s.3d.	5,685,096	1,226,160
Pack	38,968	—

Withdrawn 29.7.66 but later put on sale again in error for a short time at the Philatelic Counter in London and at the Philatelic Bureau in Edinburgh

W79.   Westminster Abbey
(Des. Sheila Robinson)

W80.   Fan Vaulting, Henry VII Chapel
(Des. and eng. Bradbury, Wilkinson)

1966 (FEBRUARY 28). 900th ANNIVERSARY OF WESTMINSTER ABBEY

Westminster Abbey, officially the Collegiate Church of St. Peter, Westminster, is the nation's Coronation Church and a mausoleum for England's greatest men and women

The 2s.6d. is recess-printed on ordinary paper by Bradbury, Wilkinson and comb perf. 11 × 12

Cat. No.	S.G. No.	Type		Description	Unused	Used
A. Ordinary						
W83	687	**W79**		3d. Black, red-brown and new	5	5
a. Diadem flaw (No dot, R. 16/2)..			75	blue		
W84	688	**W80**		2s.6d. Black	40	40
W83/4				First Day Cover	†	60
W83/4				Presentation Pack	1·25	
B. Phosphor						
WP83	687p	**W79**		3d. One band	10	10
a. Diadem flaw (No dot, R. 16/2)..			1·25	*b.* Two bands	50	
WP83				First Day Cover	†	50

Listed Variety

W83*a*, WP83*a*

Cylinder and Plate Numbers (Blocks of four)

	Cyl. or Plate Nos.						Perforation Type A	
							No dot	Dot
3d.	2A (blue)–1B (black)–1C (brown). Ordinary			..	..		40	40
3d.	2A (blue)–1B (black)–1C (brown). Phosphor			..	..		50	50
2s.6d. Plate 1. Ordinary		..	..	..	..	..	2·00	†
2s.6d. Plate 1A. Ordinary		..	..	..	..	..	2·50	†

Minor Constant Flaws

Minimum prices as singles: 3d. ordinary 40p; phosphor 50p; 2s.6d. 75p

3d. Cyls. 2A–1B–1C no dot
  1/6 Vertical scratch to right of Queen's head and running through bottom frame of panel (Th. D–E12), OP
  15/1 Small white dots touching E and second A of ANNIVERSARY, OP

2s.6d. Plate 1
  2/2 Broken horizontal line in top margin over Y of ANNIVERSARY (Th. A1)
  6/1 Scratch in bottom margin below Y of ABBEY (Th. I13–14)
  10/2 Second o of 900 joined to t of th

2s.6d. Plate 1A
  5/3 Horizontal line in margin left of Y of ANNIVERSARY and vertical line in top margin at left (Th. A1 and A2)
  7/4 Scratch through Y of ANNIVERSARY

Sheet Details

Sheet sizes:
  3d. 120 (6 × 20). Double pane sheet-fed
  2s.6d. 40 (4 × 10). Double pane sheet-fed
Sheet markings:
  Cylinder numbers: 3d. R. 19/1, boxed
  Plate numbers: 2s.6d. Bottom margin below vertical rows 3/4
  Guide holes:
    3d. In double "S O N" box opposite rows 14/15, at left (no dot) or right (dot)
    2s.6d. In circle opposite row 6, at left (Pl. 1) or right (Pl. 1A)
  Marginal arrows (photo-etched): 3d. "W" shaped, at top, bottom and sides; 2s.6d. none
  Marginal rule: 3d at bottom of sheet; 2s.6d. none.
  Colour register marks: None
  Coloured cross (black): 2s.6d. opposite row 6, at right (Pl. 1) or left (Pl. 1A)
  Autotron marks (solid):
    3d. Blue, black, red-brown opposite rows 6/7, at right (no dot) or left (dot); 2s.6d. none
  Colour designations: None
  Traffic lights (boxed):
    3d. Blue, black, red-brown opposite R. 19/6

Quantities Sold

	Ordinary	Phosphor
3d.	48,703,426	5,247,720
2s.6d.	2,819,056	—
Pack	24,272	—

Withdrawn 31.8.66 3d. (2s.6d. sold out in April 1966)

The 3d. was later put on sale again in error for a short time at the Philatelic Counter in London and at the Philatelic Bureau in Edinburgh

W81. View near Hassocks, Sussex

W82. Antrim, Northern Ireland

W83. Harlech Castle, Wales

W84. Cairngorm Mountains, Scotland

(Des. L. Rosomon. Queen's portrait adapted by D. Gentleman from coinage)

1966 (MAY 2). LANDSCAPES

Britain's first special pictorial stamps featuring scenes in England, Northern Ireland, Wales and Scotland

This issue also marks the change in the Queen's portrait

Cat. No.	S.G. No.	Type		Description	Unused	Used
A. Ordinary						
W85	689	**W81**		4d. Black, yellow-green and	5	5
a. Dash before ENGLAND (No dot, R. 20/5)		..	1·25	new blue		
b. Green flaw on tree trunk (Dot, R. 3/4) ..		..				
W86	690	**W82**		6d. Black, emerald and new	5	5
a. Watermark inverted	..	..	1·50	blue		
b. AN for AND (R. 10/3) ..		..	15·00			
W87	691	**W83**		1s.3d. Black, greenish yellow	12	10
a. Broken D (R. 14/2)	..	..	1·50	and greenish blue		
W88	692	**W84**		1s.6d. Black, orange and	15	12
a. Watermark inverted	..	..	4·50	Prussian blue		
W85/8				First Day Cover	†	60
B. Phosphor						
WP85	689p	**W81**		4d. Three bands	8	5
a. Green flaw on tree trunk (Dot, R. 3/4) ..		..				
WP86	690p	**W82**		6d. Three bands	12	10
a. Watermark inverted	..	..	12·00			
b. AN for AND (R. 10/3)		..	3·25			
WP87	691p	**W83**		1s.3d. Three bands	15	15
a. Broken D (R. 14/2)	..	..	1·75			
WP88	692p	**W84**		1s.6d. Three bands	20	20
WP85/8				First Day Cover	†	1·00

These are known postmarked 26th April in Winchester

Listed Varieties
W86b and WP86b. 40,000 sheets were printed before this was discovered and the D was then added to the cylinder

W85a
(Later retouched)

W85b, WP85a

W87a, WP87a

Cylinder Numbers (Blocks of four)
(a) Ordinary

	Cyl. Nos.				Perforation Type A	
					No dot	Dot
4d.	2A (blue)–1B (black)–1C (yellow-green)	..	..	..	40	40

						No dot	
						Type F	Type F(L)
6d.	1A (blue)–3B (black)–1C (green)	..	..	..	..	40	†
1s.3d.	2A (blue)–2B (black)–1C* (yellow)	..	..	..	..	75	†
1s.6d.	1A (blue)–1B (orange)–1C (black)	..	..	..	..	1·00	1·00

(b) Phosphor

					Perforation Types		
					A	A	F
					No dot	Dot	No dot
4d.	2A (blue)–1B (black)–1C (yellow-green)	..	..	..	50	50	†
6d.	1A (blue)–3B (black)–1C (green)	..	..	..	†	†	75
1s.3d.	2A (blue)–2B (black)–1C* (yellow)	..	..	..	†	†	75
1s.6d.	1A (blue)–1B (orange)–1C (black	..	..	..	†	†	1·00

*The figure one of this cylinder is inverted

Minor Constant Flaws
Minimum prices as singles:

	Ordinary	Phosphor		Ordinary	Phosphor
4d.	40	50	1s.3d.	60	75
6d.	40	60	1s.6d.	75	90

4d. Cyls. 2A–1B–1C no dot
11/2 Pale area behind Queen's collar above value (Th. E–F12–13), OP
14/5 Dark spot in green field at top left corner (Th. A1–2), OP

4d. Cyls. 2A–1B–1C dot
2/4 Retouching in sky between clouds (Th. A2), OP

6d. Cyls. 1A–1B–1C no dot
2/2 Horizontal blue line across Queen's neck, later retouched on ordinary (Th. D11), OP
5/4 Green spot between N. and I, OP
17/2 Curved green flaw on trees opposite Queen's chin (Th. D9), OP
18/1 Blue mark in field left of cottage (Th. F5), OP
19/2 Green line running across Queen's head (Th. B10–12), OP
20/6 Diagonal black flaw below second R of HARRISON, OP

1s.3d. Cyls. 2A–2B–1C no dot
6/1 Pale diagonal white line above ES of WALES, OP
9/2 Pale area between 1 and 3 of value (Th. F11–12), OP

1s.6d. Cyls. 1A–1B–1C no dot
1/6 Blurred area at back of Queen's hair (Th. B–C12), OP
4/6 Several blemishes in background between mountains which appear as italic figures 20 (Th. A4–5), OP
8/1 Retouch above d of value (Th. F13), OP
13/4 Retouch behind Queen's neck (Th. D12), OP
18/3 White spot between AN of SCOTLAND and foot of A is enlarged, OP

Sheet Details
Sheet size: 120 (6 × 20). 4d. double pane reel-fed; others single pane sheet-fed
Sheet markings:
    Cylinder numbers: R. 19/1, boxed

Guide holes:
  4d. In single "S O N" box opposite rows 14/15, at left (no dot) or right (dot). The centre bar of the double
    box has been erased
  Others: None
Marginal arrows (photo-etched): "W" shaped, at top, bottom and sides
Marginal rule: At bottom of sheet
Colour register marks:
  4d. None
  Others: Above and below vertical rows 1/2 and 5/6
Autotron marks (solid):
  4d. Blue, black, yellow-green opposite rows 5/6, at right (no dot) or left (dot); others, none
Colour designations: None
Traffic lights (boxed):
  4d. Blue, black, yellow-green opposite R. 19/6
  6d. Blue, black, green opposite R. 19/6
  1s.3d. Blue, black, yellow opposite R. 19/6
  1s.6d. Black, blue, orange opposite R. 19/6

Quantities Sold

	Ordinary	Phosphor		Ordinary	Phosphor
4d.	80,326,440	11,283,720	1s.3d.	5,286,000	1,242,720
6d.	11,531,760	2,459,280	1s.6d.	5,462,640	1,204,200

Withdrawn 1.5.67 but 6d. phosphor was sold out in January

W86. Goalmouth Mêlée
(Des. W. Kempster)

W85. Players with Ball
(Des. D. Gentleman)

W87. Goalkeeper saving Goal
(Des. D. Caplan)

1966 (JUNE 1). WORLD FOOTBALL CUP COMPETITION

Sixteen countries took part in the final stages of the World Football Competition for the
Jules Rimet Cup in England during July, 1966

Watermark sideways on 4d.

Cat. No.	S.G. No.	Type		Description	Unused	Used
A. Ordinary						
W89	693	**W85**		4d. Red, reddish purple, bright	5	5
a. Patch on thigh (No dot, R. 3/20)			75	blue, flesh and black		
b. Red patch below ball (No dot,						
R. 4/16) ..	..	..	60			
W90	694	**W86**		6d. Black, sepia, red, apple-	5	5
a. Black omitted ..	..	..	45·00	green and blue		
b. Apple-green omitted	..					
c. Red omitted	..	..		*d.* Watermark inverted ..	..	75
W91	695	**W87**		1s.3d. Black, blue, yellow, red	12	10
a. Blue omitted ..	..		£180	and light yellow-olive		
b. Watermark inverted	..	..	25·00			
c. Darned stocking (R. 19/2)		..	1·25			
W89/91				First Day Cover	†	60
W89/91				Presentation Pack	75	

Cat. No.	S.G. No.	Type	Description	Unused	Used

B. Phosphor

WP89   693p   **W85**   4d. Two bands   5   5
a. Patch on thigh (No dot, R. 3/20)   1·00
b. Red patch below ball (No dot, R. 4/16)   75

WP90   694p   **W86**   6d. Three bands   12   10
a. Black omitted .. .. .. 75·00

WP91   695p   **W87**   1s.3d. Three bands   20   25
a. Watermark inverted .. .. 1·00
b. Darned stocking (R. 19/2) .. 1·50

WP89/91   First Day Cover   †   75

The 4d. ordinary has been seen postmarked 31st May in Hereford.

Listed Varieties

W89*a*, WP89*a*, W96*a*

W89*b*, WP89*b*, W96*b*

W91*c*, WP91*b*

Cylinder Numbers (Blocks of six)

(a) Ordinary

Cyl. Nos.

Perforation Type A

	No dot	Dot
4d. 1A (black)–1B (blue)–1C (red)–1D (purple)– 1E (flesh)* ..	40	40

Perforation Types

	F No dot	F(L) No dot
6d. 1A (blue)–1B (green)–1C (red)–1D (sepia)–1E (black) ..	50	†
2A (blue)–1B (green)–1C (red)–1D (sepia)–1E (black) ..	60	†
1s.3d. 1A (black)–1B (yellow)–1C (yellow-olive)–1D (blue)–1E (red) 1·50*		2·50*
1A (black)–1B (yellow)–1C (yellow-olive)–1D (blue)–2E (red) 1·50*		2·00*

(b) Phosphor

Perforation Types

	A No dot	A Dot	F No dot
4d. 1A (black)–1B (blue)–1C (red)–1D (purple)–1E (flesh)*	50	50	†
6d. 1A (blue)–1B (green)–1C (red)–1D (sepia)–1E (black)	†	†	1·00
1s.3d. 1A (black)–1B (yellow)–1C (yellow-olive)–1D (blue)			
–2E (red)	†	†	2·50*

*In the 4d. no dot pane the flesh cylinder is expressed in error thus: "1E.".

The 4d. is with sheet orientated showing head to left.

Minor Constant Flaws

Minimum prices as singles.

	Ordinary	Phosphor
4d.	40	50
6d.	50	60
1s.3d.	75	1·00

4d. Cyls. 1A–1B–1C–1D–1E no dot
3/1 Horizontal scratch through top of ball (Th. K1–2), OP
5/6 Blue patch below u of Cup, OP
6/18 Blue spots over T of LTD, OP

4d. Cyls. 1A–1B–1C–1D–1E dot
4/20 Red line joins head and left arm of player at left (Th. F3), OP
5/10 Dark spot on ball (Th. K1), OP
5/17 Grey coloured spur to top of l of World, OP

6d. Cyls. 1B–1C–1D–1E in combination with blue cyls. 1A or 2A no dot
5/4 Diagonal scratch on barrier next to grass below crowd (Th. G5–7), OP

6d. Cyl. 1A no dot
17/4 Pale area around top of 1 of 1966, OP

1s.3d. Cyls. 1A–1B–1C–1D no dot in combination with red cyls. 1E or 2E
1/3 Patch on sock of central player (Th. G2), OP
9/2 Black spur on head of right-hand player (Th. B7), OP
14/5 Break in black frame line around players opposite U of CUP, OP
18/1 Black spot to right of stroke of 1/3; also black spot below second R of HARRISON OP
20/1 Black spot below second A of CAPLAN, OP

1s.3d. Cyl. 2E no dot
1/6 Red scratch on face of central player ,OP

Sheet Details

Sheet size:
  4d. 120 (20 × 6). Double pane reel-fed
  6d. and 1s.3d. 120 (6 × 20). Single pane sheet-fed
Sheet markings:
  Cylinder numbers:
    4d. Above vertical rows 2/3, boxed
    6d. and 1s.3d. Opposite rows 18/19 at left, boxed
  Guide holes:
    4d. In single photo-etched box above vertical rows 6/7 (no dot) or below (dot). On the no dot pane the
      box is now lettered "S N", the "S" being on the left in the box (usually trimmed off), and the "N"
      above the right line. On the dot pane the sequence is reversed.
    6d. and 1s.3d. None
  Marginal arrows (photo-etched): "W" shaped, at top, bottom and sides, except that early printings of the
    6d. from cylinder 1A both ordinary and phosphor were without any arrow markings in the margins
    These were later inserted by hand.
    Minimum price for marginal strip showing arrow omitted: ordinary £5; phosphor £8
  Marginal rule:
    4d. At left of sheet
    6d. and 1s.3d. At bottom of sheet
  Colour register marks:
    4d. Above vertical rows 3/4 and 18/19 (no dot) or below (dot)
    6d. and 1s.3d. Above and below vertical rows 1/2 and 6
  Coloured crosses:
    4d. None
    6d. Above and below vertical row 3
    1s.3d. Above and below vertical rows 3/4
  Autotron marks (solid):
    4d. Red, purple, flesh, black below vertical rows 15/18 (no dot) or above (dot)
    6d. and 1s.3d. None
  Colour designations:
    4d. "5 BLACK G4 BLUE MAROON G3 G2 RED G1 LIGHT RED" below vertical rows 11/16 on dot
      panes only
    6d. and 1s.3d. None
  Traffic lights (boxed):
    4d. Black, blue, red, purple, flesh reading left to right below vertical rows 2/3
    6d. Blue, green, red, sepia, black opposite rows 18/19 at right
    1s.3d. Black, yellow, yellow-olive, blue, red opposite rows 18/19 at right

Quantities Sold

	Ordinary	Phosphor
4d.	129,764,160	16,397,880
6d.	17,086,680	3,357,480
1s.3d.	7,026,240	1,761,240
Pack	48,673	—

Withdrawn   31.5.67

W88. Black-headed Gull

W89. Blue Tit

W90. Robin

W91. Blackbird

(Des. J. Norris Wood)

1966 (AUGUST 8). BRITISH BIRDS

These were the first British stamps to be printed in eight colours

Issued together in *se-tenant* blocks of four within the sheet

Cat. No.	S.G. No.	Type	Description	Unused	Used
A. Ordinary					
W92	696	**W88**	4d. Grey, black, red, emerald-green, bright blue, greenish yellow and bistre	5	5
Missing colours:					
a. Black (value, etc.), blue and bistre .. .. .. 80·00					
b. Black (value, etc.)					
c. Greenish yellow .. .. .. 7·50					
d. Red .. .. 15·00			*g.* Bistre	5·00	
e. Emerald-green .. .. .. 10·00			*h.* Watermark inverted	50	
f. Bright blue .. .. .. 12·00			*i.* HARRISO omitted (No dot, R. 15/5)*.. .. .. .. 10·00		
W93	697	**W89**	4d. Black, greenish yellow, grey, emerald-green, bright blue and bistre	5	5
Missing colours:					
a. Black, blue and bistre .. .. 80·00					
b. Black					
c. Greenish yellow .. .. .. 7·50					
d. Emerald-green .. .. .. 10·00			*f.* Bistre	5·00	
e. Bright blue .. .. .. 12·00			*g.* Watermark inverted	50	
W94	698	**W90**	4d. Red, greenish yellow, black, grey, bistre, reddish brown and emerald-green	5	5
Missing colours:					
a. Black, bistre and reddish brown 80·00					
b. Black					
c. Greenish yellow .. .. .. 7·50					
d. Red .. .. 15·00					
e. Emerald-green .. .. .. 10·00			*g.* Reddish brown .. .. 10·00		
f. Bistre .. .. .. 5·00			*h.* Watermark inverted	50	
W95	699	**W91**	4d. Black, reddish brown, greenish yellow and grey	5	5
Missing colours:					
a. Black and reddish brown .. 60·00					
b. Black					
c. Greenish yellow .. .. .. 7·50					
d. Reddish brown .. .. .. 10·00			*e.* Watermark inverted	50	
W92/5			First Day Cover	†	30
W92/5			Presentation Pack	60	

Cat. No.	S.G. No.	Type	Description	Unused	Used

B. Phosphor

WP92   696p   **W88**   4d. Three bands   5   5

Missing colours:
a. Emerald-green ..   ..   .. 10·00   *c.* Bistre   ..   .. 10·00
b. Bright blue   ..   ..   .. 30·00   *d.* Watermark inverted   ..   .. 6·00

WP93   697p   **W89**   4d. Three bands   5   5

Missing colours:
a. Emerald-green ..   ..   .. 10·00   *c.* Bistre   ..   .. 10·00
b. Bright blue   ..   ..   .. 30·00   *d.* Watermark inverted   ..   .. 6·00

WP94   698p   **W90**   4d. Three bands   5   5

Missing colours:
a. Emerald-green ..   ..   .. 10·00   *c.* Reddish brown ..   ..   .. 13·00
b. Bistre   ..   .. 10·00   *d.* Watermark inverted   ..   .. 6·00

WP95   699p   **W91**   4d. Three bands   5   5

Missing colour:
a. Reddish brown ..   ..   .. 13·00   *b.* Watermark inverted   ..   .. 6·00

WP92/5   First Day Cover   †   40

Prices for missing colour errors in blocks of four:

	Ordinary	Phosphor				Ordinary	Phosphor
Black, bright blue, bistre				Emerald-green	.. ..	30 00	30·00
and reddish brown	.. £300	†		Bright blue	.. ..	25·00	60·00
Black	—	†		Bistre ..	.. ..	20 00	40·00
Greenish yellow ..	.. 30·00	†		Reddish brown	.. ..	17·50	25·00
Red	.. 30·00	†					

*"HARRISON" is omitted except for fragments of the "N" and on the stamp below (W94) the imprint is very faint, particularly "AND SO". The price is for a block containing both varieties. The damage was quickly discovered and repaired during the early stages of the printing.

These are known postmarked at various places in Cheshire on 18th July from a sheet accidentally released by the Philatelic Bureau. Other covers are known with dates from 17th July from various places in England from supplies prematurely released by the Philatelic Bureau.

Cylinder Numbers (Blocks of eight)

           Cyl. Nos.   Perforation Type F. No dot

	Ordinary	Phosphor
2A (black)–1B (grey)–1C (yellow)–1D (red)–1E (green)–2F (blue)–2G (bistre)–1H (brown)	75	1·00
2A (black)–1B (grey)–1C (yellow)–1D (red)–1E (green)–2F (blue)–2G (bistre)–2H (brown)	6·00	†

Minor Constant Flaws

Minimum prices as singles: Ordinary 40p; phosphor 50p

4d. Cyls. 2A–1B–1C–1D–1E–2F–2G with 1H or 2H no dot
     1/2 Small brown dot under main twig (Th. B3), OP
     4/3 Small brown dot to right of Robin's tail (Th. B7), OP
     5/1 Small black dot in gull's wing (Th. D5), OP
     6/2 Red spot between blackbird's claws (Th. F6), OP
     7/1 Small black dot in gull's wing (Th. D6), OP
     7/4 Extension to main twig at right (Th. A6), OP
     9/6 Horizontal bistre line above main twig at left (Th. A–B3–4), O

Sheet Details

Sheet size: 120 (6 × 20). In *se-tenant* blocks of four, single pane sheet-fed
Sheet markings:
     Cylinder numbers: Opposite rows 17/19 at left, boxed
     Guide holes: None
     Marginal arrows (photo-etched): "W" shaped, at top, bottom and sides
     Marginal rule: At bottom of sheet
     Colour register marks: Above and below vertical rows 1/3 and 5/6
     Coloured crosses: Above and below vertical rows 3/4
     Autotron marks and colour designations: None
     Traffic lights (boxed): In same order as cylinder numbers opposite rows 18/19 at right

Quantities Sold

     Ordinary 88,047,742; phosphor 14,613,120; Pack (ordinary) 42,888

Withdrawn   7.8.57

W92. Cup Winners
(Des. D. Gentleman)

1966 (AUGUST 18). ENGLAND'S WORLD CUP FOOTBALL VICTORY

England won the World Cup Football Competition by defeating West Germany 4–2 at Wembley on July 30th, 1966

Watermark sideways

Cat. No.	S.G. No.	Type		Description	Unused	Used
Ordinary only						
W96	700	**W92**		4d. Red, reddish purple, bright		
a. Patch on thigh (No dot, R. 3/20)			1·00	blue, flesh and black	10	20
b. Red patch below ball (No dot, R. 4/16) ..	..	..	75			
W96				First Day Cover	†	50

The above was only put on sale at post offices in England, the Channel Islands and the Isle of Man, and at the Philatelic Bureau in London and also, on August 22nd, in Edinburgh on the occasion of the opening of the Edinburgh Festival as well as at Army post offices at home and abroad.

It was also pre-released on 17th August at an Army Camp P.O. in Great Britain.

Listed Varieties

W96a and W96b. See illustrations after Nos. WP89/91.

Cylinder Numbers (Block of six)

		Perforation Type A	
Cyl. Nos.		No dot	Dot
4d 1A (biack)–1B (blue)–1C (red)–1D (purple)–1E (flesh)* ..		70	70

*In the no dot pane the flesh cylinder is expressed in error thus: "1E.".

The above is with sheet orientated showing head to left.

Minor Constant Flaws

Minimum price as singles: 50p

4d. Cyls. 1A–1B–1C–1D–1E no dot
  1/15 Black dot in second N of ENGLAND
  2/9 Black spur on left player's right boot (Th. J–K5)
  3/1 Horizontal scratch through top of ball (Th. K1–2)
  5/6 Blue patch below u of Cup
  6/13 White patch on heel of left player's left boot (Th. J3)
  6/18 Blue spots over T of LTD

4d. Cyls. 1A–1B–1C–1D–1E dot
  4/11 Black dot between W and I of WINNERS
  5/10 Dark spot on ball (Th. K1)
  5/17 Grey coloured spur to top of l of World

Sheet Details

Sheet size: 120 (20×6). Double pane reel-fed
Sheet markings:
    Cylinder numbers: Above vertical rows 2/3, boxed
    Guide holes: In single "S N" box above vertical rows 6/7 (no dot) or below (dot)
    Marginal arrows (photo-etched): "W" shaped, at top, bottom and sides
    Marginal rule: At left of sheet
    Colour register marks: Above vertical rows 3/4 and 18/19 (no dot) or below (dot)
    Autotron marks (solid): Red, purple, flesh, blue, black below vertical rows 15/18 (no dot) or above (dot)
    Colour designations: "5 BLACK G4 BLUE MAROON G3 G2 RED G1 LIGHT RED" below vertical rows
      11/16 on dot panes only
    Traffic lights (boxed): Black, blue, red, purple, flesh reading left to right below vertical rows 2/3

Quantity Sold 12,452,640

Sold Out Soon after issue

W93. Jodrell Bank Radio Telescope   **W94.** British Motor-cars
(Des. D. and A. Gillespie)

W95. SRN 6 Hovercraft   **W96.** Windscale Reactor
(Des. J. A. Restall)

1966 (SEPTEMBER 19). BRITISH TECHNOLOGY

The designs represent British Technological achievements

Cat. No.	S.G. No.	Type		Description	Unused	Used
					5	5
A. Ordinary						
W97	701	**W93**		4d. Black and lemon	5	5
a. Struts flaw (No dot, R. 4/6)			1·10			
W98	702	**W94**		6d. Red, deep blue and orange	5	5
a. Red (Mini-cars) omitted			£150			
b. Blue (Jaguar and inscr.) omitted			£180	*c.* Broken D (R. 19/6)	1·25	
W99	703	**W95**		1s.3d. Black, orange-red, slate and light greenish blue	12	10
W100	704	**W96**		1s.6d. Black, yellow-green, bronze-green, lilac and deep blue	15	15
W97/100				First Day Cover	†	50
W97/100				Presentation Pack	60	
B. Phosphor						
WP97	701p	**W93**		4d. Three bands	5	5
a. Pair, with and without phosphor			10·00			
b. Struts flaw (No dot, R. 4/6)			1·40			
WP98	702p	**W94**		6d. Three bands	5	8
a. Phosphor back and front			1·50			
b. Broken D (R. 19/6)			1·50			
WP99	703p	**W95**		1s.3d. Three bands	12	15
WP100	704p	**W96**		1s.6d. Three bands	15	20
a. Phosphor back and front			5·00			
WP97/100				First Day Cover	†	90

Listed Varieties

W97a, WP97b
Strong retouch consisting of three strong
black strokes in the form of an arrow

W98c, WP98b

Cylinder Numbers (Blocks of six)

(a) Ordinary

		Cyl. Nos.					Perforation Type A	
							No dot	Dot
4d.	1A (lemon)–1B (black)	..	..	..	..	..	40	40
6d.	1A (orange)–1B (red)–1C (blue)	..	..	..	50	†
1s.3d.	1A (blue)–1B (slate)–1C (orange)–1D (black)	..	.. 1·00	†
1s.6d.	1A (bronze-green)–1B (lilac)–1C (black)–1D (yellow-green)–						
	1E (blue)	..	..	..	..	..	.. 1·40	†

(b) Phosphor

4d.	1A (lemon)–1B (black)	..	..	..	..	..	50	50
6d.	1A (orange)–1B (red)–1C (blue)	..	..	..	60	†
1s.3d.	1A (blue)–1B (slate)–1C (orange)–1D (black)	..	.. 1·00	†
1s.6d.	1A (bronze-green)–1B (lilac)–1C (black)–1D (yellow-green)–						
	1E (blue)	..	..	..	..	..	.. 1·50	†

Minor Constant Flaws

Minimum prices as singles:

	Ordinary	Phosphor		Ordinary	Phosphor
4d.	40	50	1s.3d.	75	90
6d.	50	60	1s.6d.	90	1.00

4d. Cyls. 1A–1B no dot
  1/1 Lines of retouching above Queen's head resemble a thumb-print (Th. A9–12); also small **pale area in** left of telescope bowl (Th. C3–4), both OP
  1/2 Retouch to background right of value (Th. B3–4), OP
  1/6 Retouch to background top left corner of stamp (Th. A1), OP
  5/4 Retouch to background in front of Queen's neck (Th. E9), OP
  10/6 Horizontal line of retouching to background behind Queen's head (Th. D12–13), OP
  19/6 Horizontal white line above ON AND SONS of imprint, OP
  20/5 Horizontal white line below portrait (Th. F10–12), OP
  20/6 As 20/5 but stronger line, OP

4d. Cyls. 1A–1B dot
   3/3 Retouch to background in front of Queen's neck (Th. E10), OP
   5/5 White scratch in right of telescope bowl (Th. B6–7), OP
   9/3 Small white patch in background below portrait (Th. F–G12), OP
   9/5 Retouch to background at left of telescope bowl (Th. E–F1), OP
   13/4 Small white patch in background bottom left of portrait (Th. F–G9), OP
   13/5 Pale patch in background to left of telescope bowl (Th. E–F2), OP
   14/6 Yellow spot in right of telescope bowl (Th. D6), OP

6d. Cyls. 1A–1B–1C no dot
   5/6 Retouch to background above Queen's head (Th. A10–11), OP
   10/3 Vertical blue line in Queen's portrait (Th. A–C10), OP
   13/3 Pale area above value (Th. A2), OP
   17/4 Spur of first S of SONS, OP

1s.3d. Cyls. 1A–1B–1C–1D no dot
   1/1 Retouch in background behind Queen's head (Th. C–D13), OP
   1/4 White spot below e of Hovercraft, OP
   1/6 Retouch in sea, bottom centre (Th. G7), OP
   12/6 Horizontal orange coloured line extends from sea to sheet margin (Th. G13–15), OP

1s.6d. Cyls. 1A–1B–1C–1D–1E no dot
   1/3 Retouch in sky in front of Queen's neck (Th. C–D10), OP
   1/5 Grey coloured flaw in sky top right of Queen's head (Th. A13), OP
   2/2 Lower part of left stroke of n of Advanced is broken off, OP
   16/3 Vertical blue line in gutter between design edge and perforation (Th. D–G13), OP
   16/5 Whispy whitish line runs vertically above **v** of Advanced (Th. F–G2), OP
   20/1 Small white flaw in large door of building (Th. F6), OP

Sheet Details

Sheet size: 120 (6 × 20). 4d. double pane reel-fed; others single pane reel-fed

Sheet markings:
   Cylinder numbers:
      4d., 6d., 1s.3d. Opposite R. 19/1, boxed
      1s.6d. Opposite rows 18/19 at left, boxed
   Guide holes:
      4d. In single "S N" box opposite rows 14/15, at left (no dot) or right (dot)
      Others. In single "S O N" box opposite rows 14/15, at both sides
   Marginal arrows (photo-etched): "W" shaped, at top, bottom and sides
   Marginal rule: None
   Colour register marks:
      4d. Opposite rows 1/2 and 20, at left (no dot) or right (dot)
      6d., 1s.3d. Opposite rows 2/3 and 17/18, at both sides
      1s.6d. Opposite rows 3/4 and 17/18, at both sides
   Autotron marks (solid):
      4d. Black, lemon, opposite row 5, at right (no dot) or left (dot)
      6d. Blue, red, orange below vertical rows 1/3
      1s.3d. Black, orange, blue, slate below vertical rows 1/3
      1s.6d. Black, lilac, bronze-green, yellow-green, blue below vertical rows 1/3
   Colour designations:
      4d. "G1 YELLOW G2 BLACK" in right margin reading upwards opposite rows 8/5 on dot panes only
      6d. "G2 RED G3 BLUE" in right margin reading upwards opposite rows 7/6
      1s.3d. "G1 GREY G2 BLUE G3 RED G4 BLACK" in right margin reading upwards opposite rows 7/4
      1s.6d. "G1 BLUE G2 YELLOW G3 GREEN G4 MAUVE G5 BLACK" in right margin reading upwards opposite rows 9/5
   Traffic lights (boxed):
      4d. Lemon, black opposite R. 19/6
      6d. Orange, red, blue opposite R. 19/6
      1s.3d. Blue, slate, orange, black opposite rows 18/19 at right
      1s.6d. Black, lilac, bronze-green, yellow-green, blue opposite rows 18/19 at right

Quantities Sold

	Ordinary	Phosphor		Ordinary	Phosphor
4d.	79,112,278	12,737,520	1s.6d.	5,284,069	1,414,320
6d.	11,087,516	2,388,720	Pack	35,437	—
1s.3d.	5,199,900	1,431,000			

Withdrawn 18.9.67

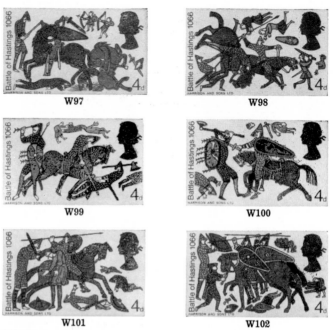

W97   W98

W99   W100

W101   W102

Types **W97/102** show battle scenes and were issued together *se-tenant* in horizontal strips of six within the sheet

W103. Norman Ship

W104. Norman Horsemen attacking Harold's Troops

(Des. D. Gentleman)

(Printed in photogravure with the Queen's head die-stamped in gold)

1966 (OCTOBER 14). 900th ANNIVERSARY OF BATTLE OF HASTINGS

The scenes depicted are all reproduced from the celebrated Bayeux Tapestry which records the Norman invasion of England

Watermark sideways on 1s.3d. (normal is top of crown pointing to left when stamps are viewed from the back)

Cat. No.	S.G. No.	Type	Description	Unused	Used
A. Ordinary					
W101	705	**W97**	4d. Black, olive-green, bistre, deep blue, orange, magenta, green, blue, grey and gold	5	5
Missing colours:					
a. Olive-green .. .. .. 8·00					
b. Bistre .. .. 7·50					
c. Deep blue .. .. .. 8·00					
d. Orange .. .. 6·00			*g.* Blue .. .. 6·00		
e. Magenta .. .. 9·00			*h.* Grey .. .. 6·00		
f. Green .. .. 6·00			*i.* Watermark inverted 75		

Cat. No.	S.G. No.	Type	Description	Unused	Used

W102 706 **W98**

4d. Black, olive-green, bistre, deep blue, orange, magenta, green, blue, grey and gold — 5 — 5

Missing colours:
- *a.* Olive-green .. .. .. 8·00
- *b.* Bistre .. .. 7·50
- *c.* Deep blue .. .. .. 8·00
- *d.* Orange .. .. 6·00
- *e.* Magenta .. .. 9·00
- *f.* Green .. .. 6·00
- *g.* Blue .. .. 6·00
- *h.* Grey .. .. 6·00
- *i.* Watermark inverted 75

W103 707 **W99**

4d. Black, olive-green, bistre, deep blue, orange, magenta, green, blue, grey and gold — 5 — 5

Missing colours:
- *a.* Olive-green .. .. .. 8·00
- *b.* Bistre .. .. 7·50
- *c.* Deep blue .. .. .. 8·00
- *d.* Orange .. .. 6·00
- *e.* Magenta .. .. 9·00
- *f.* Green .. .. 6·00
- *g.* Blue .. .. 6·00
- *h.* Grey .. .. 6·00
- *i.* Watermark inverted 75

W104 708 **W100**

4d. Black, olive-green, bistre, deep blue, magenta, green, blue, grey and gold — 5 — 5

Missing colours:
- *a.* Olive-green .. .. .. 8·00
- *b.* Bistre .. .. 7·50
- *c.* Deep blue .. .. .. 8·00
- *d.* Magenta .. .. 9·00
- *e.* Green .. .. 6·00
- *f.* Blue .. .. 6·00
- *g.* Grey .. .. 6·00
- *h.* Watermark inverted 75

W105 709 **W101**

4d. Black, olive-green, bistre, deep blue, orange, magenta, green, blue, grey and gold — 5 — 5

Missing colours:
- *a.* Olive-green .. .. .. 8·00
- *b.* Bistre .. .. 7·50
- *c.* Deep blue .. .. .. 8·00
- *d.* Orange .. .. 6·00
- *e.* Magenta .. .. 9·00
- *f.* Green .. .. 6·00
- *g.* Blue .. .. 6·00
- *h.* Grey .. .. 6·00
- *i.* Watermark inverted 75

W106 710 **W102**

4d. Black, olive-green, bistre, deep blue, orange, magenta, green, blue, grey and gold — 5 — 5

Missing colours:
- *a.* Olive-green .. .. .. 8·00
- *b.* Bistre .. .. 7·50
- *c.* Deep blue .. .. .. 8·00
- *d.* Orange .. .. 6·00
- *e.* Magenta .. .. 9·00
- *f.* Green .. .. 6·00
- *g.* Blue .. .. 6·00
- *h.* Grey .. .. 6·00
- *i.* Watermark inverted 75

W107 711 **W103**

6d. Black, olive-green, violet, blue, green and gold — 8 — 5

- *a.* Watermark inverted .. .. 12·00
- *b.* Yellowish gold 15

W108 712 **W104**

1s.3d. Black, lilac, bronze-green, rosine, bistre-brown and gold — 12 — 10

- *a.* Lilac omitted .. .. .. 75·00
- *b.* Watermark sideways inverted (top of crown pointing to right) 2·00
- *c.* Club flaw (R. 7/2) .. .. 1·00

W101/8 First Day Cover — † — 60

W101/8 Presentation Pack — 75

B. Phosphor

WP101 705p **W97**

4d. Three bands — 5 — 5

Missing colours:
- *a.* Olive-green .. .. .. 8·00
- *c.* Deep blue .. .. .. 8·00
- *d.* Orange .. .. 6·00
- *e.* Magenta .. .. 9·00
- *f.* Green .. .. 6·00
- *h.* Grey .. .. 6·00
- *i.* Magenta and green .. .. 15·00
- *j.* Watermark inverted 35

WP102 706p **W98**

4d. Three bands — 5 — 5

Missing colours:
- *a.* Olive-green .. .. .. 8·00
- *c.* Deep blue .. .. .. 8·00
- *d.* Orange .. .. 6·00
- *e.* Magenta .. .. 9·00
- *f.* Green .. .. 6·00
- *h.* Grey .. .. 6·00
- *i.* Magenta and green .. .. 15·00
- *j.* Watermark inverted 35

WP103 707p **W99**

4d. Three bands — 5 — 5

Missing colours:
- *a.* Olive-green .. .. .. 8·00
- *c.* Deep blue .. .. .. 8·00
- *d.* Orange .. .. 6·00
- *e.* Magenta .. .. 9·00
- *f.* Green .. .. 6·00
- *h.* Grey .. .. 6·00
- *i.* Magenta and green .. .. 15·00
- *j.* Watermark inverted 35

Cat. No.	S.G. No.	Type	Description	Unused	Used
WP104	708p	**W100**	4d. Three bands	5	5

Missing colours:

a. Olive-green	..	..	..	8·00	f. Green .. .. 6·00
c. Deep blue	..	..	..	8·00	h. Magenta and green .. .. 15·00
d. Magenta ..	..	..	..	9·00	i. Watermark inverted 35

WP105	709p	**W101**	4d. Three bands	5	5

Missing colours:

a. Olive-green	..	..	..	8·00	f. Green .. .. 6·00
c. Deep blue	..	..	..	8·00	h. Grey .. .. 6·00
d. Orange ..	..	..	..	6·00	i. Magenta and green .. .. 15·00
e. Magenta ..	..	..	..	9·00	j. Watermark inverted .. 35

WP106	710p	**W102**	4d. Three bands	5	5

Missing colours:

a. Olive-green	..	..	..	8·00	f. Green .. .. 6·00
c. Deep blue	..	..	..	8·00	h. Grey .. .. 6·00
d. Orange ..	..	..	..	6·00	i. Magenta and green .. .. 15·00
e. Magenta ..	..	..	..	9·00	j. Watermark inverted 35

WP107	711p	**W103**	6d. Three bands	8	10
a. Watermark inverted	..	..	25·00		
b. Yellowish gold ..	..	..	20		

WP108	712p	**W104**	1s.3d. Four bands	12	12
a. Lilac omitted	..	..	75·00		
b. Three bands ..	..	1·50		
c. Watermark sideways inverted (top of crown pointing to right)		2·00	d. Club flaw (R. 7/2) .. .. 1·10

WP101/8			First Day Cover	† 1·00

4d. *Prices for missing colour errors in strips of six:*

			Ordinary	Phosphor					Ordinary	Phosphor
Olive-green	..	..	50·00	50·00	Green	..	..	..	40·00	40·00
Bistre	..	..	45·00	†	Blue	..	..	..	40·00	†
Deep blue	..	..	50·00	50·00	Grey	..	..	..	40·00	40·00
Orange (on five stamps)	..	30·00	30·00	Magenta and green		..	†	£100
Magenta	..	..	55·00	55·00						

Nos. W101 and W105 with grey and blue omitted have been seen commercially used, posted from Middleton-in-Teesdale.

The 6d. and 1s.3d. were also issued with the die-stamped gold head omitted but as these can also be removed by chemical means we are not prepared to list them unless a way is found of distinguishing the genuine stamps from the fakes which will satisfy the Expert Committees. However, three copies of No. W108 in a right-hand top corner block of 10 (2 × 5) are known with the Queen's head omitted as a result of a double paper fold prior to die-stamping. The perforation is normal. Of the other seven stamps, four have the Queen's head misplaced and three are normal.

Listed Variety

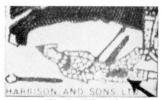

W108c, WP108d
The fallen knight has what appears to be a
large black club at his right hand

Cylinder Numbers (Blocks of 24 (4d.), six (6d.), eight (1s.3d.))

	Cyl. Nos.	Perforation Types

		F No dot
		Ordinary Phosphor
4d.	1A (black)–1B (olive-green)–1C (bistre)–1D (deep blue)– 1E (orange)–1F (magenta)–1G (green)–1H (blue)–1J (grey)	1·50 1·50
	2A (black)–1B (olive-green)–1C (bistre)–1D (deep blue)– 1E (orange)–1F (magenta)–1G (green)–1H (blue)–1J (grey)	2·50 †

	Cyl. Nos.		Perforation Types			
				G		
			No dot	Dot	No dot	Dot
			Ordinary		Phosphor	
6d.	1A (black)–1B (olive-green)–1C (violet)–1D (blue)–					
	1E (green)		75	75	60	60
				A(T)	No dot	
				Ordinary	Phosphor	
1s.3d.	1A (black)–1B (lilac)–1C (bronze-green)–1D (rosine)–					
	1E (bistre-brown)		1·40		1·40	

Minor Constant Flaws

Minimum prices as singles:

	Ordinary	Phosphor		Ordinary	Phosphor
4d.	40	50	1s.3d.	75	75
6d.	50	50			

4d. Cyls. 1B–1C–1D–1E–1F–1G–1H–1J no dot in combination with black cyls. 1A or 2A
3/4 Spur on second S of HASTINGS, OP
4/1 Horizontal black line to left of Queen's forehead (Th. A10–11), OP (1A only)
4/5 Black line under Queen's chin (Th. C11), OP (1A only)
9/1 Right hind leg of dark horse is paler than normal (Th. F–G8), OP
9/2 Second S of SONS pale and distorted, possibly hand drawn (OP) (1A only)
19/4 White spot on horseman's leg (Th. F7), OP (1A only)
20/3 LTD heavier than normal, OP (1A only)
20/4 HARRISON AND heavier than normal, OP (1A only)

4d. Cyl. 2A no dot
10/1 H of HARRISON is indistinct, O
11/1 Hastings 1066 weaker than normal, O

6d. Cyls. 1A–1B–1C–1D–1E no dot
1/1 Blue patch on hull due to lack of black shading (Th. F9) OP
4/1 Small dot after final s of Hastings, OP
6/1 Diagonal black line through figures in small boat (Th. C3–B5), OP
8/4 diagonal spur on first t of Battle, OP

6d. Cyls. 1A–1B–1C–1D–1E dot
1/1 Partial break in main left-hand rigging of main vessel (Th. D3), OP
3/1 Extra gold enlarges Queen's throat at both sides (Th. C–D12), P
8/5 Horizontal black line in upper part of first 6 of 1966, OP
8/6 Horizontal black line through HAR of HARRISON, OP

1s.3d. Cyls. 1A–1B–1C–1D–1E no dot
6/2 Dot in g of Hastings, OP
8/1 Diagonal hairline runs from bottom of red shield of second soldier through toes of right foot to bottom of stamp (Th. E–H12), P
9/1 Line continues to right-hand arm of first soldier (Th. A12), P
10/4 Bronze-green dot upper left of 1 of 1/3 (Th. F8), OP

Sheet Details

Sheet sizes:
4d. 120 (6×20). In *se-tenant* strips of six, single pane sheet-fed
6d. 60 (6×10). Double pane reel-fed
1s.3d. 60 (6×10). Single pane reel-fed
Sheet markings:
Cylinder numbers:
4d. Opposite rows 17/19 at left, boxed
6d. Opposite rows 8/9 at left, boxed
1s.3d. Opposite rows 7/8 at left, boxed
Guide holes: None
Marginal arrows (photo-etched): "W" shaped, at top, bottom and sides
Marginal rule: None
Colour register marks:
4d. Above and below vertical rows 1 and 5/6
6d. Above vertical rows 1 and 5/6 (no dot) or below them (dot)
1s.3d. Opposite rows 1/2 and 9/10, at both sides
Coloured crosses:
4d. Above and below vertical rows 3/4
6d. Above vertical rows 3/4 (no dot) or below them (dot)
1s.3d. Opposite rows 5/6, at both sides
Autotron marks and colour designations: None
Traffic lights (boxed and in same order as cylinder numbers):
4d. Opposite rows 17/19 at right
6d. Opposite rows 8/9 at right
1s.3d. Opposite rows 7/8 at right

Quantities Sold

	Ordinary	Phosphor
4d.	89,197,226	15,861,960
6d.	12,012,328	2,820,360
1s.3d.	5,721,426	1,646,280
Pack	51,332	—

Withdrawn 13.10.67 (6d. phosphor sold out in September)

W105. King of the Orient
(Des. Miss T. Shemza)

W106. Snowman
(Des. J. Berry)

(Printed in photogravure with the Queen's head die-stamped in gold)

1966 (DECEMBER 1). CHRISTMAS

These designs, executed by two six-year-old children, were chosen from nearly 5,000 entries in a Post Office competition for Britain's first adhesive Christmas stamps

Watermark sideways on 3d.

Cat. No.	S.G. No.	Type	Description	Unused	Used
A. Ordinary					
W109	713	**W105**	3d. Black, blue, green, yellow, red and gold	5	5
a. Green omitted ..		— 25·00			
b. Missing T (No dot, R. 6/2) ..		50			
W110	714	**W106**	1s.6d. Blue, red, pink, black and gold	12	12
a. Pink (hat) omitted		85·00			
b. Watermark inverted		2·50			
W109/10			First Day Cover	†	30
W109/10			Presentation Pack	50	
B. Phosphor					
WP109	713p	**W105**	3d. One band (at left or right)	8	8
a. Pair, with and without phosphor		5·00			
b. Missing T (No dot, R. 6/2) ..		65			
WP110	714p	**W106**	1s.6d. Two bands	20	20
a. Watermark inverted		10·00			
WP109/10			First Day Cover	†	75

Listed Variety

W109b, WP109b

Both values were also issued with the die-stamped gold head omitted but as these can also be removed by chemical means we are not prepared to list them unless a way is found of distinguishing the genuine stamps from the fakes which will satisfy the Expert Committees. However, the gold head and embossing omitted also occurred on the last vertical row of a sheet of the 3d. ordinary due to major displacement to the left. Copies in horizontal marginal pairs can be considered to be genuine.

Cylinder Numbers (Blocks of six)

(a) Ordinary

		Cyl. Nos.		Perforation Types	
				A	A
				No dot	Dot
3d.	1A (blue)–2B (black)–1C (green)–1D (yellow)–1E (red)		..	12·00	12·00
	1A (blue)–3B (black)–1C (green)–1D (yellow)–1E (red)		..	60	60
	1A (blue)–4B (black)–1C (green)–1D (yellow)–1E (red)		..	60	40
				A	A(T)
				No dot	No Dot
1s.6d.	1A (blue)–1B (black)–2C (red)–1D (pink)	..	..	1·00	1·75

(b) Phosphor

		Cyl. Nos.		Perforation Types	
				A	A
				No dot	Dot
3d.	1A (blue)–3B (black)–1C (green)–1D (yellow)–1E (red)	..		75	75
	1A (blue)–4B (black)–1C (green)–1D (yellow)–1E (red)	..		75	75
				A	A(T)
				No dot	No dot
1s.6d.	1A (blue)–1B (black)–2C (red)–1D (pink)	..	..	1·50	2·50

The above are with sheets orientated showing head to left.
In the dot panes of the 3d. the dot is missing after B in the black colour.

Minor Constant Flaws

Minimum prices as singles:

	Ordinary	Phosphor
3d.	40	60
1s.6d.	60	90

3d. Cyls. 1A–1C–1D–1E no dot in combination with black cyls. 3B or 4B
2/1 During the course of printing a diagonal cut developed at base of Queen's neck and later the piece of gold foil separated and dropped downwards (Th. C–D5), OP
2/3 Blue dot in front of H of HARRISON, OP
2/8 A of AND in imprint shorter than normal, OP
3/4 White patch at top left corner of panel is larger than normal (Th. A1), OP
3/8 Extra stop after T. of T. SHEMZA, OP
7/1 Damaged top to A of AND, OP
8/8 Red dot under first leg of H of HARRISON, OP

3d. Cyls. 1A–1C–1D–1E dot in combination with black cyls. 3B or 4B
1/5 Two red dots in the yellow above red circle in crown (Th. F–G3), OP (3B only)
2/1 As for no dot cyls.
4/6 Background retouch between points of crown at right (Th. F5), OP
4/7 First S of SONS incomplete, OP
5/5 Red spot in white area below Queen's portrait (Th. D5), OP (3B only)
8/1 Top of S of HARRISON incomplete, OP

1s.6d. Cyls. 1A–1B–2C–1D no dot
3/1 White spot normally found in red scarf is filled in (Th. E4), OP
6/7 Dark blue spot inside 6 of 1/6, OP
8/2 Small blue projection into right-hand margin (Th. L7), OP
9/1 Second R of BERRY is damaged, OP

Sheet Details

Sheet size: 80 (8 × 10)
    3d. double pane reel-fed, with dot pane above no dot pane
    1s.6d. single pane sheet-fed
Sheet markings:
  Cylinder numbers:
    3d. Above vertical rows 2/3, boxed
    1s.6d. Opposite R. 8/1, boxed
  Guide holes: 3d. Boxed above vertical rows 6/7; 1s.6d. none
  Marginal arrows (photo-etched): "W" shaped, at top, bottom and sides
  Marginal rule: None
  Colour register marks:
    3d. None; 1s.6d. above and below vertical rows 1/2 and 7/8
  Coloured crosses: 3d. None; 1s.6d. above and below vertical rows 4/5
  Autotron marks (solid):
    3d. Green, yellow, red, black, blue opposite rows 8/10, left margin (dot); 1s.6d. none
  Colour designations: None
  Traffic lights (boxed):
    3d. Black, blue, green, yellow, red below vertical rows 2/3
    1s.6d. Blue, red, pink, black opposite R. 8/10

Quantities Sold

	Ordinary	Phosphor
3d.	153,318,160	20,774,000
1s.6d.	8,756,960	2,109,280
Pack	33,672	—

Withdrawn

The 3d. phosphor was sold out in January, the 3d. ordinary and 1s.6d. phosphor were sold out in October, and the 1s.6d. ordinary was withdrawn on 30.11.67

W107. Sea Freight   **W108.** Air Freight

(Des. C. Abbott)

1967 (FEBRUARY 20). EUROPEAN FREE TRADE ASSOCIATION

Issued to commemorate the movement of trade between Austria, Denmark, Norway, Portugal, Sweden, Switzerland and the United Kingdom. Finland is an associate member

Cat. No.	S.G. No.	Type	Description	Unused	Used
A. Ordinary					
W111	715	**W107**	9d. Deep blue, red, lilac, green, brown, new blue, yellow and black	8	5
Missing colours:					
a. Black (Queen's head), brown, new blue and yellow		£200			
b. Lilac		8·00			
c. Green			f. Yellow		
d. Brown		12·00	g. Watermark inverted		
e. New blue		8·50	h. Quay flaw (R. 8/3)	75	
W112	716	**W108**	1s.6d. Violet, red, deep blue, brown, green, blue-grey, new blue, yellow and black	12	12
Missing colours:					
a. Red					
b. Deep blue		14·00			
c. Brown		9·00			
d. Blue-grey					
e. New blue		12·00	g. Broken ribbon (R. 11/3)	1·00	
f. Yellow		12·00	h. Broken strut (R. 13/6)	1·00	
W111/2			First Day Cover	†	25
W111/2			Presentation Pack	35	
B. Phosphor					
WP111	715p	**W107**	9d. Three bands	10	8
Missing colours:					
a. Lilac					
b. Green		3·50	e. Yellow		
c. Brown		12·00	f. Watermark inverted		
d. New blue		7·50	g. Quay flaw (R. 8/3)	85	
WP112	716p	**W108**	1s.6d. Three bands	15	15
Missing colours:					
a. Red			e. New blue		
b. Deep blue		12·00	f. Watermark inverted	14·00	
c. Brown		8·50	g. Broken ribbon (R. 11/3)	1·10	
d. Blue-grey			h. Broken strut (R. 13/6)	1·10	
WP111/2			First Day Cover	†	30

Listed Varieties

W111*h*, WP111*g*
Black protuberance on
quay between trucks

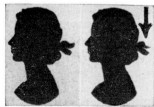

Normal   W112*g*, WP112*g*

W112*h*, WP112*h*
Broken strut below wing

Cylinder Numbers (Blocks of eight)

	Cyl. Nos.	Perforation Type F No dot	
		Ordinary	Phosphor
9d.	1A (deep blue)–1B (red)–1C (lilac)–1D (green)– 1E (brown)–1F (new blue)–1G (yellow)–1H (black)	1·00	1·00
1s.6d.	2A (violet)–1B (red)–1C (deep blue)–1D (green)– 1E (brown)–1F (new blue)–1G (yellow)–2H (blue- grey)–2J (black)	1·50	2·00

Minor Constant Flaws

Minimum prices as singles:

	Ordinary	Phosphor
9d.	50	60
1s.6d.	60	75

9d. Cyls. 1A–1B–1C–1D–1E–1F–1G–1H no dot
  6/5 Black colour on roof of bridge is smudged (Th. D8–9), OP
  11/5 Small blue dot in base of letter E (Th. B–C2), OP
  12/5 White spot in lilac superstructure (Th. E11), OP
1s.6d. Cyls. 2A–1B–1C–1D–1E–1F–1G–2H–2J no dot
  10/1 small violet dot in top of letter E (Th. A2), OP
  19/1 White spur in 6 of 1/6, OP

Sheet Details

Sheet size: 120 (6 × 20). Single pane sheet-fed
Sheet markings:
  Cylinder numbers:
    9d. Opposite rows 17/19 at left, boxed
    1s.6d. Opposite rows 17/20 at left, boxed
  Guide holes: None
  Marginal arrows (photo-etched): "W" shaped, at top, bottom and sides
  Marginal rule: At bottom of sheet
  Colour register marks: Above and below vertical rows 1/2 and 5/6
  Coloured crosses: Above and below vertical rows 4/5
  Autotron marks and colour designations: None
  Traffic lights (boxed):
    9d. Opposite rows 17/19 at right, in same order as cylinder numbers
    1s.6d. Violet, red, deep blue, brown, green, blue-grey, new blue, yellow, black opposite rows 17/19 at right

Quantities Sold

	Ordinary	Phosphor
9d.	6,553,738	5,557,104
1s.6d.	6,363,483	4,237,944
Pack	42,906	—

Withdrawn 19.2.68

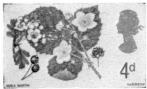

W109. Hawthorn and Bramble

W110. Larger Bindweed and Viper's Bugloss

W111. Ox-eye Daisy, Coltsfoot and Buttercup

W112. Bluebell, Red Campion and Wood Anemone

The above were issued together *se-tenant* in blocks of four within the sheet
(Des. Rev. Keble Martin)

W113. Dog Violet   **W114.** Primroses

(Des. Mary Grierson)

1967 (APRIL 24). BRITISH WILD FLOWERS

Cat. No.	S.G. No.	Type		Description	Unused	Used
A. Ordinary						
W113	717	**W109**		4d. Grey, lemon, myrtle-green, red, agate and slate-purple	5	5
a. Grey double*	..	..	..			
b. Red omitted	..	..	..			
c. Watermark inverted	..	..	35			
W114	718	**W110**		4d. Grey, lemon, myrtle-green, red, agate and violet	5	5
a. Grey double*	..	..	..			
b. Red omitted	..	..	..			
c. Watermark inverted	..	..	35			
W115	719	**W111**		4d. Grey, lemon, myrtle-green, red and agate	5	5
a. Grey double*	..	..	..			
b. Red omitted	..	..	..			
c. Watermark inverted	..	..	35			
W116	720	**W112**		4d. Grey, lemon, myrtle-green, reddish purple, agate and violet	5	5
a. Grey double*	..	..	..			
b. Watermark inverted	..	..	35			
W117	721	**W113**		9d. Lavender-grey, green, reddish violet and orange-yellow	8	8
a. Watermark inverted	..	..	50			
b. Notch in leaf (R. 20/2)	..	..	1·10			
W118	722	**W114**		1s.9d. Lavender-grey, green, greenish yellow and orange	15	15
W113/8				First Day Cover	†	60
W113/8				Presentation Pack	50	
B. Phosphor						
WP113	717p	**W109**		4d. Three bands	5	5
a. Agate omitted	..	..	..			
b. Slate-purple omitted	..	..		c. Watermark inverted	25	
WP114	718p	**W110**		4d. Three bands	5	5
a. Agate omitted	..	..	..			
b. Violet omitted	..	..		c. Watermark inverted	25	
WP115	719p	**W111**		4d. Three bands	5	5
a. Agate omitted	..	..	..			
b. Watermark inverted	..	..	25			
WP116	720p	**W112**		4d. Three bands	5	5
a. Agate omitted	..	..	..			
b. Violet omitted	..	..		c. Watermark inverted	25	
WP117	721p	**W113**		9d. Three bands	8	8
a. Notch in leaf (R. 20/2)	..	..	1·10			
WP118	722p	**W114**		1s.9d. Three bands	15	15
WP113/8				First Day Cover	†	60

4d. *Prices for missing colour errors in blocks of four:*

			Ordinary	Phosphor				Ordinary	Phosphor
Red	..	..	—	†	Violet	..	..	†	—
Agate	..	..	†	—	Slate purple	..	..	†	—

*The double impression of the grey printing affects the Queen's head, value and inscription.

The 1s.9d. is known postmarked 20th April in the Bristol area.

Listed Variety

W117*b*, WP117*a*

Cylinder Numbers (Blocks of eight (4d.) or six (others))

	Cyl. Nos.	Perforation Types

		Ordinary	Phosphor
		F No dot	
4d.	3A (grey)–1B (lemon)–2C (myrtle-green)–1D (reddish purple)–1E (red)–1F (agate)–2G (violet)–1H (slate-purple)	60	60

		A No dot	
9d.	2A (lavender-grey)–3B (green)–3C (reddish violet)–2D (orange-yellow)	1·10*	1·25*
1s.9d.	2A (lavender-grey)–2B (green)–2C (greenish yellow)–2D (orange)	1·25	1·25

Minor Constant Flaws

Minimum prices as singles:

	Ordinary	Phosphor
4d.	40	40
9d.	50	50
1s.9d.	60	50

4d. Cyls. 3A–1B–2C–1D–1E–1F–2G–1H no dot
   1/4 Green flaw in large leaf above flower (Th. A4), OP
   4/6 Yellow spot by Queen's chin (Th. C10), P
   8/6 Small spot by upper leaf of wood anemone (Th. A6), OP
   10/2 Small green spot in lower wood anemone (Th. D9), OP
   15/6 Style on left-hand flower of right-hand plant is incomplete (Th. A6), OP
   16/2 Green spot at left of bluebell leaf (Th. E1), P

9d. Cyls. 2A–3B–3C–2D no dot
   9/6 Diagonal hairline running down from small right-hand leaf (Th. F10), OP
   13/5 Green spot between left leaf and centre violet flower (Th. D3), OP
   14/1 Fine vertical yellow line at right of right-hand leaf on top left-hand stamen (Th. B–C3), OP
   20/6 Green spot in lower left-hand leaf (Th. G1), OP

1s.9d. Cyls. 2A–2B–2C–2D no dot
   1/2 Diagonal yellow hairline in the white portion from Queen's neck to top of value (Th. C–E11), OP
   1/6 Retouch between top of stroke and 9 of value (Th. F12), OP
   2/2 Retouch over 9 of value (Th. F13), OP
   10/1 M of MARY is weak, OP
   15/1 Line of green dots between two right-hand primroses (Th. E9), OP
   19/4 Dotted green line projecting left from top left-hand leaf (Th. C–D1), OP
   19/5 Horizontal green hairline on central primrose (Th. D4), OP
   19/6 N of HARRISON is weak, OP
   20/1 Break in outline of petals in topmost primrose (Th. B7), OP

Sheet Details

Sheet size: 120 (6 × 20)
   4d. In *se-tenant* blocks of four, single pane sheet-fed
   9d. and 1s.9d. Single pane reel-fed
Sheet markings:
   Cylinder numbers:
      4d. Opposite rows 17/19 at left, boxed
      9d., 1s.9d. Opposite rows 18/19 at left, boxed
   Guide holes:
      4d. None
      9d., 1s.9d. Opposite row 15 (boxed), at both sides
   Marginal arrows (photo-etched): "W" shaped, at top, bottom and sides
   Marginal rule: At bottom of sheet
   Colour register marks:
      4d. Above and below vertical rows 1/2 and 5/6
      9d., 1s.9d. Opposite rows 1/2 and 20, at both sides
   Coloured crosses:
      4d. Above and below vertical rows 3/4
      9d., 1s.9d. None

Autotron marks (solid):
4d. None
9d. Lavender-grey, green, reddish violet, green over orange, below vertical rows 1/3
1s.9d. Lavender-grey, orange, green, greenish yellow, below vertical rows 1/3
Colour designations:
4d. None
9d. "G1 GREEN G2 MAUVE G3 ORANGE G4 GREY" in right margin reading upwards opposite
rows 9/3
1s.9d. "G1 YELLOW G2 GREEN G3 ORANGE G4 GREY" in right margin reading upwards opposite
rows 13/7
Traffic lights (boxed and in same order as cylinder numbers):
4d. Opposite rows 17/19 at right
9d., 1s.9d. Opposite rows 18/19 at right

Quantities Sold

	Ordinary	Phosphor
4d.	78,331,778	37,133,952
9d.	5,873,042	5,701,608
1s.9d.	3,259,521	4,929,648
Pack	53,446	—

Withdrawn   23.4.68

PHOSPHOR BANDS

All the following commemorative issues were normally issued with phosphor bands only; however, most also exist with phosphor omitted in error.

W115.   "Master Lambton"
(Sir Thomas Lawrence)

W116.   "Mares and Foals in a
Landscape" (George Stubbs)

W117.   "Children Coming Out of
School" (L. S. Lowry)

1967 (JULY 10). BRITISH PAINTINGS

This is the first issue of British Paintings for which Harrisons made photographs from the originals

No watermark. Two phosphor bands

Cat. No.	S.G. No.	Type	Description	Unused	Used
W119	748	**W115**	4d. Multicoloured	8	5
a. Gold omitted (value and Queen's head) £100					
b. Blue omitted			*c.* Phosphor omitted	3·00	
W120	749	**W116**	9d. Multicoloured	12	10
a. Black omitted (Queen's head and value)			*b.* Phosphor omitted	70·00	
W121	750	**W117**	1s.6d. Multicoloured	12	12
a. Gold omitted (Queen's head).. £100					
b. New blue omitted .. .. 25·00			*d.* Phosphor omitted	10·00	
c. Grey omitted .. .. .. 5·00			*e.* Extra window (No dot, R. 9/1)..	1·00	
W119/21			First Day Cover	†	60
W119/21			Presentation Pack	60	

The 9d. also exists with Queen's head only omitted, and also with value at right of Queen's head but they are due to a major colour shift.

All values were put on sale in error on 30th June at the Lincoln head post office.

Listed Variety

W121*e*

Cylinder Numbers (Blocks of four (4d.) or six (others))

	Cyl. Nos.	Perforation Type A(T)	
		No dot	Dot
4d.	3A (gold)–1B (lemon)–1C (rose-red)–1D (new blue)– 1E (brown)–1F (black)	50	50
	3A (gold)–1B (lemon)–2C (rose-red)–1D (new blue)– 1E (brown)–1F (black)	50	50
	4A (gold)–1B (lemon)–1C (rose-red)–1D (new blue)– 1E (brown)–1F (black)	50	50
	4A (gold)–1B (lemon)–2C (rose-red)–1D (new blue)– 1E (brown)–1F (black)	50	50
	5A (gold)–1B (lemon)–2C (rose-red)–1D (new blue)– 1E (brown)–1F (black)	50	50
9d.	2A (black)–1B (greenish yellow)–1C (Venetian red)– 1D (ochre)–1E (new blue)–3F (grey-black)	1·00	1·00
1s.6d.	2A (grey-black)–1B (greenish yellow)–1C (rose)– 1D (new blue)–1E (grey)–1F (bistre)	1·00	1·00

The 4d. is with sheet orientated showing head to right. In the 4A dot pane the dot is omitted for the gold cylinder and it appears before the C in the rose-red cylinder.

In the 9d. the greenish yellow 1B is very faint in the dot pane and is sometimes almost invisible. Also in the dot pane the dot appears before the 2A.

In the 1s.6d. dot pane the dot appears before the 1F.

Minor Constant Flaws

Minimum prices as singles: 4d. 50p; 9d. 60p; 1s.6d. 60p

4d. Cyls. 1B–2C–1D–1E–1F in combination with gold cyls. 3A, 4A or 5A no dot
  2/1 Two small dots on boy's left leg (Th. K6, L6)
  3/1 Gold dot on boy's right collar (Th. F5)
  5/4 Dark spot on right leg of boy's breeches (Th. I4)

4d. Cyls 1B–2C–1D–1E–1F in combination with gold cyls. 3A, 4A or 5A dot
  1/11 Red spot in left gutter, sometimes lost in perforations (Th. JO)
  2/11 Small red spot on boy's right collar (Th. E5)
  3/4 Small spot in the "V" of boy's collar (Th. F5)
  5/3 Dark spot on inside of boy's left elbow (Th. F7)

9d. Cyls. 2A–1B–1C–1D–1E–3F no dot
  3/1 Break in first S of STUBBS
  4/3 Dark spot in foliage of lower centre branch (Th. C5)
  7/1 Dark spot between right-hand foal's forelegs (Th. G7) and another in the grass just below (Th. H7)

9d. Cyls. 2A–1B–1C–1D–1E–3F dot
  2/5 Slight nick in upright stroke of d of value
  9/3 Small retouch in sky above white horse (Th. D10)
  10/1 Break in first R of HARRISON
  11/1 Dark dot below horse's hind hoof in bottom left corner (Th. H1)

1s.6d. Cyls. 2A–1B–1C–1D–1E–1F no dot
  1/1 Circular patch in building below 1 of value (Th. C2)
  1/5 Small dot by leg of foreground figure left of centre (Th. I6)
  9/4 Small spot above roof of small house in side street (Th. E9)

1s.6d. Cyls. 2A–1B–1C–1D–1E–1F dot
  1/1 Break in Y of LOWRY
  1/4 Lack of colour on second red door from right (Th. F–G11)
  12/1 Line of small dots in top gutter

Sheet Details

Sheet size: 4d. 60 (12 × 5), others (5 × 12). All double pane sheet-fed
Sheet markings:
  Cylinder numbers:
    4d. Opposite R. 4/1, boxed
    Others. Opposite rows 10/11 at left, boxed
  Guide holes: None
  Marginal arrows (photo-etched): "W" shaped, at top and bottom (4d.) or at both sides (others
  Marginal rule: At bottom of sheet
  Colour register marks, coloured crosses, autotron marks and colour designations: None
  Traffic lights (boxed and in same order as cylinder numbers):
    4d. Opposite R. 4/12
    Others. Opposite rows 10/11 at right

Quantities Sold

  4d. 102,443,229; 9d. 9,568,991; 1s.6d. 9,660,509; Pack 46,017

Withdrawn

  9.7.68 (4d. sold out October 1967, 9d. sold out January 1968)

W118. *Gipsy Moth IV*
(Des. M. and S. Goaman)

1967 (JULY 24). SIR FRANCIS CHICHESTER'S WORLD VOYAGE

Sir Francis Chichester voyaged single-handed from England to Australia and back in *Gipsy Moth IV* and was knighted by the Queen on his return.

No watermark. Three phosphor bands.

Cat. No.	S.G. No.	Type	Description	Unused	Used
W122	751	**W118**	1s.9d. Black, brown-red, light	15	15
a. Broken ribbon (R. 19/3)	..	75	emerald and blue		
W122			First Day Cover	†	50

Listed Variety

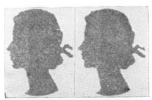

Normal   W122*a*

Cylinder Numbers (Blocks of six)

Cyl. Nos.

Perforation Type A

No dot

1s.9d. 2A (black)–1B (emerald)–1C (blue)–1D (brown-red)   ..   ..   1·40

Minor Constant Flaws

Minimum price as singles: 50p

1s.9d. Cyls. 2A–1B–1C–1D no dot
1/6 Dark flaw in Queen's hair below ribbon (Th. B12–13)
2/1 Grey flaw at top of main sail (Th. A7) and flaw in rear sail (Th. C8–9)
6/5 Diagonal line running across main sail (Th. D6–7)
13/1 Line of small blue dots in rear sail (Th. D–E8)
14/4 White flaw in figure 1 of value (Th. G12)
17/6 Line of blue dots on hull below main sail (Th. E4–5)
18/5 Scratch through rear sail to grey clouds (Th. E8–D11)
18/6 Same scratch extends to foresail (Th. C1–B5)
19/1 Small spur protrudes from top right of rear sail (Th. B–C9)
20/1 Curved dotted blue line between rear sail and Queen's portrait (Th. C9)
20/2 Diagonal blue line in top gutter (Th. 9–13 in gutter)
20/3 Vertical white line at bottom left of main sail (Th. D–E5)
20/4 Blue flaw at top of main sail (Th. A7)
20/6 Dot between ON of HARRISON

Sheet Details

Sheet size: 120 (6 × 20). Single pane reel-fed
Sheet markings:
  Cylinder numbers: Opposite rows 18/19 at left, boxed
  Guide holes: Boxed, opposite row 14, at both sides. Boxes without holes also appear opposite row 15, at both sides
  Marginal arrows (photo-etched): "W" shaped, at top, bottom and sides
  Marginal rule: At bottom of sheet
  Colour register marks: Opposite rows 1/2 and 20, at both sides
  Autotron marks (solid):
    Black, blue, emerald, brown-red, below vertical rows 1/3
  Coloured crosses and colour designations: None
  Traffic lights (boxed and in same order as cylinder numbers): Opposite rows 18/19 at right

Quantity Sold   10,060,867

Withdrawn   23.7.68

W119.   Radar Screen

W120.   Penicillin Mould

(Des. C. Abbott)

W121.   "VC–10" Jet Engines

W122.   Television Equipment

(Des. Negus-Sharland team)

1967 (SEPTEMBER 19).   BRITISH DISCOVERY AND INVENTION

Watermark Multiple Crowns, sideways on 1s.9d. This was the last commemorative issue to bear a watermark.

Three phosphor bands (4d.) or two phosphor bands (others)

Cat. No.	S.G. No.	Type			Description	Unused	Used
W123	752	**W119**			4d. Greenish yellow, black and vermilion	5	5
a. Phosphor omitted	..		..	50			
b. Major scale break (R. 10/2)	..			50			
W124	753	**W120**			1s. Blue-green, light greenish blue, slate-purple and bluish violet	10	8
a. Phosphor omitted		..	..	2·00			
b. Watermark inverted		..	..	10·00			
W125	754	**W121**			1s.6d. Black, grey, Royal blue, ochre and turquoise-blue	12	10
a. Phosphor omitted		..	..				
b. Watermark inverted		..	..	12·00			
c. Cowling flaw (R. 1/2)		..	..	75			
W126	755	**W122**			1s.9d. Black, grey-blue, pale olive-grey, violet and orange	15	12
a. Phosphor omitted		..	..	20·00			
W123/6					First Day Cover	†	50
W123/6					Presentation Pack	50	

All values are known on a special cover prepared by the Edinburgh G.P.O. Philatelic Bureau but postmarked 8th August.

Listed Varieties

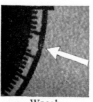

W123*b*

W125*c*

Cylinder Numbers (Blocks of six)

	Cyl. Nos. (No dot)		Perforation Types	
			A	F
4d.	1A (vermilion)–1B (yellow)–1C (black)		50	†
1s.	1A (violet)–1B (green)–1C (blue)–1D (slate-purple) ..		†	90
1s.6d.	1A (black)–1B (ochre)–1C (blue)–1D (grey)–1E (turquoise-blue)		†	1·00
1s.9d.	1A (black)–1B (violet)–1C (olive-grey)–1D (grey-blue)–1E (orange)		†	1·25

The 1s.9d. is with sheet orientated showing head to right.

Minor Constant Flaws

Minimum prices as singles: 4d. 40p; 1s. 50p; 1s.6d. 60p; 1s.9d. 75p

4d. Cyls. 1A–1B–1C
   2/2 Break in outer ring of radar screen at top centre (Th. A6)
   8/5 Break in scale division of radar screen just to left of centre bottom mark (Th. G5)
   14/5 Break in scale division of radar screen in centre left mark (Th. D3)

1s. Cyls. 1A–1B–1C–1D
   19/3 Retouch to background at right of value (Th. F12–13)
   19/6 Violet coloured flaw in bottom right of white outer ring (Th. G6)

1s.6d. Cyls. 1A–1B–1C–1D–1E
   12/3 Small break in outer frame-line to right of 1/6 (Th. G13)
   13/2 Pale area in background above first e of engine (Th. F8)
   19/5 White scratch to background—extends to next stamp (Th. G3–10)
   19/6 White scratch to background—extending from previous stamp (Th. G4–10)
   20/3 The small grey coloured projection of the tailplane at right of the engines is malformed (Th. C8)

1s.9d. Cyls. 1A–1B–1C–1D–1E
   1/18 Two of the holes of the disc at left are joined (Th. E1)
   5/1 One of the slits in grey-blue disc below portrait is joined to hub by white flaw (Th. E5)

Sheet Details

Sheet sizes:
   4d. 120 (6 × 20). Single pane reel-fed
   1s. and 1s.6d. 120 (6 × 20). Single pane sheet-fed
   1s.9d. 120 (20 × 6). Single pane sheet-fed

Sheet markings:
   Cylinder numbers:
      4d. and 1s. Opposite R. 19/1, boxed
      1s.6d. Opposite rows 18/19 at left, boxed
      1s.9d. Opposite rows 5/6 at left, boxed
   Guide holes:
      4d. Opposite rows 14/15 (boxed), at both sides; others, none
   Marginal arrows (photo-etched): "W" shaped, at top, bottom and sides
   Marginal rule: At bottom of sheet
   Colour register marks:
      4d. Opposite rows 3/4 and 17/18, at both sides
      1s. and 1s.6d. Above and below vertical rows 1 and 6
      1s.9d. Opposite rows 1 and 6 bottom margin, at both sides
   Coloured crosses:
      4d. None
      1s. and 1s.6d. Above and below vertical rows 2/3
      1s.9d. Opposite rows 4/5, at both sides
   Autotron marks (solid):
      4d. Black, yellow, vermilion below vertical rows 1/3. An additional semi-solid mark in red appears below vertical row 1; others, none
   Colour designations: None
   Traffic lights (boxed):
      4d. and 1s. In same order as cylinder numbers opposite R. 19/6
      1s.6d. In reverse order to cylinder numbers opposite rows 18/19 at right
      1s.9d. Violet, black, olive-grey, grey-blue, orange opposite rows 5/6 at right

Quantities Sold

   4d. 104,165,625; 1s. 10,718,389; 1s.6d. 10,380,413; 1s.9d. 7,469,585; Pack 59,117

Withdrawn 18.9.68

NO WATERMARK

All commemorative stamps from here onwards are printed on paper without watermark.

W123.   "The Adoration of the
Shepherds" (School of Seville)

W124.   "Madonna and Child"
(Murillo)

W125.   "The Adoration of the Shepherds"
(Louis Le Nain)

1967. CHRISTMAS

The 4d. was issued on October 18th and the others were put on sale on November 27th.
One phosphor band (3d.) or two phosphor bands (others)

Cat. No.	S.G. No.	Type	Description	Unused	Used
W127	756	**W123**	3d. Multicoloured	5	5
a. Gold omitted (value and Queen's head) .... 45·00					
b. Rose omitted .. .. .. 25·00					
c. Imperforate between stamp and left margin			*d.* Phosphor omitted 20		
			e. Printed on the gummed side .. 15·00		
W128	757	**W124**	4d. Multicoloured	5	5
a. Gold omitted (value and Queen's head) .. .. .. 50·00					
b. Phosphor omitted .. .. 25·00			*c.* Right band omitted		
			d. Brown flaw (Dot, R. 2/3) .. 1·00		
W129	758	**W125**	1s.6d. Multicoloured	15	12
a. Gold omitted (value and Queen's head)					
b. Ultramarine omitted .. .. 40·00			*c.* Phosphor omitted .. .. 4·00		
W128			First Day Cover	†	10
W127 and W129			First Day Cover	†	25

There is a wide variation on shades of the 3d. and 4d. but they are not listed as there are a
number of intermediate shades. In the 4d. value, stamps emanating from one machine show
a darker background and give the appearance of the yellow being omitted, but this is not so.

The 3d. and 4d. are known with value omitted resulting from colour shifts.

Listed Variety

No. W128d. This marked variety on the 4d. consists of a large brown area in the lower right corner (Th. J–K 8–9) which can be clearly seen by the naked eye but which would not show up in an enlarged illustration. It occurs on cylinders 2B–2C–2D–2E dot in conjunction with gold cylinders 2A or 3A.

Cylinder Numbers (Blocks of six)

	Cyl. Nos.	Perforation Types	
		A	
		No dot	Dot
3d.	1A (gold)–1B (olive-yellow)–1C (rose)–1D (blue)–1E (black) ..	40	†
	2A (gold)–1B (olive yellow)–1C (rose)–1D (blue)–1E (black) ..	40	†
4d.	2A (gold)–1B (bright purple)–1C (new blue)–1D (greenish yellow)–1E (grey-black) ..	50	50
	2A (gold)–2B (bright purple)–2C (new blue)–2D (greenish yellow)–2E (grey-black) ..	75	75
	3A (gold)–2B (bright purple)–2C (new blue)–2D (greenish yellow)–2E (grey-black) ..	50	50
	6A (gold)–3B (bright purple)–3C (new blue)–3D (greenish yellow)–3E (grey-black) ..	60	†
	8A (gold)–3B (bright purple)–3C (new blue)–3D (greenish yellow)–3E (grey-black) ..	75	†
		A(T) No dot	
1s.6d.	2A (gold)–1B (ultramarine)–1C (bright purple)–1D (orange-red)–1E (lemon)–1F (bistre)–2G (black)	1·25	

The 3d. and 4d. are with the sheet orientated showing the head to right.

The gold of the Queen's portrait and the value is normally further to the left on the 6A and 8A cylinders.

Minor Constant Flaws

Minimum prices as singles: 3d. 40p; 4d. 40p; 1s.6d. 60p

3d. Cyls. 1B–1C–1D–1E in conjunction with gold cyls. 1A or 2A no dot
  1/7 Black horizontal line across triangle of red above Mary's head (Th. E2–3)

3d. Cyls. 1A–1B–1C–1D–1E no dot
  1/11 Break in upright wall of building shows against sky (Th. D6)

3d. Cyls. 2A–1B–1C–1D–1E no dot
  3/10 Small black spot in Joseph's cloak (Th. D5)
  4/9 Background retouch in left pillar (Th. D2)

4d. Cyls. 2B–2C–2D–2E in conjunction with gold cyls. 2A or 3A no dot
  1/5 Prominent pale area in background at bottom right (Th. K–L 8–9)

4d. Cyls. 3A–2B–2C–2D–2E no dot
  2/12 A cut at top of diagonal of 4 of value
  7/5 Dark spot in Mother's right hand (Th. E5)

4d. Cyls. 2B–2C–2D–2E in conjunction with gold cyls. 2A or 3A dot
  4/5 Line of pale dots over 4 of value (Th. J1)

4d. Cyls. 3A–2B–2C–2D–2E dot
  2/12 Black dot over first R of HARRISON
  3/6 Black dot on Child's forehead (Th. C6)
  4/9 Spot on lower left margin of stamp (Th. K1)
  7/2 Small spot just beyond little finger of Madonna's right hand Th. E6)
  7/12 Two small red dots over H of HARRISON

1s.6d. Cyls. 2A–1B–1C–1D–1E–1F–2G no dot
  1/2 Background disturbance above ll of shilling
  3/6 Curved green flaw left of cow's tail (Th. E1)
  4/9 Background disturbance below n of One

Sheet Details

Sheet sizes:
  3d. 120 (12 × 10). Single pane sheet-fed
  4d. 120 (12 × 10). Double pane reel-fed for gold cyls. 2A and 3A and single pane reel-fed for gold cyls. 6A and 8A
  1s.6d. 60 (10 × 6). Single pane sheet-fed
Sheet markings:
  Cylinder Numbers:
    3d. Opposite R. 9/1, boxed
    4d. Below vertical row 11, boxed
    1s.6d. Opposite rows 4/5 at right, boxed
  Guide holes:
    3d. and 1s.6d. None
    4d. Above and below vertical row 8

Marginal arrows (photo etched): "W" shaped, at top, bottom and sides
Marginal rule: None
Colour register marks:
    3d. Above and below vertical rows 1/2 and 11/12
    4d. Above and below vertical rows 1/3 (dot) and 8/10 (no dot)
    1s.6d. Opposite rows 1/2 and 6, at both sides
Coloured crosses:
    3d. Above and below vertical rows 3/4
    4d. None
    1s.6d. Next to cylinder numbers at left and traffic lights at right
Autotron marks (solid):
    3d. and 1s.6d. None
    4d. Greenish yellow, bright purple, new blue, grey-black, gold opposite rows 6/8, right margin (dot) with
    the 3A–2B–2C–2D–2E cylinders but the order of the colours is reversed with the 2A–1B–1C–1D–1E
    cylinders
Colour designations:
    3d. and 1s.6d. None
    4d. "G1 YELLOW" above vertical row 12 on the dot pane and "G2 GREY G3 GREEN G4 RED
    G5 GOLD" above vertical rows 1/4 on the no dot pane, the whole inscription being upside down.
    The "G3 GREEN" is printed in blue
Traffic lights (boxed):
    3d. In the same order as the cylinder numbers opposite R. 9/12
    4d. Greenish yellow, bright purple, gold, new blue, grey-black above vertical rows 10/11
    1s.6d. Lemon, bright purple, orange-red, ultramarine, black, bistre, gold opposite rows 4/5 at right

In the case of the 4d. value all the above information relates to the stamps printed from gold cylinders 2A and 3A in double panes. We have not been able to examine full sheets from the single pane cylinders 6A and 8A on which some of the markings may well be different. However, we have seen part of the top which showed the following differences: colour register marks above row 1/1 and 1/12 and colour designations inverted but reading "G1 YELLOW G2 RED G3 GREEN (printed in blue) G4 GREY G5 GOLD" above vertical rows 1/6, with the yellow above row 6 and the gold above row 1. There was no perforation guide hole.

Quantities Sold   3d. 270,349,845; 4d. 287,827,440; 1s.6d. 17,913,209

Withdrawn   3d. Sold out July 1968; 4d. 17.10.68; 1s.6d. 26.11.68

1967 (NOVEMBER 27). GIFT PACK 1967
WGP1 Comprising Nos. W111/29   2·00

Quantity Sold 105,577

PVA GUM
All commemorative issues from here onwards printed by Harrisons are on paper with PVA gum. For further particulars about this gum see notes at the beginning of Section U1 on the Machin definitive issues.

W126.   Tarr Steps, Exmoor
(Des. J. Matthews)

W127.   Aberfeldy Bridge
(Des. A. Restall)

W128.   Menai Bridge
(Des. L. Rosoman)

W129.   M4 Viaduct
(Des. J. Matthews)

1968 (APRIL 29). BRITISH BRIDGES

Two phosphor bands

Cat. No.	S.G. No.	Type		Description	Unused	Used

W130   763   **W126**
  a. Printed on the gummed side..   3·00
  b. Phosphor omitted   ..   ..   1·00
  c. "O" retouch (R. 20/6)   50

4d.   Black,   bluish   violet, turquoise-blue and gold   5   5
  d. No curve to slab (R.10/6)   ..   50

W131   764   **W127**
  a. Gold (Queen's head) omitted ..   75·00
  b. Ultramarine omitted   ..   ..
  c. Phosphor omitted   ..   ..   1·50
  d. Phosphor bands diagonal   ..
  e. HARRISON redrawn (R. 18/3)   75

9d.   Red-brown,   myrtle-green, ultramarine, olive-brown, black and gold   8   8
  f. RESTALL redrawn (R. 18/4)   75

W132   765   **W128**
  a. Gold (Queen's head) omitted ..
  b. Red-orange omitted   ..   ..
  c. Phosphor omitted   ..   ..
  d. Broken corner stones (R. 15/1)   75

1s.6d. Olive-brown, red-orange, bright green, turquoise-green and gold   12   12

W133   766   **W129**
  a. Gold (Queen's head) omitted ..   £100
  b. Phosphor omitted   ..   ..   1·00
  c. One band at left   ..   ..

1s.9d. Olive-brown,   greenish yellow, dull green, deep ultramarine and gold   15   15

W130/3   First Day Cover   †   40
W130/3   Presentation Pack   60

Listed Varieties

W130*c*

W130*d*
No curve at left to central slab

W132*d*

Normal

W131*e*   W131*f*
Inscriptions redrawn by hand

Cylinder Numbers (Blocks of eight)

	Cyl. Nos.	Perforation Type
		F No dot
4d.	3A (black)–1B (turquoise-blue)–2C (bluish violet)–2D (gold).. ..	60
9d.	1A (black)–1B (red-brown)–1C (ultramarine)–1D (olive-brown)–1E (myrtle-green)–1F (gold)	90
1s.6d.	2A (olive-brown)–1B (red-orange)–1C (bright green)–2D (turquoise-green)–3E (gold)	1·40
1s.9d.	2A (olive-brown)–1B (gold)–1C (dull green)–1D (deep ultramarine)–1E (greenish yellow)	1·60

Minor Constant Flaws

Minimum prices as singles: 4d. 40p; 9d. 50p; 1s.6d. 50p; 1s.9d. 60p

4d. Cyls. 3A–1B–2C–2D no dot
  4/1 Diagonal dotted line across top of bridge near far end (Th. C10)
  9/1 Lack of screening dots in left of pale green patch left of Tarr (Th. G4–5)
  11/1 Similar variety but more pronounced (Th. G4–5)
  12/2 Broken tip to horizontal bar of T of Tarr
  14/2 Scratch across lower stones near far end of bridge (Th. D10–C12)
  17/2 Weakness behind and below hi of Prehistoric (Th. G11)
  19/4 Damaged H in HARRISON

9d. Cyls. 1A–1B–1C–1D–1E–1F no dot
  9/4 Break in olive-brown line at left of ultramarine area under main arch (Th. F6)
  20/4 Small dark spot under r of Bridge
1s.6d. Cyls. 2A–1B–1C–2D–3E no dot
  5/5 Two diagonal lines in sky at right (Th. B–C13)
  5/6 Diagonal line in sky extending to base of Queen's neck (extension of one of the lines in 5/5) (Th. C1
  6/1 Small curved flaw in front of H of HARRISON
  6/2 White flaw in first arch beyond the far tower (Th. E12)
  14/5 Small white flaw at top right of near tower (Th. B8)
  19/1 Green spot on near tower above right-hand arch (Th. D7-8)
1s.9d. Cyls. 2A–1B–1C–1D–1E no dot
  2/5 Retouch in centre lane (Th. C–D8)
  10/4 Disturbance at right of pale green area below Queen (Th. D3-4)
  14/5 Vertical line appears as radio mast above building on skyline (Th. A6)
  15/1 Retouch between buildings at bend in motor way (Th. C10)
  17/4 Break at foot of s in value

Sheet Details

Sheet size: 120 (6 × 20). Single pane sheet-fed
Sheet markings:
  Cylinder numbers: Opposite rows 17/18 at left, boxed
  Guide holes: None
  Marginal arrows (photo-etched): "W" shaped, at top, bottom and sides
  Marginal rule: At bottom of sheet
  Colour register marks:
    4d. and 1s.9d. Above and below vertical rows 1/2 and 6
    9d. and 1s.6d. Above and below vertical rows 1 and 5/6
  Coloured crosses:
    4d. and 1s.6d. Above and below vertical row 3
    9d. Above and below vertical rows 3/4
    1s.9d. Above and below vertical rows 2/3
  Autotron marks and colour designations: None
  Traffic lights (boxed):
    4d. Gold, bluish violet, turquoise-blue, black above vertical row 5
    9d. Black, red-brown, ultramarine, myrtle-green, gold, olive-brown above vertical rows 4/5
    1s.6d. Gold, turquoise-green, bright green, red-orange, olive-brown above vertical row 5
    1s.9d. Gold, dull green, olive-brown, deep ultramarine, greenish yellow above vertical row 5

Quantities Sold

4d. 97,458,120; 9d. 8,773,080; 1s.6d. 9,451,400; 1s.9d. 5,924,800; Pack 69,646

Withdrawn 28.4.69

W130. "T U C" and Trade Unionists

W131. Mrs. Emmeline Pankhurst (statue)

W132. Sopwith "Camel" and "Lightning" Fighters

W133. Captain Cook's *Endeavour* and Signature

(Des. D. Gentleman (4d.), C. Abbott (others))

1968 (MAY 29). BRITISH ANNIVERSARIES

Four famous anniversaries, with the events described on the stamps

Two phosphor bands

Cat. No.	S.G. No.	Type		Description	Unused	Used
W134	767	**W130**		4d. Emerald, olive, blue and black	5	5
a. Phosphor omitted*		.. ..				
b. Retouch on large C (No dot, R. 3/2)	75					
W135	768	**W131**		9d. Reddish violet, grey and black	8	8
a. Phosphor omitted	.. ..	50				
W136	769	**W132**		1s. Olive-brown, blue, red, slate-blue and black	8	12
a. Phosphor omitted	.. ..	1·50				
W137	770	**W133**		1s.9d. Ochre, brownish ochre and blackish brown	15	15
a. Phosphor omitted†	8·00					
b. Broken bulwarks (R. 8/2) ..	1·00					
W134/7				First Day Cover	†	40
W134/7				Presentation Pack	50	

*The phosphor lines are normally faint and difficult to see and care is needed in identifying the phosphor omitted on the 4d. value.

†The 1s.9d. is known with phosphor removed by chemical means but these can be detected and care is needed in identifying genuine copies

Listed Varieties

W134b   W137b

Cylinder Numbers (Blocks of eight (4d., 1s.), four (9d.), six (1s.9d.))

	Cyl. Nos.	Perforation Types	
		A	A
		No dot	Dot
4d.	1A (black)–1B (blue)–1C (olive)–1D (emerald)	60	60
		F No dot	
9d.	1A (black)–1B (reddish violet)–1C (grey)	75	
1s.	1A (black)–1B (olive-brown)–1C (blue)–1D (slate-blue)–1E (red)	90	
1s.9d.	2A (blackish brown)–1B (brownish ochre)–1C (ochre)	1·60	

Minor Constant Flaws

Minimum prices as singles: 4d. 40p; 9d. 40p; 1s. 50p; 1s.9d. 60p

4d. Cyls. 1A–1B–1C–1D no dot
1/1 Small retouch in right cross bar of large T
2/2 Stop between Union and Congress
4/1 Retouch at top of large C (not as prominent as No. W134b)
10/6 Small retouch at top left of large U
11/3 Small flaw in 6 of 1968
11/6 Vertical green line from right cross bar of large T (Th. B–E3)

4d. Cyls. 1A–1B–1C–1D dot
2/6 Small spot right of 4 of value
4/5 Green spots by d of Trades (Th. F–G1)
5/5 Dotted line across back of Queen's hair (Th. B–C12)
19/1 Retouch on cheek of face shown in large T (Th. D1–2)
20/5 Two tiny dots above g of Congress

9d. Cyls. 1A–1B–1C no dot
9/4 Spur at top right of Queen's head (Th. A13)
14/6 Dark flaw on collar (Th. D10/11) and small flaw on left sleeve (Th. F11)

1s. Cyls. 1A–1B–1C–1D–1E no dot
3/1 Dot over O of ROYAL
4/4 Extension of wing joining it to last T of ABBOTT

1s.9d. Cyls. 2A–1B–1C no dot
  10/3 Small flaws in background above Y of DISCOVERY level with value (Th. F10-11)
  11/2 Small cut in Y of VOYAGE
  13/2 Flaw in lower part of S of DISCOVERY
  20/5 Tail of 9 of 1968 slightly shortened

Sheet Details

Sheet size: 120 (6 × 20). 4d. double pane reel-fed; others single pane sheet-fed
Sheet markings:
  Cylinder numbers:
    4d. and 1s. Opposite rows 17/18 at left, boxed
    9d. Opposite R. 19/1, boxed
    1s.9d. Opposite R. 18/1, boxed
  Guide holes:
    4d. In double " S O N " box opposite rows 14/15, at left (no dot) or right (dot).
    Others: None
  Marginal arrows (photo-etched): "W" shaped, at top, bottom and sides
  Marginal rule: 4d. None· others at bottom of sheet
  Colour register marks:
    4d. Opposite rows 2/4 and 18/20 at left (no dot) or right (dot)
    Others: Above and below vertical rows 1 and 6
  Coloured crosses:
    4d. None
    9d. and 1s.9d. Above and below vertical row 3
    1s. Above and below vertical rows 2/3
  Autotron marks (solid):
    4d. Black, blue, olive, emerald opposite rows 4/6, at right (no dot) or left (dot); others, none
  Colour designations: None
  Traffic lights (boxed):
    4d. In same order as cylinder numbers opposite rows 1/2, at right
    9d. Black, grey, reddish violet above vertical row 5
    1s. Olive-brown, blue, slate-blue, red, black above vertical row 5
    1s.9d. Brownish ochre, blackish brown, ochre above vertical row 5

Quantities Sold

  4d. 97,757,920; 9d. 9,135,240; 1s. 9,872,160; 1s.9d. 6,217,440; Pack 67,639

Withdrawn 28.5.69

W134. "Queen Elizabeth I"
(Unknown Artist)

W135. "Pinkie"
(Lawrence)

W136. "Ruins of St. Mary
Le Port" (Piper)

W137. "The Hay Wain"
(Constable)
(Printed in photogravure with the Queen's head embossed in gold)

1968 (AUGUST 12). BRITISH PAINTINGS

This is the second issue of British Paintings for which Harrisons made photographs from the originals

Two phosphor bands

Cat. No.	S.G. No.	Type	Description	Unused	Used
W138	771	**W134**			
a. Gold omitted (value and Queen's head)		75·00	4d. Multicoloured	5	5
b. Gold (value and Queen's head) and phosphor omitted					
c. Vermilion omitted			*d.* Phosphor omitted	20	
			e. Blister on hand (No dot, R. 2/8)	75	
W139	772	**W135**	1s. Multicoloured	8	10
a. Gold omitted (value and Queen's head)		£100			
b. Gold (value and Queen's head), embossing and phosphor omitted			*c.* Phosphor omitted	75	
W140	773	**W136**	1s.6d. Multicoloured	12	12
a. Gold omitted (value and Queen's head)		£100	*b.* Phosphor omitted	1·00	
W141	774	**W137**	1s.9d. Multicoloured	15	15
a. Gold (value and Queen's head), embossing and phosphor omitted		80·00	*b.* Phosphor omitted	2·50	
W138/41			First Day Cover	†	45
W138/41			Presentation Pack	50	
W138/41			Presentation Pack (German)		

The 4d. also exists with the value only omitted resulting from a colour shift.

This issue is known pre-released on a first day cover postmarked 10th August from Vauxhall Bridge P.O., S.W.1.

Listed Variety

KNOWN c.157

W138*e*

Cylinder Numbers (Blocks of six)

Cyl. Nos.		Perforation Type A(T)	
		No dot	Dot
4d.	2A (gold)–1B (embossing)–3C (black)–2D (grey)–3E (vermilion)–2F (greenish yellow)	50	50
1s.	2A (gold)–1B (embossing)–2C (black)–2D (new blue)–2E (mauve)–2F (magenta)–2G (greenish yellow)	75	75
	2A (gold)–2B (embossing)–2C (black)–2D (new blue)–2E (mauve)–2F (magenta)–2G (greenish yellow)	75	75
1s.6d.	1A (gold)–1B (embossing)–1C (black)–1D (ultramarine)–1E (slate)–1F (mauve)–1G (orange)–1H (greenish yellow)	1·00	1·00
1s.9d.	2A (gold)–1B (embossing)–1C (black)–1D (new blue)–1E (red)–1F (greenish yellow)	1·50	1·50

The 4d., 1s and 1s.6d. are with sheet orientated showing head to right.

In each value the 1B cylinder number appears in colourless embossing; it is difficult to see but can often be discerned with the aid of a magnifying glass.

Minor Constant Flaws

Minimum prices as singles: 4d. 40p; 1s. 40p; 1s.6d. 50p; 1s.9d. 60p

4d. Cyls. 2A–1B–3C–2D–3E–2F no dot
  6/8 Thick A in HARRISON

4d. Cyls. 2A–1B–3C–2D–3E–2F dot
  4/2 Black flaw on dress above Queen's right hand (Th. J4–5)

1s. Cyls. 2A–1B–2C–2D–2E–2F–2G no dot
  2/4 Diagonal black line across Pinkie's shoulder (Th. D4)
  5/1 Black spur to A of HARRISON
  6/1 Thin diagonal black line across dress (Th. H3–5)

1s.6d. Cyls. 1A–1B–1C–1D–1E–1F–1G–1H no dot
   6/1 Dark coloured spot in top right corner of dark blue area (Th. A8–9)

1s.6d. Cyls. 1A–1B–1C–1D–1E–1F–1G–1H dot
   1/8 ? shaped black flaw in doorway (Th. J5)
   6/6 Extra patch at upper left corner of yellow wall (Th. E8)

1s.9d. Cyls. 2A–1B–1C–1D–1E–1F no dot
   9/2 Blue spot after HARRISON
   10/1 Green instead of brown bush in bottom left-hand corner

Sheet Details

Sheet size: 1s.9d. 60 (6 × 10), others 60 (10 × 6). All double pane sheet-fed

Sheet markings:

  Cylinder numbers:
    4d. Opposite row 5, left margin, boxed
    1s. and 1s.6d. Opposite rows 4/5, left margin, boxed
    1s.9d. Opposite rows 8/9, left margin, boxed

  Guide holes: None

  Marginal arrows (photo-etched): "W" shaped, at top, bottom and sides

  Marginal rule: None

  Colour register marks:
    4d., 1s. and 1s.6d. Above vertical rows 1/2 and 9/10 (no dot) or below (dot)
    1s.9d. Opposite rows 1/2 and 9/10, left margin (no dot) or right margin (dot)

  Coloured crosses:
    4d. and 1s. Above vertical rows 6/7 (no dot) or below (dot)
    1s.6d. Above vertical rows 7/8 (no dot) or below (dot)
    1s.9d. Opposite rows 7/8, left margin (no dot) or right margin (dot)

  Autotron marks, colour designations: None

  Traffic lights (boxed):
    4d., 1s. and 1s.6d. In same order as cylinder numbers, except that on the 1s.6d. the gold and embossing "lights" are transposed, reading left to right above vertical rows 8/9
    1s.9d. In same order as cylinder numbers, except that the gold and embossing "lights" are transposed, reading left to right above vertical row 5

Quantities Sold

4d.	185,034,000	English Pack	93,829
1s.	17,953,440	German Pack	7,880
1s.6d.	8,878,440		
1s.9d.	5,739,000		

Withdrawn   11.8.69

1968 (SEPTEMBER 16). GIFT PACK 1968

WGP2 Comprising Nos. W130/41   1·25
  a. German text   ..   ..   ..

Quantities Sold   Ordinary 41,308; German 1,650

1968 (SEPTEMBER 16). COLLECTORS PACK 1968

WCP1 Comprising Nos. W123/41   1.60

Quantity Sold   26,284

W139. Girl with
Doll's House

W138. Boy and Girl with
Rocking Horse

W140. Boy with
Train Set

(Des. Rosalind Dease)

(Printed in photogravure with the Queen's head embossed in gold)

1968 (NOVEMBER 25). CHRISTMAS

The joy of giving is emphasised on this Christmas issue; all three designs show children playing with their Christmas toys

One centre phosphor band (4d.) or two phosphor bands (others)

Cat. No.	S.G. No.	Type			Description	Unused	Used
W142	775	**W138**			4d. Black, orange, vermilion,		
a. Gold omitted	..	..	..	— 50.00	ultramarine, bistre and		
b. Vermilion omitted*	..	..	40·00		gold	5	5
c. Ultramarine and		phosphor					
omitted ..	..	..	..	55·00			
d. Embossing omitted	..	..	75		f. Retouched dapples (Cyl. 1A,		
e. Phosphor omitted	..	..	15		R. 12/4)	50	
W143	776	**W139**			9d. Yellow-olive, black, brown,		
a. Yellow omitted ..	..	..	7·50		yellow, magenta, orange,		
b. Embossing and		phosphor			turquoise-green and gold	8	8
omitted ..	..	..	4·00				
c. Embossing omitted	..	..	4·50		f. Phosphor omitted	50	
W144	777	**W140**			1s.6d. Ultramarine, yellow-		
a. Embossing omitted	..	..			orange, bright purple,		
b. Phosphor omitted	..	..	1·50		blue-green, black and		
					gold	12	15
W142/4					First Day Cover	†	25
W142/4					Presentation Pack	35	
W142/4					Presentation Pack (German)		

*The effect of the missing vermilion is shown on the rocking horse, saddle and faces which appear orange instead of red.

No. W142 is known pre-released on 24th November at Edinburgh.

Two machines were used for printing the 4d. value:
Stamps from cylinders 1A–1B–2C–1D–1E in combination with 1F, 2F or 3F (gold) were printed entirely on the Rembrandt sheet-fed machine. They invariably have the Queen's head level with the top of the boy's head and the sheets are perforated through the left side margin (perforation type F).

Stamps from cylinders 2A–2B–3C–2D–2E in combination with 1F, 2F, 3F or 4F (gold) were printed on the reel-fed Thrissell machine in five colours (its maximum colour capacity) and subsequently sheet-fed on the Rembrandt machine for the gold Queen's head and the embossing. The position of the Queen's head is generally lower than on the stamps printed at one operation but it varies in different parts of the sheet and is not, therefore, a sure indication for identifying single stamps. Another small difference is that the boy's grey pullover is noticeably "moth-eaten" in the Thrissell printings and is normal on the Rembrandt. The Thrissell printings are perforated through the top margin (perforation type A).

Marginal copies can usually be identified by the characteristics of the perforation (if any) in the sheet margin. Ideally, cylinder blocks of six are required to show examples of the two printing machines used.

Listed Variety

Grey dapples on the horse nearest to the boy and extending to the boy's belt and trousers, are heavily retouched

Normal   W142*f*

Cylinder Numbers (Blocks of six)

		Cyl. Nos. (No dot)	Perforation Types	
			A	F
A.	"Rembrandt" only printings			
	4d.	1A (black)–1B (orange)–2C (vermilion)–1D (ultramarine)–1E (bistre)–1F (gold) ..	†	50
		1A (black)–1B (orange)–2C (vermilion)–1D (ultramarine)–1E (bistre)–2F (gold) ..	†	50
		1A (black)–1B (orange)–2C (vermilion)–1D (ultramarine)–1E (bistre)–3F (gold)..	†	60
	9d.	1A (black)–1B (brown)–1C (yellow)–2D (magenta)–1E (orange)–1F (turquoise-green)–1G (yellow-olive)–1H (gold) ..	†	60
	1s.6d.	1A (black)–1B (ultramarine)–1C (yellow-orange)–1D (bright purple)–1E (blue-green)–1F (gold) ..	†	90
B.	"Thrissell" and "Rembrandt" printings			
	4d.	2A (black)–2B (orange)–3C (vermilion)–2D (ultramarine)–2E (bistre)–1F (gold)..	50	†
		2A (black)–2B (orange)–3C (vermilion)–2D (ultramarine)–2E (bistre)–2F (gold)..	50	†
		2A (black)–2B (orange)–3C (vermilion)–2D (ultramarine)–2E (bistre)–3F (gold)..	60	†
		2A (black)–2B (orange)–3C (vermilion)–2D (ultramarine)–2E (bistre)–4F (gold)..	75	†

The 9d. and 1s.6d. are with sheet orientated showing head to right.

Minor Constant Flaws

Minimum prices as singles: 4d. 40p; 9d. 40p; 1s.6d. 50p

4d. Cyls. 1A–1B–2C–1D–1E in combination with gold cyls. 1F, 2F, 3F, or 4F
    3/6 Small black flaw in m of Christmas
    12/5 Small nick on right edge of upright stroke of 4 of value

4d. Cyls. 2A–2B–3C–2D–2E in combination with gold cyls. 1F, 2F, 3F or 4F
    16/4 Small black flaw above horse's left foreleg by boy's waist (Th. D9)
    20/4 Break in outline at top centre of near rocker (Th. F4–5)

9d. Cyls. 1A–1B–1C–2D–1E–1F–1G–1H
    4/3 Small black flaw between a and s of Christmas
    6/18 Break in middle of final s of Christmas

1s.6d. Cyls. 1A–1B–1C–1D–1E–1F
    2/18 Pale patch on boy's left shoulder (Th. F4)
    3/8 Thick horizontal spur on left of lower central purple slotted plate (Th. D–E4
    5/2 Black flaws in background lower right of Queen's head (Th. C–D7)
    5/3 Two black dots between 1 and stroke of 1/6
    6/20 Purple coloured flaws in background below boy's foot (Th. J7)

Sheet Details

	Rembrandt	Thrissell/Rembrandt
Sheet sizes:		
4d. 120 (6 × 20)	Single pane sheet-fed	Single pane reel-fed for five colours, and then single pane sheet fed for the gold and embossing
9d. and 1s.6d. 120 (20 × 6)	Single pane sheet-fed	

Sheet markings:

	Rembrandt	Thrissell/Rembrandt
Cylinder numbers:		
4d.	Opposite rows 18/19, left margin, boxed	Opposite rows 18/19, left margin, boxed
9d. and 1s.6d.	Opposite rows 4/5, left margin, boxed	
Guide holes:		
4d.	None	Opposite rows 14/15 (boxed), at both sides
9d. and 1s.6d.	None	
Marginal arrows (photo-etched):		
4d.	"W" shaped, at top, bottom and sides	"W" shaped, at top, bottom and sides
9d. and 1s.6d.	As 4d.	
Marginal rule:	None	None
Colour register marks:		
4d.	Above and below vertical rows 1/2 and 6	Opposite rows 2/3 and 19/20 at both sides
9d. and 1s.6d.	Opposite rows 1/2 and 5/6 at both sides	
Coloured crosses:		
4d.	Above and below vertical row 3	Gold only below vertical row 3
9d. and 1s.6d.	Opposite rows 3/4 at both sides	
Autotron marks (solid):		
4d.	None	Black, bistre, ultramarine, vermilion, orange below vertical rows 4/6
9d. and 1s.6d.	None	
Colour designations:	None	None
Traffic lights (boxed):		
4d.	Orange, vermilion, ultramarine, bistre, black, gold, embossing opposite rows 18/19, right margin; also above vertical row 5 reading left to right	Orange, vermilion, ultramarine, bistre, black, gold, embossing opposite rows 18/19, right margin; also gold and embossing (unboxed) above vertical row 5 reading left to right
9d.	Gold, olive, green, orange, magenta, yellow, brown, black opposite rows 4/5, right margin; also embossing, gold, olive, green, orange, magenta, yellow, brown, black above vertical rows 17/19 reading left to right	
1s.6d.	Embossing, gold, green, purple, orange, ultramarine, black opposite rows 4/5, at right; also gold, green, purple, orange, ultramarine, black, above vertical rows 18/19 reading left to right	

Although the Traffic Light box in the right margin on the 9d. and the upper margin on the 1s.6d. were designed to accommodate an embossing "light" the space was not in fact used.

Quantities Sold

4d.	326,078,360	English Pack	72,474
9d.	17,102,520	German Pack	7,298
1s.6d.	21,344,760		

Withdrawn 24.11.69

W141.   R.M.S. *Queen Elizabeth 2*

W142.   Elizabethan Galleon

W145.   S.S. *Great Britain*

W143.   East Indiaman

W146.   R.M.S. *Mauretania*
(Des. D. Gentleman)

W144.   *Cutty Sark*

1969 (JANUARY 15).   BRITISH SHIPS

Issued as a tribute to British shipbuilders and seamen, these stamps depict five famous ships of the past and of the *Queen Elizabeth 2* which sailed on her maiden voyage to New York on 2nd May 1969

The 9d. values were issued together *se-tenant* in strips of three throughout the sheet and the 1s. values were issued together *se-tenant* in pairs throughout the sheet.

Two phosphor bands at right (1s.), one horizontal phosphor band (5d.) or two phosphor bands (9d.)

Cat. No.	S.G. No.	Type	Description	Unused	Used
W145	778	**W141**	5d. Black, grey, red and turquoise	5	5
a. Black omitted (Queen's head, value, hull and inscr.) £110					
b. Grey omitted (decks, etc.) .. 50·00					
c. Red omitted .. .. .. 12·00		*d.* Phosphor omitted	40	
W146	779	**W142**	9d. Red, blue, ochre, brown, black and grey	10	10
a. Red, blue and phosphor omitted £110					
b. Blue omitted .. .. .. 85·00					
c. Phosphor omitted .. .. 2·00					
W147	780	**W143**	9d. Ochre, brown, black and grey	10	10
a. Phosphor omitted .. .. 2·00					
W148	781	**W144**	9d. Ochre, brown, black and grey	10	10
a. Phosphor omitted .. .. 2·00					
W149	782	**W145**	1s. Brown, black, grey, green and greenish yellow	12	12
a. Greenish yellow omitted ..					
b. Phosphor omitted .. .. 4·00					

Cat. No.	S.G. No.	Type	Description	Unused	Used
W150	783	**W146**	1s. Red, black, brown, carmine and grey	12	12
a. Phosphor omitted	..	.. 4·00			
W145/50			First Day Cover	†	50
W145/50			Presentation Pack*	60	
W145/50			Presentation Pack (German)		

*In addition to the generally issued Presentation Pack (inscribed "RMS Queen Elizabeth 2 . . . she sailed on her maiden voyage to New York on 17th January 1969") a further pack (inscribed "RMS Queen Elizabeth 2 . . . she sails on her maiden voyage early in 1969") was issued for sale exclusively on board the Q.E.2 during her maiden voyage which had been postponed. (*Price* £1.25).

9d. *Prices for missing colour errors in strips of three:*
Red, blue and phosphor ..	..	..	..	..	..	..	..	£110
Blue	..	..	..	..	..	..	..	80·00

1s. *Price for missing colour error in pair:*
Greenish yellow ..	..	..	..	..	..	..	—

Cylinder Numbers (Blocks of six (5d. and 1s.) or twelve (9d.))

	Cyl. Nos. (No dot)		Perforation Types	
			A(T)	F
5d.	1A (black)–1B (grey)–1C (red)–1D (turquoise)		50	†
9d.	1A (black)–2B (brown)–1C (ochre)–1D (grey)–1E (red)– 1F (blue)		†	90
1s.	2A (black)–1B (grey)–1C (green)–1D (red)–1E (carmine)– 1F (brown)–1G (yellow)		75	†

Minor Constant Flaws

Minimum prices as singles: 5d. 40p; 9d. 40p; 1s. 50p

5d. Cyls. 1A–1B–1C–1D
2/5 Disturbance in sea over liz of Elizabeth
3/2 Blue flaw on superstructure halfway between funnel and stern (Th. E6) (later removed)
4/5 Weak patch in hull directly below funnel (Th. F9)

9d. Cyls. 1A–2B–1C–1D–1E–1F
16/2 Rope between second and third masts is broken (Th. D5)

1s. Cyls. 2A–1B–1C–1D–1E–1F–1G
1/6 Small brown flaw lower right of stern mast (Th. D6)
2/8 Curved black flaw just above third funnel (Th. C10)
4/2 Weak patch in hull directly below fore mast (Th. E17)
10/1 Whispy black flaw in front of Queen's chin (Th. B–C17)

Sheet Details

Sheet sizes:
All single pane sheet-fed
5d. 72 (8 × 9)
9d. 120 (6 × 20). In *se-tenant* strips of three
1s. 80 (8 × 10). In *se-tenant* pairs
Sheet markings:
Cylinder numbers:
5d. Opposite rows 7/8, left margin, boxed
9d. Opposite rows 17/18, left margin, boxed
1s. Below vertical row 7, boxed
Guide holes: None
Marginal arrows (photo-etched): "W" shaped, at top and bottom (5d); "W" shaped, at top, bottom and sides (others)
Marginal rule: None
Colour register marks:
5d. Opposite rows 1/2 and 8/9 at both sides
9d. Above and below vertical rows 1 and 6
1s. Opposite rows 1/2 and 10 at both sides
Coloured crosses:
5d. Opposite rows 5/6 at both sides
9d. Above and below vertical rows 3/4
1s. Opposite rows 5/7 at both sides
Autotron marks, colour designations: None
Traffic lights (boxed):
5d. In same order as cylinder numbers opposite rows 7/8, right margin; also above vertical row 7 reading left to right
9d. In same order as cylinder numbers opposite rows 18/19, right margin; also above vertical rows 5/6 but in reverse order to cylinder numbers reading left to right
1s. In reverse order to cylinder numbers opposite rows 8/9, right margin; also above vertical row 8 in reverse order to cylinder numbers reading left to right

Quantities Sold

5d.	67,584,528	English Pack	116,526
9d.	14,351,160	German Pack	4,416
1s.	10,784,480		

Withdrawn 14.1.70

W147. "Concorde" in Flight
(Des. M. and Sylvia Goaman)

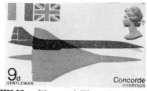

W148.   Plan and Elevation Views   **W149.**   "Concorde's" Nose and Tail
(Des. D. Gentleman)

1969 (MARCH 3). FIRST FLIGHT OF "CONCORDE"

Issued to commemorate the first flight of the "Concorde" supersonic airliner developed and produced jointly by Britain and France

Two phosphor bands

Cat. No.	S.G. No.	Type		Description	Unused	Used
W151	784	**W147**		4d. Yellow-orange, violet, greenish blue, blue-green and pale green	5	5
a. Violet omitted (value, etc.)		..	75·00			
b. Yellow-orange and phosphor omitted			25·00			
c. Yellow-orange omitted		..				
d. Phosphor omitted		..	20	*e.* "Oil slick" flaw (R.13/2) ..	80	
W152	785	**W148**		9d. Ultramarine, emerald, red and grey-blue	8	8
a. Phosphor omitted		..	10·00			
W153	786	**W149**		1s.6d. Deep blue, silver-grey and light blue	12	10
a. Silver-grey omitted*		..	90·00			
b. Phosphor omitted		..	1·75			
W151/3				First Day Cover	†	30
W151/3				Presentation Pack	35	
W151/3				Presentation Pack (German)		

*No. W153*a* affects the Queen's head which appears in the light blue colour.

Listed Variety

Dark flaw in Atlantic Ocean appears as an oil slick

W151*e*

Cylinder Numbers (Blocks of six)

	Cyl. Nos. (No dot)	Perforation Type F	
4d.	1A (violet)–1B (orange)–1C (greenish blue)–1D (pale green)–		
	1E (blue-green)	..	50
9d.	2A (grey-blue)–1B (red)–1C (emerald)–1D (ultramarine)	..	50
1s.6d.	1A (deep blue)–1B (silver-grey)–3C (light blue)	.. ..	90

Minor Constant Flaws

Minimum prices as singles: 4d. 40p; 9d. 40p; 1s.6d. 50p

4d. Cyls. 1A–1B–1C–1D–1E
 1/2 Disturbance in background below tail (Th. F–G11)
 2/2 Disturbance in background below tail (Th. F–G12)

9d. Cyls. 2A–1B–1C–1D
 11/2 Flaw on Queen's hair below ribbons (Th. B13)

1s.6d. Cyls. 1A–1B–3C
 18/2 Small white patch below tip of Concorde's nose (Th. F13)

Sheet Details

Sheet size: 120 (6 × 20). Single pane sheet-fed

Sheet markings:

 Cylinder numbers:
  4d. Opposite rows 1/2 and 18/19, at both sides, boxed
  9d. Opposite rows 2/3 and 18/19, at both sides, boxed
  1s.6d. Opposite rows 2 and 19, at both sides, boxed

 Guide holes: None

 Marginal arrows (photo-etched): "W" shaped, at top, bottom and sides

 Marginal rule: At bottom of sheet

 Colour register marks:
  4d. Above and below vertical rows 1/2 and 6
  9d. Above and below vertical rows 1 and 5/6
  1s.6d. Above and below vertical rows 1/2 and 6

 Coloured crosses: Above and below vertical rows 2/3

 Autotron marks, colour designations: None

 Traffic lights (boxed):
  4d. Blue-green, orange, violet, greenish blue, pale green reading left to right above vertical row 5
  9d. Ultramarine, emerald, red, grey-blue reading left to right above vertical row 5
  1s.6d. Deep blue, light blue, silver-grey reading left to right above vertical row 5

Quantities Sold

4d.	91,551,720	English Pack	100,608
9d.	9,488,520	German Pack	2,827
1s.6d.	9,874,560		

Withdrawn 2.3.70

W150. Page from *Daily Mail*, and Vickers "Vimy" Aircraft
(Des. P. Sharland)

W151. Europa and CEPT Emblems
(Des. M. and Sylvia Goaman)

W152. ILO Emblem
(Des. P. Sharland)

W153. Flags of NATO Countries
(Des. P. Sharland)

W154.   Vickers "Vimy" Aircraft and
Globe showing Flight
(Des. M. and Sylvia Goaman)

1969 (APRIL 2). NOTABLE ANNIVERSARIES

Five famous anniversaries, with the events described on the stamps
Two phosphor bands

Cat. No.	S.G. No.	Type	Description	Unused	Used
W154	791	**W150**	5d. Black, pale sage-green, chestnut and new blue	5	5
a. Missing windshield (R. 3/4) ..		65			
W155	792	**W151**	9d. Pale turquoise, deep blue, light emerald-green and black	8	8
a. Phosphor omitted .. .. 1·00					
W156	793	**W152**	1s. Bright purple, deep blue and lilac	10	10
a. Phosphor omitted .. .. 1·25					
W157	794	**W153**	1s.6d. Red, Royal blue, yellow-green, black, lemon and new blue	12	15
a. Black omitted .. .. .. 25·00					
b. Yellow-green omitted .. .. 30·00					
c. Yellow-green and phosphor omitted .. .. 15·00			e. Shadow variety (R.18/6) ..	80	
d. Phosphor omitted 75					
W158	795	**W154**	1s.9d. Yellow-olive, greenish yellow and pale turquoise-green	15	15
a. Uncoated paper*			First Day Cover	†	60
b. Phosphor omitted .. .. 1·50					
W154/8			Presentation Pack	65	
W154/8			Presentation Pack (German)		
W154/8					

*Uncoated paper—see General Notes for Section U1.

Listed Varieties

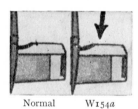

Normal   W154a

W157e
Deficient shading in shadow
by fold

Cylinder Numbers (Blocks of six (5d., 1s., 1s.9d.) or eight (9d., 1s.6d.))

	Cyl. Nos. (No dot)	Perforation Types	
		A	F
5d.	1A (blue)–1B (chestnut)–1C (sage-green)–1D (black) ..	50	†
9d.	1A (blue)–1B (green)–1C (black)–1D (turquoise)	†	75
1s.	1A (blue)–1B (purple)–1C (lilac)	†	75
1s.6d.	1A (new blue)–1B (lemon)–1C (red)–1D (Royal blue)–1E (black)–1F (green)	†	90
1s.9d.	2A (yellow-olive)–2B (green)–1C (yellow)	†	1·60

Minor Constant Flaws

Minimum prices as singles: 5d. 40p; 9d. 40p; 1s. 40p; 1s.6d. 50p; 1s.9d. 60p

5d. Cyls. 1A–1B–1C–1D
   3/4 Black horizontal line extending through the engine and fuselage (Th. E9–12)
   4/6 Vertical black scratch top left of photograph of Alcock (Th. A–B3)
   15/3 Retouch to base of engine (Th. E10)
   15/5 White flaw on Brown's cap (Th. B6). Later retouched

9d. Cyls. 1A–1B–1C–1D
   14/1 Retouch to background below O of EUROPA (Th. F–G4)
   15/3 Weak patch in background to left of CEPT symbol (Th. E11)
   19/3 Retouch to background below EU of EUROPA (Th. F2)
   20/2 Weak patch in background above O of EUROPA (Th. B–C4)

1s. Cyls. 1A–1B–1C
   19/1 Dark patch in upper jaw of spanner (Th. F1)

1s.9d. Cyls. 2A–2B–1C
   17/4 Horizontal scratch through value (Th. A1–3)
   20/6 Pale patch in East Asia on globe (Th. B12)

Sheet Details

Sheet size: 120 (6 × 20). 5d. single pane reel-fed; others single pane sheet-fed

Sheet markings:

Cylinder numbers:
   5d. Opposite rows 18/19, left margin, boxed
   9d. Opposite rows 17/18, left margin, boxed
   1s. Opposite row 18, left margin, boxed
   1s.6d. Opposite rows 17/18, left margin, boxed
   1s.9d. Opposite row 18, left margin, boxed

Guide holes:
   5d. Opposite rows 14/15 (boxed), at both sides
   Others: None

Marginal arrows (photo-etched): "W" shaped, at top, bottom and sides

Marginal rule: None

Colour register marks:
   5d. Opposite rows 1/2 and 19/20 at both sides
   Others: Above and below vertical rows 1 and 6

Coloured crosses:
   5d. None
   9d., 1s. and 1s.9d. Above and below vertical row 3
   1s.6d. Above and below vertical rows 3/4

Autotron marks (solid):
   5d. Black, sage-green, blue, chestnut below vertical rows 1/3
   Others: None

Colour designations:
   5d. "G1 BROWN G2 BLUE G3 (blank) G4 BLACK" in right margin reading upwards opposite rows 14/9
   Others: None

Sheet values: Opposite rows 4/7 and 14/17 reading upwards in left margin and downwards in right margin

Traffic lights (boxed):
   5d. Black, sage-green, blue, chestnut opposite rows 18/19, right margin; also in same order opposite rows 1/2, left margin
   9d. Black, green, blue, turquoise opposite rows 17/18, right margin; also in reverse order reading left to right above vertical row 5
   1s. In same order as cylinder numbers opposite row 18, right margin; also in reverse order reading left to right above vertical row 5
   1s.6d. In same order as cylinder numbers opposite rows 17/18, right margin; also in reverse order reading left to right above vertical row 5
   1s.9d. In same order as cylinder numbers opposite row 18, right margin; also in reverse order reading left to right above vertical row 5

Quantities Sold

5d.	82,285,680	English Pack	90,282
9d.	9,823,200	German Pack	4,539
1s.	10,302,360		
1s.9d.	6,155,760		

Withdrawn 1.4.70

W155.   Durham Cathedral

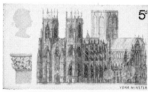
W156.   York Minster

W157.   St. Giles', Edinburgh

W158.   Canterbury Cathedral

W159.   St. Paul's Cathedral

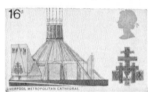
W160.   Liverpool Metropolitan Cathedral

(Des. P. Gauld)

1969 (MAY 28). BRITISH ARCHITECTURE (CATHEDRALS)

The designs show six famous British Cathedrals dating from medieval times to the present day, the Liverpool Metropolitan Cathedral being completed in 1967

The 5d. values were issued together *se-tenant* in blocks of four throughout the sheet

Two phosphor bands

Cat. No.	S.G. No.	Type	Description	Unused	Used
W159	796	**W155**	5d. Grey-black, orange, pale bluish violet and black	5	5
a. Pale bluish violet omitted	..				
W160	797	**W156**	5d. Grey-black, pale bluish violet, new blue and black	5	5
a. Pale bluish violet omitted	..				
W161	798	**W157**	5d. Grey-black, purple, green and black	5	5
a. Green omitted* ..	..	.. 15·00			
W162	799	**W158**	5d. Grey-black, green, new blue and black	5	5
W163	800	**W159**	9d. Grey-black, ochre, pale drab, violet and black	8	8
a. Black omitted (value) ..	..	25·00			
b. Phosphor omitted	..	.. 2·50			
W164	801	**W160**	1s.6d. Grey-black, pale turquoise-blue, pale reddish violet, pale yellow-olive and black	12	15
a. Black omitted (value) ..	..	90·00			
b. Phosphor omitted	..	.. 10·00			
W159/64			First Day Cover	†	50
W159/64			Presentation Pack	50	
W159/64			Presentation Pack (German)		

5d. *Prices for missing colour errors in blocks of four:*

Pale bluish violet	..	..	..	..	..	..	..	..	..	
Green ..	..	..	..	..	..	..	..	..	15·00

*The missing green on the roof top is known on R. 2/5, R. 8/5 and R. 10/5 but all from different sheets and it only occurred in part of the printing, being "probably caused by a batter on the impression cylinder". Examples are also known with the green partly omitted.

Cylinder Numbers (Blocks of eight (5d.) or six (9d., 1s., 1s.6d.))

	Cyls. Nos.	Perforation Types		
		A No dot	A Dot	F No dot
5d.	1A (black)–1B (purple)–1C (blue)–1D (orange)– 2E (green)–2F (grey-black)–1G (violet)* ..	60	60	†
	1A (black)–1B (purple)–2C (blue)–1D (orange)– 2E (green)–2F (grey-black)–1G (violet)* ..	60	60	†
9d.	1A (black)–1B (grey-black)–2C (violet)– 1D (drab)–1E (ochre)**	†	†	50
1s.6d.	1A (black)–1B (violet)–1C (turquoise-blue)– 1D (yellow-olive)–1E (grey-black)	†	†	90

* In the 5d. dot panes the violet cylinder is expressed in error thus: "1.G" and the black cylinder "1.A".
**In the 9d. the violet "2C" often appears battered, the "2" sometimes being hardly discernible.

Minor Constant Flaws

Minimum prices as singles: 5d. 40p; 9d. 40p; 1s.6d. 50p

5d. Cyls. 1A–1B–1D–2E–2F no dot in combination with blue cyls. 1C or 2C no dot
  12/4 Thin diagonal green line joins portrait to inset design (Th. C–E2)

5d. Cyls. 1A–1B–1D–2E–2F dot in combination with blue cyls. 1C or 2C dot
  1–4/3 Green coloured scratch extends from bottom of third stamp in row 1 to top of third stamp in row 4.
    Most noticeable in the sky of R. 3/3
  4/1 Damaged first S of ST. GILES'
  10/3 Grey-black coloured spur at right of angel (Th. F13)

9d. Cyls. 1A–1B–2C–1D–1E
  8/5 Dark spot in window on first floor just to right of centre of St. Paul's (Th. F7)

1s.6d. Cyls. 1A–1B–1C–1D–1E
  1/1 Retouch on Queen's head (Th. A11)
  15/1 Spur at left of third spike of central tower (Th. A5); also dot before C of CATHEDRAL

Sheet Details

Sheet sizes:
  5d. 72 (6×12). In *se-tenant* blocks of four, double pane reel-fed, with dot pane above no dot pane
  9d. and 1s.6d. 120 (6×20). Single pane sheet-fed

Sheet markings:
  Cylinder numbers:
    5d. Opposite rows 10/11, left margin, boxed
    9d. and 1s.6d. Opposite rows 18/19, left margin, boxed
  Guide holes:
    5d. Opposite rows 6/7 (boxed), at both sides
    Others: None
  Marginal arrows (photo-etched): "W" shaped, at top, bottom and sides
  Marginal rule: None
  Colour register marks:
    5d. Opposite rows 10/12, left margin, although usually trimmed off
    9d. and 1s.6d. Above and below vertical rows 1 and 6
  Coloured crosses:
    5d. None
    9d. and 1s.6d. Above and below vertical rows 3/4
  Autotron marks:
    5d. Normally trimmed off
    9d. and 1s.6d. None
  Colour designations: None
  Sheet values:
    5d. Opposite rows 2/5 and 8/11 reading upwards in left margin and downwards in right margin
    9d. and 1s.6d. Opposite rows 5/6 and 15/16 reading upwards in left margin and downwards in right margin
  Traffic lights (boxed):
    5d. In same order as cylinder numbers opposite rows 10/11, right margin; also in same order reading
      left to right above vertical rows 4/5
    9d. In reverse order to cylinder numbers opposite rows 18/19, right margin; also above vertical row 5
      but in same order as cylinder numbers reading left to right
    1s.6d. Black, yellow-olive, turquoise-blue, violet, grey-black opposite rows 18/19, right margin; also
      grey-black, yellow-olive, turquoise-blue, violet and black reading left to right above vertical row 5

Quantities Sold

5d.	65,354,076	English Pack	119,828
9d.	11,065,920	German Pack	7,200
1s.6d.	11,423,880		

Withdrawn 27.5.70

W161. The King's Gate, Caernarvon Castle **W162.** The Eagle Tower, Caernarvon Castle **W163.** Queen Eleanor's Gate, Caernarvon Castle

W164. Celtic Cross, Margam Abbey **W165.** H.R.H. The Prince of Wales (after photograph by G. Argent)

(Des. D. Gentleman)

1969 (JULY 1). INVESTITURE OF H.R.H. THE PRINCE OF WALES

The ceremony of Investiture dates back to 1284 when King Edward I presented his son to the people of Caernarvon as the first Prince of Wales

The 5d. values were issued together *se-tenant* in strips of three throughout the sheet

Two phosphor bands

Cat. No.	S.G. No.	Type			Description	Unused	Used
W165	802	**W161**			5d. Deep olive-grey, light olive-grey, deep grey, light grey, red, pale turquoise-green, black and silver	5	5
a. Black omitted (value and inscr.)			..	80·00			
b. Red omitted*	..	..		5·00			
c. Deep grey omitted**	..			13·00			
d. Phosphor omitted		..		20			
W166	803	**W162**			5d. Deep olive-grey, light olive-grey, deep grey, light grey, red, pale turquoise-green, black and silver	5	5
a. Black omitted (value and inscr.)			..	80·00			
b. Red omitted*	..	..		5·00			
c. Deep grey omitted**	..			13·00			
d. Phosphor omitted		..		20			
W167	804	**W163**			5d. Deep olive-grey, light olive-grey, deep grey, light grey, red, pale turquoise-green, black and silver	5	5
a. Black omitted (value and inscr.)			..	80·00			
b. Red omitted*	..	..		5·00			
c. Deep grey omitted**	..			13·00			
d. Phosphor omitted		..		20			
W168	805	**W164**			9d. Deep grey, light grey, black and gold	8	8
a. Phosphor omitted	..	..		3·00			
W169	806	**W165**			1s. Blackish yellow-olive and gold	10	10
a. Phosphor omitted	..	.		1·50			
b. One band at right	..	..					
W165/9					First Day Cover	†	35
W165/9					Presentation Pack†	40	
W165/9					Presentation Pack (German)		

5d. *Prices for missing colour errors in strips of three:*

Black	..	..	..	..	..	..	..	..	..	..	£250
Red ..	..	..	..	..	..	..	..	..	..	..	—
Deep grey	..	..	..	..	..	..	..	..	..	..	—

*The 5d. is also known with the red misplaced downwards and where this occurs the red printing does not take very well on the silver background and in some cases is so faint that it could be mistaken for a missing red. However, the red can be seen under a magnifying glass and caution should therefore be exercised when purchasing copies of W165/7b.

**The deep grey affects the dark portions of the windows and doorways.

†In addition to the generally issued Presentation Pack a further pack in different colours and with all texts printed in both English and Welsh was made available exclusively through Education Authorities for free distribution to all schoolchildren in Wales and Monmouthshire. (*Price* 75p).

First Day Covers are known postmarked in error "1 JUL 1968" at London N.W.1.

Cylinder Numbers (Blocks of nine (5d.) or four (9d., 1s.))

Cyl. Nos.	Perforation Types		
	A No dot	A Dot	F No dot
5d. 1A (black)–1B (red)–1C (silver)–1D (green)– 1E (deep olive-grey)–1F (light olive-grey)– 1G (deep grey)–1H (light grey)	†	†	75
9d. 1A (black)–1B (gold)–1C (deep grey)–1D (light grey)	40	40	†
1s. 1A (gold)–2B (blackish yellow-olive)	50	50	†

The above are with sheets orientated showing head to right.

Minor Constant Flaws

Minimum prices as singles: 5d. 40p; 9d. 40p; 1s. 50p

9d. Cyls. 1A–1B–1C–1D dot
  5/9 yw of Tywysog are joined together

1s. 1A–2B no dot
  1/10 Retouch to right of Prince's lower lip (Th. J–K6)
  3/4 Small retouch below Prince's left eye (Th. G6)

Sheet Details

Sheet sizes:
  5d. 72 (12 × 6). In *se-tenant* strips of three, single pane sheet-fed
  9d. and 1s. 60 (10 × 6). Double pane sheet-fed, with no dot pane above dot pane

Sheet markings:
  Cylinder numbers:
    5d. Opposite rows 4/5, left margin, boxed
    9d. and 1s. Opposite row 6, left margin, boxed
  Guide holes: None
  Marginal arrows (photo-etched):
    5d. None
    9d. and 1s. "W" shaped, at top, bottom and sides
  Marginal rule: None
  Colour register marks:
    5d. Opposite rows 1 and 6, at both sides
    9d. Above (no dot) or below (dot) vertical rows 1/2 and 10
    1s. Above (no dot) or below (dot) vertical rows 1/2 and 9/10
  Coloured crosses:
    5d. Opposite rows 3/4, at both sides
    9d. and 1s. Above (no dot) or below (dot) vertical row 4
  Autotron marks, colour designations: None
  Sheet values:
    5d. Above and below vertical rows 2/5 and 8/11 reading left to right in top margin and right to left (upside-down) in bottom margin
    9d. and 1s. Opposite rows 1/3 and 4/6 reading upwards in left margin and downwards in right margin
  Traffic lights (boxed):
    5d. In same order as cylinder numbers opposite rows 4/5, right margin; also in same order reading left to right above vertical rows 10/11
    9d. In same order as cylinder numbers opposite row 5, right margin; also in same order reading left to right above vertical row 9
    1s. In reverse order to cylinder numbers opposite row 6, right margin; also in reverse order reading left to right above vertical row 9

Quantities Sold

5d.	99,467,496	English Pack	256,709
9d.	13,384,380	German Pack	9,360
1s.	12,972,720		

Withdrawn 30.6.70

W166.   Mahatma Gandhi
(Des. Biman Mullick)

1969 (AUGUST 13). GANDHI CENTENARY YEAR

This stamp marking the Gandhi Centenary Year was also the first United Kingdom postage stamp to commemorate an overseas leader and the first to be designed by an overseas artist

Two phosphor bands

Cat. No.	S.G. No.	Type	Description	Unused	Used
W170	807	**W166**	1s.6d. Black, green, red-orange		
a. Printed on the gummed side ..			and grey	12	15
b. Phosphor omitted	1·50		*c.* Tooth Flaw (R.20/3)	75	
W170			First Day Cover	†	15

The above is known pre-released on 12th August at Penyfai (Bridgend), Glamorgan and also postmarked Paisley, Renfrewshire 13th July, the latter being due to the use of an incorrect date-stamp on a first day cover.

Listed Variety

White patch in Gandhi's mouth appears as tooth. Later retouched to near normal

W170*c*

Cylinder Numbers (Block of six)

Cyl. Nos. (No dot)   Perforation Type F

1s.6d. 2A (black)–1B (grey)–2C (green)–1D (orange)   90

Minor Constant Flaws

Minimum price as singles: 50p

1s.6d. Cyls. 2A–1B–2C–1D

    1/6 Second white spot in Gandhi's right eye (Th. D6). Later retouched; also small nick in left arm of Y of Year
    3/4 Dark patch on arm of spectacles (Th. C4)
    3/5 Retouch on Gandhi's nose (Th. E6)
    5/3 Dark spot in front of Gandhi's right ear (Th. D3)
    8/2 Dark spot on Gandhi's temple (Th. C4). Later retouched
    12/4 White patch on Gandhi's right lapel (Th. G2)
    16/1 Retouched G of Gandhi

Sheet Details

Sheet size: 120 (6×20). Single pane sheet-fed

Sheet markings:
    Cylinder numbers: Opposite rows 18/19, left margin, boxed
    Guide holes: None
    Marginal arrows (photo-etched): "W" shaped, at top, bottom and sides
    Marginal rule: None
    Colour register marks: Above and below vertical rows 1 and 6
    Coloured crosses: Above and below vertical row 3
    Autotron marks and colour designations: None
    Sheet values: Opposite rows 4/7 and 14/17 reading upwards in left margin and downwards in right margin
    Traffic lights (boxed): Black, grey, green, orange opposite rows 19/20, right margin; also in reverse order reading left to right above vertical row 5

Quantity Sold 10,804,920

Withdrawn 12.8.70

1969 (SEPTEMBER 15). COLLECTORS PACK

WCP2 Comprising Nos. W142/70   2·00

Quantity Sold 63,890

W167. National Giro
"G" Symbol

W168. Telecommunications—
International Subscriber Dialling

W169. Telecommunications—
Pulse Code Modulation

W170. Postal Mechanisation—
Automatic Sorting

(Des. D. Gentleman)
(Lithographed by De La Rue)

1969 (OCTOBER 1). POST OFFICE TECHNOLOGY COMMEMORATION

Issued on the day the Post Office became a public corporation, these stamps depict some of its technological achievements. This issue in itself was a technical departure for the Post Office being the first British stamps to be printed by lithography

Comb perforation $13\frac{1}{2} \times 14$. Two phosphor bands applied by typography

Cat. No.	S.G. No.	Type	Description	Unused	Used
W171	808	**W167**	5d. New blue, greenish blue,		
a. Phosphor omitted	.. ..		pale lavender and black	5	5
b. One band at right					
W172	809	**W168**	9d. Emerald, violet-blue and		
a. One band at right	.. ..		black	8	10
W173	810	**W169**	1s. Emerald, lavender and		
a. One band at right	.. ..		black	10	12
W174	811	**W170**	1s.6d. Bright purple, light		
a. One band at right	.. ..		turquoise-blue, grey-blue		
			and black	12	15
W171/4			First Day Cover	†	40
W171/4			Presentation Pack	40	

The 1s. is known postmarked at Gloucester on 29th September and the 1s.6d. at Gutcher, Yell (Shetland Isles) on 26th September.

For advance publicity the Post Office produced sample sets of stamps sealed in a sheet of perspex (size 4 × 6 in.) together with details of the designs, and names of the stamp designer and printer.

Cylinder Numbers (Blocks of four)

		Cyl. Nos. (all Dot)			Pertoration Type F (L)	
5d.	2A (new blue)–2B (greenish blue)–2C (lavender)–2D (black) ..			..		40
	2A (new blue)–3B (greenish blue)–2C (lavender)–2D (black)					40
	2A (new blue)–3B (greenish blue)–2C (lavender)–3D (black) ..					40
	3A (new blue)–4B (greenish blue)–3C (lavender)–4D (black) ..					40
9d.	2A (emerald)–2B (violet-blue)–2C (black)		..	..	..	40
1s.	1A (emerald)–1B (lavender)–1C (black) ..		..	..	..	75
	1A (emerald)–1B–(lavender)–2C (black)		..	..	..	60
	1A (emerald)–1B (lavender)–3C (black) ..		..	..	..	60
1s.6d.	1A (purple)–1B (light turquoise-blue)–1C (grey-blue)–1D (black) ..					75

Although all the cylinder numbers are followed by a dot they were in fact only printed in single panes.

Minor Constant Flaws

Numerous minor flaws caused by specks of dust settling on the printing plate and preventing the ink from reaching the area appear as white inkless rings and are known as litho "ring" flaws. Minor flecks of colour are similarly caused. As such flaws only affect part of a printing and cannot be regarded as constant we have decided not to record them.

Sheet Details

Sheet size: 120 (10 × 12). Single pane sheet-fed

Sheet markings:
  Cylinder numbers: Opposite rows 1/2, left margin, unboxed
  Guide holes: Above and below vertical row 6 in crossed box. Reserve guide-hole boxes appear above and
    below vertical row 4 but these were not used
  Marginal arrows (solid): "W" shaped, at top, bottom and sides
  Marginal rule: None
  Colour register marks:
    5d., 9d. and 1s. Below vertical rows 1 and 10 and opposite rows 1 and 12, at both sides
    1s.6d. Above and below vertical rows 1 and 10 and opposite rows 1 and 12, at both sides
  Coloured crosses, autotron marks, colour designations: None
  Sheet values: Above and below vertical rows 2/4 and 7/9 reading left to right in top margin and right to
    left (upside down) in bottom margin
  Traffic lights (unboxed):
    5d. Opposite rows 8/10, right margin
    9d. and 1s. Opposite rows 9/10, right margin
    1s.6d. Opposite rows 9/11, right margin

Quantities Sold   5d. 72,405,720; 9d. 10,872,000; 1s. 10,656,120; 1s.6d. 10,757,040; Pac
  104,230

Withdrawn 30.9.70

W171.   Herald Angel

W172.   The Three Shepherds

W173.   The Three Kings

(Des. F. Wegner)

(Printed in photogravure with the Queen's head (and stars 4d., 5d. and scroll-work 1s.6d.
  embossed in gold)

1969 (NOVEMBER 26).   CHRISTMAS

Traditional religious themes are featured on these stamps by Austrian-born designe
Fritz Wegner

One 7 to 8 mm. centre phosphor band (4d.) or two phosphor bands (others)

Cat. No.	S.G. No.	Type	Description	Unused	Use
W175	812	**W171**	4d. Vermilion, new blue,		
a. Gold (Queen's Head) omitted..		£100	orange, bright purple,		
b. Centre band 3½ mm. ..	..	5 5	light green, bluish		
			violet, blackish brown		
			and gold	5	
W176	813	**W172**	5d. Magenta, light blue, Royal		
a. Light blue (sheep, etc.) omitted	25·00		blue, olive-brown, green,		
b. Red omitted* ..	..	..	greenish yellow, red and		
c. Embossing omitted	..	50	gold	5	
d. Phosphor omitted	..	25			
W177	814	**W173**	1s.6d. Greenish yellow, bright		
a. Embossing omitted	..	2·50	purple, bluish violet,		
b. Embossing and	phosphor		deep slate, orange, green,		
omitted ..	..	2·00	new blue and gold	12	1
c. Phosphor omitted	..	1·00			
d. Broken arch (R.1/6)	..	65			
W175/7			First Day Cover	†	3
W175/7			Presentation Pack	30	

274

The 4d. is known postmarked at Dudley, Worcs. on 25th November.

*The effect of the missing red is shown on the hat, leggings and purse which appear as ull orange.

No. W175 has one centre band 8 mm. wide but this was of no practical use in the automatic acing machines and after about three-quarters of the stamps had been printed the remainder were printed with a 3½ mm. band (No. W175b). The wide band is sometimes difficult to see. stamps have also been seen with very wide "phantom" band measuring about 20 mm. which only reacts very faintly under the lamp and with a clear 3½ mm. band over it.

isted Variety

W177d

Break in the arch above the crown of King at right

ylinder Numbers (Blocks of six (4d.) or eight (5d., 1s.6d.))

Cyl. Nos.		Perforation Types			
		A			
		7–8 mm. band		3½ mm. band	
		No dot	Dot	No dot	Dot
4d.	1A (brown)–1B (vermilion)–2C (orange)–1D (purple)–1E (new blue)–1F (green)–1G (violet)–1H (gold)	40	40	†	†
	1A (brown)–1B (vermilion)–2C (orange)–1D (purple)–1E (new blue)–2F (green)–1G (violet)–1H (gold)	40	40	40	40
		F No dot		F (L) No dot	
5d.	1A (Royal blue)–1B (yellow)–1C (magenta)–1D (green)–2E (brown)–1F (light blue)–1G (red)–1H (gold)	50		5·00	
1s.6d.	3A (slate)–1C (gold)–1D (blue)–1E (yellow)–1F (green)–1G (violet)–1H (purple)–1J (orange)	1·00		†	

On the 4d. cylinder numbers 1A and 1H often appear as " 1A1 " and " 1H1 " on the dot and no dot panes respectively; the 1B and 1E have what appear to be small letters "IN" in place of dot, whilst the 2C is an alteration from "1C", all on the dot panes.

Minor Constant Flaws

Minimum price as singles: 4d. 40p

d. Cyls. 1A–1B–2C–1D–1E–2F–1G–1H dot

   5/3 White flaw in hem of angel's gown (later corrected) (Th. E1)
   11/1 A break in the pattern of the pillar on the right (Th. E13)
   11/4 White flaw in the pattern of the arch over the Queen's head (Th. A11)

Sheet Details

Sheet sizes:
   4d. 72 (6×12). Double pane reel-fed (one pane above the other) for four colours and phosphor, and then single pane sheet-fed for remaining four colours and embossing
   5d. and 1s.6d. 120 (6×20). Single pane sheet-fed
Sheet markings:
Cylinder numbers:
   4d. Opposite rows 10/12, left margin, boxed
   5d. and 1s.6d. Opposite rows 17/19, left margin, boxed
Guide holes:
   4d. Opposite rows 6/7 (boxed), at both sides
   5d. and 1s.6d. None
Marginal arrows (photo-etched): " W " shaped, at top, bottom and sides
Marginal rule: None
Colour register marks:
   4d. None
   5d. and 1s.6d. Above and below vertical rows 1/2 and 5/6
Coloured crosses:
   4d. Usually trimmed off
   5d. and 1s.6d. Above and below vertical rows 3/4
Autotron marks, colour designations: None
Sheet values:
   4d. Opposite rows 3/4 and 9/10 reading upwards in left margin and downwards in right margin
   5d. Opposite rows 4/7 and 14/17 reading upwards in left margin and downwards in right margin
   1s.6d. Opposite rows 5/6 and 15/16 reading upwards in left margin and downwards in right margin
Traffic lights (boxed):
   4d. Vermilion, orange, purple, new blue, green, brown, violet, gold and embossing opposite rows 9/11, right margin; also in same order reading left to right above vertical rows 4/5
   5d. Embossing and then as cylinder numbers but in reverse order opposite rows 17/19, right margin; also in same order as cylinder numbers followed by embossing above vertical rows 4/5
   1s.6d. Embossing, gold, blue, yellow, slate, green, violet, purple and orange opposite rows 17/19, right margin; also in reverse order reading left to right above vertical rows 4/5

Quantities Sold 4d. 271,244,808; 5d. 139,845,600; 1s.6d. 19,136,520; Pack

Withdrawn 25.11.70

W174. Fife Harling

W175. Cotswold Limestone

(Des. D. Gentleman)

W176. Welsh Stucco

W177. Ulster Thatch

(Des. Sheila Robinson)

1970 (FEBRUARY 11). BRITISH RURAL ARCHITECTURE

The designs feature typical cottage architecture in Scotland, England, Wales and Northern Ireland respectively

Two phosphor bands

Cat. No.	S.G. No.	Type			Description	Unused	Used
W178	815	**W174**			5d. Grey, grey-black, black, lemon, greenish blue, orange-brown, ultramarine and green	5	5
a. Yellow omitted ..		..	..	7·00			
b. Phosphor omitted		..	..	25			
c. Yellow omitted from chimney at left (R.12/2)		..	..	75			
W179	816	**W175**			9d. Orange-brown, olive-yellow, bright green, black, grey-black and grey	8	10
a. Phosphor omitted		..	..	2·00			
W180	817	**W176**			1s. Deep blue, reddish lilac, drab and new blue	10	10
a. New blue omitted		..	..	6·00			
b. Phosphor omitted		..	..	60			
c. One band at left		..	..				
W181	818	**W177**			1s.6d. Greenish yellow, black, turquoise-blue and lilac	12	12
a. Phosphor omitted		..	..	50			
b. Broken panes in middle window (No dot, R.3/2) ..		..	..	75			
W178/81					First Day Cover	†	40
W178/81					Presentation Pack	40	

A single used copy of No. W178 is known with the grey-black omitted. This affects the inscription "Fife harling" and also detail on the roof, the walls of the buildings and the foreground.

Listed Varieties

No. W178c. The yellow is omitted from the chimney at left once in every sheet (later added to cylinder and appearing normal)

W181b

Cylinder Numbers (Blocks of eight (5d.), six (9d.), four (1s., 1s.6d.))

	Cyl. Nos.	F No dot	A (T) No dot	A (T) Dot
			Perforation Types	
5d.	1A (black)–1B (grey-black)–1C (brown)–1D (ultra- marine)–1E (greenish blue)–1F (green)–1G (grey)– 1H (lemon)	45	†	†
9d.	1A (grey-black)–1B (yellow)–1C (brown)–1D (black)– 1E (green)–1F (grey)	60	†	†
1s.	1A (deep blue)–2B (lilac)–1C (new blue)–1D (drab)..	†	50	50
1s.6d.	1A (black)–1B (yellow)–1C (turquoise-blue)– 1D (lilac)	†	60	60

Minor Constant Flaws

Minimum prices as singles: 5d. 40p; 9d. 50p; 1s.6d. 50p

5d. Cyls. 1A–1B–1C–1D–1E–1F–1G–1H no dot
    4/2 Right leg of h of harling is broken
    9/6 Pale patch on wall above left-hand first-floor window of building at right (Th. D8)
    20/6 Pale patch on wall by top of upright at the bottom of the banisters and similar patch with grey
        spot in it just above (Th. F1); coloured spur to centre chimney (Th. A7); and orange-brown flaw
        below F of Fife (Th. A2)

9d. Cyls. 1A–1B–1C–1D–1E–1F no dot
    19/1 Dark flaw on gate at left (Th. G2)

1s.6d. Cyls. 1A–1B–1C–1D no dot
    2/3 Pale flaw on left stroke of U of ULSTER and two yellow dots in front of Queen's neck

1s.6d. Cyls. 1A–1B–1C–1D dot
    5/5 White flaw to right of sixth brick from bottom (Th. G7)

Sheet Details

Sheet sizes:
    5d. and 9d. 120 (6 × 20). Single pane sheet-fed
    1s. and 1s.6d. 60 (6 × 10). Double pane sheet-fed
Sheet markings:
    Cylinder numbers:
        5d. Opposite rows 17/19, left margin, boxed
        9d. Opposite rows 18/19, left margin, boxed
        1s. and 1s.6d. Opposite rows 9/10, left margin, boxed
    Guide holes: None
    Marginal arrows (photo-etched): " W " shaped, at top, bottom and sides
    Marginal rule: None
    Colour register marks:
        5d. and 9d. Above and below vertical rows 1/2 and 6
        1s. Opposite rows 1/2 and 6, at left (no dot) or right (dot)
        1s.6d. Opposite rows 1 and 6, at left (no dot) or right (dot)
    Coloured crosses:
        5d. and 9d. Above and below vertical rows 3/4
        1s. Opposite row 7, at left (no dot) or right (dot)
        1s.6d. Opposite rows 6/7, at left (no dot) or right (dot)
    Autotron marks, colour designations: None
    Sheet values:
        5d. and 9d. Opposite rows 4/7 and 14/17 reading upwards in left margin and downwards in right margin
        1s. Opposite row 2/4 and 7/9 reading upwards in left margin and downwards in right margin
        1s.6d. As 1s. but reading downwards in left margin and upwards in right margin
    Traffic lights (boxed):
        5d. In same order as cylinder numbers opposite rows 18/19, right margin; also in reverse order reading
        left to right above vertical rows 4/6
        9d. In reverse order to cylinder numbers opposite rows 18/19; also in same order as cylinder numbers
        above vertical row 5
        1s. In same order as cylinder numbers opposite rows 6/7, right margin; also same order reading left to
        right above vertical row 5
        1s.6d. In same order as cylinder numbers opposite rows 7/8 at both sides; also in reverse order above
        vertical row 5

Withdrawn   10.2.71

W178.   Signing the Declaration
of Arbroath

W179.   Florence Nightingale
attending Patients

(Des. F. Wegner)

W180. Signing the International
Co-operative Alliance
(Des. Marjorie Saynor)

W181. Pilgrims and *Mayflower*

(Des. F. Wegner)

W182. Sir William Herschel, Francis Baily,
Sir John Herschel and Telescope
(Des. Marjorie Saynor)
(Printed in photogravure with the Queen's head embossed in gold)

1970 (APRIL 1). GENERAL ANNIVERSARIES

Five famous anniversaries, with the events described on the stamps

An additional feature of this issue was the introduction of cylinder numbers for the cylinders printing the phosphor bands. They are not easy to see but are printed below the ordinary cylinder numbers. The Post Office expects all future special issues to have phosphor cylinder numbers

Two phosphor bands

Cat. No.	S.G. No.	Type		Description	Unused	Used
W182	819	**W178**		5d. Black, yellow-olive, blue,		
a. Gold (Queen's head) omitted ..				emerald, greenish yellow,		
b. Emerald omitted	..	..		rose-red, gold and		
c. Phosphor omitted	..	..		orange-red	5	5
d. White flaw in desk (R.2/6)	..	50				
e. White spot in hem (R.5/5)	..	50				
f. Missing portions of desk and foot						
(R.20/4) ..	..	..	50			
W183	820	**W179**		9d. Ochre, deep blue, carmine,		
a. Ochre omitted ..	..	..	14·00	black, blue-green, yellow-		
b. Embossing omitted	..	..	60	olive, gold and blue	8	10
c. Phosphor omitted	..	..	75			
W184	821	**W180**		1s. Green, greenish yellow,		
a. Gold (Queen's head) omitted ..		20·00		brown, black, cerise,		
b. Green and embossing omitted	..	40·00		gold and light blue	10	10
c. Green omitted ..	..	..	40·00			
d. Brown and phosphor omitted ..				*g.* Embossing omitted	..	..	1·00	
e. Brown omitted ..	..	..		*h.* Phosphor omitted	..	..	1·00	
f. Embossing and phosphor						
omitted ..	..	..	6·00			
W185	822	**W181**		1s.6d. Greenish yellow, car-		
a. Emerald omitted	..	..	15·00	mine, deep yellow-olive,		
b. Embossing omitted	..	..	1·25	emerald, black, blue,		
c. Phosphor omitted	..	..	1·75	gold and sage-green	12	12
d. Flag flaw (R.20/5)	..	..	75			
W186	823	**W182**		1s.9d. Black, slate, lemon,		
a. Phosphor omitted	..	..	1·25	gold and bright purple	15	15
W182/6				First Day Cover	†	50
W182/6				Presentation Pack	50	

The 5d. is known with the gold partly omitted, possibly due to under-inking. Of a complete sheet seen the cylinder number did not show, the traffic lights appeared smaller and the back of the Queen's head on every stamp was rounded with no ribbons.

We have seen a copy of the 1s.9d. on cover with the lemon colour omitted and two or three other covers have been reported. This error may only exist in used condition.

Listed Varieties

W182*d*

W182*e*
Amount of white varies
with the registration
of colours

W182*f*
Large part of base of
desk and front of shoe
missing

All the above are multipositive flaws which appear on no dot and dot panes

W185*d*

Portion of blue in
bottom right-hand
corner of Union Jack
is missing

Cylinder Numbers (Blocks of eight (5d., 9d., 1s., 1s.6d.) or six (1s.9d.))

Cyl. Nos.		Perforation Types		
		A (T)	F	F (L)
		No dot Dot	No dot	No dot
5d.	1A (black)–1B (gold)–1C (blue)–1D (emerald)–1E (olive)–1F (rose-red)–1G (yellow)–1H (orange-red)–P1 (phosphor)	45 45	†	
9d.	2A (blue)–1B (ochre)–1C (deep blue)–1D (green)–1E (gold)–2F (black)–1G (olive)–1H (carmine)–P2 (phosphor)	†	70	†
1s.	1A (black)–1B (blue)–1C (yellow)–1D (brown)–1E (gold)–2F (cerise)–1G (green)–P2 (phopshor) ..	†	90	10·00
1s.6d.	1A (black)–1B (sage-green)–1C (yellow)–1D (carmine)–1E (gold)–2F (blue)–1G (deep yellow-olive)–1H (emerald)–P2 (phosphor)	†	1·00	†
1s.9d.	1A (black)–1E (gold)–1B (slate)–1C (lemon)–2D (bright purple)–P2 (phosphor)	†	1·10	†

The phosphor cylinder numbers appear below the ordinary cylinder numbers opposite R.20/1. In the 5d. the " P1 " is indented into the phosphor band but in the other values the " P2 " is to the left of the phosphor band.

In the 5d. the "1" of "1C" and the bar below it are sometimes missing.

In the 1s.9d. the cylinder numbers are always out of sequence.

Minor Constant Flaws

Minimum prices as singles: 5d. 40p; 9d. 50p; 1s. 50p; 1s.6d. 50p; 1s.9d. 60p

5d. Cyls. 1A–1B–1C–1D–1E–1F–1G–1H–P1 no dot

    2/1 Weak patches in background below r and t of Declaration
    6/1 Vertical scratch in background, through and below th of Arbroath (Th. A10 to C11)
    7/1 As 6/1

9d. Cyls. 2A–1B–1C–1D–1E–2F–1G–1H–P2 no dot
    8/6 Pale area surrounds final e of Florence
    19/4 Dark patch in background below second g of Nightingale

1s. Cyls. 1A–1B–1C–1D–1E–2F–1G–P2 no dot
   3/4 Missing top to t in Co-operative
   8/3 Dark flaw by top of first l of Alliance

1s.6d. Cyls. 1A–1B–1C–1D–1E–2F–1G–1H–P2 no dot
   8/3 Letters flo of Mayflower have hazy appearance

1s.9d. Cyls. 1A–1E–1B–1C–2D–P2 no dot
   2/3 Pale patch in background above on of Astronomical
   2/6 Small break in t of Astronomical
   19/1 Dark patch on left leg of figure at right (Th. F6)
   19/5 Bright purple coloured flaw on left sleeve of man at left due to lack of screening dots on black
      cylinder (Th. D3)
   20/4 Black dot on e of Society

Sheet Details

Sheet sizes: 120 (6 × 20). 5d. double pane reel-fed; others single pane sheet-fed
Sheet markings:
   Cylinder numbers:
      1s.9d. Opposite rows 18/19, left margin, boxed. Others: Opposite rows 17/19, left margin, boxed.
   Guide holes: 5d. Opposite rows 6/7 (boxed), at both sides. Others: None
   Marginal arrows (photo-etched): " W " shaped, at top, bottom and sides
   Marginal rule: None
   Colour register marks:
      5d. Opposite rows 9/12 at right (no dot) or left (dot). Others: Above and below vertical rows 1 and 6
   Coloured crosses: 5d. None. Others: Above and below vertical rows 3/4
   Autotron marks (solid):
      5d. Gold, black, blue, emerald, olive, rose-red, yellow, orange-red above left margin and above vertical
      rows 1/4. Others: None
   Colour designations: None
   Sheet values:
      1s. Opposite rows 5/6 and 15/16 reading upwards in left margin and downwards in right margin
      Others: Opposite rows 4/7 and 14/17 reading upwards in left margin and downwards in right margin
   Traffic lights (boxed):
      5d. Embossing, gold, black, blue, emerald, olive, rose-red, yellow and orange-red opposite rows 16/18,
      right margin; also in same order reading left to right above vertical rows 4/5
      9d. Blue, ochre, deep blue, green, gold, embossing, black, olive and carmine opposite rows 17/19, right
      margin; also in reverse order reading left to right above vertical rows 4/5
      1s. Green, black, cerise, gold, embossing, brown, yellow and blue opposite rows 18/19, right margin; also
      blue, yellow, embossing, gold, brown, cerise, black and green reading left to right above vertical rows
      4/5
      1s.6d. Sage-green, yellow, carmine, blue, gold, embossing, deep yellow-olive, black and emerald opposite
      rows 17/19, right margin; also in reverse order reading left to right above vertical rows 4/5
      1s.9d. Black, gold, embossing, slate, lemon and bright purple opposite rows 18/19, right margin; also
      embossing, gold, black, slate, lemon and bright purple reading left to right above vertical row 5

Withdrawn 31.3.71

W183.   " Mr. Pickwick and Sam "   **W184.**   " Mr. and Mrs. Micawber "
        (Pickwick Papers)   *(David Copperfield)*

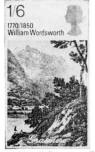

W185. "David Copperfield and Betsy Trotwood" *(David Copperfield)*

W186. "Oliver asking for more" *(Oliver Twist)*

W187. "Grasmere" (from engraving by J. Farrington, R.A.)

(Des. Rosalind Dease. 5d. based on etchings by "Phiz" and George Cruickshank)
(Printed in photogravure with the Queen's head embossed in gold)

1970 (JUNE 3). LITERARY ANNIVERSARIES

The four 5d. stamps, commemorating the death centenary of Charles Dickens, feature popular characters from his novels. The 1s.6d. stamp commemorates the birth bicentenary of Lakeland poet William Wordsworth

The 5d. values were issued together *se-tenant* in blocks of four throughout the sheet
Two phosphor bands

Cat. No.	S.G. No.	Type		Description	Unused	Used
W187	824	**W183**		5d. Black, orange, silver, gold and magenta	5	5
a. Imperf. (block of four) £300						
W188	825	**W184**		5d. Black, magenta, silver, gold and orange	5	5
W189	826	**W185**		5d. Black, light greenish blue, silver, gold and yellow-bistre	5	5
a. Yellow-bistre (value) omitted ..						
W190	827	**W186**		5d. Black, yellow-bistre, silver, gold and light greenish blue	5	5
a. Yellow-bistre (background) omitted						
b. Light greenish blue (value) omitted*						
W191	828	**W187**		1s.6d. Light yellow-olive, black, silver, gold and bright blue	10	10
a. Gold (Queen's head) omitted ..						
b. Silver ("Grasmere") omitted .. 12·00						
c. Embossing and phosphor omitted						
d. Embossing omitted						
e. Phosphor omitted				f. Retouch in slope (R.1/16) ..	75	
				g. Extra road (R.6/8) ·· ..	75	
W187/91				First Day Cover	†	30
W187/91				Presentation Pack	25	

*No. W190b (unlike No. W189a) results from a partial missing colour. Although it is completely missing on No. W190, it is only partially omitted on No. W189.

Listed Varieties

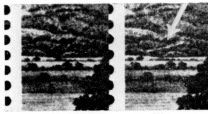

W191f
Retouch consists of diagonal black lines over triangular green patch N.E. of Grasmere

Normal **W191g**
Green line gives the impression of an extra road leading up the foothill

Cylinder Numbers (Blocks of eight (5d.) or four (1s.6d.))

		Perforation Types		
	Cyl. Nos.	A		F
		No dot	Dot	No dot
5d.	1A (orange)–1B (magenta)–3C (bistre)–1D (blue)–1E (black)–1F (silver)–			
	1G (gold)–P4 (phosphor)	35	35	†
1s.6d.	1A (blue)–1B (gold)–1C (silver)–1D (black)–1E (olive)–P3 (phosphor) ..	†		45

The above are with sheets orientated showing head to right.
In the 5d. the 1F is printed over a figure "2" in both panes.

Minor Constant Flaws

Minimum price as singles: 5d. 40p

5d. Cyls. 1A–1B–3C–1D–1E–1F–1G dot
 5/17 Extra "button" on Sam's coat under armpit (Th. B6)
 5/19 Dot by 7 of 1870 level with centre of 8

Sheet Details

Sheet size: 120 (20 × 6)
 5d. In *se-tenant* blocks of four, double pane reel-fed
 1s.6d. Single pane sheet-fed
Sheet markings:
 Cylinder numbers:
  5d. above vertical rows 1/3, boxed
  1s.6d. Opposite row 5, left margin, boxed
 Guide holes:
  5d. In single box above and below vertical rows 14/15
  1s.6d. None
 Marginal arrows (photo-etched): " W " shaped, at top, bottom and sides
 Marginal rule: None
 Colour register marks:
  5d. None
  1s.6d. Opposite rows 1 and 6 at both sides
 Coloured crosses:
  5d. None
  1s.6d. Opposite rows 3/4 at both sides
 Autotron marks (solid):
  5d. Opposite rows 1/4 at right on no dot pane only
  1s.6d. None
 Colour designations: None
 Sheet values: Above and below vertical rows 4/7 and 14/17
 Traffic lights (boxed):
  5d. Embossing, gold, silver, blue, bistre, magenta, orange and black opposite rows 5/6, right margin;
   also in reverse order below vertical rows 3/4
  1s.6d. Embossing, gold, silver, blue, black and olive opposite row 5, right margin; also in same order
   above vertical rows 18/19

Withdrawn 3.6.71

W188. Runners

W189. Swimmers

W190. Cyclists

(Des. A. Restall)
(Lithographed by De La Rue)

1970 (JULY 15). BRITISH COMMONWEALTH GAMES

These were issued on the eve of the Ninth British Commonwealth Games which were held in Edinburgh. Like the Post Office Technology issue these were printed by lithography by De La Rue.

Comb perforation 13½ × 14. Two phosphor bands applied by typography

Cat. No.	S.G. No.	Type		Description	Unused	Used
W192	832	**W188**		5d. Pink, emerald, greenish yellow and deep yellow-green		
a. Phosphor omitted		.. ..	10·00		5	5
W193	833	**W189**		1s.6d. Light greenish blue, lilac, bistre-brown and Prussian blue		
a. Phosphor omitted		.. ..	10·00		12	12
W194	834	**W190**		1s.9d. Yellow-orange, lilac, salmon and deep red-brown	15	15
W192/4				First Day Cover	†	40
W192/4				Presentation Pack	30	

Cylinder Numbers (Blocks of Four)

	Cyl. Nos.		Perforation Type F (L)	
			No dot	Dot
5d.	1A (yellow)–1B (emerald)–1C (pink)–1D (green)		20	20
	2A (yellow)–1B (emerald)–1C (pink)–1D (green)		20	20
1s.6d.	1A (bistre-brown)–1B (greenish blue)–1C (lilac)–1D (indigo) ..		50	50
	2A (bistre-brown)–2B (greenish blue)–2C (lilac)–2D (indigo) ..		50	50
1s.9d.	1A (salmon)–1B (lilac)–1C (yellow-orange)–1D (red-brown) ..		60	60
	1A (salmon)–2B (lilac)–1C (yellow-orange)–1D (red-brown) ..		60	60

Minor Constant Flaws

The notes relating to minor flaws in lithographed stamps under the 1969 Post Office Technology issue also apply here.

Sheet Details

Sheet size: 120 (10 × 12). Double pane sheet-fed with no dot pane at top and dot pane below
Sheet markings:
  Cylinder numbers: Opposite rows 1/2, left margin, unboxed
  Guide holes: Above and below vertical row 4 in crossed box on no dot pane and below vertical row 4 in crossed box on dot pane; the reserve box in top margin was not used. In addition reserve guide-hole boxes appear above and below vertical row 6 in both panes but these were not used
  Marginal arrows (solid): "W" shaped, at top, bottom and sides
  Marginal rule: None
  Colour register marks: Below vertical rows 1 and 12 and in right-hand margin opposite rows 1 and 12 in both panes; in addition, they occur in the left-hand margin opposite row 12 in the no dot pane
  Coloured crosses, autotron marks, colour designations: None
  Sheet values: Above and below vertical rows 2/4 and 7/9 reading left to right in top margin and right to left (upside down) in bottom margin
  Traffic lights (unboxed): Opposite rows 9/10, right margin in same order as cylinder numbers

Withdrawn 15.7.71

1970 (SEPTEMBER 14). COLLECTORS PACK 1970

WCP3 Comprises Nos. W171/94   1·75

Withdrawn 13.9.71

W191. 1d. Black (1840)

W192. 1s. Green (1847)
(Des. D. Gentleman)

W193. 4d. Carmine (1855)

1970 (SEPTEMBER 18). "PHILYMPIA 70" STAMP EXHIBITION

Issued for the opening of the International Philatelic Exhibition held at the Olympia Exhibition Hall, London. The 5d. depicts the first adhesive postage stamp ever issued, the famous Penny Black. This is shown with the check letters "P" and "L" for "Philympia" and "London". The 9d. and 1s.6d. show the first Great Britain stamps using the embossed and surface-printed processes respectively.

Two phosphor bands

Cat. No.	S.G. No.	Type		Description	Unused	Used
W195	835	**W191**		5d. Grey-black, brownish bistre,		
a. Phosphor omitted*	..	..	1·00	black and dull purple	5	5
b. One phosphor band	..	..				
c. White blob (No dot, R.5/6)	..	40		d. Weak entry (Dot, R.1/2)	..	40	
W196	836	**W192**		9d. Light drab, bluish green,		
a. Phosphor omitted	..	..	3·00	stone, black and dull		
				purple	8	8
W197	837	**W193**		1s.6d. Carmine, light drab,		
a. Phosphor omitted	..	..	1·00	black and dull purple	12	15
b. Missing dot over i (R.6/12)	..	50				
W195/7				First Day Cover	†	35
W195/7				Presentation Pack	25	

The 5d. is known postmarked at Boughton, King's Lynn on 17th September.

*The phosphor is sometimes difficult to see on the 5d. due to "dry" prints so care is needed in identifying true missing phosphors.

Listed Varieties

W195c
Large white blob between OS
of POSTAGE (later retouched)

W195d
Weak entry of frameline
in top left corner

In No. W197b the dot is missing over the i of printed

Cylinder Numbers (Blocks of Four)

Cyl. Nos.

		Perforation Types		
		A		A (T)
		No dot	Dot	No dot
5d.	1A (black)–1B (dull purple)–1C (brownish bistre)–1D (grey-black)–P6 (phosphor)	35	35	†
9d.	1A (black)–1B (stone)–2C (bluish green)–1D (dull purple)–1E (light drab)– P10 (phosphor)	†		35
1s.6d.	1A (black)–1B (light drab)–1C (dull purple)–1D (carmine)–P5 (phosphor)	†		50

The above are with sheets orientated showing head to right.

Minor Constant Flaws

Minimum prices as singles: 5d. 30p; 9d. 35p; 1s.6d. 40p
1s.6d. Cyls. 1A–1B–1C–1D–P5 no dot
   1/1 Frame flaw below N of PENCE

Sheet Details

Sheet size: 120 (12×10). 5d. double pane reel-fed; others single pane sheet-fed
Sheet markings:
  Cylinder numbers: Opposite row 9, left margin, boxed but the phosphor number is opposite row 10, left
    margin
  Guide holes: 5d. Above and below vertical row 6 (boxed). Others: None
  Marginal arrows (photo-etched): "W" shaped, at top, bottom and sides
  Marginal rule: None
  Colour register marks:
    5d. None. Others: Above and below vertical rows 1 and 10/11
  Coloured crosses: 5d. None. Others: Above and below vertical rows 3/4
  Autotron marks and colour designations: None
  Sheet values: Opposite rows 2/4 and 7/9 at both sides, reading up at left and down at right
  Traffic lights (boxed):
    5d. Dull purple, black, brownish bistre, grey-black opposite row 10 right margin; also in same order
      reading from left to right above vertical rows 11/12
    9d. Bluish green, stone, dull purple, black, brownish bistre opposite row 10 right margin; also in same
      order reading from left to right above vertical rows 11/12
    1s.6d. Light drab, dull purple; carmine, black opposite 9/10 right margin; also in reverse order reading
      from left to right above vertical row 12

Withdrawn 18.9.71

W194. Shepherds and
Apparition of the Angel

W195. Mary, Joseph and
Christ in the Manger
(Des. Sally Stiff)

W196. The Wise Men
bearing Gifts

(Printed in photogravure with the Queen's head in gold and then embossed)

1970 (NOVEMBER 25). CHRISTMAS

    The designs depict traditional Nativity scenes taken from the de Lisle Psalter in the
Arundel Collection at the British Museum.
    The 4d. stamps were printed by the Wood machine which has a capacity for ten cylinders.
Eight were used for the colours and the others for simultaneous application of the embossing
and phosphor bands.
    One central 4 mm. phosphor band (4d.) or two phosphor bands (others)

Cat. No.	S.G. No.	Type		Description	Unused	Used
W198	838	**W194**		4d Brown-red, blue, turquoise-		
a. Phosphor omitted			15·00	green, pale chestnut,		
b. Imperf. between stamp and left				brown, grey-black, gold		
margin				and vermilion	5	5
c. Thinned frame (No dot, R.4/6)..			40			
W199	839	**W195**		5d. Emerald, gold, blue, brown-		
a. Green omitted			35·00	red, ochre, grey-black and		
b. Imperforate (pair)			90·00	violet	5	5
c. Embossing omitted						
d. Phosphor omitted			50			
W200	840	**W196**		1s.6d. Gold, grey-black, pale		
a. Salmon omitted			45·00	turquoise-green, salmon,		
b. Ochre omitted				ultramarine, ochre, red		
c. Embossing and phosphor omitted				and yellow-green	12	15
d. Embossing omitted			12 15			
e. Phosphor omitted			1·00			
W199/200				First Day Cover	†	20
W199/200				Presentation Pack	25	

Listed Variety

Gold frame at right by shepherd's arm is thinned and has been strengthened by two parallel chestnut lines

W198c

Cylinder Numbers (4d. Blocks of Ten; Others Blocks of Six)

	Cyl. Nos.	Perforation Type A	
		No dot	Dot
4d.	1A (vermilion)–1B (grey-black)–1C (brown)–1D (brown-red)–1E (turquoise-green)–1F (blue)–1G (pale chestnut)–1J (gold)–P9 (phosphor)	40	40
5d.	1A (violet)–1B (brown-red)–1C (blue)–1D (ochre)–3E (grey-black)–1F (emerald)–1G (gold)–P7 (phosphor)	40	†
1s.6d.	1A (yellow-green)–1B (grey-black)–1D (red)–1E (salmon)–1F (pale turquoise-green)–1G (gold)–1J (ochre)–1C (ultramarine)–P7 (phosphor)	75	†

The above are with sheets orientated showing head to right.
On some sheets of the 4d. the J is completely omitted.

Minor Constant Flaws

Minimum prices as singles: 4d. 30p; 5d. 30p; 1s.6d. 40p

4d. Cyls. 1A–1B–1C–1D–1E–1F–1G–1J–P9 no dot
5/5 Dotted line across central shepherd's temple and through hair (Th. G6–7)

5d. Cyls. 1A–1B–1C–1D–3E–1F–1G–P7 no dot
8/8 Diagonal line over Mary's left hand (Th. J3)

1s.6d. Cyls. 1A–1B–1D–1E–1F–1G–1J–1C–P7 no dot
1/12 Horizontal scratch across cloaks of Three Wise Men (Th. K2–6)

The Thirkell Position Finder readings are taken with the finder over the perforations.

Sheet Details

Sheet size: 120 (12 × 10). 4d. double pane reel-fed; others single pane sheet-fed
Sheet markings:
Cylinder numbers:
4d. Bottom margin, unboxed, reading down below vertical rows 5/2
5d. Opposite rows 8/9, left margin, boxed but the phosphor number is opposite row 10, left margin
1s.6d. Opposite rows 8/10, left margin, boxed. The 1C was added at the bottom opposite row 10
Guide holes: 4d. Above and below vertical row 6 (boxed). Others: None
Marginal arrows (photo-etched): "W" shaped, at top, bottom and sides
Marginal rule: None
Colour register marks:
4d. Above and below vertical rows 2/5. Others: Above and below vertical rows 1/2 and 12
Autotron marks and colour designations: None
Coloured crosses: 4d. None. Others: Above and below vertical rows 3/4
Sheet values: Opposite rows 2/4 at both sides and rows 7/8 at left and 7/9 at right, reading up at left and down at right
Traffic lights (boxed):
4d. Vermilion, grey-black, brown, brown-red, turquoise-green, blue, pale chestnut, gold, embossing* opposite rows 9/10 right margin; also in same order reading from left to right above vertical rows 11/12
5d. Violet, brown-red, blue, ochre, grey-black, emerald, gold, embossing opposite rows 9/10 right margin; also in same order reading from left to right above vertical rows 10/11
1s.6d. Yellow-green, grey-black, ultramarine; red, salmon, pale turquoise-green, gold, ochre, embossing; also in same order reading from left to right above vertical rows 9/11

*The embossing is usually very faint on the 4d. traffic lights.

Withdrawn 25.11.71

W197. "A Mountain Road"
(T. P. Flanagan)

W198. "Deer's Meadow"
(Tom Carr)

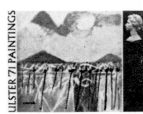

W199. "Slieve na brock"
(Colin Middleton)

(Layout des. Stuart Rose)

1971 (JUNE 16). "ULSTER '71" PAINTINGS

This issue featuring paintings by contemporary artists living and working in Belfast marks the "Ulster '71" Festival aimed at tourists and industrialists.

Two phosphor bands

Cat. No.	S.G. No.	Type		Description	Unused	Used
W201	861	**W197**		3p. Yellow-buff, pale yellow, Venetian red, black, blue		
a. Phosphor omitted	..	..	40	and drab	5	5
W202	862	**W198**		7½p. Olive-brown, brownish		
a. Pale olive-grey omitted*	..	4·00	grey, pale olive-grey,		
b. Phosphor omitted	..	..	1·50	deep blue, cobalt and		
c. One wide phosphor band	..	30	grey-blue	10	12
W203	863	**W199**		9p. Greenish yellow, orange,		
a. Phosphor omitted	..	..	1·00	grey, lavender - grey,		
b. One wide phosphor band	..	1·00	bistre, black, pale ochre-		
				brown and ochre-brown	12	15
W201/3				First Day Cover	†	30
W201/3				Presentation Pack	35	

* This only affects the boulder in the foreground, which appears whitish, and it is only applied to some stamps in the sheet.

Cylinder Numbers (Blocks of Six)

	Cyl. Nos. (No dot)	Perforation Type A (T)
3p.	2A (black)–1B (yellow-buff)–1C (pale yellow)–2D (blue)–1E (Venetian red)–1F (drab)–P14 (phosphor)	35
7½p.	1A (brownish grey)–1B (cobalt)–2C (deep blue)–1D (grey-blue)–1E (olive-brown)–1F (pale olive-grey)–P18 (phosphor)	60
9p.	1A (black)–2B (grey)–1C (lavender-grey)–1D pale (ochre-brown)–1E (ochre-brown)–1F (bistre)–1G (greenish yellow)–1H (orange)–P18 (phosphor)	75

Minor Constant Flaws

Minimum prices as singles: 3p. 30p; 7½p. 40p; 9p. 45p

7½p. Cyls. 1A–1B–2C–1D–1E–1F–P14 no dot

    3/3 Dark spot on top of grass stalks at right (Th. F10)
    6/6 Blue spot in second N of PAINTINGS
    9/7 Blue spot under second N of PAINTINGS
    9/9 Brown spot in Queen's bust (Th. C12)

9p. Cyls. 1A–2B–1C–1D–1E–1F–1G–1H–P18 no dot

    1/6 Brown speck in hill at right (Th. E9–10)
    7/9 Dark speck in panel below Queen's head (Th. D11)

Sheet Details

Sheet size: 100 (10 × 10). Single pane sheet-fed (cylinders arranged sideways)

Sheet markings:
    Cylinder numbers:
        3p. Opposite rows 8/9, left margin, boxed
        Others. Opposite rows 8/10, left margin, boxed
    Guide holes: None
    Marginal arrows (photo-etched): "W" shaped, at top, bottom and sides
    Marginal rule: None
    Colour register marks: Crossed circle type opposite rows 1 and 19 at both sides. The 3p has two in each
        position and the others one
    Autotron marks and colour designations: None
    Coloured crosses: 3p. Opposite rows 7/8 at both sides. Others: Opposite rows 6/8 at both sides
    Sheet values: Above and below vertical rows 2/4 and 6/8 reading left to right in top margin and right to left
        (upside-down) in bottom margin
    Traffic lights (boxed):
        3p. Drab, yellow-buff, black, blue, Venetian red, pale yellow opposite rows 8/9 right margin; also in
        same order reading from left to right above vertical rows 9/10
        7½p. Brownish grey, cobalt, deep blue, grey-blue, olive-brown, pale olive-grey opposite rows 8/10 right
        margin; also in same order reading from left to right above vertical rows 9/10
        9p. Grey, lavender-grey, pale ochre-brown, ochre-brown, black, bistre, greenish yellow, orange opposite
        rows 8/10 right margin; also in same order reading from left to right above vertical rows 9/10

SECTION X1

Regional Issues

1958-70. £.s.d. Issues. Photogravure

General Notes

INTRODUCTION. On 18th August 1958 the first Great Britain Regional issues were put on sale for use in Northern Ireland, Scotland and Wales and Monmouthshire and in the islands of Guernsey, Jersey and the Isle of Man. The ordinary postage stamps of Great Britain in the same values are not on sale at post offices in these regions except at the Philatelic Counters in Belfast, Cardiff, Edinburgh and Glasgow, apart from Monmouthshire where the Welsh Regionals and Great Britain postage stamps are on sale concurrently.

Although specifically issued for regional use, these issues were initially valid for use throughout Great Britain. However, they ceased to be valid in Guernsey and Jersey from 1st October 1969 when these islands each established their own independent postal administrations and introduced their own stamps. Guernsey and Jersey Regionals were withdrawn locally on 30th September 1969 but remain on sale at British Philatelic Counters until 30th September 1970.

Following the practice set by Great Britain, these issues do not bear the names of the regions, these being indicated by various devices and symbols which relate to them. The three island issues are inscribed "Postage" only and have no usage as revenue stamps as they have their own Parliaments.

The portrait used is by Dorothy Wilding, Ltd.

PRINTERS. All the Regional issues were printed in photogravure by Harrison & Sons on continuous reels of paper "on the web". The 3d., 4d. and 5d. values of Northern Ireland, Scotland and Wales and Monmouthshire were printed in double pane width, i.e. 480 stamps consisting of two panes (no dot and dot) each of 240 stamps arranged in twenty rows of twelve stamps, the panes being guillotined before issue. All the island issues and the 6d., 9d., 1s.3d., and 1s.6d. values from the other regions were made from single cylinders printing sheets of 240 stamps (i.e. no dot panes only).

PAPER AND WATERMARK. As with the Wilding definitives, for the first few years the Regional issues were printed on a creamy paper but starting in February 1962 a whiter paper was gradually introduced as new printings were made. See the General Notes for Section S for further information. Exceptionally, a chalk-surfaced paper was used for a printing of the Isle of Man 3d. in 1963.

Only the Crowns watermark, as illustrated in Section S, has been used for the Regional issues. From 1967 new printings of a number of values were on the chalk-surfaced paper without watermark, as used for the Machin definitives.

GUM. Gum arabic was used from 1958 to 1968 after which PVA gum was introduced.

The distinction between gum arabic and PVA gum is explained in the General Notes to Section U1. It is worth noting that gum arabic was used on the creamy, white and unwatermarked chalk-surfaced papers but that PVA gum exists only on the last of these.

PERFORATION. Harrisons used the same 15 × 14 comb perforation as for the Wilding definitives. A number of different perforators were used and these are described and illustrated in Appendix O. The cylinder numbers are listed and priced according to the type of perforator used.

PHOSPHOR BANDS. See the General Notes for Section S for a detailed description of these. In the Regional issues it is sufficient to state that these were applied as follows:

"Blue" 8 mm. bands: 1963–64
"Violet" 8 mm. bands: 1965–66
"Violet" 9·5 mm. bands: 1967 to date
The one centre band stamps in the "violet" period were always 4 mm. bands.

A number of values have appeared with the phosphor omitted in error and these are listed separately. All values are believed to have the bands applied in photogravure.

DATES OF ISSUE. Conflicting dates of issue have been announced for some of the issues, partly explained by their being released on different dates by the Philatelic Bureau in Edinburgh or the Philatelic Counter in London and in the regions. We give the earliest date, since once released the stamps could have been used anywhere in the U.K.

FIRST DAY COVERS.   Prices for these are only quoted where there was a specific service provided by the Post Office.

SHEET MARKINGS.   Reference should be made to the descriptions of sheet markings given in the General Notes for Sections S and U1, as most of them apply to this Section and the information given there is not repeated here. Additional information is given here.

Cylinder Numbers. In the Regional issues these appear in the left-hand margin opposite Row 18 No. 1 in the style as illustrated in Section S.

Phosphor Cylinder Numbers. The notes in the General Notes for Section U £.s.d. Low Values also apply here but they are only found on the Scottish 5d. and the Welsh 5d.

Marginal Arrows. In the Regional issues these are " W " shaped (photo-etched) at top, bottom and sides, except for the Jersey and Isle of Man 3d. and the Northern Ireland, Scotland and Wales and Monmouthshire 3d., 6d. and 1s.3d. which are all " V " shaped (hand engraved) at top and bottom of the sheet and " W " shaped (photo-etched) at both sides (only cyl. 4 Scotland 1s.3d.).

---

*PRICES FOR CYLINDER BLOCKS WITH ASTERISKS
These denote cylinder blocks containing a listed variety and the price includes the variety.

A. Guernsey

XG1

XG2

(Des. E. A. Piprell)

2½d., Type **XG1** (1964)

Cat. No.	S.G. No.		Shades	Unused	Used
1964 (JUNE 8). WATERMARK CROWNS					
XG1	6		(1) Pale rose-red (Cyl. 1)	35	25
			(2) Rose-red (Cyl. 3)	30	25
XG1			First Day Cover	†	75

Cylinder Numbers (Blocks of Six)

Single pane cylinders.   Perforation Type F (L).

Cyl. Nos.					No dot
1	..	..	..	..	2·75
3	..	..	..	..	2·50

Minor Constant Flaws

Minimum price as singles: 50p

Cyl. 1   1/4 Small retouch over TA
 1/5 White patch over left part of diadem to left of central cross (Th. A3)
 17/12 Background disturbance in top loop of left-hand ribboning (Th. B1)
 19/2 White patch below left leg of R

Cyl. 3   17/5 Dark spot under topmost tip of ribboning at right (Th. B6)
 17/12 and 19/2. As on cyl. 1 (multipositive flaws)

Sheet Markings

Guide holes: Through marginal arrow above vertical rows 6/7 and below vertical row 10
Others: As given in General Notes

Withdrawn 31.8.66

Quantity Sold 3,485,760 including 10,100 on First Day Covers

3d., Type XG2 (1958–62)

Cat. No.   S.G. No.   Shades   Unused Used

1958 (AUGUST 18).   WATERMARK CROWNS

A. Cream Paper

XG2   —   Deep lilac   30   8

B. White Paper (5 July 1962)

XG3   7   Deep lilac   20   5

Cylinder Numbers (Blocks of Six)

	Cream Paper					Whiter Paper			
Cyl. No.	(No dot)			Perf. Types B C		Cyl. No.	(No dot)		Perf. Types B C F (L)
4	..	..	..	..	2·50 2·50	4	..	..	..	1·50 1·50 1·50
						5	..	..	..	† † 1·25

Minor Constant Flaws

Minimum price as singles: 40p

Cyl. 5   4/1 Background scratch above right-hand petal (Th. C–D2)
          7/10 Dark spot in left-hand margin (opposite Th. C1)
          9/10 Pale scratch in background from petal at far right down to Queen's chin (Th. D–E3)
          11/11 Diagonal background scratch from base of lily's stem to base of Queen's neck (Th. F3–E4)
          13/1 Flaw in background above centre stamen of lily (Th. C2)
          18/6 Smudge in background near Queen's mouth (Th. D3)

Sheet Markings

Guide holes: Perf. Type F (L), as for No. XG1 except that there are also boxes opposite rows 14/15 at left and right.   Perf. Types B and C, not known.
Others: As given in General Notes.

Sold Out 6.3.68

Quantity Sold 25,812,360

1967 (MAY 24).   ONE CENTRE PHOSPHOR BAND REACTING VIOLET.   WATERMARK CROWNS

XG4   7p   1) Deep lilac   5   5
                                       (2) Deep reddish lilac   8   5

Cylinder Numbers (Blocks of Six)

Single pane cylinder.   Perforation Type F (L)

	Cyl. No.				No dot
	5	..	..	..	50

Minor Constant Flaws

Minimum price as singles: 40p

As for flaws on Cyl. 5 of No. XG3

Sheet Markings

Guide holes: As for Perf. Type F (L) on No. XG3
Others: As given in General Notes

Sold Out 11.68

4d., Type XG2 (1966–69)

Cat No.	S.G. No.			Shades	Unused	Used

1966 (FEBRUARY 7). WATERMARK CROWNS

XG5	8			Ultramarine	12	6
a. Stem flaw (R. 12/8)	..	1·10				
XG5				First Day Cover	†	25

Listed Variety

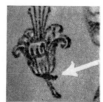

Coloured line across top of stem

XG5*a*, XG6*a*, XG7*b*, XG8*c*

Cylinder Numbers (Blocks of Six)

Single pane cylinder.   Perforation Type F (L)

Cyl. No.				No dot
1	..	..	..	90

Minor Constant Flaws

Minimum price as singles: 50p

Cyl. 1   1/1 Small spot above centre stamen of lily (Th. C2)
            9/5 White dot between two stamens on left-hand side (Th. D2)
            13/4 White spot on right-hand petal (Th. D3)
            20/12 Pale flaw in background to right of central diadem (Th. A5)
These are generally more marked on later issues from this cylinder.

Sheet Markings

Guide holes: Through marginal arrow above vertical rows 6/7 and below vertical row 10
Others: As given in General Notes

Sold Out 6.3.68

Quantity Sold 4,415,040 including 12,350 on First Day Covers

1967 (OCTOBER 24). TWO 9·5 mm. PHOSPHOR BANDS REACTING VIOLET. WATERMARK CROWNS

XG6	8p			Ultramarine	5	5
a. Stem flaw (R. 12/8)	..	1·10				

For illustration of No. XG6*a*, see No. XG5*a*.

Cylinder Numbers (Blocks of Six)

Single pane cylinder.   Perforation Type F (L)

Cyl. No.				No dot
1	..	..	..	50

Minor Constant Flaws

Minimum price as singles: 40p

Cyl. 1   5/10 Circular background retouch below Queen's chin (Th. E4)
           16/12 Break in centre stamen (Th. C–D2)
           17/10 Break in second stamen from left (Th. C2)
Others: As on No. XG5

Sheet Markings

As for No. XG5

Sold Out 10.68

Cat. No.	S.G. No.	Shades	Unused	Used

1968 (APRIL 14*). NO WATERMARK. CHALKY PAPER. PVA GUM. TWO 9·5 mm. PHOSPHOR BANDS REACTING VIOLET

XG7   9   Pale ultramarine   5   5
a. Phosphor omitted   ..   ..   12·00
b. Stem flaw (R. 12/8)   90

*This was not issued in Guernsey until 22nd April.
For illustration of No. XG7*b*, see No. XG5*a*.

Cylinder Numbers (Blocks of Six)

Single pane cylinder. Perforation Type F (L)

Cyl. No.   No dot
1   50

Minor Constant Flaws

Minimum price as singles: 40p

Cyl. 1   2/8 Weak patch in background at upper left (Th. A1)
19/6 Small retouch between A and G
Others: As on Nos. XG5 and XG6

Sheet Markings

As for No. XG5

Sold Out 3.69

1968 (SEPTEMBER 4). CHANGE OF COLOUR. NO WATERMARK. CHALKY PAPER. PVA GUM. ONE CENTRE PHOSPHOR BAND REACTING VIOLET

XG8   10   Olive-sepia   5   5
a. Phosphor omitted   ..   ..   1·50
b. Phosphor horizontal ..   ..   2·50
c. Stem flaw (R.12/8)   60   *d.* Retouched 4 (R. 16/10)   ..   60

Listed Varieties

For illustration of No. XG8*c*, see No. XG5*a*.

XG8*d*
Spot over 4 has been retouched
Corrected on No. XG9

Cylinder Numbers (Blocks of Six)

Single pane cylinder. Perforation Type F (L)

Cyl. No.   No dot
1   45

Constant Minor Flaws

Minimum price as singles: 40p

As for No. XG7 except that flaw on R.5/10 does not show

Sheet Markings

As for No. XG5

Withdrawn 30.9.70

1969 (FEBRUARY 26). FURTHER CHANGE OF COLOUR. NO WATERMARK. CHALKY PAPER. PVA GUM. ONE CENTRE PHOSPHOR BAND REACTING VIOLET

XG9   11   Bright vermilion   5   5
a. Stem flaw retouched (R.12/8)   50

293

Listed Variety

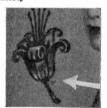

The stem flaw has been retouched but still shows as a smudge to right of stem

XG9*a*

Cylinder Numbers (Blocks of Six)

Single pane cylinder.   Perforation Type F (L)

Cyl. No.					No dot
1	..	..	..	..	45

Minor Constant Flaws

Minimum price as singles: 40p
  As for No. XG8

Sheet Markings
  As for No. XG5

Withdrawn 30.9.70

5d., Type XG2 (1968)

Cat. No.	S.G. No.			Shades		Unused	Used

1968 (SEPTEMBER 4).   NO WATERMARK.   CHALKY PAPER.   PVA GUM.   TWO 9·5 mm. PHOSPHOR BANDS REACTING VIOLET

XG10	12			Royal blue		5	5
a. Stamen flaw (R.12/1)		..	60				
b. Retouched	..	..	..	2·00			

XG8 and XG10 (52,449 posted)

First Day Cover   †   25

Listed Variety

XG10*a*

X10*b*

Still visible after retouch on late printing

Cylinder Numbers (Blocks of Six)

Single pane cylinder.   Perforation Type F (L)

Cyl. No.					No dot
1	..	..	..	..	50

Minor Constant Flaws

Minimum price as singles: 40p
  Cyl. 1   12/6 Small white flaw to left of Queen's mouth (Th. D3)

Sheet Markings
  As for No. XG5

Withdrawn 30.9.70

INVALIDATION. The regional issues for Guernsey were invalidated for use in Guernsey and Jersey on 30 September 1969 but remained valid for use in the rest of the United Kingdom. Those still current remained on sale at philatelic sales counters until 30 September 1970.

B. Jersey

XJ1
(Des. E. Blampied)

XJ2
(Des. W. M. Gardner)

2½d., Type XJ1 (1964)

Cat. No.	S.G. No.	Shades	Unused	Used
1964 (JUNE 8). WATERMARK CROWNS				
XJ1	9	Carmine-red	30	25
a. Imperf. three sides (pair)	.. £200			
b. Thin POSTAGE (R.18/1)	.. 1·50			
XJ1		First Day Cover	†	75

Listed Varieties

Letters of POSTAGE are thinner, resulting in more white showing in the O and G

Normal   XJ1*b*

Cylinder Numbers (Blocks of Six)

Single pane cylinder.   Perforation Type F (L)

	Cyl. No.				No dot
	1	..	..	..	..	3·75*

Minor Constant Flaws

Minimum price as singles: 50p

 Cyl. 1 11/1 Two tiny dots on Queen's nose
    18/2 Spot to right of mace level with O of POSTAGE

Sheet Markings

 Guide holes: Through marginal arrow above vertical rows 6/7 and below vertical row 10
 Others: As given in General Notes

Withdrawn 31.8.66

Quantity Sold 4,770,000 including 12,800 on First Day Covers

3d., Type XJ2 (1958–67)

1958 (AUGUST 18).   WATERMARK CROWNS

A. Cream Paper

XJ2	—	Deep lilac	20	8
a. Joined tomato (Cyl. 1, R.19/9)	.. .. .. 1·50	*b.* "Halberd" flaw (Cyl. 1, R.20/3) 1·10		

B. Whiter Paper (23 September 1962)

XJ3	10	Deep lilac	10	5
a. Scratched collar (Cyl. 2, R. 9/8)	50			

295

Listed Varieties

| XJ2a | XJ2b | XJ3a, XJ4a |

Both these varieties were later retouched to normal

Cylinder Numbers (Blocks of Six)

	Cream Paper				Whiter Paper		
Cyl. No.	(No dot)		Perf. Types	Cyl. No.	(No dot)		Perf. Types
			B C				B C F (L)
1	.. ..		2·00 2·00	1	.. .. ..		1·50 1·50 1·50
				2	.. .. ..		† † 5·00

Minor Constant Flaws

Minimum price as singles: 40p

Cyl. 1 20/4 Short white line extends below left of D
Cyl. 2 3/7 Weak background below left-hand berry of middle pair on right-hand plant (Th. E5)
14/12 Dot in left-hand margin (Opposite Th. D1)
16/1 Dot on top left leaf of right-hand plant (Th. C5–6)
16/12 Dot in top margin (Above Th. A4)
20/3 Dot in top margin (Above Th. A4)

Sheet Markings

Guide holes: Perf. Types F (L), through marginal arrow above vertical rows 6/7 and below vertical row 10. Other perfs. not known. Cyl. 2 also has boxes opposite rows 14/15 at left and right.
Others: As given in General Notes and also a trimming line above and below vertical rows 8/9.

Sold Out 10.67

Quantity Sold 35,169,720

Cat. No.	S.G. No.		Shades		Unused Used

1967 (JUNE 9). ONE CENTRE PHOSPHOR BAND REACTING VIOLET. WATERMARK CROWNS

XJ4	10p		(1) Deep lilac		5 5
a.	Scratched collar (Cyl. 2, R. 9/8)	60	(2) Dull reddish lilac		8 5

For illustration of No. XJ4a, see No. XJ3a.

Cylinder Numbers (Blocks of Six)

Single pane cylinder. Perforation Type F (L)

	Deep lilac				Dull reddish lilac	
Cyl. No.			No Dot	Cyl. No.		No dot
2	.. ..		40	2	.. ..	60

Minor Constant Flaws

Minimum price as singles: 40p

As for flaws on Cyl. 2 of No. XJ3

Sheet Markings

Guide holes: Through marginal arrow above vertical rows 6/7 and below vertical row 10 with boxes opposite rows 14/15 at left and right.
Others: As given in General Notes and also a trimming line above and below vertical rows 8/9

Sold Out 10.68

4d., Type XJ2 (1966–69)

Cat. No.	S.G. No.	Shades	Unused	Used

1966 (FEBRUARY 7). WATERMARK CROWNS

XJ5	11	Ultramarine	10	5

  a. Leaf flaw (R.3/6) .. .. 1·50
  b. Neck flaw (R.18/9) .. .. 1·00

XJ5   First Day Cover   †   25

Listed Varieties

Arrow-like flaw over top leaf at left. Later retouched and does not occur on phosphor issues

XJ5*a*   XJ5*b*, XJ6*a*/8*a*

Cylinder Numbers (Blocks of Six)

Single pane cylinder.   Perforation Type F (L)

	Cyl. No.	No dot
	1	60

Minor Constant Flaws

Minimum price as singles: 40p

Cyl. 1   3/4 Diagonal scratch under Queen's chin (Th. E2–3)
           3/11 Spot in top margin (close to perf. hole) (Above Th. A4)
          9/10 Slight dent in left-hand frame line (Opposite Th. D–E1)
       11/10 White flaw in background behind Queen's hair (Th. C5)
        15/1 Dark patch in background to left of top leaf on left-hand side of sceptre (Th. D1).   This
                 varies in intensity and is particularly strong on No. XJ7.
      15/12 Two small white flaws in front of Queen's collar (Th. F2–3)
       18/8 Break in top frame line (Above Th. A5)
       20/8 Diagonal scratch to right of Queen's left eye (Th. C3–4)

Sheet Markings

Guide holes: Through marginal arrow above vertical rows 6/7 and below vertical row 10.
Others: As given in General Notes.

Sold Out 11.67

Quantity Sold 6,623,040 including 14,487 on First Day Covers

1967 (SEPTEMBER 5). TWO 9·5 mm. PHOSPHOR BANDS REACTING VIOLET. WATERMARK CROWNS

XJ6	11p	Ultramarine	5	5

  a. Neck flaw (R.18/9) 75
  For illustration of No. XJ6*a*, see No. XJ5*b*.

Cylinder Numbers (Blocks of Six)

Single pane cylinder.   Perforation Type F (L)

	Cyl. No.	No dot
	1	40

Minor Constant Flaws

Minimum price as singles: 40p

  As for No. XJ5

Sheet Markings

  As for No. XJ5

Sold Out 10.68

Cat. No.	S.G. No.	Shades	Unused	Used

1968 (SEPTEMBER 4). CHANGE OF COLOUR. NO WATERMARK. CHALKY PAPER. PVA GUM. ONE CENTRE PHOSPHOR BAND REACTING VIOLET

XJ7	12	Olive-sepia	5	5
a.	Neck flaw (R.18/9)	75		

For illustration of No. XJ7*a*, see No. XJ5*b*.

Cylinder Numbers (Blocks of Six)

Single pane cylinder. Perforation Type F (L)

Cyl. No.	No dot
1	40

Minor Constant Flaws

Minimum price as singles: 40p

As for No. XJ5

Sheet Markings

As for No. XJ5

Withdrawn 30.9.70

1969 (FEBRUARY 26). FURTHER CHANGE OF COLOUR. NO WATERMARK. CHALKY PAPER. PVA GUM. ONE CENTRE PHOSPHOR BAND REACTING VIOLET

XJ8	13	Bright vermilion	5	5
a.	Neck flaw (R.18/9)	75		

For illustration of No. XJ8*a*, see No. XJ5*b*.

Cylinder Numbers (Blocks of Six)

Single pane cylinder. Perforation Type F (L)

Cyl. No.	No dot
1	40

Minor Constant Flaws

Minimum price as singles: 40p

As for No. XJ5

Sheet Markings

As for No. XJ5

Withdrawn 30.9.70

5d., Type XJ2 (1968)

1968 (SEPTEMBER 4). NO WATERMARK. CHALKY PAPER. PVA GUM. TWO 9·5 mm. PHOSPHOR BANDS REACTING VIOLET

XJ9	14	Royal blue	5	5
a.	Leaf dot (R.16/6)	60		
b.	Shield flaw (R.19/12) ..	60		
XJ7 and XJ9 (57,500 posted)		First Day Cover	†	25

Listed Varieties

XJ9*a*
White dot above lowest leaf

XJ9*b*
Leaf joined to shield

Cylinder Numbers (Blocks of Six)
Single pane cylinder.   Perforation Type F (L)

	Cyl. No.				No dot
	I	..	..	..	..	40

Minor Constant Flaws
Minimum price as singles: 40p

Cyl. I	5/1	Dot in top margin (Above Th. A2)
	6/5	White scratch from back of Queen's collar to back of neck (Th. E–F4)
	9/11	Flaw in background above middle right-hand jewel of sceptre (Th. A2)
	10/4	White scratch extending from Queen's chin to top of P
	11/1	Tiny break in left-hand frame line (Th. C1)
	14/12	Small white flaw on Queen's collar (Th. F3–4)
	17/12	Dotted line extending from right of top leaf below flower at right of sceptre across Queen's face and plant at right (Th. E2–6)

Sheet Markings
As for No. XJ5

Withdrawn 30.9.70

INVALIDATION. The regional issues for Jersey were invalidated for use in Jersey or Guernsey on 30 September 1969 but remained valid for use in the rest of the United Kingdom. Those still current remained on sale at philatelic sales counters until 30 September 1970.

C. Isle of Man

XM1

XM2

(Des. J. H. Nicholson)

2½d., Type **XM1** (1964)

Cat. No.	S.G. No.	Shades	Unused	Used

1964 (JUNE 8).   WATERMARK CROWNS

XM1	IM1	Carmine-red	25	30
XM1		First Day Cover	†	60

Cylinder Numbers (Blocks of Six)
Single pane cylinder.   Perforation Type F (L)

	Cyl. No.				No dot
	I	..	.	..	..	2·00

Minor Constant Flaws
Minimum price as singles: 50p

Cyl. I   11/1 Red dot to right of lower cross of crown (Th. C5)

Sheet Markings:

Guide holes: Through marginal arrow above vertical rows 6/7 and below vertical row 10
Others: As given in General Notes

Withdrawn 31.8.66

Quantity Sold 4,298,160 including 9,237 on First Day Covers

3d., Type XM2 (1958–68)

Cat. No.	S.G. No.	Shades	Unused	Used

1959 (AUGUST 18). WATERMARK CROWNS

A. Cream Paper

| XM2 | — | Deep lilac | 25 | 8 |

B. Chalky Paper (17 May 1963)

| XM3 | IM2a | Deep lilac | 2·00 | 2·00 |

C. Whiter Paper (1965)

| XM4 | IM2 | Deep lilac | 5 | 5 |

No. XM3 was released in London on 17 May 1963 but was not put on sale in Northern Ireland until 15 July 1963.

Cylinder Numbers (Blocks of Six)

	Cream Paper					Chalky Paper		
Cyl. No.	(No dot)		Perf. Types		Cyl. No.	(No dot)		Perf. Type
			B	C				I
I	.. ..		2·25	2·25	I	.. ..		15·00

	Whiter Paper					
Cyl. No.	(No dot)			Perf. Types		
				B	C	F (L)
I	.. ..			75	75	75

Minor Constant Flaws

Minimum price as singles: 50p

Cyl. I   19/6 Fine curved line to right of second link from bottom at left (Th. G1)

Sheet Markings

Guide holes:
Perf. Types B and C, opposite rows 1 and 7/8 at both sides and also boxed opposite rows 14/15 at both sides
Perf. Types F (L) and I, through marginal arrow above vertical rows 6/7 and below vertical row 10. Boxes only opposite rows 14/15
Others: As given in General Notes

Sold Out 12.68

Quantity Sold 35,959,420 up to 31.3.68 and including 1,080,000 on chalky paper (No. XM3)

1968 (JUNE 27). ONE CENTRE PHOSPHOR BAND REACTING VIOLET. WATERMARK CROWNS

| XM5 | IM2p | Deep lilac | 5 | 5 |

Four sheets are said to have been pre-released in Douglas on 24th May 1968 but we do not know if any were used.

Cylinder Numbers (Blocks of Six)

Single pane cylinder.   Perforation Type F (L)

Cyl. No.					No dot
I	..	..	..	..	40

Minor Constant Flaws

Minimum price as singles: 40p

As for Nos. XM2/4

Sheet Markings

Guide holes: As for perf. Type F (L) of No. XM4
Others: As given in General Notes

Sold Out 4.69

4d., Type **XM2** (1966–69)

Cat. No.	S.G. No.	Shades	Unused	Used

1966 (FEBRUARY 7). WATERMARK CROWNS

XM6	IM3	Ultramarine	8	5
XM6		First Day Cover	†	25

Cylinder Numbers (Blocks of Six)

Single pane cylinder. Perforation Type F (L)

	Cyl. No.				No dot
	1	..	..	..	..	60

Minor Constant Flaws

Minimum price as singles: 40p

Cyl. 1 7/12 Fine line from top of diadem to inner frame at right (Th. B3–5)
      8/7 Coloured dot left of inner frame line at right (Th. C5–6)
      17/1 Coloured scratches below Queen's left eye (Th. D3–4)
      19/1 Coloured scratch behind Queen's neck (Th. F5)

Sheet Markings

Guide holes: Through marginal arrow above vertical rows 6/7 and below vertical row 10
Others: As given in General Notes

Sold Out 11.67

Quantity Sold 4,353,840 including 7,553 on First Day Covers

**1967 (JULY 5). TWO 9·5 mm. PHOSPHOR BANDS REACTING VIOLET.
WATERMARK CROWNS**

XM7	IM3p	Ultramarine	5	5

Cylinder Numbers (Blocks of Six)

Single pane cylinder. Perforation Type F (L)

	Cyl. No.				No dot
	1	..	..	..	..	40

Minor Constant Flaws

Minimum price as singles: 40p

As for No. XM6

Sheet Markings

As for No. XM6

Sold Out 12.68

**1968 (JUNE 24). NO WATERMARK. CHALKY PAPER. PVA GUM. TWO 9·5 mm.
PHOSPHOR BANDS REACTING VIOLET**

XM8	IM4	Blue	5	5

Cylinder Numbers (Blocks of Six)

Single pane cylinder. Perforation Type F (L)

	Cyl. No.				No dot
	1	..	..	..	..	40

Minor Constant Flaws

Minimum price as singles: 40p

Cyl. 1 6/7 Flaw behind lower cross of diadem (Th. D5)
      14/2 White background spot just above Queen's right eye (Th. C–D2)
      Others as for No. XM6

Sheet Markings

As for No. XM6

Sold Out 16.7.69

Cat. No.	S.G. No.	Shades	Unused	Used

1968 (SEPTEMBER 4). CHANGE OF COLOUR. NO WATERMARK. CHALKY PAPER. PVA GUM. ONE CENTRE PHOSPHOR BAND REACTING VIOLET

XM9	IM5	Olive-sepia	5	5
a. Phosphor omitted	.. .. 14·00			

Cylinder Numbers (Blocks of Six)

Single pane cylinder.   Perforation Type F (L)

	Cyl. No.				No dot
	I	..	..	..	40

Minor Constant Flaws

Minimum price as singles: 40p

  As for No. XM8

Sheet Markings

  As for No. XM6

1969 (FEBRUARY 26). FURTHER CHANGE OF COLOUR. NO WATERMARK. CHALKY PAPER. PVA GUM. ONE CENTRE PHOSPHOR BAND REACTING VIOLET

XM10	IM6	Bright vermilion	5	5

Cylinder Numbers (Blocks of Six)

Single pane cylinder.   Perforation Type F (L)

	Cyl. No.				No dot
	I	..	..	..	40

Minor Constant Flaws

Minimum price as singles: 40p

  As for No. XM8

Sheet Markings

  As for No. XM6

5d., Type XM2 (1968)

1968 (SEPTEMBER 4). NO WATERMARK. CHALKY PAPER. PVA GUM. TWO 9·5 mm. PHOSPHOR BANDS REACTING VIOLET

XM11	IM7	Royal blue	5	5
a. Phosphor omitted .. .. 4·00		*c.* Frame flaw (bottom left)		
b. Frame flaw (top right) (R.20/1) 50		(R.20/12)..	50	

XM9 and XM11 (42,910 posted)	First Day Cover	†	25

Listed Varieties

XM11*b*

XM11*c*

Cylinder Numbers (Blocks of Six)

Single pane cylinder.   Perforation Type F (L)

	Cyl. No.				No dot
	I	..	..	..	75*

Sheet Markings

  As for No. XM6

D. Northern Ireland

XN1

(Des. W. Hollywood)

XN2

(Des. L. Pilton)

XN3

(Des. T. Collins)

3d., Type XN1 (1958–67)

Cat. No.	S.G. No.	Shades	Unused	Used

1958 (AUGUST 18). WATERMARK CROWNS

A. Cream Paper

XN1	—	Deep lilac	25	8

B. Whiter Paper (21 February 1962)

XN2	N11	Deep lilac	8	5

Cylinder Numbers (Blocks of Six)

Cream Paper			Whiter Paper		
Perforation Type A			**Perforation Type A**		
Cyl. No.	No dot	Dot	Cyl. No.	No dot	Dot
3	2·00	2·00	3	60	60
			Perforation Type F (L)*		
			3		

Minor Constant Flaws

Minimum price as singles: 50p

Cyl. 3 4/9 White flaw on edge of lowest flax flower (Th. G2)

Sheet Markings

Guide holes: Boxed opposite rows 14/15, at left (no dot) or right (dot)
Others: As given in General Notes

Sold Out 10.67

Quantity Sold 365,417,400

1967 (JUNE 9). ONE CENTRE PHOSPHOR BAND REACTING VIOLET. WATERMARK CROWNS

XN3	N11p	Deep lilac	5	5

Cylinder Numbers (Blocks of Six)

Perforation Type A			Perforation Type F (L)*		
Cyl. No.	No dot	Dot	Cyl. No.	No dot	Dot
3	40	40	3	40	40

Minor Constant Flaws

Minimum price as singles: 40p

As for flaw on Nos. XN1/2

Sheet Markings

Guide holes: Boxed opposite rows 14/15, at left (no dot) or right (dot) but in the case of perforation Type F (L)* the boxes remain on both panes but the holes are unboxed above and boxed below the eighth vertical row in the no dot pane only
Others: As given in General Notes

4d., Type XN1 (1966–69)

Cat. No.	S.G. No.	Shades	Unused Used

1966 (FEBRUARY 7). WATERMARK CROWNS

XN4   NI2   Ultramarine   5   5

a. Dot on leaf (No dot,
    R.3/12)   ..   ..   1·00   c.   Dot under S of POSTAGE
b. Flower flaw (No dot, R.7/7)   1·00   (Dot, R.2/4) ..   ..   ..   1·00

Listed Varieties

XN4a, XN5a, XN6a,   XN4b   XN4c
XN7a, XN8b

White dot on leaf of plant.   White spot on top flower.   White dot under S of
Retouched on No. XN9   The above only exists on   POSTAGE. Retouched on
                                 No. XN4. It was retouched   No. XN5
                                 and shows as a dark patch
                                 on Nos. XN5b, XN6b,
                                 XN7b, XN8c and XN9b

Cylinder Numbers (Blocks of Six)

Perforation Type A

Cyl. No.					No dot	Dot
1	..	..	..	..	40	40

Minor Constant Flaws

Minimum price as singles: 40p

Cyl. 1   16/5 Small white spot to right of second leaf down on upright flax plant (Th. B6)
Cyl. 1.   2/1 Small coloured projection above upper frame line (Th. A2)
        3/12 Small white dot below lower right leaf of flax plant (Th. G4)
      10/6 Coloured flaw in lower left of badge (Th. E1)
      12/1 Pale patch below P of POSTAGE (Th. F1)

Sheet Markings

Guide holes: In double "SON" box opposite rows 14/15, at left (no dot) or right (dot)
Cylinder number: Opposite R.18/1. In addition, early printings of both no dot and dot panes bore a
trace of cylinder numbers reading "1A" and "1A." with two sides of a box opposite R.19/1. These
had been inserted in error. Attempts to remove them were only partially successful, so that they
exist in varying degrees of faintness.
Others: As given in General Notes

Sold Out 11.68

Quantity Sold 61,449,360

**1967 (OCTOBER). TWO 9·5 mm. PHOSPHOR BANDS REACTING VIOLET.
WATERMARK CROWNS**

XN5   NI2p   Ultramarine   5   5

a. Dot on leaf (No dot, R.3/12)
b. Flower flaw retouch (No dot,   75
    R.7/7)   75

    For illustration of No. XN5a and for description of No. XN5b, see Nos. XN4a/b respec-
tively.

Cylinder Numbers (Blocks of Six)

Perforation Type F (L)*

Cyl. No.					No dot	Dot
1	..	..	..	..	40	40

Minor Constant Flaws

Minimum price as singles: 40p

Cyl. 1   16/5 Small white spot to right of second leaf down on upright flax plant (Th. B6)

Cyl. 1.   2/1 Small coloured projection above upper frame line (Th. A2)
2/4 Dark patch below S of POSTAGE where former white dot, No. XN4*a*, existed (Th. F2)
3/12 Small white dot below lower right leaf of flax plant (Th. G4)
10/6 Coloured flaw in lower left of badge (Th. E1)
12/1 Pale patch below P of POSTAGE (Th. F1)

Sheet Markings

Guide holes: Unboxed above and boxed below the eighth vertical row in the no dot pane only. The double "S O N" boxes opposite rows 14/15 remain
Others: As given in General Notes

Sold Out 1.70

Cat. No.	S.G. No.	Shades	Unused	Used

1968 (JUNE 27). NO WATERMARK. CHALKY PAPER. TWO 9·5 mm. PHOSPHOR BANDS REACTING VIOLET

A. Gum Arabic

XN6	NI7	Deep bright blue	5	5

a. Dot on leaf (No dot, R.3/12)
b. Flower flaw retouch (No dot, R.7/7) ..   ..   75 / 75

B. PVA Gum* (23 October 1968)

XN7	NI7Ev	Deep bright blue	2·50

a. Dot on leaf (No dot, R.3/12)
b. Flower flaw retouch (No dot, R.7/7) ..   4·00 / 4·00

For illustration of Nos. XN6*a* and XN7*a* and for description of Nos. XN6*b* and XN7*b*, see Nos. XN4*a*/*b* respectively.

* No. XN7 was never issued in Northern Ireland. After No. XN6 (gum arabic) had been withdrawn from Northern Ireland but whilst still on sale at the philatelic counters elsewhere, about fifty sheets with PVA gum were sold over the London Philatelic counter on 23 October 1968, and some were also on sale at the British Philatelic Exhibition Post Office.

Cylinder Numbers (Blocks of Six)

Gum Arabic			PVA Gum		
Perforation Type A			Perforation Type A		
Cyl. No.	No dot	Dot	Cyl. No.	No dot	Dot
1	40	40	1 .. .. •• ..	30·00	†

Minor Constant Flaws

Minimum price as singles: 40p

Cyl. 1.   2/1 Small coloured projection above upper frame line (Th. A2)
2/4 Dark patch below S of POSTAGE where former white dot, No. XN4*a*, existed (Th. F2)
3/12 Small white dot below lower right leaf of flax plant (Th. G4)
6/12 Small coloured flaws on leaf above NU of REVENUE
10/6 Coloured flaw in lower left of badge (Th. E1)
12/1 Pale patch below P of POSTAGE (Th. F1)

Sheet Markings

Guide holes: In double " S O N " box opposite rows 14/15, at left (no dot) or right (dot). In addition a single hand-engraved box appears below the eighth vertical row in the no dot pane only (latter only used in conjunction with perforation Type F (L)*).
Others: As given in General Notes

Withdrawn No. XN7 on the same day as released

Sold Out No. XN6, 4.70

1968 (SEPTEMBER 4). CHANGE OF COLOUR. NO WATERMARK. CHALKY PAPER. PVA GUM. ONE CENTRE PHOSPHOR BAND REACTING VIOLET

XN8	NI8	Olive-sepia	5	5

a. Phosphor omitted   ..   ..   *c.* Flower flaw retouch (No dot,
b. Dot on leaf (No dot, R.3/12)   50   R.7/7)   50

For illustration of No. XN8*b* and for description of No. XN8*c*, see Nos. XN4*a*/*b* respectively.

Cylinder Numbers (Blocks of Six)

Perforation Type A

Cyl. No.	No dot	Dot
1	40	40

Minor Constant Flaws

Minimum price as singles: 40p

As for Nos. XN6/7

Sheet Markings

As for Nos. XN6/7

Cat. No.	S.G. No.	Shades	Unused	Used

1969 (FEBRUARY 26). FURTHER CHANGE OF COLOUR. NO WATERMARK. CHALKY PAPER. PVA GUM. ONE CENTRE PHOSPHOR BAND REACTING VIOLET

XN9	NI9	Bright vermilion	5	5

a. Phosphor omitted .. .. 4·00
b. Flower flaw retouch (No dot, R.7/7) 50

For description of No. XN9*b*, see No. XN4*b*.

Cylinder Numbers (Blocks of Six)

Perforation Type A

Cyl. No.	No dot	Dot
1	40	40

Minor Constant Flaws

Minimum price as singles: 40p

Cyl. 1.   2/4 Dark patch below S of POSTAGE where former white dot, No. XN4*a*, existed (Th. F2)
6/12 Small coloured flaws on leaf above NU of REVENUE
10/6 Coloured flaw in lower left of badge (Th. E1)
12/1 Pale patch below P of POSTAGE (Th. F1)

Sheet Markings

Guide holes: As for Nos. XN6/7.
Cylinder number: Opposite R.18/1. In addition both no dot and dot panes bear traces of cylinder numbers reading " 1A" and " 1A." with two sides of a box opposite R.19/1. These exist in varying degrees of faintness
Others: As given in General Notes

5d., Type XN1 (1968)

1968 (SEPTEMBER 4). NO WATERMARK. CHALKY PAPER. PVA GUM. TWO 9·5 mm. PHOSPHOR BANDS REACTING VIOLET

XN10	NI10	Royal blue	5	5

a. Phosphor omitted .. .. 2·00
b. "Extra leaf" (No dot, R.13/2) 50   (¹)

XN8 and XN10	First Day Cover	†	25

Listed Variety

XN10*b*

White flaw near junction of flax plant stalks appears as an extra leaf

Cylinder Numbers (Blocks of Six)
Perforation Type A

Cyl. No.					No dot	Dot
1	..	..	..	..	40	40

Sheet Markings
Guide holes: In double "S O N" box opposite rows 14/15, at left (no dot) or right (dot). In addition a single "traffic light" type box appears above and below the eighth vertical row in the no dot pane only. (These would only be used in conjunction with perforation Type F (L)*).
Others: As given in General Notes

6d., Type XN2 (1958–62)

Cat. No.	S.G. No.	Shades	Unused	Used
1958 (SEPTEMBER 29). WATERMARK CROWNS				
A. Cream Paper				
XN11	—	Deep claret	50	10
B. Whiter Paper (4 June 1962)				
XN12	N13	Deep claret	8	5

Cylinder Numbers (Blocks of Six)

	Cream Paper				Whiter Paper		
Cyl. No.	(No dot)		Perf. Types		Cyl. No.	(No dot)	Perf. Types
			B	C			B C F (L)
1	..	..	..	..	4·00 4·00	1	.. .. 75 75 50

Minor Constant Flaws
Minimum price as singles: 50p

Cyl. 1   1/12 Flaw in background to right of diadem (Th. A4)
       2/11 White coloured spur on lowest leaf of left flax plant (Th. F1)
       3/9 Dot in diamond to right of 6D (Th. F4); also similar dot in diamond to right of Queen's collar (Th. E–F5)
       3/10 "Ring" on little finger of hand at left (Th. F2)
       3/12 Dark spot in centre of central cross of diadem (Th. B3)
       4/2 Coloured line in background to right of 6D (Th. G4)
      10/2 White bulge half way down stalk at left (Th. D1)
      12/2 Coloured spot in background to right of Queen's hair (Th. D5)

Sheet Markings
Guide holes:
    Perf. Types B and C, unboxed opposite rows 1 and 7/8 at both sides and also boxed opposite rows 14/15 at both sides
    Perf. Type F (L), through marginal arrow above vertical rows 6/7 and below vertical row 10. Boxes only opposite rows 14/15 at both sides
Others: As given in General Notes

Withdrawn 11.68

Quantity Sold 28,531,180 up to 31.3.68

9d., Type XN2 (1967)

1967 (MARCH 1). WATERMARK CROWNS. TWO 9·5 mm. PHOSPHOR BANDS REACTING VIOLET

XN13	N14	Bronze-green	5	8

Cylinder Numbers (Blocks of Six)
Single pane cylinder.   Perforation Type F (L)

	Cyl. No.				No dot
	1	..	..	..	40

Sheet Markings
Guide holes: Through marginal arrow above vertical rows 6/7 and below vertical row 10
Others: As given in General Notes

1s.3d., Type XN3 (1958–62)

Cat. No.	S.G. No.		Shades	Unused	Used
1958 (SEPTEMBER 29). WATERMARK CROWNS					
A. Cream Paper					
XN14	—		Green	80	15
B. Whiter Paper (9 November 1962)					
XN15	NI5		Green	10	8

Cylinder Numbers (Blocks of Six)

	Cream Paper				Whiter Paper		
Cyl. No.	(No dot)			Perf. Types	Cyl. No.	(No dot)	Perf. Types
				B C			B C F (L)
1	..	..	..	..	6·50 6·50	1	..	..	..	.. 1·25 1 25 80

Minor Constant Flaws

Minimum price as singles: 50p

Cyl. 1   1/1 White dot in upper loop of S of POSTAGE; also small area of retouching above emblems in diadem (Th. A4)

3/7 White spur to O of POSTAGE (Th. E1)

Sheet Markings

Guide holes:
Perf. Types B and C, not known
Perf. Type F (L), through marginal arrow above vertical rows 6/7 and below vertical row 10. Boxes only opposite rows 14/15 at both sides
Others: As given in General Notes

1s.6d., Type XN3 (1967–69)

1967 (MARCH 1). WATERMARK CROWNS. TWO 9·5 mm. PHOSPHOR BANDS REACTING VIOLET

XN16	NI6				Grey-blue	10	15
a. Phosphor omitted	..	..	40·00				
XN13 and XN16					First Day Cover	†	35

Cylinder Numbers (Blocks of Six)

Single pane cylinder.   Perforation Type F (L)

	Cyl. No.				No dot
	1	..	..	..	..	80

Minor Constant Flaws

Minimum price as singles: 50p

Cyl. 1   4/12 Small area of retouching behind Queen's head. Consists of several small dark coloured dots (Th. E5)

14/1 Dark coloured spot on Queen's cheek (Th. D4)

15/12 A multitude of tiny coloured spots over the Queen's face, neck and collar, and in the background behind her neck

17/8 Coloured spot to right of Queen's left eye (Th. D3–4)

Sheet Markings

Guide holes: Through marginal arrow above vertical rows 6/7 and below vertical row 10
Others: As given in General Notes

Cat. No.	S.G. No.	Shades	Unused	Used

1969 (MAY 20). NO WATERMARK. CHALKY PAPER. PVA GUM. TWO 9·5 mm. PHOSPHOR BANDS REACTING VIOLET

XN17	NI11		Grey-blue	12	12

Cylinder Numbers (Blocks of Six)

Single pane cylinder. Perforation Type F (L)

	Cyl. No.				No dot
	1	..	..	..	..	90

Minor Constant Flaws

Minimum price as singles: 50p

Cyl. 1   4/12 Small area of retouching behind Queen's head. Consists of several small dark coloured dots (Th. E5)
   11/12 Small dark coloured flaw on Queen's neck, just above necklace (Th. E4)
   14/1 Small dark coloured flaw on Queen's cheek (Th. D4)
   15/12 A multitude of tiny dark coloured spots over the Queen's face, neck and collar, and in the background behind her neck
   17/8 Area of retouching to right of Queen's left eye (Th. D3–4)

Sheet Markings

As for No. XN16

Presentation Pack

XNPP1 (9.12.70)	Seven stamps	80

Comprises Nos. XN3, 8/10, 13, and 15/16

E. Scotland

XS1
(Des. G. F. Huntly)

XS2
(Des. J. B. Fleming)

XS3
(Des. A. B. Imrie)

3d., Type XS1 (1958–68)

1958 (AUGUST 18). WATERMARK CROWNS

A. Cream Paper

XS1	—		Deep lilac	12	5

a. Spot on U of REVENUE (Cyl. 3., R.19/8) .. .. 1·50
b. Dot in d of 3d (Cyl. 3., R.20/12) 65

c. Spot after last E of REVE-NUE (Cyl. 5., R. 20/2) .. 1·50

B. Whiter Paper (9 July 1962)

XS2	S1		Deep lilac	8	5

Listed Varieties

XS1a

XS1b
Later retouched

XS1c, XS3a, XS4b,
XS5b, XS7b, XS8b

Cylinder Numbers (Blocks of Six)

	Cream Paper					Whiter Paper			

Perforation Type A

Cyl. No.					No dot	Dot
3	..	..	..	..	1·00	1·00
4	..	..	..	..	1·00	1·00

Perforation Type A

Cyl. No.					No dot	Dot
4	..	..	..	..	60	60
5	..	..	..	..	60	2·00·

Perforation Type H

4	..	..	..	..	†	—

Sheet Markings

Guide holes: Boxed opposite rows 14/15, at left (no dot) or right (dot)
Others: As given in General Notes

Sold Out 18.3.68

Quantity Sold 1,487,481,480

1962. Miniature Sheet. On the occasion of SCOTEX the 1962 Scottish Stamp Exhibition, a miniature sheet, size 105 x 60 mm., was produced comprising Types **XS1/3** printed *se-tenant* in black, imperforate and surrounded by a decorative frame and inscription in blue on white chalk-surfaced gummed paper watermarked "HARRISON AND SONS LTD" sideways. The sheet was printed by Harrison & Sons with the use of actual stamp positives. It had no franking value. 15,000 printed.

Cat. No.	S.G. No.	Shades	Unused	Used

1963 (JANUARY 29). PHOSPHOR BANDS REACTING BLUE. WATERMARK CROWNS

A. Two 8 mm. Bands

XS3	S1p		Deep lilac	1·75	8

    a. Spot after last E of REVE-
       NUE (Cyl. 5., R.20/2)   ..   4·00

B. One Side Band* (30 April 1965)

XS4	—		Deep lilac (band at left)	60	8

    a. Band at right   60
    b. Spot after last E of REVE-
       NUE (Cyl. 5., R.20/2)   ..   1·50   —

*The one side band stamps were produced by an 8 mm. band applied down alternate vertical rows of the sheets over the perforations so that alternate stamps have the band at left (No. XS4) or right (No. XS4a). In theory the width of the band on a single stamp should be 4 mm. but this will vary if the bands have not been perfectly positioned.

    For illustration of Nos. XS3a and XS4b, see No. XS1c.

Cylinder Numbers (Blocks of Six)

	Two Bands					One Side Band			

Perforation Type A

Cyl. No.					No dot	Dot
4	..	..	..	..	12·00	12·00
5	..	..	..	..	12·00	14·00*

Perforation Type A

Cyl. No.					No dot	Dot
5	..	..	..	..	6·00	8·00*

Sheet Markings

As for Nos. XS1/2

Sold Out No. XS3, 1968

1965 (DECEMBER 16). PHOSPHOR BANDS REACTING VIOLET. WATERMARK CROWNS

A. One Side Band*

XS5	S1pa		Deep lilac (band at left)	8	5

    a. Band at right   8   5
    b. Spot after last E of REVE-
       NUE (Cyl. 5., R.20/2)   ..   75

B. One 4 mm. Centre Band (9 November 1967)

XS6	S1pb	Deep lilac	5	5

    *The note *re* one side band stamps after No. XS4b also applies here.
    For illustration of No. XS5b, see No. XS1c.

Cylinder Numbers (Blocks of Six)

One Side Band				One Centre Band			
Perforation Type A				Perforation Type A			
Cyl. No.		No dot	Dot	Cyl. No.		No dot	Dot
5		60	1·50*	4		40	40

Sheet Markings

As for Nos. XS1/2

Sold Out No. XS5, 15.7.68; No. XS6, 11.68

Cat. No.	S.G. No.		Shades		Unused	Used

1968 (MAY 16). NO WATERMARK. CHALKY PAPER. ONE CENTRE PHOSPHOR BAND REACTING VIOLET

A. Gum Arabic

XS7	S7		Deep lilac		5	5
a.	Phosphor omitted	1·50				
b.	Spot after last E of REVE-NUE (Cyl. 5., R.20/2) ..	50				

B. PVA Gum (July 1968)

XS8	S7Ev		Deep lilac		5	
a.	Phosphor omitted	1·00				
b.	Spot after last E of REVE-NUE (Cyl. 5., R.20/2) ..	50				

For illustration of Nos. XS7*b* and XS8*b*, see No. XS1*c*.

Cylinder Numbers (Blocks of Six)

Gum Arabic				PVA Gum			
Perforation Type F (L)*				Perforation Type F (L)*			
Cyl. No.		No dot	Dot	Cyl. No.		No dot	Dot
5		40	40	5		40	40

Minor Constant Flaws

Minimum price as singles: 40p

Cyl. 5   8/6 Retouching on Queen's forehead, nose and around lips (Th. B–D3)
13/3 Pale patch on Queen's collar (Th. E–F4)
15/3 Small dark flaw surrounded by white area on right side of thistle (Th. G6)
17/7 Area of retouching on Queen's neck (Th. E4–5)
18/1 Horizontal coloured line through G of POSTAGE

Sheet Markings

Guide holes: Unboxed above and boxed below the eighth vertical row in the no dot pane only. The boxes opposite rows 14/15 remain.
Others: As given in General Notes

4d., Type XS1 (1966–69)

1966 (FEBRUARY 7). WATERMARK CROWNS

XS9	S2		Ultramarine		5	5
a.	Dot before second E of REVENUE (Dot, R.10/9) ..	50				

Listed Variety

Retouched on
No. XS10

XS9*a*

Cylinder Numbers (Blocks of Six)
Perforation Type A

	Cyl. No.				No dot	Dot
	2	..	..	..	.. 40	40

Minor Constant Flaws
Minimum price as singles: 40p

Cyl. 2 7/11 White spot to left of crown at right (Th. F5)
    8/6 Small blue flaw on top left-hand leaf of thistle (Th. F5)
    20/5 Small dark flaw in background to right of d of 4d (Th. F4–5)

Sheet Markings
Guide holes: In double "S O N" box opposite rows 14/15, at left (no dot) or right (dot)
Others: As given in General Notes

Sold Out 7.70.

Cat. No.	S.G. No.	Shades	Unused Used

1966 (FEBRUARY 7). TWO 8 mm. PHOSPHOR BANDS REACTING VIOLET. WATERMARK CROWNS

XS10	S2p		Ultramarine	5	5

Cylinder Numbers (Blocks of Six)
Perforation Type A

	Cyl. No.				No dot	Dot
	2	..	..	..	.. 40	40

Minor Constant Flaws
Minimum price as singles: 40p

Cyl. 2 7/11 White spot to left of crown at right (Th. F5)
    8/6 Small blue flaw on top left-hand leaf of thistle (Th. F5)
    20/5 Small dark flaw in background to right of d of 4d (Th. F4–5)
Cyl. 2. 8/12 Blue spot below Queen's left eye (Th. C3)
    11/7 Small blue spot on Queen's forehead (Th. B2)
    12/8 Small dark flaw in background to left of EV of REVENUE (Th. B5); also retouching on Queen's temple and cheek (Th. C3–4)
    20/3 Small coloured flaw above Queen's left eye (Th. B3); also small blue spot on top left-hand leaf of thistle (Th. F5)

Sheet Markings
As for No. XS9

Sold Out 7.70.

1967 (NOVEMBER 28). NO WATERMARK. CHALKY PAPER. TWO 9·5 mm. PHOSPHOR BANDS REACTING VIOLET

A. Gum Arabic

XS11	S8		Deep bright blue	5	5
a. Phosphor omitted	..	.. 1·00			

B. PVA Gum (25 July 1968) 5

XS12	S8Ev		Deep bright blue		

Cylinder Numbers (Blocks of Six)

Gum Arabic				PVA Gum			
Perforation Type F (L)*				Perforation Type A			
Cyl. No.			No dot Dot	Cyl. No.			No dot Dot
2	.. .. ..	.. 40	40	2	.. .. ..	.. 40	40

Minor Constant Flaws
Minimum price as singles: 40p

Cyl. 2 1/7 Retouch on Queen's forehead (Th. B3). PVA only
    3/7 Retouch on Queen's collar (Th. E4–5). PVA only
    5/10 White patches on Queen's nose and forehead
    8/6 Small blue flaw on top left-hand leaf of thistle (Th. F5)
    10/11 Retouch to right of Queen's mouth (Th. D3). PVA only
    14/10 Retouch on Queen's forehead (Th. B3) Less pronounced on PVA
    15/4 Retouch on Queen's cheek (Th. C–D3)
    19/7 White spot on Queen's cheek (Th. C3). Retouched on PVA where it shows as three dark spots

20/5 Small dark flaw in background to right of d of 4d (Th. F4–5). Less pronounced on PVA but can be confirmed by additional retouches on Queen's nose and forehead (Th. C2 and B3)

20/6 Small blue flaw on Queen's cheek (Th. C3). On PVA there is an additional white flaw on Queen's right cheek (Th. C2)

Cyl. 2. 1/5 Coloured spot above Queen's left eye (Th. B3). PVA only

2/6 Retouch on Queen's collar (Th. E4)

6/11 White spot on Queen's cheek (Th. C–D3). Retouched on PVA where it shows as a dark spot

8/12 White spot below Queen's left eye where former blue spot appeared (Th. C3). Further retouched on PVA

11/7 Small blue spot on Queen's forehead (Th. B2)

12/8 Small blue spot in background to left of EV of REVENUE (Th. B5); also retouching on Queen's temple and cheek, the latter much more pronounced on PVA (Th. C3–4)

15/1 Small retouch on Queen's temple (Th. C3–4). PVA only

15/2 Small retouch on Queen's forehead (Th. B2). PVA only

18/4 Weak patches on Queen's chin (Th. D2–3). PVA only

18/6 Blue spot on Queen's collar (Th. E4). Retouched on PVA but a scratch now appears across Queen's neck and collar (Th. E4)

19/3 White spot on Queen's left cheek (Th. D3). Shows larger on PVA

20/3 Small coloured flaw above Queen's left eye (Th. B3); also small blue spot on top left-hand leaf of thistle (Th. F5)

20/4 Coloured spots around Queen's eyes and nose (Th. C2–3)

Sheet Markings

Guide holes:
Perf. Type A, in double "S O N" box opposite rows 14/15, at left (no dot) or right (dot). In addition a single hand-engraved box appears above and below the eighth vertical row in the no dot pane only (latter only used in conjunction with perforation Type F (L)*).
Perf. Type F (L)*, boxed above and below the eighth vertical row in the no dot pane only. The usual "S O N" boxes opposite rows 14/15 remain
Others: As given in General Notes

Cat. No.	S.G. No.			Shades		Unused	Used

1968 (SEPTEMBER 4). CHANGE OF COLOUR. NO WATERMARK. CHALKY PAPER. PVA GUM. ONE CENTRE PHOSPHOR BAND REACTING VIOLET

XS13	S9			Olive-sepia		5	5
a. Phosphor omitted	..	..	1·00				

Cylinder Numbers (Blocks of Six)

Perforation Type A

Cyl. No.				No dot	Dot
2	..	..	..	40	40

Minor Constant Flaws

Minimum price as singles: 40p

Cyl. 2. 1/5 Coloured spot above Queen's left eye (Th. B3)

2/6 Retouch on Queen's collar (Th. E4)

6/11 Retouch on Queen's cheek (Th. C–D3)

8/12 Retouch below Queen's left eye (Th. C3)

11/7 Coloured spot on Queen's forehead (Th. B2)

12/8 Small dark flaw in background to left of EV of REVENUE (Th. B5); also retouching on Queen's temple and cheek (Th. C3–4)

15/1 Small retouch on Queen's temple (Th. C3–4)

15/2 Small retouch on Queen's forehead (Th. B2)

18/4 Weak patches on Queen's chin (Th. D2–4)

18/6 Retouch on Queen's collar and also scratch across her neck and collar (Th. E4)

19/3 Large white spot on Queen's left cheek (Th. D3)

20/3 Small coloured flaw above Queen's left eye (Th. B3); also small coloured spot on top left-hand leaf of thistle (Th. F5)

20/4 Coloured spots around Queen's eyes and nose (Th. C2–3)

Sheet Markings

Guide holes: As for Perf. Type A under Nos. XS11/12
Others: As given in General Notes

1969 (FEBRUARY 26). FURTHER CHANGE OF COLOUR. NO WATERMARK. CHALKY PAPER. PVA GUM. ONE CENTRE PHOSPHOR BAND REACTING VIOLET

XS14	S10			Bright vermilion		5	5
a. Phosphor omitted	..	..	1·00				

Cylinder Numbers (Blocks of Six)

Perforation Type A						Perforation Type A						
Cyl. No.				No dot	Dot	Cyl. No.					No dot	Dot
2	..	..	..	40	40	4	..	..	..	..	40	40

Minor Constant Flaws

Minimum price as singles: 40p

Cyl. 2   1/7 Retouch on Queen's forehead (Th. B3)
3/7 Retouch on Queen's collar (Th. E4–5)
5/10 Retouching on Queen's nose and forehead where former white patches appeared
8/11 Retouch by Queen's ear (Th. C–D4)
10/11 Retouch to right of Queen's mouth (Th. D3)
14/10 Heavy retouching on Queen's forehead (Th. B3)
15/4 Retouch on Queen's cheek (Th. C–D3)
19/7 Retouch on Queen's cheek where former white spot appeared (Th. C3)
20/5 Retouches on Queen's nose and forehead (Th. C2 and B3). Small dark flaw in background to right of d of 4d now hardly shows (Th. F4–5)
20/6 Retouches on both of the Queen's cheeks where former flaws appeared (Th. C2–3)

Cyl. 2.   1/5 Coloured spot above Queen's left eye (Th. B3)
2/6 Retouch on Queen's collar (Th. E4)
6/11 Heavy area of retouching on Queen's cheek (Th. C–D3)
8/12 Retouch below Queen's left eye (Th. C3)
10/5 Extensive area of retouching on Queen's temple and cheek (Th. B3 and C3–4)
11/7 Area of retouching on Queen's forehead where former coloured spot appeared (Th. B2)
12/8 Small dark flaw in background to left of EV of REVENUE (Th. B5) is now less noticeable but retouches on Queen's temple and cheek remain (Th. C3–4)
15/1 Small retouch on Queen's temple (Th. C3–4)
15/2 Small retouch on Queen's forehead (Th. B2)
18/4 Weak patches on Queen's chin (Th. D2–4)
18/6 Retouch on Queen's collar and also scratch across her neck and collar (Th. E4)
20/3 Small coloured flaw above Queen's left eye (Th. B3); also small coloured spot on top left-hand leaf of thistle (Th. F5)
20/4 Coloured spots around Queen's eyes and nose (Th. C2–3)

Sheet Markings

Guide holes: As for Perf. Type A under Nos. XS11/12
Others: As given in General Notes

5d., Type XS1 (1968)

Cat. No.	S.G. No.	Shades	Unused	Used

1968 (SEPTEMBER 4). NO WATERMARK. CHALKY PAPER. PVA GUM. TWO 9·5 mm. PHOSPHOR BANDS REACTING VIOLET

XS15	S11	Royal blue	5	5
a. Phosphor omitted .. .. 12·00		*b.* Shoulder retouch (Cyl. 2., R.16/6)	50	
XS13 and XS15		First Day Cover	†	25

Listed Variety

Large retouch on Queen's shoulder

XS15*b*

Cylinder Numbers (Blocks of Six)

Perforation Type A

Cyl. No.					No dot	Dot
2	..	..	..	..	40	40
3	..	..	..	..	40	40

Sheet Markings

Phosphor cylinder number: "Ph 1" found on cyl. 3 dot, right margin
Guide holes: In double "S O N" box opposite rows 14/15, at left (no dot) or right (dot)
Others: As given in General Notes

Cat. No.	S.G. No.	Shades	Unused	Used

6d., Type XS2 (1958–66)

1958 (SEPTEMBER 29). WATERMARK CROWNS

A. Cream Paper

XS16	—	Reddish purple	10	30

   a. Broken V of REVENUE (Cyl. 1, R.11/12) .. .. 4·00

       b. Curled leaf (Cyl. 1, R.7/7) .. 2·00

B. Whiter Paper (28 May 1962)

XS17	S3	Deep reddish purple	5	5

   a. Broken V of REVENUE (Cyl. 1, R.11/12) .. .. 2·00

   b. Curled leaf (Cyl. 1, R.7/7) .. 75

       c. Cut leaf (Cyl. 4, R.2/10) .. 60

Listed Varieties

XS16*a*, XS17*a*
This is a multipositive flaw. It was later retouched on Cyl. 1. On Cyls. 2 and 4 it is only known retouched and it shows as a much thicker V than normal

XS16*b*, XS17*b*
Later retouched

XS17*c*, XS18*a*
Leaf half-way down at right has V-shaped cut in solid colour

Cylinder Numbers (Blocks of Six)

	Cream Paper				Whiter Paper				
Cyl. No.	(No dot)		Perf. Types		Cyl. No.	(No dot)		Perf. Types	
			B	C				B C	F (L)
1	.. ..		2·50	2·50	1	.. .. ..	..	† †	75
					2	.. .. ..	..	60 60	†
					4	.. .. ..	..	† †	40

Minor Constant Flaws

Minimum price as singles: 50p

   Cyl. 1   5/8 Small white flaw by left thistle just outside oval frame (Th. B2)

   Cyl. 2 11/12 V of REVENUE retouched. It is thicker than normal and has a fuzzy appearance

   Cyl. 4 11/12 As for Cyl. 2

Sheet Markings

Guide holes:
   Perf. Types B and C, unboxed opposite rows 1 and 7/8 at both sides and also boxed opposite rows 14/15 at both sides
   Perf. Type F (L), through marginal arrow above vertical rows 6/7 and below vertical row 10. Boxes only opposite rows 14/15 at both sides

Marginal rule:
   Cyl. 1: Instead of the usual "stamp width" rule below each stamp in the bottom row the rules on this cylinder are shorter (approx. 17 mm.) and are arranged alternately with a 1 mm. wide rectangular rule, the latter being perforated through. The rules below vertical rows 9/12 are damaged
   Cyls 2 and 4: As given in General Notes

Others: As given in General Notes

1963 (JANUARY 29). TWO 8 mm. PHOSPHOR BANDS REACTING BLUE. WATERMARK CROWNS

XS18	—	Deep reddish purple	75	12

   a. Cut leaf (Cyl. 4, R.2/10) .. 1·75

Cylinder Numbers (Blocks of Six)

Single pane cylinder. Perforation Type F (L)

	Cyl. No.				No dot
	4	..	..	..	..	6·00

Minor Constant Flaws

Minimum price as singles: £1·25

    Cyl. 4 11/12 V of REVENUE retouched. It is thicker than normal and has a fuzzy appearance

Sheet Markings

    Guide holes: Through marginal arrow above vertical rows 6/7 and below vertical row 10. Boxes only
      opposite rows 14/15 at both sides
    Others: As given in General Notes

Cat. No.	S.G. No.	Shades	Unused	Used

1966 (FEBRUARY 2). TWO 8 mm. PHOSPHOR BANDS REACTING VIOLET. WATERMARK CROWNS

XS19	S3p		Deep reddish purple	15	5

Cylinder Numbers (Blocks of Six)

Single pane cylinder. Perforation Type F (L)

	Cyl. No.				No dot
	4	..	..	..	..	1·25

Sheet Markings

    As for No. XS18

Sold Out 10.68

Quantity Sold 26,758,320 (including No. XS18) up to 31.3.68

9d., Type XS2 (1967-70)

1967 (MARCH 1). WATERMARK CROWNS. TWO 9·5 mm. PHOSPHOR BANDS REACTING VIOLET

XS20	S4	Bronze-green	5	8

Cylinder Numbers (Blocks of Six)

Single pane cylinder. Perforation Type F (L)

	Cyl. No.				No dot
	1	..	..	..	..	40

Sheet Markings

    Guide holes: Through marginal arrow above vertical rows 6/7 and below vertical row 10
    Others: As given in General Notes

1970 (SEPTEMBER 28). NO WATERMARK. CHALKY PAPER. PVA GUM. TWO 9·5 mm. PHOSPHOR BANDS REACTING VIOLET

XS21	S12		Bronze-green	5	8
a. Phosphor omitted	..	..	30·00		

Cylinder Numbers (Blocks of Six)

Single pane cylinder. Perforation Type F (L)

	Cyl. No.				No dot
	1	..	..	..	..	40

Sheet Markings

    As for No. XS20

1s.3d., Type XS3 (1958–65)

Cat. No.	S.G. No.	Shades	Unused	Used

1958 (SEPTEMBER 29). WATERMARK CROWNS

A. Cream Paper

XS22 — Green 75 12
    a. Broken oblique in value
      (Cyl. 4, R.15/2) .. .. 4·00

B. Whiter Paper (31 July 1962)

XS23 S5 Green 10 8
    a. Broken oblique in value
      (Cyl. 4, R.15/2) .. .. 1·00

Listed Variety

XS22*a*, XS23*a*, XS24*a*, XS25*a*

Cylinder Numbers (Blocks of Six)

	Cream Paper				Whiter Paper			
Cyl. No.	(No dot)		Perf. Types		Cyl. No.	(No dot)		Perf. Types
			B	C				B C F,(L)
4	.. ..		6·00	6·00	4	.. .. ..		1·25 1·25 75

Minor Constant Flaws

Minimum price as singles: 50p

Cyl. 4   3/7 Green spot on shoulder of right-hand unicorn (Th. D6)
         11/12 Small break in inner frame line at right of value tablet (Th. G4)
         15/2 Hind leg of lion on standard is severed (Th. B1)

Sheet Markings

Guide holes:
    Perf. Types B and C, unboxed opposite rows 1 and 7/8 at both sides and also boxed opposite rows
    14/15 at both sides
    Perf. Type F (L), through marginal arrow above vertical rows 6/7 and below vertical row 10. Boxes
    only opposite rows 14/15 at both sides
Marginal arrows:
    " V " shaped, hand engraved at top and bottom; " W " shaped, photo-etched at both sides. Early
    printings have the arrows omitted from the top and bottom of the sheet. *Price for marginal strip of*
    7 stamps £8.
Others: As given in General Notes

**1963 (JANUARY 29). TWO 8 mm. PHOSPHOR BANDS REACTING BLUE.
WATERMARK CROWNS**

XS24 — Green 1·00 12
    a. Broken oblique in value
      (Cyl. 4, R.15/2) .. .. 4·00

    For illustration of No. XS24*a*, see No. XS22*a*

Cylinder Numbers (Blocks of Six)

Single pane cylinder. Perforation Type F (L)

Cyl. No.	No dot
4	8·00

Minor Constant Flaws

Minimum price as singles: £1·75

As for Nos. XS22/3

Sheet Markings

Guide holes: Through marginal arrow above vertical rows 6/7 and below vertical row 10. Boxes only
    opposite rows 14/15 at both sides
Others: As given in General Notes

Cat. No.	S.G. No.	Shades	Unused	Used

1965 (NOVEMBER 26). TWO 8 mm. PHOSPHOR BANDS REACTING VIOLET. WATERMARK CROWNS

| XS25 | S5p | Deep Green | 10 | 10 |

a. Broken oblique in value (Cyl. 4, R.15/2) .. .. 1·00

For illustration of No. XS25*a*, see No. XS22*a*

Cylinder Numbers (Blocks of Six)

Single pane cylinders. Perforation Type F (L)

Cyl. No.		No dot		Cyl. No.				No dot
4 ..	..	80		8 ..	..	..	..	1·25

Minor Constant Flaws

Minimum price as singles: 60p

Cyl. 4 As for Nos. XS22/3

Sheet Markings

As for No. XS24

1s.6d., Type XS3 (1967–68)

1967 (MARCH 1). WATERMARK CROWNS. TWO 9·5 mm. PHOSPHOR BANDS REACTING VIOLET

| XS26 | S6 | Grey-blue | 10 | 15 |
| XS20 and XS26 | | First Day Cover | † | 35 |

Cylinder Numbers (Blocks of Six)

Single pane cylinder. Perforation Type F (L)

Cyl. No.			No dot
1 ..	..	..	80

Minor Constant Flaws

Minimum price as singles: 60p

Cyl. 1 1/11 Coloured spot in background to right of Queen's neck, below her hair (Th. E4)

Sheet Markings

Guide holes: Through marginal arrow above vertical rows 6/7 and below vertical row 10
Others: As given in General Notes

1968 (DECEMBER 12). NO WATERMARK. CHALKY PAPER. PVA GUM. TWO 9·5 mm. PHOSPHOR BANDS REACTING VIOLET

| XS27 | S13 | Grey-blue | 10 | 10 |

Cylinder Numbers (Blocks of Six)

Single pane cylinder. Perforation Type F (L).

Cyl. No.			No dot
1 ..	..	..	80

Minor Constant Flaws

Minimum price as singles: 60p

As for No. XS26

Sheet Markings

As for No. XS26

Presentation Pack

| XSPP1 (9.12.70) | Eight stamps | 1·00 |

Comprises Nos. XS8, 13/15, 17, 21, 25 and 27.

F. Wales and Monmouthshire

XW1

XW2

XW3

(Des. Reynolds Stone)

3d., Type XW1 (1958–67)

Cat. No.	S.G. No.	Shades	Unused	Used

1958 (AUGUST 18). WATERMARK CROWNS

A. Cream Paper

XW1   —   Deep lilac   25   8
    a. Bulge on oval value tablet
        (Cyl. 1, R.6/3) ..   ..   ..   1·75
    b. Wing-tail flaw (Cyl. 2, R.16/1)   1·75

B. Whiter Paper (30 April 1962)

XW2   W1   Deep lilac   8   5
    a. Wing-tail flaw (Cyl. 2, R.16/1)   75

Listed Varieties

XW1*a*
Later retouched

XW1*b*, XW2*a*
White flaw joins spine
of dragon's wing to its tail

Cylinder Numbers (Blocks of Six)

Cream Paper				Whiter Paper			
Perforation Type A				Perforation Type A			
Cyl. No.		No dot	Dot	Cyl. No.		No dot	Dot
1		5·00	5·00	2		75	75
2		2·00	2·00	3		75	75

Minor Constant Flaws

Minimum price as singles: 50p

Multipositive flaws

No dot 1/12 Small coloured flaw on dragon's neck (Th. F–G3)
       17/10 Known in three states:
            Cyl. 1 Two pale coloured dots on back of Queen's neck just below hair (Th. D4)
            Cyl. 2 Cylinder retouched to almost normal
            Cyl. 3 Cylinder retouched but still leaving one coloured dot on back of neck

Cyl. 1   15/7 White flaw in middle of central cross of diadem (Th. A3)
Cyl. 2   6/11 White spot on end of top horizontal bar of first E of REVENUE

Sheet Markings

Guide holes: Boxed opposite rows 14/15, at left (no dot) or right (dot)
Others: As given in General Notes

Sold Out 12.67

Quantity Sold 902,289,240

1967 (MAY 16). ONE CENTRE PHOSPHOR BAND REACTING VIOLET. WATERMARK CROWNS

XW3   W1p   Deep lilac   5   5

Cylinder Numbers (Blocks of Six)

Perforation Type A

Cyl. No.					No dot	Dot
3	..	..	..	..	25	25

Minor Constant Flaws

Minimum price as singles: 40p

Multipositive flaws

No dot 1/12 Small coloured flaw on dragon's neck (Th. F–G3)
        17/10 Pale coloured dot on back of Queen's neck just below hair (Th. D4)
Cyl. 3   1/7 Coloured spot on oval frame line opposite R of REVENUE (Th. A5)
         1/8 Small coloured flaw just inside oval frame opposite G of POSTAGE (Th. E2)
         7/11 Small coloured flaw on Queen's collar (Th. E5)
         10/11 Small dot on leaf to right of final E of REVENUE (Th. E6)
         11/10 Small dot on leaf to left of second E of REVENUE (Th. C6)
Cyl. 3.   1/6 Small retouch to right of Queen's mouth (Th. D3)
         1/8 Retouch on Queen's cheek (Th. C–D4)
         3/5 Small dot on leaf above E of POSTAGE (Th. E1)
         3/9 Coloured flaw on Queen's neck just above collar (Th. E4)
         4/9 Coloured diagonal flaw in front of Queen's neck (Th. E3)
         5/9 Coloured spot inside lower loop of 3 of right-hand 3D
         8/1 Two white flaws on dragon's front left foot (Th. G–H2)
         10/2 Coloured spot on Queen's collar (Th. E4)
         11/6 Small retouch on back of Queen's collar (Th. E4–5)
         18/10 Retouch to background within oval to right of O of POSTAGE (Th. A–B2)
         18/11 Small dot on leaf to right of T of POSTAGE (Th. C1–2)
         20/6 Pale patch on Queen's shoulder (Th. E4)

Sheet Markings

As for Nos. XW1/2

Sold Out   1.68

Cat. No.	S.G. No.		Shades		Unused	Used

1967 (DECEMBER 6). NO WATERMARK. CHALKY PAPER. ONE CENTRE PHOSPHOR BAND REACTING VIOLET

XW4	W7		Deep lilac		5	5
a. Phosphor omitted		..	..			

Cylinder Numbers (Blocks of Six) ——

Perforation Type F (L)*

Cyl. No.					No dot	Dot
3	..	..	..	..	40	40

Minor Constant Flaws

Minimum price as singles: 40p

As for multipositive and cylinder flaws on No. XW3 with the addition of the following cylinder flaws:

Cyl. 3   5/9 Retouch on Queen's cheek (Th. D3–4)
Cyl. 3.   5/8 Retouch on Queen's chin (Th. D3)
         14/1 Retouch on Queen's cheek (Th. D4)
         20/5 Retouch on Queen's chin (Th. D3–4) and several dark spots on her forehead, cheek and neck

Sheet Markings

Guide holes: Unboxed above and boxed below the eighth vertical row in the no dot pane only. The boxes opposite rows 14/15 remain
Others: As given in General Notes

4d., Type XW1 (1966–69)

1966 (FEBRUARY 7). WATERMARK CROWNS

XW5	W2		Ultramarine		8	8

Cylinder Numbers (Blocks of Six)

Perforation Type A

Cyl. No.					No dot	Dot
1	..	..	..	..	40	40

Sheet Markings

Guide holes: In double "SON" box opposite rows 14/15, at left (no dot) or right (dot)
Others: As given in General Notes

Sold Out 7.2.68

Quantity Sold 148,137,600

Cat. No.	S.G. No.	Shades	Unused	Used

1967 (OCTOBER). TWO 9·5 mm. PHOSPHOR BANDS REACTING VIOLET. WATERMARK CROWNS

XW6	W2p	Ultramarine	5	5

Cylinder Numbers (Blocks of Six)

Perforation Type F (L)*

Cyl. No.				No dot	Dot
1	..	..	..	40	40

Sheet Markings

Guide holes: Unboxed above and boxed below the eighth vertical row in the no dot pane only. The double "SON" boxes opposite rows 14/15 remain
Others: As given in General Notes

Sold Out 4.70

1968 (JUNE 21). NO WATERMARK. CHALKY PAPER. PVA GUM. TWO 9·5 mm. PHOSPHOR BANDS REACTING VIOLET

XW7	W8		Deep bright blue	5	5

a. White spot before E of POSTAGE (No dot, R.17/12) .. — 65

b. White spot after E of POSTAGE (No dot, R.18/10) .. — 65

c. White spot above dragon's hind leg (No dot, R.20/1) .. .. — 55

Listed Varieties

XW7*a*, XW8*a*
Later retouched on
No. XW8

XW7*b*, XW8*b*
Later retouched
on No. XW8

XW7*c*, XW8*c*
Retouched on No.
XW9

Cylinder Numbers (Blocks of Six)

Perforation Type A

Cyl. No.				No dot	Dot
2	..	..	..	80*	40

Minor Constant Flaws

Minimum price as singles: 40p

Cyl. 2   6/9 Small dot on leaf to left of second E of REVENUE (Th. C6)
12/6 Coloured flaw on Queen's left eye-brow (Th. C4)
13/2 Small dot on leaf above U of REVENUE (Th. D6)
18/5 Coloured spots over Queen's face and background
20/12 Coloured flaw over D of left-hand 4D

Cyl. 2.   1/6 Small dot on leaf above U of REVENUE (Th. D6)
3/12 Small dot on leaf to left of N of REVENUE (Th. D6)
4/3 Small dot on leaf to right of T of POSTAGE (Th. C1–2)
4/6 White spot in background of oval frame opposite R of REVENUE (Th. A4)
4/9 White spot on right-hand frame line by first E of REVENUE (Th. B6–7)
7/2 Small dot on leaf to right of E of POSTAGE (Th. E2)
7/11 Small coloured flaw in background of oval frame opposite VE of REVENUE (Th. C5)
8/6 Small white flaw to right of dragon's left hind foot (Th. H5)
11/7 Coloured spot in left-hand margin opposite P of POSTAGE (opposite Th. A1)
12/2 Retouch on Queen's chin (Th. D3)
12/6 White flaw over Queen's upper lip (Th. D3)
16/10 Small coloured flaw on Queen's shoulder just above collar (Th. E4)

Sheet Markings

Guide holes: In double "S O N" box opposite rows 14/15, at left (no dot) or right (dot)
Others: As given in General Notes

Sold Out 4.70

Cat. No.	S.G. No.	Shades	Unused Used

**1968 (SEPTEMBER 4). CHANGE OF COLOUR. NO WATERMARK. CHALKY PAPER.
PVA GUM. ONE CENTRE PHOSPHOR BAND REACTING VIOLET**

XW8   W9   Olive-sepia   5   5

    a. White spot before E of
       POSTAGE (No dot, R.17/12) ..   75
    b. White spot after E of   *c.* White spot above dragon's hind
       POSTAGE (No dot, R.18/10) ..   60   leg (No dot, R.20/1)   60

For illustrations of Nos. XW8*a/c*, see Nos. XW7*a/c*.
Note. Varieties XW8*a/b* were later retouched.

Cylinder Numbers (Blocks of Six)

Perforation Type A

	Cyl. No.				No dot	Dot
	2	..	..	..	.. 90*	40

Minor Constant Flaws

Minimum price as singles: 40p

   As for No. XW7

Sheet Markings

   As for No. XW7

**1969 (FEBRUARY 26). FURTHER CHANGE OF COLOUR. NO WATERMARK.
CHALKY PAPER. PVA GUM. ONE CENTRE PHOSPHOR BAND REACTING VIOLET**

XW9   W10   Bright vermilion   5   5

    a. Phosphor omitted   ..   ..

Cylinder Numbers (Blocks of Six)

Perforation Type A

	Cyl No.				No dot	Dot
	2	..	..	..	.. 40	40

Minor Constant Flaws

Minimum price as singles: 40p

Cyl. 2 As for flaws on No. XW7 except that flaw on R.13/2 has been retouched
Cyl. 2. Sheet not yet examined

Sheet Markings

   As for No. XW7

5d., Type XW1 (1968)

**1968 (SEPTEMBER 4). NO WATERMARK. CHALKY PAPER. PVA GUM. TWO
9·5 mm. PHOSPHOR BANDS REACTING VIOLET**

XW10   W11   Royal blue   5   5

    a. Phosphor omitted   ..   ..

XW8 and XW10   First Day Cover   †   2

Cylinder Numbers (Blocks of Six)

Perforation Type A

	Cyl. No.				No dot	Dot
	2	..	..	..	.. 35	35

Minor Constant Flaws

Minimum price as singles: 40p

Cyl. 2 2/3 Coloured spot in background of oval frame just above central cross of diadem (Th. A3)
16/5 Coloured flaws in background of oval frame to left of Queen's nose (Th. C–D2)
20/4 White flaw on bottom frame line below dragon's left hind foot (Th. H4)

Sheet Markings

Phosphor cylinder number: "Ph 1" found on cyl. 2 dot, right margin
Guide holes: In double "S O N" box opposite rows 14/15, at left (no dot) or right (dot). In addition a single
"traffic light" type box appears above and below the eighth vertical row in the no dot pane only. (These
would only be used in conjunction with perforation Type F (L)*.)
Others: As given in General Notes

6d., Type XW2 (1958–62)

Cat. No.	S.G. No.	Shades	Unused	Used

1958 (SEPTEMBER 29). WATERMARK CROWNS

A. Cream Paper

XW11	—	Deep claret	50	15

B. Whiter Paper (18 July 1962)

XW12	W3	Reddish purple	15	10

Cylinder Numbers (Blocks of Six)

	Cream Paper				Whiter Paper		
	(No dot)		Perf. Types		(No dot)		Perf. Types
Cyl. No.			B C	Cyl. No.			B C F (L)
2	.. .. ..		.. 3·50 3·50	3	.. .. ..		..1·25 1·25 1·00

Minor Constant Flaws

Minimum price as singles: 75p

Cyl. 3 16/4 Coloured spot on dragon's tail (Th. F5)

Sheet Markings

Guide Holes:
Perf. Types B and C, unboxed opposite rows 1 and 7/8 at both sides and also boxed opposite rows 14/15
at both sides
Perf. Type F (L), through marginal arrow above vertical rows 6/7 and below vertical row 10. Boxes only
opposite rows 14/15 at both sides
Marginal rule: Cyl. 2, 2½ mm. wide; Cyl. 3, 2 mm. wide
Others: As given in General Notes

Sold Out 3.68

Quantity Sold 66,754,200

9d., Type XW2 (1967)

**1967 (MARCH 1). WATERMARK CROWNS. TWO 9·5 mm. PHOSPHOR BANDS
REACTING VIOLET**

XW13	W4	Bronze-green	5	8
a. Phosphor omitted	.. .. 50·00			

Cylinder Numbers (Blocks of Six)

Single pane cylinder. Perforation Type F (L)

Cyl. No.				No dot
1	.. .. ..			.. 50

Sheet Markings

Guide holes: Through marginal arrow above vertical rows 6/7 and below vertical row 10
Others: As given in General Notes

1s.3d., Type **XW3** (1958-64)

Cat. No.	S.G. No.	Shades	Unused	Used

1958 (SEPTEMBER 29). WATERMARK CROWNS

A. Cream Paper

XW14	—	Green	1·00	30

B. Whiter Paper (11 May 1964)

XW15	W5	(1) Myrtle-green	20	12
		(2) Deep dull green	15	10
		(3) Deep myrtle-green	15	10

Cylinder Numbers (Blocks of Six)

	Cream Paper				Whiter Paper	
Cyl. No.	(No dot)	Perf. Types B C		Cyl. No.	(No dot)	Perf. Type F (L)
2	.. .. ..	.. 6·50 6·50		2	.. ..	1·00
				3	.. ..	75

Sheet Markings

Guide holes:
Perf. Types B and C, unboxed opposite rows 1 and 7/8 at both sides and also boxed opposite rows 14/15 at both sides
Perf. Type F (L), through marginal arrow above vertical rows 6/7 and below vertical row 10. Boxes only opposite rows 14/15 at both sides
Others: As given in General Notes

Sold Out 7.70.

1s.6d., Type **XW3** (1967–69)

1967 (MARCH 1). WATERMARK CROWNS. TWO 9·5 mm. PHOSPHOR BANDS REACTING VIOLET

XW16	W6	Grey-blue	10	15
a. Phosphor omitted	.. ..			
XW13 and XW16		First Day Cover	†	35

Cylinder Numbers (Blocks of Six)

Single pane cylinder. Perforation Type F (L)

Cyl. No.	No dot
1	 75

Minor Constant Flaws

Minimum price as singles: 60p

Cyl. 1   3/11 Small dot in top of left fork of V of REVENUE
6/7 Coloured flaw in base of second E of REVENUE
10/1 Small dot on upper right-hand leaf of leak (Th. F6)
10/3 Small coloured flaw on Queen's neck (Th. D4)
15/9 Retouch on Queen's shoulder just above collar (Th. E4)

Sheet Markings

Guide holes: Through marginal arrow above vertical rows 6/7 and below vertical row 10
Others: As given in General Notes

1969 (AUGUST 1). NO WATERMARK. CHALKY PAPER. PVA GUM. TWO 9·5 mm. PHOSPHOR BANDS REACTING VIOLET

XW17	W12	Grey-blue	12	12

Cylinder Numbers (Blocks of Six)

Single pane cylinder. Perforation Type F (L)

Cyl. No.	No dot
1	 90

Minor Constant Flaws

Minimum price as singles: 60p

As for No. XW16

Sheet Markings

Guide holes: Through marginal arrow above vertical rows 6/7 and boxed below vertical row 10
Others: As given in General Notes

Presentation Pack

XWPP1 (9.12.70)   Six stamps   60
Comprises Nos. XW4, 8/10, 13 and 16.

Presentation Pack (Six Regions)

XPP1 (issued 1960)   Twelve values   5·00

The issued pack contained one each of the ordinary 3d., 6d. and 1s.3d. stamps from Northern Ireland, Scotland and Wales and Monmouthshire and one each of the ordinary 3d. stamps from Guernsey, Jersey and the Isle of Man together with 6-page printed leaflet describing the stamps.

Island Issues

Many islands off the coast of Great Britain have issued local carriage labels to cover the cost of ferrying mail to the nearest mainland post office. As they are not recognised as valid for national or international mail they are not listed here. They are classed as British Private Local issues and the following places are known to have issued them: Calf of Man, Canna, Davaar, Herm, Jethou, Lihou, Lundy, Pabay, Sanda, Sark-Alderney-Guernsey, Shuna and Stroma.

Labels inscribed Soay are bogus and issues inscribed Staffa are Tourist Souvenir Labels.

Regional Issues

1971. Decimal Issues. Photogravure

General Notes

INTRODUCTION. On 7th July 1971 new stamps appeared in decimal currency showing a reduced size Machin head accompanied by emblems representing the Isle of Man, Northern Ireland, Scotland and Wales and Monmouthshire. They were all designed by Jeffery Matthews.

The ordinary postage stamps of Great Britain in the same values are not on sale at post offices in these regions except at the Philatelic Counters in Belfast, Cardiff, Edinburgh and Glasgow, apart from Monmouthshire where the Welsh Regionals and Great Britain stamps are on sale concurrently. All regional stamps are valid for use throughout Great Britain with the exception of the Channel Islands.

PRINTERS. All were printed in photogravure by Harrison & Sons. As with the ordinary decimal Machin issues they were printed in double pane width, i.e. 400 stamps consisting of two panes (no dot and dot) each of 200 stamps arranged in twenty rows of ten stamps, the panes being guillotined before issue. The 2½p and 3p values were reel-fed and the 5p and 7½p were sheet-fed.

PAPER AND GUM. Unwatermarked chalk-surfaced paper with PVA gum was used.

PERFORATION. All stamps are perforated 15 × 14 as before. Cylinder numbers are listed according to the perforation types used and these are illustrated in Appendix O.

PHOSPHOR BANDS. See the General Notes for Section S for a detailed description of these. In these issues the " violet " phosphor was used throughout and the bands were applied in photogravure in the same operation as the printing.

PHOSPHOR CYLINDER NUMBERS. See the General Notes for Section U3. They always appear synchronised in the box to the left of the cylinder number in the form illustrated in Section U3 and on both panes. In the case of double figure numbers in the dot pane the margins are often narrow so that the first figure is liable to be trimmed off.

SHEET MARKINGS.

Cylinder Numbers. Boxed opposite R. 18/1 (Section U3).

Marginal Arrows. These are " W " shaped (photo-etched) and occur above and below vertical rows 5/6 and at sides opposite rows 10/11 (Section W).

Perforation Guide Holes. For the 2½p and 3p they are in double " S O N " box (Type (a) Section W) opposite rows 14/15, at left on no dot panes and at right on dot panes. There are none on the 5p and 7½p values.

Marginal Rules. Wide co-extensive rule below the bottom row (Section S).

Coloured Cross. These occur above and below vertical row 5 on the no dot panes of the 5p and 7½p only (Section W).

Total Sheet Values. These are preceded by " I O MAN ", " N. IRELAND ", " SCOTLAND " or " WALES " and occur four times on each pane opposite rows 5/7 and 15/17, reading up at left and down at right (Section W).

A. Isle of Man

XM3

(Des. J. Matthews)

1971. Type **XM3**

Cat. No.	S.G. No.	Shades	Unused	Used

1971 (JULY 7). 2½p. ONE 4 mm. CENTRE PHOSPHOR BAND

XM12	IM8	Bright magenta	5	5

Cylinder Numbers (Blocks of Six)

Perforation Type A

Cyl. No.	Phos. No.			No dot	Dot
3	5	..	..	20	20

1971 (JULY 7). 3p. TWO 9·5 mm. PHOSPHOR BANDS

XM13	IM9	Ultramarine	5	5

Cylinder Numbers (Blocks of Six)

Perforation Type A

Cyl. No.	Phos. No.			No dot	Dot
I	4	..	..	20	20

1971 (JULY 7). 5p. TWO 9·5 mm. PHOSPHOR BANDS

XM14	IM10	Reddish violet	8	5

Cylinder Numbers (Blocks of Six)

Perforation Type F*

Cyl. No.	Phos. No.			No dot	Dot
4	12	..	..	50	50

1971 (JULY 7). 7½p. TWO 9·5 mm. PHOSPHOR BANDS

XM15	IM11	Chestnut	10	8
XM12/15		First Day Cover	†	35
XM12/15		Presentation Pack	35	

Cylinder Numbers (Blocks of Six)

Perforation Type F*

Cyl. No.	Phos. No.			No dot	Dot
4	10			70	70

B. Northern Ireland

XN4

(Des. J. Matthews)

1971. Type XN4

Cat. No.	S.G. No.	Shades	Unused	Used

1971 (JULY 7). 2½p. ONE 4 mm. CENTRE PHOSPHOR BAND

XN18	NI12	Bright magenta	5	5

Cylinder Numbers (Blocks of Six)

Perforation Type A

Cyl. No.	Phos. No.			No dot	Dot
4	5	..	..	20	20

1971 (JULY 7). 3p. TWO 9·5 mm. PHOSPHOR BANDS

XN19	NI13	Ultramarine	5	5

Cylinder Numbers (Blocks of Six)

Perforation Type F*

Cyl. No.	Phos. No.			No dot	Dot
1	4	..	..	20	20

1971 (JULY 7). 5p. TWO 9·5 mm. PHOSPHOR BANDS

XN20	NI14	Reddish violet	8	5

Cylinder Numbers (Blocks of Six)

Perforation Type F*

Cyl. No.	Phos. No.			No dot	Dot
4	10	..	..	50	50

1971 (JULY 7). 7½p. TWO 9·5 mm. PHOSPHOR BANDS

XN21	NI15	Chestnut	10	8
XN18/21		First Day Cover	†	35
XN18/21		Presentation Pack	35	

Cylinder Numbers (Blocks of Six)

Perforation Type F*

Cyl. No.	Phos. No.			No dot	Dot
6	12	..	..	70	70

C. Scotland

XS4

(Des. J. Matthews)

1971.   Type XS4

Cat. No.	S.G. No.	Shades	Unused	Used

1971 (JULY 7). 2½p. ONE 4 mm. CENTRE PHOSPHOR BAND

XS28	S14	Bright magenta	5	5

Cylinder Numbers (Blocks of Six)

Perforation Type A

Cyl. No.	Phos. No.			No dot	Dot
2	5	..	..	20	20

1971 (JULY 7). 3p. TWO 9·5 mm. PHOSPHOR BANDS

XS29	S15	Ultramarine	5	5

Cylinder Numbers (Blocks of Six)

Perforation Type A

Cyl. No.	Phos. No.			No dot	Dot
1	4	..	..	20	20

1971 (JULY 7). 5p. TWO 9·5 mm. PHOSPHOR BANDS

XS30	S16	Reddish violet	8	5

Cylinder Numbers (Blocks of Six)

Perforation Type F*

Cyl. No.	Phos. No.			No dot	Dot
3	12	..	..	50	50

1971 (JULY 7). 7½p. TWO 9·5 mm. PHOSPHOR BANDS

XS31	S17	Chestnut	10	8
XS28/31		First Day Cover	†	35
XS28/31		Presentation Pack	35	

Cylinder Numbers (Blocks of Six)

Pefforation Type F*

Cyl. No.	Phos. No.			No dot	Dot
6	10	..	..	70	70

D. Wales and Monmouthshire

XW4

(Des. J. Matthews)

1971. Type XW4

Cat. No.	S.G. No.	Shades	Unused	Used

1971 (JULY 7). 2½p. ONE 4 mm. CENTRE PHOSPHOR BAND

| XW18 | W13 | | Bright magenta | | 5 | 5 |

Cylinder Numbers (Blocks of Six)

Perforation Type A

Cyl. No.	Phos. No.			No dot	Dot
3	5	..	..	20	20

1971 (JULY 7). 3p. TWO 9·5 mm. PHOSPHOR BANDS

| XW19 | W14 | | Ultramarine | | 5 | 5 |

Cylinder Numbers (Blocks of Six)

Perforation Type A

Cyl. No.	Phos. No.			No dot	Dot
1	4	..	..	20	20

1971 (JULY 7). 5p. TWO 9·5 mm. PHOSPHOR BANDS

| XW20 | W15 | | Reddish violet | | 8 | 5 |

Cylinder Number (Blocks of Six)

Perforation Type F*

Cyl. No.	Phos. No.			No dot	Dot	
3	12	..	..	50		50

1971 (JULY 7). 7½p. TWO 9·5 mm. PHOSPHOR BANDS

XW21	W16		Chestnut		10	8
XW18/21			First Day Cover		†	35
XW18/21			Presentation Pack		35	

Cylinder Numbers (Blocks of Six)

Perforation Type F*

Cyl. No.	Phos. No.			No dot	Dot
7	10	..	..	70	70

SECTION Z

Postage Due Stamps

1954-69 (Typographed) and 1968-71 (Photogravure)

General Notes

£.s.d. Issues

INTRODUCTION. These stamps generally fulfil two functions: the lower values, inscribed "POSTAGE DUE", are affixed to understamped and unstamped correspondence by the Post Office, to indicate to the postman and to the addressee the amount which is to be collected on delivery (usually twice the excess). The higher values, inscribed "TO PAY", are affixed to mail from abroad for the collection of customs charges. The same basic stamp design has been in continual use since 1914.

PRINTERS. All the Postage Due stamps were typographed by Harrison & Sons with the exception of the 4d. and 8d. values of 1969 and 1968 respectively which were printed in photogravure.

They were printed on sheet-fed machines in single panes of 240 each arranged in twelve rows of twenty stamps and this applies to both printing processes.

PAPER. As with the Wilding definitives, for about the first ten years the Postage Due stamps were printed on a creamy paper but starting in 1964 a whiter paper was gradually introduced as new printings were made. See the General Notes for Section S for further information. Exceptionally the 2s.6d. to £1 values were always printed on a yellow paper which did not change its appearance.

From 1968 unwatermarked chalk-surfaced paper, as used for the Machin definitives, was introduced for a number of values.

WATERMARKS. These were used as follows:

W.22 Tudor Crown	Nos. Z1/6 (1954–55)
W.23 St. Edward's Crown	Nos. Z7/16 (1955–57)
W.24 Crowns	Nos. Z17/37 (1959–64)
No watermark	No. Z38 onwards (1968–69)

See the General Notes for Section S for illustrations of these.

The watermarks are *always* sideways and *when seen from the front of the stamp* the normal watermark has the top of the Crowns pointing to left. In cases where the sheets were fed into the press the wrong way round, the watermark appears as sideways with the Crowns pointing to right.

GUM. This was used as follows:

Gum Arabic	Nos. Z1/39 (1954–68)
PVA Gum	No. Z40 onwards (1968–69)

The distinction between gum arabic and PVA gum is explained in the General Notes relating to Section U1.

PERFORATION. All values are comb perforated 14 × 15. The perforation types used are given following each issue, and are described and illustrated in Appendix O. In the photogravure-printed values the cylinder numbers are listed and priced according to the type of perforator used. The typographed issues do not have cylinder or plate numbers.

DATE OF ISSUE. The dates given are those on which the stamps were first issued by the Supplies Dept. to postmasters except in the case of dates for changes to chalky paper or to PVA gum when we have usually quoted dates of release by the Philatelic Bureaux.

SHEET MARKINGS. Compared with other stamps the Postage Due stamps show very few markings.

Cylinder Numbers. These only occur on the photogravure-printed stamps, opposite Row 11 No. 1 (4d.) or opposite Row 10 No. 1 (8d.). They are similar in style to the illustration in Section S.

Marginal Arrows. These are "W" shaped at top and bottom of the sheet only. They appear solid (typographed issues) or photo-etched (photogravure issues) as illustrated in Section S.

Marginal Rule. This occurs on all four sheet margins in the typographed issues only. It is similar in style to the "Narrow Rule" illustration in Section S. In the 1½d., 6d., 5s., 10s. and £1 values an additional 1 mm. square appears at each corner of the sheet thus giving a neater appearance.

   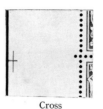

"Morse Code" marking   Cross

Other Markings. On the typographed issues "Morse Code" markings as illustrated appear opposite rows 6/7 at both sides of the sheet. These are possibly allied to the way in which the printing plate is fixed to the press.

In photogravure issues the "Morse Code" markings are replaced by a cross as illustrated. These are often trimmed off.

Decimal Issues

These were also printed by Harrison and Sons and particulars of sheet sizes and markings are given at the end of the listing.

WATERMARK. The normal sideways watermark *when seen from the front of the stamp* has the top of the Crowns pointing to left.

Z1. "POSTAGE DUE"   **Z2.** "TO PAY"

Cat. No.	S.G. No.	Date	Description	Unused	Used
1954-55. TYPE Z1 AND Z2 (2s.6d.). TYPOGRAPHED. WATERMARK TUDOR CROWN, TYPE W.22					
Z1	D40	8.6.55	½d. Orange	10	8
a. Wmk. Crown to right ..		.. 2·75			
Z2	D41	28.7.55	2d. Agate	25	15
Z3	D42	4.5.55	3d. Violet	75	40
Z4	D43	14.7.55	4d. Blue	90	35
a. Imperf. (pair) ..		.. 70·00			
Z5	D44	19.5.55	5d. Yellow-brown	1·00	30
Z6	D45	–.11.54	2s.6d. Purple/*yellow*	1·50	50

Perforation Type

Type A, all values

Cat. No.	S.G. No.	Date	Description	Unused	Used

1955-57. TYPE Z1 AND Z2 (2s.6d., 5s.). TYPOGRAPHED. WATERMARK ST. EDWARD'S CROWN, TYPE W.23

Z 7	D46	16.7.56	½d. Orange	5	5
a. Wmk. Crown to right ..	..	2·25			
Z 8	D47	7.5.56	1d. Violet-blue	5	5
Z 9	D48	13.2.56	1½d. Green	20	15
a. Wmk. Crown to right	..	2·25			
b. Stop after "THREE" (Row 1)	1·50				
Z10	D49	22.5.56	2d. Agate	12	10
Z11	D50	5.3.56	3d. Violet	12	10
a. Wmk. Crown to right ..	..				
Z12	D51	24.4.56	4d. Blue	15	12
Z13	D52	23.3.56	5d. Yellow-brown	15	12
Z14	D53	22.11.55	1s. Bistre-brown	25	20
Z15	D54	28.6.57	2s.6d. Purple/*yellow*	60	50
Z16	D55	25.11.55	5s. Scarlet/*yellow*	1·25	35
a. Wmk. Crown to right ..	..				

The 2d. (No. Z10) is known bisected (June 1956) and also the 4d. (Poplar, London, April 1959).

Listed Variety

Stop after "THREE". Occurs on most stamps in row 1

Z9*b*, Z19*a*

Perforation Types

Type A, all values, except that in the case of the 5s. the left-hand sheet margin is perforated through, possibly due to the use of a wider comb-head

1959-70. TYPE Z1 AND Z2 (2s.6d. to £1). TYPOGRAPHED. WATERMARK CROWNS, TYPE W.24

A. Cream Paper

Z17	—	18.10.61	½d. Orange	5	5
Z18	—	9.5.60	1d. Violet-blue	5	5
Z19	D58	5.10.60	1½d. Green	35	35
a. Stop after "THREE" (Row 1)	75				
Z20	—	14.9.59	2d. Agate	5	5
Z21	—	24.3.59	3d. Violet	5	5
Z22	—	17.12.59	4d. Blue	5	5
Z23	—	6.11.61	5d. Yellow-brown	5	5
Z24	—	29.3.62	6d. Purple	5	5
Z25	—	11.4.69	1s. Bistre-brown	8	5
Z26	D65	11.5.60	2s.6d. Purple/*yellow*	20	12
a. Wmk. Crown to right ..	..	20			
Z27	D66	8.5.61	5s. Scarlet/*yellow*	35	15
a. Wmk. Crown to right ..	..	35			
Z28	D67	2.9.63	10s. Blue/*yellow*	75	25
a. Wmk. Crown to right ..	4·70	75			
Z29	D68	2.9.63	£1 Black/*yellow*	1·50	50

Whilst the 2s.6d. and 5s. already existed with watermark Crown to right further printings were issued in 1970, as also of the 10s., on highly fluorescent paper and with watermark Crown to right. These can only be distinguished by the use of a u.v. lamp and so are not listed separately.

Cat. No.	S.G. No.	Date	Description	Unused	Used
B. Whiter Paper					
Z30	D56	22.9.64	½d. Orange	5	5
a. Wmk. Crown to right ..	..	5			
Z31	D57	1964	1d. Violet-blue	5	5
a. Wmk. Crown to right ..	..	5			
Z32	D59	1964	2d. Agate	5	5
a. Wmk. Crown to right ..	..	5			
Z33	D60	1.6.64	3d. Violet	5	5
a. Wmk. Crown to right ..	..	5			
Z34	D61	3.3.64	4d. Blue	5	5
a. Wmk. Crown to right ..	..	8			
Z35	D62	9.6.64	5d. Yellow-brown	5	5
a. Wmk. Crown to right ..	..	5			
Z36	D63	30.1.64	6d. Purple	5	5
a. Wmk. Crown to right ..	..				
Z37	D64	28.8.64	1s. Bistre-brown	8	5
a. Wmk. Crown to right ..	..	10			

For illustration of No. Z19*a*, see No. Z9*b*.

Perforation Types
Type A, all values; 2s.6d. also Type A (T)

Withdrawn. The 1½d. was withdrawn from sale to the public on 26.4.65. It had ceased to be issued on 31.1.65 but post offices continued to use existing stocks until exhausted

Sold Out 1s. 11.68; 2d. 1.69; 4d. 11.69

1968-69. TYPE Z1. TYPOGRAPHED. NO WATERMARK. CHALKY PAPER

A. Gum Arabic

Z38	D69	11.4.68	2d. Agate	5	5
Z39	D71	6.5.68	4d. Blue	5	5

B. PVA Gum

Z40	D69Ev	26.11.68	2d. Agate	5	
Z41	D70	9.9.68	3d. Violet	5	5
Z42	D72	3.1.69	5d. Yellow-brown	5	5
Z43	D73	9.9.68	6d. Purple	5	5
Z44	D74	19.11.68	1s. Bistre-brown	8	8

Perforation Types
4d., 6d. Type A; other values Type A (T), except that in the case of the 2d. the right-hand sheet margin is perforated through and in the 4d. the left-hand sheet margin is perforated through, both possibly due to the use of a wider comb-head

1968-69. TYPE Z1. SMALLER FORMAT, 21½ × 17½ mm. PHOTOGRAVURE. NO WATERMARK. CHALKY PAPER. PVA GUM

Z45	D75	12.6.69	4d. Blue	5	5
Z46	D76	3.10.68	8d. Red	5	5

Cylinder Numbers (Block of four (4d.) or six (8d.))
Perforation Type A (T)

	Cyl. No.			No dot
4d.	1	..	..	25
8d.	1	..	..	35

Z3   Z4

(Des. J. Matthews. Printed in photogravure.)

Cat. No.	S.G. No.	Type	Date	Description	Unused	Used
1970-71. DECIMAL CURRENCY. CHALKY PAPER. NO WATERMARK. PVA GUM. PERF. 14 × 15						
Z47	D77	**Z3**	15.2.71	½p. Turquoise-blue	5	5
Z48	D78	**Z3**	15.2.71	1p. Deep reddish purple	5	5
Z49	D79	**Z3**	15.2.71	2p. Myrtle-green	5	5
Z50	D80	**Z3**	15.2.71	3p. Ultramarine	5	8
Z51	D81	**Z3**	15.2.71	4p. Yellow-brown	5	8
Z52	D82	**Z3**	15.2.71	5p. Violet	8	10
Z53	D83	**Z4**	17.6.70	10p. Carmine	15	12
Z54	D84	**Z4**	17.6.70	20p. Olive-brown	30	15
Z55	D85	**Z4**	17.6.70	50p. Ultramarine	74	25
Z56	D86	**Z4**	17.6.70	£1 Black	1·50	50

Cylinder Numbers (Blocks of Six)

Perforation Type A (T)

Value	Cyl. No.		No dot		Value	Cyl. No.		No dot
½p	2	..	8		5p	8	..	45
1p	1	..	10		10p	2	..	90
2p	1	..	20		20p	2	..	1·75
3p	2	..	25		50p	1	..	4·50
4p	3	..	35		£1	2	..	8·00

Sheet Details

Sheet sizes: 200 (20 × 10) single pane sheet-fed

Sheet markings:
    Cylinder numbers: Above R. 1/3, unboxed
    Guide holes: None
    Marginal arrows (photo-etched): "W" shaped at top, bottom and sides
    Marginal rule: None
    Coloured cross: Opposite rows 6/7, at both sides
    Sheet values: Above and below vertical rows 5/6 and 15/16 reading left to right in top margin and right to
      left (upside down) in bottom margin

APPENDIX O

Perforators

General Notes

INTRODUCTION. Basically, two kinds of perforating machines are used for British stamps: sheet-fed and reel-fed. The sheet-fed machines generally employ a two-row comb and the reel-fed machines a three-row comb. Both kinds are full width, i.e. they are able to perforate two panes side by side.

Types A to I and N are the different *sheet perforation types* recorded in this catalogue, produced either by the sheet-fed or the reel-fed machines but they should not be regarded as representing the use of ten different machines, rather they are ten different sheet perforation types produced by various perforating machines.

Types J to M relate to booklet panes for the Machin issues.

GUIDE HOLES. Perforation guide holes can be an indication of the type of perforator used and these are recorded, where known, following the sheet perforation characteristics for each type. For reasons unknown these may not always appear in the sheet margins.

ORDER. This Appendix is divided into four sections:
1. Low Value Definitive Stamps (including Regionals and Postage Due Stamps)
2. High Value Definitive Stamps
3. Special Issues
4. Machin Booklet Panes

ILLUSTRATIONS. The illustrations are all from definitive stamps but they are equally representative of the High Value and Special issues where the same types occur.

TABLE OF PERFORATION TYPES. The useful tabulated list of Perforation Types at the end of this Appendix is primarily designed to be used for Special issues, although, the first part may also be used in conjunction with the Low and High Value definitive stamps for Types A, A (T), B, C, E (no dot panes only) and F (L).

BOOKLETS. We list the perforation types used for the Machin booklets as they are fairly simple and easily collected. The Wilding booklet perforations are more complicated.

1. Low Value Definitive Stamps

This section deals with the small size Wilding and Machin definitives, the Regionals and the Postage Due Stamps.

Type A. Horizontal two-row comb. Sheet-fed.

No dot and dot panes—	Top margin	Perforated through
	Bottom margin	Imperforate
	Left margin	A single extension hole
	Right margin	A single extension hole
	Guide holes	Opposite rows 14/15, at left (no dot panes) or right (dot panes)

In this machine an appropriate number of sheets (usually six to eight) are impaled through the guide holes and they go forward together under the comb. The imperf. margin (at the bottom) indicates the point of entry.

Type A (T). Horizontal two-row comb. Sheet-fed.

Single pane printing—	Top margin	Imperforate
	Bottom margin	Perforated through
	Left margin	A single extension hole
	Right margin	A single extension hole
	Guide holes	None

This is simply a top (T) instead of a bottom feed ot Type A. In the definitive stamps it only occurs in the Postage Due Stamps. Cylinder blocks are identical in appearance with Type C.

336

Types B and C. Horizontal three-row comb. Reel-fed.

Type B. No dot panes—	Top margin	Perforated through
	Bottom margin	Perforated through
	Left margin	Imperforate
	Right margin	A single extension hole
	Guide holes	Usually opposite rows 1, 7/8 and 14/15 at both sides of pane

Type C. No dot and dot panes—	Top margin	Perforated through
	Bottom margin	Perforated through
	Left margin	A single extension hole
	Right margin	Imperforate
	Guide holes	As Type B, above

Type B is the left and Type C the right halves of the same reel-fed perforator. The outer ends of the comb are without extension pins, there being only single extension pins in the interpane margin. In this machine the continuous web of paper advances under the comb in a single thickness and without interruption, hence both top and bottom margins are perforated.

It often happened that two narrow reels were perforated together by placing them side by side on the machine so that single pane printings (i.e. no dot panes only) occur perforated with Type B and also Type C. It is only when double pane printings are perforated on this machine that no dot panes will always be Type B and dot panes will always be Type C, except that in the Special issues, the 4d. Scout Jamboree stamp from Cyl. 1 dot is known with perforation Type B and Type C.

Type E. Horizontal two-row comb. Sheet-fed.

No dot panes—	Top margin	Perforated through
	Bottom margin	Imperforate
	Left margin	A single extension hole on alternate rows only
	Right margin	A single extension hole
	Guide hole	Opposite rows 14/15, at left

Dot panes—	Top margin	Perforated through
	Bottom margin	Imperforate
	Left margin	A single extension hole
	Right margin	A single extension hole on alternate rows only
	Guide hole	Opposite rows 14/15, at right

This is a simple variation of Type A (*q.v.*) that may result from the removal of a perforating pin or a repair to a comb-head. Therefore, no dot cylinder blocks are as Type A but left margin has the single extension hole missing on alternate rows.

Cylinder blocks from the dot pane would be indistinguishable from Type A, hence only no dot cylinder blocks are recorded with Type E.

Type F*. Vertical two-row comb. Sheet-fed.

No dot panes—	Top margin	A single extension hole
	Bottom margin	A single extension hole
	Left margin	Perforated through
	Right margin	Perforated through
	Guide holes	None

Dot panes—	Top margin	A single extension hole
	Bottom margin	A single extension hole
	Left margin	Perforated through
	Right margin	Imperforate
	Guide holes	None

This is similar to Type F (L)* except that the vertical comb has perforated horizontally from *right* to *left* (instead of from *left* to *right*) across both panes prior to guillotining into single sheets. Because the interpane margin is perforated no dot and dot cylinder blocks are identical. This perforation type was used exclusively for the Regional decimal definitives.

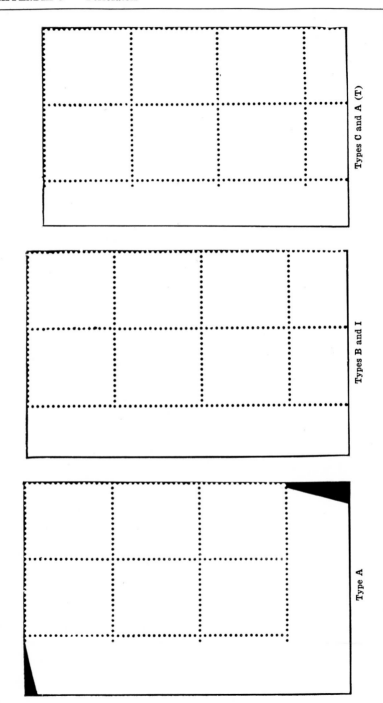

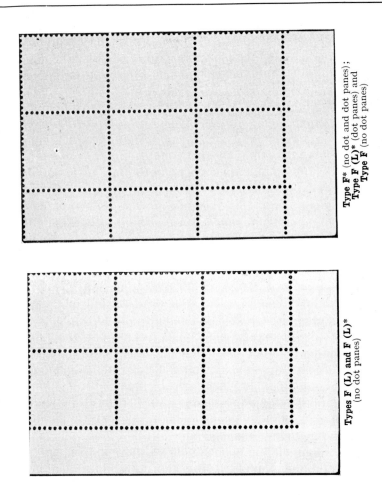

Type F* (no dot and dot panes) ;
Type F (L)* (dot panes) and
Type F (no dot panes)

Types F (L) and F (L)*
(no dot panes)

Type F (L). Vertical two-row comb. Sheet-fed.

No dot panes—

Top margin	A single extension hole
Bottom margin	A single extension hole
Left margin	Imperforate
Right margin	Perforated through
Guide holes	Through marginal arrow above vertical rows 6/7 and below vertical row 10

This type perforates from the left (L) through to the right side of the sheet. In this catalogue the use of this type has been restricted to single pane printings (i.e. no dot panes only).

Type F (L)*. Vertical two-row comb. Sheet-fed.

No dot panes—

Top margin	A single extension hole
Bottom margin	A single extension hole
Left margin	Imperforate
Right margin	Perforated through
Guide holes	Above and below eighth vertical row

339

Type F (L)* Contd.

Dot panes—

Top margin	A single extension hole
Bottom margin	A single extension hole
Left margin	Perforated through
Right margin	Perforated through
Guide holes	None (occur on no dot panes *only*)

This is the same perforator as used for Type F (L) and it is given in this catalogue when double pane printings (i.e. no dot and dot panes) have been perforated together prior to their being guillotined into single sheets. This gives no dot cylinder blocks exactly as Type F (L) but because the vertical comb has perforated horizontally from left to right across *both* panes the interpane margin is also perforated and, therefore, the dot cylinder blocks are perforated through the left margin.

Type H. Horizontal two-row comb. Sheet-fed.

No dot panes—

Top margin	Perforated through
Bottom margin	Imperforate
Left margin	A single extension hole
Right margin	Perforated through
Guide hole	Opposite rows 14/15, at left

Dot panes—

Top margin	Perforated through
Bottom margin	Imperforate
Left margin	Perforated through
Right margin	A single extension hole
Guide hole	Opposite rows 14/15, at right

This is a further variation of Type A (*q.v.*) differing by the fact that the interpane margin is perforated through instead of there being single extension holes at the end of every row at right on the no dot pane and at the end of every row at left on the dot pane. Therefore, dot cylinder blocks are as Type A but left margin is perforated through. Cylinder blocks from the no dot pane would be indistinguishable from Type A, hence only dot cylinder blocks are recorded with Type H.

Type I. Vertical two-row comb. Sheet-fed.

Single pane printing—

Top margin	A single extension hole
Bottom margin	Perforated through
Left margin	Imperforate
Right margin	Perforated through
Guide holes	Through marginal arrow above vertical rows 6/7 and below vertical row 10

This is similar to Type F (L) (*q.v.*), except that the bottom sheet margin is perforated through instead of there being only a single extension hole at the end of every row. Cylinder blocks are identical in appearance with Type B.

2. High Value Definitive Stamps

This section deals with the Wilding and Machin High Value stamps.

Wilding High Values

Perforation Type A, as described at the beginning of this Appendix, was used exclusively for these stamps. Waterlow and De La Rue both used a single-row comb and Bradbury, Wilkinson a two-row comb.

The guide holes appear opposite row 6, at left on left-hand panes and at right on right-hand panes.

Machin £.s.d. High Values

The printer's sheet was perforated with Type A prior to being guillotined into four panes, so that the characteristics of each individual Post Office pane are different and this has, therefore, been described as perforation Type A*. The description of Type A, given at the beginning of this Appendix, applies equally to Type A*, except that Bradbury, Wilkinson used a single-row comb.

For diagram showing the printer's sheet, the method of perforation and the position of plate numbers and guide holes see the General Notes for Section U2.

Machin Decimal High Values

Type N has only been used for this issue.

Type N. Horizontal single-row comb. Sheet-fed.

Single pane printing—

Top margin	Perforated through
Bottom margin	Imperforate
Left margin	Perforated through
Right margin	Perforated through
Guide holes	None

3.   Special Issues

This section deals with all the special stamps issued to date.

Type A. In the special issues this type is exactly as described at the beginning of this Appendix except that with single pane printings (i.e. no dot panes only) the guide holes are opposite rows 14/15, at both sides of the sheet.

Type A (T). In the special issues this type is exactly as described at the beginning of this Appendix and it applies equally to both no dot and dot panes. Guide holes very rarely appear in the sheet margins but where they do this is given under "Sheet Details" in Section W.

Types B and C. In the special issues these types are exactly as described in the first part of this Appendix.

Type D. Vertical single-row comb. Sheet-fed.

Single pane printing—		
	Top margin	Perforated through
	Bottom margin	A single extension hole
	Left margin	Imperforate
	Right margin	Perforated through

This is similar to Type F (L) except that the top margin is perforated through. It only occurs on the 3d. Post Office Savings Bank stamp where the cylinder number appears in the bottom margin below vertical row 5.

Type E. Horizontal two-row comb. Sheet-fed.

Right-hand panes—		
	Top margin	Perforated through
	Bottom margin	Imperforate
	Left margin	A single extension hole on alternate rows only
	Right margin	A single extension hole
	Guide hole	Opposite rows 14/15, at right

This is a variation of Type A that may result from the removal of a perforating pin or a repair to a comb-head. Therefore, cylinder blocks are as Type A but left margin has the single extension hole missing on alternate rows.

This type is only known on the 1s.3d. Freedom from Hunger and the 3d. Red Cross on the right-hand panes only (i.e. no dot* pane of 1s.3d. F.F.H. and dot pane of 3d. Red Cross). The left-hand panes in both cases are believed to be Type A but it is possible that the right margin has single extension holes on alternate rows to match the left margin of the right-hand pane.

*The panes of the 1s.3d. Freedom from Hunger issue are transposed, i.e. the dot pane is on the left and the no dot pane is on the right.

Types F and F (L). Vertical single-row comb. Sheet-fed.
Single pane printings.

Type F. Right feed—		
	Top margin	A single extension hole
	Bottom margin	A single extension hole
	Left margin	Perforated through
	Right margin	Imperforate

Type F (L). Left feed—		
	Top margin	A single extension hole
	Bottom margin	A single extension hole
	Left margin	Imperforate
	Right margin	Perforated through

Type F perforates from the right through to the left side of the sheet and Type F (L) perforates from the left through to the right side of the sheet. Both types are used for single pane printings (i.e. no dot panes only). Guide holes very rarely appear in the sheet margins but where they do this is given under "Sheet Details" in Section W.

Type G. Vertical single-row comb. Sheet-fed.

No dot and dot panes—		
	Top margin	Perforated through
	Bottom margin	Perforated through
	Left margin	Perforated through
	Right margin	Imperforate
	Guide holes	None

This was a special perforator used exclusively for the 6d. Battle of Hastings issue. The cylinder block is perforated through in both the bottom and left margins.

TABLE OF SPECIAL ISSUE PERFORATION TYPES

The table below combines a list of the different *sheet perforation types* recorded in Section W, together with the characteristics of the four sheet margins. Following the basic perforation type the characteristics given relate to the sheet viewed with the stamps the right way up.

The identification of a particular perforation type from a cylinder block (or any corner block) can easily be established by referring to this table in conjunction with the recorded types under "Cylinder Numbers" in Section W.

Whilst this table is mainly designed to be used for the special stamps, the first part may also be used in conjunction with the Low and High Value definitive stamps for Types A, A (T), B, C, E (no dot panes only) and F (L).

I. HORIZONTAL FORMAT STAMPS

Perforation Type	Top margin	Bottom margin	Left margin	Right margin
Type A (*bottom feed*)	Perforated through	Imperforate	Single extension hole	Single extension hole
Type A (T) (*top feed*)	Imperforate	Perforated through	Single extension hole	Single extension hole
Type B	Perforated through	Perforated through	Imperforate	Single extension hole
Type C	Perforated through	Perforated through	Single extension hole	Imperforate
Type D	Perforated through	Single extension hole	Imperforate	Perforated through
Type E	Perforated through	Imperforate	Single extension hole alternate rows only	Single extension hole
Type F (*right feed*)	Single extension hole	Single extension hole	Perforated through	Imperforate
Type F (L) (*left feed*)	Single extension hole	Single extension hole	Imperforate	Perforated through
Type G	Perforated through	Perforated through	Perforated through	Imperforate

II. VERTICAL FORMAT STAMPS*

Perforation Type	Top margin	Bottom margin	Left margin	Right margin
Type A (*head to right*)	Single extension hole	Single extension hole	Perforated through	Imperforate
Type A (*head to left*)	Single extension hole	Single extension hole	Imperforate	Perforated through
Type A (T) (*head to right*)	Single extension hole	Single extension hole	Imperforate	Perforated through
Type A (T) (*head to left*)	Single extension hole	Single extension hole	Perforated through	Imperforate
Type B (*head to right*)	Single extension hole	Imperforate	Perforated through	Perforated through
Type C (*head to right*)	Imperforate	Single extension hole	Perforated through	Perforated through
Type F (*head to right*)	Imperforate	Perforated through	Single extension hole	Single extension hole

*The position of the head on vertical format stamps is determined by viewing the sheet with the marginal rule (normally on a short side) at the bottom. In most instances the head (or top of the stamp) is to the right; the head to the left occuring on the 3d. Post Office Tower, 4d. World Football Cup, 4d. World Cup Victory and the 3d. and 1s.6d. 1966 Christmas issue, although the latter does not in fact bear marginal rules but it should be regarded as being "head to left".

From the 1966 Christmas issue onwards many sheets did not bear marginal rules. Where this is the case with vertical format designs the correct orientation of the sheets to determine the perforation type is given below the "Cylinder Numbers" in the listings.

Exceptionally, the 1967 British Paintings 4d. and the British Discovery and Inventions 1s.9d. show the marginal rule on a *long* side and this should be orientated to the left-hand side to show perforation Types A (T) (head to right) and F (head to right) respectively.

1. Machin Booklet Panes

1. £.s.d. Booklets

(a) 2s. Booklets (Panes of Four)

Three perforation types exist:—

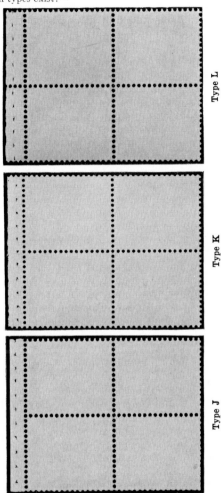

Type J.   Margin imperforate

Type K.   Margin perforated through but alternate rows imperforate

Type L.   Margin fully perforated through

(b) 4s.6d., 5s., 6s. and 10s. Booklets (Panes of Six)

These, of course, are arranged horizontally and all panes are Type J except for No. UB3 which also exists Type L and No. UB4 which only exists Type L.

(c) £1 "Stamps for Cooks" Booklet (Panes of Fifteen)

These panes only exist Type J.

The Machin £.s.d. Booklets are printed continuously "on the web" from 21-row cylinders. The perforated web is cut at every 20th row to make sheets of 480 (two panes of 240 (12 × 20)). Consequently on successive sheets the cylinder number appears one row lower so that a pane can have it adjoining the top or bottom row. In the listing of cylinder blocks for stamps from the 4/6, 5/–, 6/– and 10/– Booklets the letter "T" after the cylinder number indicates that it is a pane with the cylinder number adjoining the top row.

In every fourth row of the imperf. type (Type J) there is an extension hole between the no dot and dot panes. This means that the cylinder number in the dot panes exists not only in two positions in the pane but also each position exists with the extension hole either at the top or bottom. We do not distinguish these sub-types of perforation.

II. Decimal Booklets

(a) 10p. Booklets (Se-tenant Panes of Four)

These exist with Types J and L in the proportion of one to four respectively. They are printed in twenty-four rows of ten arranged sideways. The left margin is Type J followed by 1p and 1½p facing down, 1½p and 1p facing up, perforated gutter margin Type L, 1p and 1½p facing down, 1½p and 1p facing up, perforated gutter margin Type L and 1p and 1½p facing down. The right margin is removed before making up.

The other pane is made up of 2p in the place of the 1p and ½p in the place of the 1½p. The cylinder numbers are trimmed off.

(b) 25p, 30p and 50p. Booklets (Panes of Six)

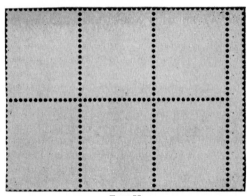

Type M

Besides Types J, K and L there is an additional Type M which is new. This is as Type K except that there is an additional vertical line of perforations in the binding margin. At the junction of this extra vertical row of perforations with each horizontal row there is an extra large perforation hole but this is not always apparent. The extra row of perforations is liable to be trimmed off in which case the pane is indistinguishable from Type K. Panes with part of the vertical row of perforations still visible can be classed as Type M.

They are printed from double-width cylinders of 480 subjects arranged similar to the diagram at the beginning of Appendix P except that there is only one cylinder number which is without dot and appears in the left-hand margin. Only 20-row cylinders are used and Booklet cylinders have the letter "B" in front of the number. They are shown in a box like in the sheet stamps as illustrated in the General Notes for Section U3 but in the issued books all that appears is the extreme right portion of the number and sides of the box.

The perforator used for part of the printing of the February 1971 edition of the 30p Booklet had Type J in the left margin and Type K in the right margin, all the gutter margins being Type L. The perforator was then altered so as to give Type K in the left margin and the new Type M in the right margin. This was used for the remainder of the February 1971 and subsequent editions of the 30p Booklet and for all 25p and 50p Booklets. Thus Type J only exists for the "£4,315" label pane, No. UB30.

For the 30p August 1971 Booklet the perforator was adapted or a new perforator was made to provide for the label to be imperforate in the binding margin to prevent it being used as a stamp by blind people.

Post Office Booklets of Stamps

General Notes

BOOKLET SHEET ARRANGEMENT. Booklets are made up from specially printed sheets which are differently arranged from normal Post Office sheets in order to facilitate economic manufacture. The arrangement of the sheet varies according to the size and format of the booklet pane required. For example, in the case of booklet panes of six, the printer's sheet of 480 stamps, consisting of two panes (no dot and dot) each of 240 stamps arranged in twenty rows of twelve stamps, has additional gutters provided between the 6th and 7th vertical rows in both panes, and the stamps in the 4th, 5th and 6th, and 10th, 11th and 12th vertical rows in both panes are inverted in relation to the others (i.e. *tête-bêche*). Two horizontal rows of the sheet (producing eight booklets) would be arranged thus:

	No dot pane				Dot pane			
	1239St	G U T T E R	1239St	G U T T E R	1239St	G U T T E R	1239St	←
Watermark	456Ɛ2I		456Ɛ2I		456Ɛ2I		456Ɛ2I	←

↑   ↑   ↑   ↑   ↑   ↑   ↑

The sheets of stamps, interleaving sheets and covers are stitched vertically, once at the two outer edges of the double pane and twice in each of the gutters as shown by the vertical rules in the diagram. Finally, the booklets are guillotined both horizontally and vertically as indicated by the arrows.

INVERTED WATERMARKS. From the diagram it is easy to see how 50% of Wilding booklets have stamps with inverted watermarks.

WATERMARK POSITIONS. Although 50% of booklet panes have the watermark inverted, in describing the contents of the booklets reference is made to the catalogue numbers of the basic stamps with normal watermark throughout the list. This is to avoid continual reference to the catalogue numbers of the inverted watermarks, etc.

WHITER PAPER. During the changeover period cream and whiter paper stamps could occur in the same booklet and we make no attempt to distinguish these.

TETE-BECHE ERRORS. These occur in booklets due to faulty manufacture, usually the result of a corner of the sheet being folded over.

ERRORS OF MAKE-UP. Such errors exist but we do not list them as it is not difficult to break up booklets and remake them to agree with known errors.

COVERS. All covers are printed in black except where otherwise stated.

BOOKLET CYLINDER NUMBERS. These occur in the left-hand margin of both panes (i.e. no dot and dot) as normal Post Office sheets. They are illustrated in Section S except that they always have prefix letters, e.g. E4, F5, G3, but the letters are liable to be partly or completely trimmed off.
    Booklet panes of six printed from 20-row cylinders always have the cylinder number adjoining the bottom row of stamps but in the case of 21-row cylinders, the perforated web is cut at every 20th row to make sheets of 480. Consequently, on successive sheets the cylinder number appears one row lower and thus a pane can have it adjoining the top or bottom row.
    Booklet panes of four and fifteen usually have the cylinders trimmed off completely.

DATES. The month and year dates are those found printed on the booklets, either on the outer back cover or on the white leaves. No dates are given on the 1s. booklets, the 2s. booklets Nos. N1/3, the 5s. "Philympia" booklet No. HP34 and the £1 booklet No. ZP1. The dates of issue of every booklet in a new cover design or composition are given in brackets where known.

QUANTITIES. The quantities given are of the numbers manufactured, but some of the figures are shared by two or more booklets and this is indicated in the listing.

CATALOGUE NUMBERS. In order to avoid confusion we have used the same booklet numbers as in the *Elizabethan Catalogue*. Many of these booklets bear the same prefix letters as other stamps listed in the *Great Britain* Specialised Catalogues so that when quoting numbers in this Appendix it should be made clear that booklets are being referred to.

TYPES OF BOOKLET COVERS

Type A
Circular GPO Cypher

Type B
Oval Type GPO Cypher

Type C
New GPO Cypher (small)

Type D
New GPO Cypher (large)

Section A. Wilding Issues without Graphite Lines or Phosphor Bands

1/- Booklets for use in Slot Machines

Composition.   Panes of two: 4 × 1½d., 4 × 1d., 4 × ½d.
I. White unprinted cover. Not interleaved. For use in experimental "D" machines
Watermark Tudor Crown (Nos. S1, S13, S25)
E1 No date (issued 2.9.53)   56,650   6£

Watermark St. Edward's Crown (Nos. S2, S14, S26)
E2 No date (issued 11.57)   7,180   1·75
    These booklets were made up from vertical rows 1 and 2 from sheets and so
do not have inverted watermarks. Booklets for "D" machines were withdrawn
in November 1960.

New composition.   Panes of four: 4 × 1½d., 4 × 1d., 4 × ½d.
II. White printed cover as Type B. Not interleaved. For use in "E" machines
Watermark Tudor Crown (Nos. S1, S13, S25)
K1 No date (issued 22.7.54)   753,260   65

Watermark St. Edward's Crown (Nos. S2, S14, S26)
K2 No date (issued 5.7.56)   1,446,000   65

Watermark Crowns (Nos. S4, S16, S28)
K3 No date (issued 13.8.59)   873,500   65
    1/- booklets are no longer issued. They were available until 1964.

2/- Booklets

Composition. Panes of four: 4×3d., $4 \times 1\frac{1}{2}$d., 4×1d., $4 \times \frac{1}{2}$d.
I. Salmon cover as Type B. Fully interleaved
Watermark St. Edward's Crown (Nos. S2. S14, S26, S68)

N1 No date (issued 22.4.59)	452,470	1·10

II. Salmon cover as Type C. Fully interleaved
Watermark Crowns (upright) (Nos. S4, S16, S28, S70)

N2 No date (issued 2.11.60)	300,500	65

III. Lemon cover as Type C. Fully interleaved
Watermark Crowns (upright) (Nos. S4, S16, S28, S70)

N3 No date (issued 9.2.61)	1,330,750	50

Watermark Crowns (sideways) (Nos. S4d or S5a, S16e or S17a, S28b or S29a,
    S70a, or S71a)

N 4 APR 1961 (issued 26.5.61)	1,381,440	1·60	N13 AUG 1963	..	..	989,000	1·60
N 5 SEPT 1961	..	..	889,000	1·60	N14 OCT 1963	..	..	1,018,800	1·60
N 6 JAN 1962	..	..	911,600	1·60	N15 FEB 1964	..	..	1,122,400	1·60
N 7 APR 1962	..	..	958,600	1·60	N16 JUNE 1964	..	..	386,570	1·75
N 8 JULY 1962	..	..	935,600	1·60	N17 AUG 1964	..	..	122,300	1·90
N 9 NOV 1962	..	..	975,000	1·60	N18 OCT 1964	..	..	1,179,800	1·60
N10 JAN 1963	..	..	1,105,400	1·60	N19 DEC 1964	..	..	109,170	1·90
N11 MAR 1963	..	..	1,090,800	1·60	N20 APR 1965	..	..	1,435,400	1·60
N12 JUNE 1963	..	..	1,014,800	1·60					

2/– booklets in this composition were withdrawn from sale on 31st August 1965.

New composition. Panes of four: 4×4d. and pane of 2×1d. and 2×3d.
    arranged *se-tenant* horizontally
Orange-yellow cover as Type C and printed in black. Fully interleaved
Watermark Crowns (sideways) (Nos. S17a, S71a, S85b)

N21 JULY 1965 (16.8.65)	..	2,671,800	50	N25 JULY 1966	..	..	1,981,800	45
N22 OCT 1965	..	..	1,852,800	45	N26 OCT 1966	..	..	1,787,400	45
N23 JAN 1966	..	..	1,633,200	45	N27 JAN 1967	..	..	644,200	50
N24 APR 1966	..	..	2,125,200	45					

In the *se-tenant* pane the 3d. appears at left or right to facilitate the application
of phosphor bands in the phosphor issue.

2/- Booklets for Holiday Resorts

Composition. Panes of four: two panes of $4 \times 2\frac{1}{2}$d. and one of $3 \times \frac{1}{2}$d. and
    $1 \times 2\frac{1}{2}$d. arranged *se-tenant*
Lemon cover as Type C and printed in red. Fully interleaved
Watermark Crowns. Chalky paper (Nos. S6, S58)

A. Black stitching

NR1 No date (issued 15.7.63)	415,000	1·75
aa. Screen damage on 2½d. (see No. SB10c)		4·50

B. White stitching

NR1a No date (issued 3.9.63)	50,000	2·50
b. Screen damage on 2½d. (see No. SB10c)		10·00

New composition. Panes of four: four panes of $2 \times \frac{1}{2}$d. and $2 \times 2\frac{1}{2}$d. arranged
    sideways, vertically *se-tenant*
Lemon cover as Type C and printed in red. Fully interleaved
Watermark Crowns (sideways) (No. SB11 $\times$ 4)

NR2 1964 (issued 1.7.64)	827,800	1·75

2/- Booklet for Christmas Cards

Composition. Panes of four: two panes of 4×3d. arranged sideways
Orange-yellow cover as Type C and printed in red. Fully interleaved
Watermark Crowns (sideways) (No. S71a)

NX1 1965 (issued 6.12.65)	1,208,000	60

The above was withdrawn on 3.1.66 but reissued on 16.5.66 as a holiday
resort booklet.

2/6 Booklets

Green covers

Composition.   Panes of six: 6 × 2½d., 6 × 1½d., 3 × 1d. (page completed by three perforated labels), 6 × ½d.

LABELS.   The wording printed on the labels differs as follows:—

"PPR"="MINIMUM INLAND PRINTED PAPER RATE 1½d." Two types exist:
    (a) 17 mm. high. Printed in photogravure
    (b) 15 mm. high. Printed by typography
"SHORTHAND"="SHORTHAND IN 1 WEEK" (covering all three labels)
"POST EARLY"="PLEASE POST EARLY IN THE DAY"
"PAP"="PACK YOUR PARCELS SECURELY" (1st label), "ADDRESS YOUR LETTERS CORRECTLY" (2nd label), "AND POST EARLY IN THE DAY" (3rd label)

I. Composite booklets containing stamps of King George VI and Queen Elizabeth II

A. K.G. VI ½d. (No. Q3) and 1d. (No. Q6) and Q.E. II 1½d. (No. S25) and 2½d. (No. S51). Cover as Type A. Not interleaved

F 1 MAY 1953 PPR 17 mm.	..	..	..	..	..	..	..	2,772,000	2·00
F 2 JUNE 1953 PPR 17 mm.	..	..	..	..	..	..	..	2,751,000	2·00
F 3 JULY 1953 PPR 17 mm.	..	..	..	..	..	..	..	2,199,000	2·25
F 4 AUG 1953 PPR 17 mm.	..	..	..	..	..	..	..	2,464,000	2·25

B. Same composition but with the addition of two interleaving pages, one at each end. Cover as Type A

F 5 SEPT 1953 PPR 17 mm.	..	..	..	..	..	..	..⎫	2·50
F 6 SEPT 1953 PPR 15 mm.	..	..	..	..	..	..	..⎭ 2,386,000	4·00

C. Same composition with interleaving as before but cover as Type B

F 7 OCT 1953 PPR 17 mm. ..	..	..	..	..	..	..	..⎫	2·00
F 8 OCT 1953 PPR 15 mm. ..	..	..	..	..	..	..	..⎭ 2,532,000	3·00
F 9 NOV 1953 PPR 17 mm. ..	..	..	..	..	..	..	..⎫	2·00
F10 NOV 1953 PPR 15 mm. ..	..	..	..	..	..	..	..⎭ 4,308,000	3·00
F11 DEC 1953 PPR 17 mm. ..	..	..	..	..	..	..	2,918,000	2·00
F12 JAN 1954 SHORTHAND	..	..	..	..	..	..	2,199,000	2·50
F13 FEB 1954 SHORTHAND	..	..	..	..	..	..	2,202,000	2·50

D. *New composition.*   ½d. Q.E.II (No. S1) in place of ½d. K.G. VI, but otherwise as Nos. F7/13

F14 MAR 1954 PPR 17 mm. ..	..	..	..	..	..	..	139,000	12·00

II. Booklets containing only Queen Elizabeth II stamps. All covers as Type B Watermark Tudor Crown (Nos. S1, S13, S25, S51)

A. Two interleaving pages, one at each end

F15 MAR 1954 PPR 15 mm. ..	..	..	..	..	..	..	2,085,000	12·00
F16 APR 1954 POST EARLY	..	..	..	..	..	..	3,176,000	3·00
F17 MAY 1954 POST EARLY	..	..	..	..	..	..	2,435,000	3·00
F18 JUNE 1954 POST EARLY	..	..	..	..	..	..	2,419,000	3·00
F19 JULY 1954 POST EARLY	..	..	..	..	..	..	2,876,000	3·00
F20 AUG 1954 POST EARLY	..	..	..	..	..	..	2,871,000	3·00
F21 SEPT 1954 POST EARLY	..	..	..	..	..	..	2,799,000	3·00
F22 OCT 1954 POST EARLY	..	..	..	..	..	..	2,803,000	3·00
F23 NOV 1954 POST EARLY	..	..	..	..	..	..	3,739,000	3·00
F24 DEC 1954 POST EARLY	..	..	..	..	..	..	2,813,000	3·00

B. Fully interleaved

F25 JAN 1955 POST EARLY	..	..	..	..	..	..	2,551,000	3·00
F26 JAN 1955 PAP ..	..	..	..	..	..	..	160,000	6·00
F27 FEB 1955 PAP ..	..	..	..	..	..	..	2,694,000	3·00
F28 MAR 1955 PAP ..	..	..	..	..	..	..	2,530,000	3·00
F29 APR 1955 PAP ..	..	..	..	..	..	..	2,522,000	3·00
F30 MAY 1955 PAP ..	..	..	..	..	..	..	2,530,000	3·00
F31 JUNE 1955 PAP ..	..	..	..	..	..	..	2,522,000	3·00
F32 JULY 1955 PAP ..	..	..	..	..	..	..	2,431,000	3·00
F33 AUG 1955 PAP ..	..	..	..	..	..	..⎫	
a. Combination TTET	..	..	..	..	..	..⎬ 2,563,000	3·00
b. Combination TEET	..	..	..	..	..	..⎭	

MIXED WATERMARKS. Nos. F33, F35/38 and F42/3 exist with mixed Tudor Crown and St. Edward's Crown watermarks, whilst No. F34 only exists with mixed watermarks. The mixed watermarks are indicated by the code letters "T" (Tudor) and "E" (Edward) starting with the first pane of the booklet, i.e. 2½d., 1½d., 1d., ½d. We only quote one price for each booklet and this is the minimum price. Some combinations are scarcer and worth more.

Mixed Tudor Crown and St. Edward's Crown watermarks

F34 SEPT 1955 PAP (TTET)	..	..	..	..	..	..	..	..	}	
a. Combination TEET	..	..	..	..	..	..	..	..	} 2,275,000	1·40
b. Combination ETET	..	..	..	..	..	..	..	..	}	
c. Combination EEET	..	..	..	..	..	..	..	..	}	

Watermark St. Edward's Crown (Nos. S2, S14, S26, S53). All have PAP labels

F35 OCT 1955	..	}		F42 MAY 1956	..		
a. Combination TEET		}		a. Combination EEET	} 2,275,000	2·50
b. Combination EEET	} 2,289,000	2·50		b. Combination TEEE	}	
c. Combination TEEE	}			F43 JUNE 1956	..	} 2,293,000	2·40
F36 NOV 1965	..	} 4,125,000	2·50	a. Combination TEEE	}	
a. Combination TEEE	}			F44 JULY 1956	..	..	2,279,400	2·40
F37 DEC 1965	..	}		F45 AUG 1956	..	..	2,264,400	2·40
a. Combination TEET	} 2,789,000	2·50		F46 SEPT 1956	..	..	2,533,000	2·40
b. Combination EEET	}			F47 OCT 1956	..	..	2,536,000	2·40
F38 JAN 1956	..	}		F48 NOV 1956	..	..	4,165,800	2·40
a. Combination EEET	} 2,001,000	2·50		F49 DEC 1956	..	..	2,724,600	2·40
F39 FEB 1956	..	..	2,031,000	2·50	F50 JAN 1957	..	..	2,212,800	2·40
F40 MAR 1956	..	..	2,289,000	2·50	F51 FEB 1957	..	..	2,772,790	2·40
F41 APR 1956	..	..	2,283,000	2·50	F52 MAR 1957	..	..	2,497,800	2·40

New composition.   Panes of six: 6 × 2½d., 6 × 2d., 6 × ½d.

Watermark St. Edward's Crown (Nos. S2, S38, S53)

F53 APR 1957	..	..	2,451,800	1·40	F58 SEPT 1957	..	..	2,482,200	1·25
F54 MAY 1957	..	..	2,062,400	1·40	F59 OCT 1957	..	..	2,505,600	1·25
F55 JUNE 1957	..	..	1,843,000	1·50	F60 NOV 1957	..	..	3,085,600	1·25
F56 JULY 1957	..	..	2,305,000	1·40	F61 DEC 1957	..	..	281,000	3·00
F57 AUG 1957	..	..	2,265,000	1·40					

The 2/6 booklets were withdrawn from sale on 27th July 1958.

3/- Booklets

Composition.   Panes of six: 6 × 3d., 6 × 1½d., 6 × 1d., 6 × ½d.

I. Red cover as Type B. Fully interleaved
Watermark St. Edward's Crown (Nos. S2, S14, S26, S68)

M1 JAN 1958	..	..	1,815,000	1·60	M7 JULY 1958	..	..	885,000	1·60
M2 FEB 1958	..	..	2,224,000	1·50	M8 AUG 1958	..	..	896,000	1·60
M3 MAR 1958	..	..	2,271,000	1·50	M9 NOV 1958	..	..	}	
M4 APR 1958	..	..	2,654,000	1·50	a. Combination EEEC	}	
M5 MAY 1958	..	..	2,146,000	1·50	b. Combination EECE	} 1,367,000	1·90
M6 JUNE 1958	..	..	2,222,000	1·50	c. Combination EECC	}	

MIXED WATERMARKS. See notes above No. F34. The mixed watermarks here are indicated by the code letters "E" (Edward) and "C" (Crowns) starting with the first pane of the booklet, i.e. 3d., 1½d., 1d., ½d.

Watermark Crowns (Nos. S4, S16, S28, S70)

M10 DEC 1958	..	}		M11 JAN 1959	..	} 1,145,000	75
a. Combination CEEE	}		a. Combination CECC	}	
b. Combination CECE	} 886,000	90	M12 FEB 1959	..	..	1,125,000	60
c. Combination CEEC	}		M13 AUG 1959	..	..	1,038,000	60
d. Combination CECC	}		M14 SEPT 1959	..	..	1,542,000	60

II. Brick-red cover as Type C. Same composition

M15 OCT 1959	..	..	1,016,000	60	M22 MAY 1960	..	..	911,000	75
M16 NOV 1959	..	..	2,287,000	60	M23 JUNE 1960	..	..	982,000	75
M17 DEC 1959	..	..	1,027,000	60	M24 JULY 1960	..	..	989,200	75
M18 JAN 1960	..	..	752,000	90	M25 AUG 1960	..	..	897,000	75
M19 FEB 1960	..	..	750,000	75	M26 SEPT 1960	..	..	1,326,600	60
M20 MAR 1960	..	..	966,000	75	M27 OCT 1960	..	..	1,343,400	60
M21 APR 1960	..	..	941,000	75	M28 NOV 1960	..	..	2,068,200	60

III. Brick red cover as Type D
Watermark Crowns (Nos. S4 or S5, S16 or S17, S28 or S29, S70 or S71)

M29 DEC 1960	..	..	905,200	60	M41 DEC 1961	..	..	356,800	60
M30 JAN 1961	..	..	731,800	60	M42 JAN 1962	..	..	447,000	60
M31 FEB 1961	..	..	727,000	60	M43 FEB 1962	..	..	654,200	50
M32 MAR 1961	..	..	754,600	60	M44 MAR 1962	..	..	655,200	50
M33 APR 1961	..	..	760,800	60	M45 APR 1962	..	..	569,600	50
M34 MAY 1961	..	..	738,000	50	M46 MAY 1962	..	..	475,000	60
M35 JUNE 1961	..	..	768,000	50	M47 JUNE 1962	..	..	468,400	50
M36 JULY 1961	..	..	783,400	50	M48 JULY 1962	..	..	729,400	50
M37 AUG 1961	..	..	747,400	50	M49 AUG 1962	..	..	691,200	50
M38 SEPT 1961	..	..	513,600	50	M50 SEPT 1962	..	..	687,400	50
M39 OCT 1961	..	..	494,600	60	M51 OCT 1962	..	..	864,600	50
M40 NOV 1961	..	..	467,600	60	M52 NOV 1962	..	..	1,125,600	50

M53 DEC 1962	..	..	1,035,000	50	M64 NOV 1963	..	..	670,000	50
M54 JAN 1963	..	..	499,400	50	M65 DEC 1963	..	..	711,400	50
M55 FEB 1963	..	..	462,400	50	M66 JAN 1964	..	..	619,600	50
M56 MAR 1963	..	..	512,800	50	M67 MAR 1964	..	..	666,600	50
M57 APR 1963	..	..	512,800	50	M68 MAY 1964	..	..	636,600	50
M58 MAY 1963	..	..	520,800	50	M69 JULY 1964	..	..	865,800	50
M59 JUNE 1963	..	..	532,400	50	M70 SEPT 1964	..	..	915,600	50
M60 JULY 1963	..	..	712,000	50	M71 NOV 1964	..	..	2,157,600	50
M61 AUG 1963	..	..	698,600	50	M72 JAN 1965	..	..	1,009,800	50
M62 SEPT 1963	..	..	503,000	50	M73 MAR 1965	..	..	944,600	50
M63 OCT 1963	..	..	660,400	50	M74 MAY 1965	..	..	765,600	50

3/9 Booklets

Composition: Panes of six: 18 × 2½d.

Red cover as Type B.

A. Two interleaving pages, one at each end
Watermark Tudor Crown (No. 51)

G1 NOV 1953	..	..	1,446,000	3·50	G7 JUNE 1955	..	..	675,000	3·75
G2 JAN 1954	..	..	1,572,000	3·50	G8 AUG 1955	..	..	636,000	3·75
G3 MAR 1954	..	..	1,474,000	3·50	G9 OCT 1955	..			
G4 DEC 1954	..	..	1,477,000	3·50	*a.* Combination TET	}		1,661,000	3·50
G5 FEB 1955	..	..	925,000	3·50	*b.* Combination EET				
G6 APR 1955	..	..	1,112,000	3·50					

Watermark St. Edward's Crown (No. S53)

G10 OCT 1955	..	..	*(incl. above)*	1·60	G11 DEC 1955	..	..	616,000	1·60

B. Fully interleaved (same composition)

G12 FEB 1956	..	..	638,000	1·60	G17 DEC 1956	..	..	1,065,800	1·60
G13 APR 1956	..	..	642,000	1·60	G18 FEB 1957	..	..	1,376,000	1·60
G14 JUNE 1956	..	..	634,000	1·60	G19 APR 1957	..	..	1,139,600	1·60
G15 AUG 1956	..	..	747,200	1·60	G20 JUNE 1957	..	..	1,115,200	1·60
G16 OCT 1956	..	..	1,762,800	1·60	G21 AUG 1957	..	..	39,600	2·75

3/9 booklets were withdrawn from sale on 30th September 1957.

4/6 Booklets

Composition. Panes of six: 18 × 3d.

I. Purple cover as Type B. Fully interleaved
Watermark St. Edward's Crown (No. S68)

L1 OCT 1957	..	..	2,249,000	2·00	L5 JUNE 1958	..	..	1,096,000	2·25
L2 DEC 1957	..	..	4,539,000	1·90	L6 OCT 1958	..	..	1,796,000	2·25
L3 FEB 1958	..	..	1,789,000	2·25	L7 DEC 1958	..	..	1,808,000	2·25
L4 APR 1958	..	..	2,691,000	2·00					

Watermark Crowns (No. S70)

L8 DEC 1958	..	*(incl. above)*	3·00

II. Purple cover as Type C (same composition)

L 9 FEB 1959	*(with L14)*		2,260,000	60	L12 OCT 1959	..	..	1,852,000	65
L10 JUNE 1959	*(with L16)*		2,195,000	60	L13 DEC 1959	*(with L17)* ..		1,409,000	65
L11 AUG 1959	..	..	1,710,000	65					

III. Violet cover as Type C (same composition)

L14 FEB 1959	..		*(incl. in L9)*	60	L19 APR 1960	..	..	1,730,000	50
L15 APR 1959	..	..	2,137,000	60	L20 JUNE 1960	..	..	1,832,000	50
L16 JUNE 1959	..		*(incl. in L10)*	60	L21 AUG 1960	..	..	1,771,600	50
L17 DEC 1959	..		*(incl. in L13)*	60	L22 OCT 1960	..	..	2,723,600	60
L18 FEB 1960	..	..	1,801,000	50					

IV. Violet cover as Type D
Watermark Crowns (No. S70 or S71)

L23 DEC 1960	••	..	1,772,000	60	L41 NOV 1963	..	..	1,821,000	60
L24 FEB 1961	..	..	1,982,200	60	L42 DEC 1963	..	..	2,431,400	60
L25 APR 1961	..	..	3,428,400	60	L43 JAN 1964	..	..	1,043,800	60
L26 JUNE 1961	..	..	1,825,600	60	L44 FEB 1964	..	..	1,069,000	60
L27 AUG 1961	..	..	2,679,800	60	L45 MAR 1964	..	..	1,014,200	60
L28 OCT 1961	..	..	3,061,000	60	L46 APR 1964	..	..	1,006,600	60
L29 DEC 1961	..	..	1,942,800	60	L47 MAY 1964	..	..	1,028,800	60
L30 FEB 1962	..	..	2,405,200	60	L48 JUNE 1964	..	..	1,067,400	60
L31 APR 1962	..	..	1,985,000	60	L49 JULY 1964	..	..	1,673,600	60
L32 JUNE 1962	..	..	2,190,600	60	L50 AUG 1964	..	..	1,622,600	60
L33 AUG 1962	..	..	2,533,800	60	L51 SEPT 1964	..	..	1,561,200	60
L34 OCT 1962	..	..	3,525,400	60	L52 OCT 1964	..	..	1,781,800	60
L35 DEC 1962	..	..	1,822,000	60	L53 NOV 1964	..	..	1,686,000	60
L36 FEB 1963	..	..	2,352,600	60	L54 DEC 1964	..	..	1,684,000	60
L37 APR 1963	..	..	2,390,200	60	L55 JAN 1965	..	..	1,519,200	60
L38 JUNE 1963	..	..	2,873,600	60	L56 FEB 1965	..	..	1,504,600	60
L39 AUG 1963	..	..	2,474,200	60	L57 MAR 1965	..	..	1,479,600	60
L40 OCT 1963	..	..	1,829,200	60	L58 APR 1965	..	..	1,438,400	60

New Composition. Panes of six: 12 × 4d., 6 × 1d.

Slate-blue cover as Type D
Watermark Crowns (Nos. S17, S85)

L59 JULY 1965				L62 JAN 1966	..	..	1,671,000	50
(issued 26.7.65) ..	..	2,191,600	50	L63 MAR 1966	..	..	1,201,600	50
L60 SEPT 1965	..	1,839,600	50	L64 JAN 1967	..	..	98,800	60
L61 NOV 1965	..	2,005,000	50	L65 MAR 1967	..	..	97,200	60

5/- Booklets

Buff covers

Composition. Panes of six: 12 × 2½d., 6 × 2d., 6 × 1½d., 6 × 1d., 6 × ½d.

I. Composite booklets containing stamps of King George VI and Queen Elizabeth II

A. K.G. VI ½d. (No. Q3), 1d. (No. Q6) and 2d. (No. Q12) and Q.E. II 1½d. (No. S25) and 2½d. (No. S51). Cover as Type A. Not interleaved

H1 MAY 1953	..	..	1,309,000	2·50	H2 JULY 1953	 1,716,000	2·50

B. Same composition but with the addition of two interleaving pages, one at each end. Cover as Type A

H3 SEPT 1953 .. .. 1,070,000 2·75

C. Same composition with interleaving as before but cover as Type B

H4 NOV 1953	..	..	2,126,000	2·00	H5 JAN 1954	 692,000	3·00

D. *New composition.* ½d. Q.E. II (No. S1) in place of ½d. K.G. VI, but otherwise as Nos. H4/5

H6 MAR 1954 .. .. 16,000 10·00

E. *New composition.* 1d. Q.E. II (No. S13) in place of 1d. K.G. VI, but otherwise as No. H6

H7 MAR 1954 .. .. 160,000 7·00

II. Booklets containing only Queen Elizabeth II stamps.

Buff covers as Type B
Watermark Tudor Crown (Nos. S1, S13, S25, S36, S51)

A. Two interleaving pages, one at each end

H 8 MAR 1954	..	..	1,092,000	2·75	H11 SEPT 1954	 1,357,000	2·75
H 9 MAY 1954	..	..	1,884,000	2·75	H12 NOV 1954	 2,309,000	2·50
H10 JULY 1954	..	..	1,351,000	2·75			

B. Fully interleaved

H13 JAN 1955	..	..	1,349,000	2·50	H15 MAY 1955	 1,461,000	2·50
H14 MAR 1955	..	..	1,450,000	2·50	H16 JULY 1955	 1,460,000	2·50

MIXED WATERMARKS. Nos. H17/19 exist with mixed Tudor Crown and St. Edward's Crown watermarks. The mixed watermarks are indicated by the code letters "T" (Tudor) and "E" (Edward), starting with the first pane of the booklet, i.e. 2½d. (2), 2d., 1½d., 1d., ½d. We only quote one price for each booklet and this is the minimum price. Some combinations are scarcer and worth more.

Watermark St. Edward's Crown (Nos. S2, S14, S26, S37, S51)

H17 SEPT 1955			*p.* Combination EEEEET	
a. Combination TTTETT			*q.* Combination EETET	(inc. in
b. Combination TTTEET			*r.* Combination TTEEEE	H17a/o) 2·00
c. Combination TTTETT			H18 NOV 1955	
d. Combination TTEEET			*a.* Combination TTEEEE	
e. Combination ETTETT			*b.* Combination EETEEE	2,147,000 1·60
f. Combination TETETT			*c.* Combination TEEEEE	
g. Combination ETTEET			*d.* Combination EEEETE	
h. Combination TETEET	1,328,000	2·00	H19 JAN 1956 ..	
i. Combination ETEETT			*a.* Combination TTTEET	1,337,000 1·75
j. Combination TEEETT			*b.* Combination EEEEET	
k. Combination ETEEET			H20 MAR 1956	1,403,000 1·75
l. Combination TEEEET			H21 MAY 1956	1,572,000 1·75
m. Combination EETETT			H22 JULY 1956	1,465,190 1·75
n. Combination EETEET			H23 SEPT 1956	1,589,000 1·75
o. Combination EEEETT			H24 NOV 1956	2,430,600 1·75
			H25 JAN 1957	100,000 3·50

Introduction of 2d. light red-brown (No. S36) in place of No. S35

H26 JAN 1957	..	..	1,417,800	1·60	H29 JULY 1957 1,453,600	1·60
H27 MAR 1957	..	..	1,435,400	1·60	H30 SEPT 1957 2,104,600	1·60
H28 MAY 1957	..	..	1,375,200	1·60	H31 NOV 1957 1,708,400	1·60

New composition. Panes of six: 12 × 3d., 6 × 2½d., 6 × 1d., 6 × ½d.
Watermark St. Edward's Crown (Nos. S2, S14, S53, S68)

H32 JAN 1958	..	..	1,528,000	2·25	H36 NOV 1958	..	
H33 MAR 1958	..	..	442,000	2·50	a. Combination EECE		
H34 MAY 1958	..	..	795,000	2·50	b. Combination EECEE		
H35 JULY 1958 (11.58)					c. Combination ECCEE		
a. Combination EEEEC					d. Combination CCEEE		
b. Combination EEEEC	}	1,313,000	2·25		e. Combination CCCEE		

(H36 group: 1,235,000   2·25)

MIXED WATERMARKS. See notes above No. H17. The mixed watermarks
here are indicated by the code letters "E" (Edward) and "C" (Crowns) starting
with the first pane of the booklet, i.e. 3d. (2), 2½d., 1d., ½d.

Blue cover as Type C fully interleaved
Watermark Crowns (Nos. S4, S16, S55, S70)

H37 JAN 1959	..				H42 JAN 1960	..	..	1,092,000	75
a. Combination CCCCE	}	1,330,000	75	H43 MAR 1960	..	..	1,042,000	75
b. Combination CCCEC				H44 MAY 1960	..	..	1,023,000	75
H38 MAR 1959	..	..	895,000	90	H45 JULY 1960	..	..	1,104,000	75
H39 JULY 1959	..	..	1,122,000	75	H46 SEPT 1960	..	..	1,158,800	75
H40 SEPT 1959	..	..	1,541,000	75	H47 NOV 1960	..	..	1,308,400	75
H41 NOV 1959	..	..	1,340,000	75				

Blue cover as Type D (same composition)
Watermark Crowns (Nos. S4 or S5, S16 or S17, S55 or S57, S70 or S71)

H48 JAN 1961	..	..	1,344,600	65	H62 MAY 1963	..	..	1,102,200	60
H49 MAR 1961	..	..	2,382,800	60	H63 JULY 1963	..	..	1,456,400	60
H50 MAY 1961	..	..	1,219,200	65	H64 SEPT 1963	..	..	1,402,200	60
H51 JULY 1961	..	..	1,148,200	65	H65 NOV 1963	..	..	1,400,000	60
H52 SEPT 1961	..	..	1,728,600	60	H66 JAN 1964	..	..	831,600	75
H53 NOV 1961	..	..	1,367,000	60	H67 MAR 1964	..	..	760,200	75
H54 JAN 1962	..	..	963,800	80	H68 MAY 1964	..	..	760,200	75
H55 MAR 1962	..	..	1,006,200	60	H69 JULY 1964	..	..	1,647,200	60
H56 MAY 1962	..	..	1,120,800	60	H70 SEPT 1964	..	..	1,574,000	60
H57 JULY 1962	..	..	1,309,600	60	H71 NOV 1964	..	..	1,152,400	60
H58 SEPT 1962	..	..	1,523,800	60	H72 JAN 1965	..	..	1,119,000	60
H59 NOV 1962	..	..	1,543,200	60	H73 MAR 1965	..	..	657,600	75
H60 JAN 1963	..	..	1,024,600	60	H74 MAY 1965	..	..	1,076,600	60
H61 MAR 1963	..	..	1,116,800	60				

6/- Booklets

Composition. Panes of six: (18 × 4d.)
Claret cover as Type D
Watermark Crowns (No. S85)

Q 1 JUNE 1965					Q12 MAY 1966	..	..	1,099,000	75
(issued 21.6.65)	..	..	1,166,800	90	Q13 JUNE 1966	..	..	1,070,400	75
Q 2 JULY 1965	..	..	1,718,000	90	Q14 JULY 1966	..	..	667,600	75
Q 3 AUG 1965	..	..	1,192,400	75	Q15 AUG 1966	..	..	1,503,200	75
Q 4 SEPT 1965	..	..	1,907,800	75	Q16 SEPT 1966	..	..	1,402,400	75
Q 5 OCT 1965	..	..	1,889,600	75	Q17 OCT 1966	..	..	986,600	75
Q 6 NOV 1965	..	..	1,788,600	75	Q18 NOV 1966	..	..	1,078,000	75
Q 7 DEC 1965	..	..	1,662,000	75	Q19 DEC 1966	..	..	1,069,400	75
Q 8 JAN 1966	..	..	1,114,800	75	Q20 JAN 1967	..	..	231,400	90
Q 9 FEB 1966	..	..	1,448,600	75	Q21 FEB 1967	..	..	253,800	90
Q10 MAR 1966	..	..	1,038,000	75	Q22 MAR 1967	..	..	395,000	90
Q11 APR 1966	..	..	1,124,200	75	Q23 APR 1967	..	..	395,400	90

10/- Booklets

I. Green cover as Type D. Fully interleaved
Composition. Panes of six: 30 × 3d., 6 × 2d., 6 × 1½d., 6 × 1d., 6 × ½d.
Watermark Crowns (Nos. S4, S16, S28, S40, S70)

X1 No date (issued 10.4.61)		902,000	1·40	X2 OCT 1961	..	..	483,200	1·60

New composition. Panes of six: 30 × 3d., 6 × 2½d., 6 × 1½d., 6 × 1d.
Watermark Crowns (Nos. S17, S29, S57, S71)

X3 APR 1962	..	..	524,680	1·40	X7 DEC 1963	..	..	606,600	1·40
X4 AUG 1962	..	..	474,600	1·40	X8 JULY 1964	..	..	599,400	1·40
X5 MAR 1963	..	..	493,200	1·40	X9 DEC 1964	..	..	415,200	1·40
X6 JULY 1963	..	..	620,600	1·40				

10/- booklets in this composition were withdrawn from sale on 31st August 1965.

II. Ochre cover as Type D
New composition. Panes of six: 24 × 4d., 6 × 3d., 6 × 1d.
Watermark Crowns (Nos. S17, S71, S85)

X10 AUG 1965					X12 FEB 1966	..	..	663,600	1·10
(issued 23.8.65)	..	..	854,200	1·10	X13 AUG 1966	..	..	686,800	1·10
X11 DEC 1965	..	..	658,800	1·10	X14 NOV 1966	..	..	796,000	1·10

Section B. Wilding Issues with Graphite Lines or Phosphor Bands

NOTE. All booklets in this Section are fully interleaved

2/- Booklets with Phosphor Bands

Composition. Panes of four: 4×3d., $4 \times 1\frac{1}{2}$d., 4×1d., $4 \times \frac{1}{2}$d.

Lemon cover as Type C

Watermark Crowns (sideways), blue phosphor (Nos. S10*b* or S11*a*, S21*b* or S22*a*, S33*b* or S34*a*, S75*b* or S76*a*)

NP1 APR 1961 (issued 14.7.61)	171,400	1·75	NP 8 FEB 1964	76,600	2·00
NP2 JULY 1962	51,600	2·25	NP 9 JUNE 1964	63,400	2·00
NP3 NOV 1962	56,200	2·25	NP10 AUG 1964	58,800	2·00
NP4 JAN 1963	58,390	2·25	NP11 OCT 1964	94,200	1·75
NP5 JUNE 1963	57,800	2·25	NP12 DEC 1964	34,000	2·50
NP6 AUG 1963	56,400	2·25	NP13 APR 1965	40,800	2·50
NP7 OCT 1963	11,200	2·50			

2/- booklets in this composition were withdrawn from sale on 31st August 1965.

New composition. Panes of four: 4×4d. and pane of 2×1d. and 2×3d. arranged *se-tenant* horizontally

Orange-yellow cover as Type C

One phosphor band on 3d.

Watermark Crowns (sideways), blue or violet phosphor (Nos. S22*a*, S23*c* or S24*b*; S77*b*, S78*b* or S80; S90*c*, S91*b* or S92*b*)

NP14 JULY 1965 (issued 16.8.65)	Blue	109,600	60
NP15 OCT 1965	Blue	223,200	60
NP15a OCT 1965	Violet 8 mm.		50
NP16 JAN 1966	Blue	350,600	60
NP16a JAN 1966	Violet 8 mm.		50
NP17 APR 1966	Violet 8 mm.	240,000	50
NP18 JULY 1966	Violet 8 mm.	97,400	60
NP19 OCT 1966	Violet 8 mm.	471,400	50
NP20 JAN 1967	Violet 8 mm.	2,100,400	50
NP21 APR 1967	Violet 8 mm.	2,330,200	50
NP22 JULY 1967	Violet 8 mm.	3,209,800	50
NP23 OCT 1967 (issued 15.9.67)	Violet 8 mm.	3,924,600	50
NP23a OCT 1967 *(error)*	Violet 9·5 mm. *(with* NP24*)*		15·00

For illustration showing how the *se-tenant* stamps with one phosphor band on the 3d. are printed, see listing of No. SB36.

Change to 3d. with two phosphor bands

Watermark Crowns (sideways) (Nos. S24*b*, S80, S92*b*)

NP24 OCT 1967	Violet 9·5 mm.	*(incl. in* NP23/3*a)*	50
NP25 JAN 1968 (issued early 11.67)	Violet 9·5 mm.	1,864,800	50
NP26 MAR 1968 (issued mid 1.68)..	Violet 9·5 mm.	3,078,800	50

3/- Booklets with Graphite Lines

Composition. Panes of six: 6×3d., $6 \times 1\frac{1}{2}$d., 6×1d., $6 \times \frac{1}{2}$d.

Watermark Crowns (Nos. S7, S18, S30, S72)

I. Red cover as Type B

MG1 AUG 1959 (issued 4.8.59)	47,000	18·00	MG2 SEPT 1959	74,000	16·00

II. Brick-red cover as Type C

MG3 OCT 1959	74,000	16·00	MG5 MAR 1960	39,600	18·00
MG4 FEB 1960	37,600	18·00	MG6 APR 1960	38,200	18·00

3/- Booklets with Phosphor Bands

Composition. Panes of six: 6×3d., $6 \times 1\frac{1}{2}$d., 6×1d., $6 \times \frac{1}{2}$d.

I. Brick-red cover as Type C

Watermark Crowns, green phosphor (Nos. S9, S20, S32, S74)

MP1 AUG 1960 (issued 14.8.60)	39,800	10·00	MP2 NOV 1960	11,900	12·00

II. Brick-red cover as Type D

Watermark Crowns, green or blue phosphor (Nos. S9 or S10, S20 or S21, S32 or S33, S74 or S75)

MP 3	DEC 1960	Green..	31,800	8·00	MP20	MAR 1963	Blue ..	39,200	50
MP 4	APR 1961	Blue ..	142,600	60	MP21	APR 1963	Blue ..	39,600	50
MP 5	JULY 1961	Blue ..	7,800	2·00	MP22	MAY 1963	Blue ..	19,400	75
MP 6	AUG 1961	Green ⎱		8·00	MP23	JUNE 1963	Blue ..	19,800	75
MP 6a	AUG 1961	Blue ⎰	54,400	75	MP24	JULY 1963	Blue ..	17,800	75
MP 7	SEPT 1961	Blue ..	19,200	90	MP25	AUG 1963	Blue ..	19,800	75
MP 8	OCT 1961	Blue ..	18,800	75	MP26	NOV 1963	Blue ..	39,400	50
MP 9	FEB 1962	Blue ..	11,800	75	MP27	DEC 1963	Blue ..	19,350	75
MP10	MAR 1962	Blue ..	19,400	75	MP28	JAN 1964	Blue ..	67,000	50
MP11	APR 1962	Blue ..	19,600	75	MP30	MAR 1964	Blue ..	30,400	50
MP12	MAY 1962	Blue ..	27,000	50	MP32	MAY 1964	Blue ..	46,600	50
MP13	JUNE 1962	Blue ..	27,200	50	MP33	JULY 1964	Blue ..	27,400	50
MP14	AUG 1962	Blue ..	28,800	50	MP34	SEPT 1964	Blue ..	39,800	50
MP15	SEPT 1962	Blue ..	11,800	75	MP35	NOV 1964	Blue ..	99,200	50
MP16	OCT 1962	Blue ..	35,200	50	MP36	JAN 1965	Blue ..	50,000	50
MP17	NOV 1962	Blue ..	51,800	50	MP37	MAR 1965	Blue ..	38,200	50
MP18	DEC 1962	Blue ..	19,200	75	MP38	MAY 1965	Blue ..	58,200	50
MP19	FEB 1963	Blue ..	39,400	50					

3/– booklets were withdrawn from sale on 31st August 1965.

4/6 Booklets with Graphite Lines

Composition.   Panes of six: 18 × 3d.

Watermark Crowns (No. S72)

I. Purple cover as Type C

LG1	AUG 1959	..	..	97,600	4·00

II. Violet cover as Type C

LG2	APR 1959	..	..	99,200	4·00	LG4	FEB 1960	..	..	79,600	4·00
LG3	JUNE 1959	..	..	99,400	4·00	LG5	APR 1960	..	..	78,800	4·00

4/6 Booklets with Phosphor Bands

Composition.   Panes of six: 18 × 3d.

I. Violet cover as Type C
Watermark Crowns, green phosphor (No. S74)

LP1	AUG 1960	..	..	39,600	2·50

II. Violet cover as Type D
Watermark Crowns, green or blue phosphor (Nos. S74 or else S75 or S76)

LP 2	FEB 1961	Green ..	27,200	10·00	LP17	NOV 1963	Blue ..	99,600	90
LP 3	APR 1961	Blue ..	297,400	90	LP18	DEC 1963	Blue ..	46,400	1·40
LP 4	AUG 1961	Green ⎱		10·00	LP19	FEB 1964	Blue ..	87,000	1·10
LP 4a	AUG 1961	Blue ⎰	63,120	1·10	LP20	MAR 1964	Blue ..	82,800	1·10
LP 5	OCT 1961	Blue ..	31,400	1·50	LP21	APR 1964	Blue ..	62,400	1·10
LP 6	FEB 1962	Blue ..	43,600	1·40	LP22	MAY 1964	Blue ..	105,200	90
LP 7	APR 1962	Blue ..	75,400	1·10	LP23	JUNE 1964	Blue ..	70,400	1·10
LP 8	JUNE 1962	Blue ..	74,000	1·10	LP24	JULY 1964	Blue ..	56,200	1·25
LP 9	AUG 1962	Blue ..	83,600	1·10	LP25	AUG 1964	Blue ..	78,200	1·10
LP10	OCT 1962	Blue ..	83,200	1·10	LP26	SEPT 1964	Blue ..	98,000	90
LP11	DEC 1962	Blue ..	82,200	1·10	LP27	OCT 1964	Blue ..	197,800	90
LP12	FEB 1963	Blue ..	117,000	90	LP28	NOV 1964	Blue ..	138,000	90
LP13	APR 1963	Blue ..	119,000	90	LP29	DEC 1964	Blue ..	119,200	90
LP14	JUNE 1963	Blue ..	178,600	90	LP30	JAN 1965	Blue ..	95,000	90
LP15	AUG 1963	Blue ..	111,000	90	LP31	FEB 1965	Blue ..	94,200	90
LP16	OCT 1963	Blue ..	99,400	90	LP31a	MAR 1965	Blue ..	18,800	2·00

New composition.   Panes of six: 12 × 4d., 6 × 1d.

Slate-blue cover as Type D. Watermark Crowns, blue or violet phosphor (Nos. S22, S23 or S24; S90, S91 or S92)

LP32	JULY 1965 (issued 26.7.65) ..	..	..	..	..	Blue		75,400	40
LP33	SEPT 1965	..	..	..	..	Blue .. ⎱			40
LP33a	SEPT 1965	..	..	..	..	Violet 8 mm. ⎰	200,800		30
LP34	NOV 1965	..	..	..	..	Blue .. ⎱			40
LP34a	NOV 1965	..	..	..	..	Violet 8 mm. ⎰	165,800		30
LP35	JAN 1966	..	..	..	..	Blue .. ⎱			40
LP35a	JAN 1966	..	..	..	..	Violet 8 mm. ⎰	334,600		30
LP36	MAR 1966	..	..	..	..	Violet 8 mm.	153,200		30
LP37	JAN 1967	..	..	..	..	Violet 8 mm.	396,600		30
LP38	MAR 1967	..	..	..	..	Violet 8 mm. ⎱			40
LP38a	MAR 1967	..	..	..	..	Violet 9·5 mm. ⎰	255,400		30
LP39	MAY 1967	..	..	..	..	Violet 9·5 mm.	697,200		30
LP40	JULY 1967	..	..	..	..	Violet 9·5 mm.	569,000		30
LP41	SEPT 1967	..	..	..	..	Violet 9·5 mm.	750,800		30
LP42	NOV 1967	..	..	..	..	Violet 9·5 mm.	1,802,600		30
LP43	JAN 1968	..	..	..	..	Violet 9·5 mm.	729,400		30
LP44	MAR 1968	..	..	..	..	Violet 9·5 mm.	729,400		30

5/- Booklets with Graphite Lines
Composition.   Panes of six: 12 × 3d., 6 × 2½d., 6 × 1d., 6 × ½d.
Blue cover as Type C. Watermark Crowns (Nos. S7, S18, S59, S72)

HG1 JULY 1959 (issued 21.8.59)	..	..	..	..	..	..	..	46,200	13·00
HG2 MAR 1960..	..	..	..	..	..	..	..	38,000	13·00
HG3 SEPT 1960	..	..	..	..	..	..	..	65,999	13·00

5/- Booklets with Phosphor Bands
Composition.   Panes of six: 12 × 3d., 6 × 2½d., 6 × 1d., 6 × ½d.
I. Blue cover as Type C
Watermark Crowns, green phosphor (Nos. S9, S20, S61, S74)

HP1 SEPT 1960   39,600   12·00

II. Blue cover as Type D
Two phosphor bands on 2½d.
Watermark Crowns, blue phosphor (Nos. S10, S21, S62, S75)

| HP2 MAR 1961 | .. | .. | 97,400 | 2·00 | HP4 SEPT 1961 | .. | .. | 15,200 | 1·60 |
| HP3 JULY 1961 | .. | .. | 7,200 | 4·00 | HP5 JAN 1962 | .. | .. | 38,600 | 1·50 |

Change to 2½d. with one band
Watermark Crowns, blue phosphor (Nos. S10 or S11, S21 or S22, S63 or S65, S75 or S76)

HP 6 MAR 1962	..	..	23,600	1·25	HP16 NOV 1963	..	..	78,800	75
HP 7 MAY 1962	..	..	50,800	1·00	HP17 JAN 1964	..	..	43,000	75
HP 8 JULY 1962	..	..	16,600	1·60	HP18 MAR 1964	..	..	55,800	75
HP 9 SEPT 1962	..	..	49,800	1·00	HP19 MAY 1964	..	..	66,000	75
HP10 NOV 1962	..	..	51,000	1·00	HP20 JULY 1964	..	..	29,400	75
HP11 JAN 1963	..	..	38,800	1·10	HP21 SEPT 1964	..	..	38,400	75
HP12 MAR 1963	..	..	15,800	1·50	HP22 NOV 1964	..	..	98,600	75
HP13 MAY 1963	..	..	78,600	75	HP23 JAN 1965	..	..	55,200	75
HP14 JULY 1963	..	..	44,600	75	HP24 MAR 1965	..	..	19,000	1·00
HP15 SEPT 1963	..	..	36,200	75	HP25 MAY 1965	..	..	56,800	75

5/– booklets were withdrawn from sale on 31st August 1965.

6/- Booklets with Phosphor Bands
Composition.   Panes of six: 18 × 4d.
Claret cover as Type D
Watermark Crowns, blue or violet phosphor (Nos. S90, S91 or S92)

QP 1	JUNE 1965 (issued 21.6.65) ..	..	..	..	Blue	101,800	65
QP 2	JULY 1965	..	..	..	Blue	136,200	50
QP 3	AUG 1965	..	..	..	Blue	87,600	50
QP 4	SEPT 1965	..	..	..	Blue .. .. }	244,400	65
QP 4a	SEPT 1965	..	..	..	Violet 8 mm.		50
QP 5	OCT 1965	..	..	..	Blue .. .. }	263,600	65
QP 5a	OCT 1965	..	..	..	Violet 8 mm.		50
QP 6	NOV 1965	..	..	..	Blue .. .. }	98,200	65
QP 6a	NOV 1965	..	..	..	Violet 8 mm.		50
QP 7	DEC 1965	..	..	..	Blue .. .. }	93,000	65
QP 7a	DEC 1965	..	..	..	Violet 8 mm.		50
QP 8	JAN 1966	..	..	..	Blue .. .. }	349,200	65
QP 8a	JAN 1966	..	..	..	Violet 8 mm.		50
QP 9	FEB 1966	..	..	..	Violet 8 mm.	116,800	50
QP10	MAR 1966	..	..	..	Violet 8 mm.	122,400	50
QP11	APR 1966	..	..	..	Violet 8 mm.	119,600	50
QP12	MAY 1966	..	..	..	Violet 8 mm.	121,000	50
QP13	JUNE 1966	..	..	..	Violet 8 mm.	121,000	50
QP14	JULY 1966	..	..	..	Violet 8 mm.	46,800	50
QP15	AUG 1966	..	..	..	Violet 8 mm.	42,400	50
QP16	SEPT 1966	..	..	..	Violet 8 mm.	227,200	50
QP17	OCT 1966	..	..	..	Violet 8 mm.	227,200	50
QP18	NOV 1966	..	..	..	Violet 8 mm.	271,200	50
QP19	DEC 1966	..	..	..	Violet 8 mm.	270,500	50
QP20	JAN 1967	..	..	..	Violet 8 mm.	622,400	40
QP21	FEB 1967	..	..	..	Violet 9·5 mm.	566,200	40
QP22	MAR 1967	..	..	..	Violet 9·5 mm.	580,800	40
QP23	APR 1967	..	..	..	Violet 9·5 mm.	632,200	40
QP24	MAY 1967	..	..	..	Violet 9·5 mm.	1,612,600	40
QP25	JUNE 1967	..	..	..	Violet 9·5 mm.	1,596,800	40
QP26	JULY 1967	..	..	..	Violet 9·5 mm.	776,600	40
QP27	AUG 1967	..	..	..	Violet 9·5 mm.	750,600	40

10/- Booklets with Phosphor Bands

Composition.   Panes of six: 24 × 4d., 6 × 3d., 6 × 1d.
Ochre cover as Type D
One side phosphor band on 3d.
Watermark Crowns, violet phosphor (Nos. S23 or S24, S78, S91 or S92)

XP1	FEB 1967	..	..	..	..	Violet 8 and 4 mm.	1·25
XP1*a*	FEB 1967	..	..	..	..	Violet 9·5 and 4 mm.	301,800	1·25

Change to 3d. with one centre band
Watermark Crowns, violet 9·5 mm. phosphor (Nos. S24, S80, S92)

XP2	AUG 1967	..	..	..	..	Violet 9·5 and 4 mm.	1,488,800	1·25
XP3	FEB 1968	..	..	..	..	Violet 9·5 and 4 mm.	474,400	1·00

Section C.   Machin £.s.d. Issues with Violet Phosphor Bands

TYPES OF BOOKLET COVERS

Type E
Pictorial Cover with GPO Cypher
Two types of Cypher:
Type I. GPO in clear letters *(as illus.)*. 10/-
   Booklets XP4/5
Type II. GPO in black letters. All 4/6, 5/–, 6/– and
   10/- (XP6/10) Booklets

Type F
Pictorial Cover with Post Office
Corporation Crown Symbol

(Pictorial covers as Types E/F.   Des. Stuart Rose)
(In Types E/F the design subject is changed from time to time and this is indicated in
brackets after the date)

NOTE.   All booklets in this Section are fully interleaved

2/- Booklets

Composition.   Panes of four: 4 × 4d. and pane of 2 × 1d. and 2 × 3d. arranged
   se-tenant horizontally
Orange-yellow cover as Type C. PVA gum (Nos. U2, U10, U12)

NP27	MAY 1968 (issued 6.4.68)	..	..	..	..	..	..	..		20
NP28	JULY 1968	..	..	..	..	..	..	..	3,112,400	20
NP29	AUG 1968	..	..	..	..	..	..	..	1,971,685	

2/–booklets containing 3d. stamps were withdrawn on 14th September 1968.

New composition.   Panes of four: 4 × 4d. and pane of 2 × 4d. *se-tenant* with two
   printed labels
Grey cover as Type C
One centre phosphor band on *se-tenant* pane. PVA gum (Nos. U12, U13)

NP30	SEPT 1968 (issued 16.9.68)	..	..	..	..	..	..	2,497,400	35
NP31	JAN 1969	..	..	..	..	..	..	2,247,600	50

Change to one centre phosphor band on 4 × 4d. pane. PVA gum (No. U13)

NP31*a*	SEPT 1968	..	..	..	..	..	..	..	(*incl. in* NP30)	75
NP32	NOV 1968	..	..	..	..	..	..	..	2,397,400	20
NP33	JAN 1969	..	..	..	..	..	..	..	(*incl. in* NP31)	20

Change to 4d. bright vermilion with one centre phosphor band. PVA gum (No. U14)

NP34 MAR 1969 (issued 3.3.69)	..	.. 1,952,000	20	NP40 MAR 1970 ..	.. 1,168,600	20
NP35 MAY 1969	..	.. 2,092,000	20	NP41 MAY 1970 ..	.. 1,390,800	20
NP36 JULY 1969	..	.. 436,000	40	NP42 JULY 1970 ..	.. 1,023,800	20
NP37 SEPT 1969	..	.. 1,612,400	20	NP43 AUG 1970 ..	.. 1,037,800	20
NP38 NOV 1969	..	.. 1,470,400	20	NP44 OCT 1970 ..	.. 2,544,600	20
NP39 JAN 1970	..	.. 1,172,000	20	NP45 DEC 1970 ..	.. 2,273,400	15

4/6 Booklets
Composition. Panes of six: 12 × 4d., 6 × 1d.
PVA gum (Nos. U2, U12)

I. Slate-blue cover as Type D
LP45 MAY 1968   742,600   40

II. Blue cover as Type E. Ships Series
LP46 JULY 1968 *(Cutty Sark)*   427,600   40

Change to one centre phosphor band on 4d. PVA gum (Nos. U2, U13)
LP47 SEPT 1968 *(Golden Hind)*   1,052,800   40
LP48 NOV 1968 *(Discovery)*   1,009,000   40

Change to 4d. bright vermilion with one centre phosphor band. PVA gum (No. U14)
LP49 JAN 1969 *(Queen Elizabeth 2)*   775,200   40
LP50 MAR 1919 *(Sirius)*   1,105,800   40
LP61 MAY 1969 *(Sirius)*   993,200   40
LP52 JULY 1969 *(Dreadnought)*   932,000   40
LP35 SEPT 1969 *(Dreadnought)*   1,318,600   40
LP54 NOV 1969 *(Mauretania)*   1,469,400   40
LP55 JAN 1970 *(Mauretania)*   1,046,600   40
LP56 MAR 1970 *(Victory)*   872,400   40
LP57 MAY 1970 *(Victory)*   515,800   40

Change to cover Type F
LP58 AUG 1970 *(The Sovereign of the Seas)*   412,600   40
LP59 OCT 1970 *(The Sovereign of the Seas)*   746,600   40

5/- Booklets
Composition. Panes of six: 12 × 5d.
Cinnamon cover as Type E. English Homes Series. PVA gum (No. U17)
HP26 DEC 1968 (Ightham Mote) (issued 27.11.68)   978,000   45
HP27 FEB 1969 (Little Moreton Hall)   1,510,200   45
HP28 APR 1969 (Long Melford Hall)   1,963,200   45
HP29 JUNE 1969 (Long Melford Hall)   1,821,000   45
HP30 AUG 1969 (Long Melford Hall)   1,660,800   45

Change to cover Type F
HP31 OCT 1969 (Mompesson House)   2,251,200   45
HP32 DEC 1969 (Mompesson House)   960,200   45
HP33 FEB 1970 (Cumberland Terrace)   910,800   45

Type P
(Des. Peter Gauld)
Issued to publicise the "Philympia" International
Philatelic Exhibition, London, September 1970

Change to cover Type P. Stitched in red

HP34 (no date) (issued 3.3.70)	..	..	..	..	..	..	.. 1,019,800	4!

Change back to cover Type F

HP35 JUNE 1970 (The Vineyard, Saffron Walden)	..	..	..	..	.. 1,814,400	4!
HP36 AUG 1970 (The Vineyard, Saffron Walden)	..	..	..	..	.. 2,076,800	4!
HP37 OCT 1970 (Mereworth Castle)	..	..	..	..	..	.. 3,301,400	4!
HP38 DEC 1970 (Mereworth Castle)	..	..	..	..	..	.. 5,517,680	4(

6/- Booklets

Composition. Panes of six: 18 × 4d.
I. Claret cover as Type D. Gum arabic (No. U11(1))

QP28 SEPT 1967	..	..	..	..	..	..	..	..	.. 1,345,000	5!
QP29 OCT 1967	..	..	..	..	..	..	..	..	.. 1,487,400	5!
QP30 NOV 1967	..	..	..	..	..	..	..	..	.. 1,522,200	55
QP31 DEC 1967	..	..	..	..	..	..	..	..	.. 1,531,000	5!
QP32 JAN 1968	..	..	..	..	..	..	..	..	.. 1,251,400	55

Change to 4d. deep olive-brown. Gum arabic (No. U11(2))

QP33 FEB 1968	..	..	..	..	..	..	..	..	.. 1,314,400	55
QP34 MAR 1968	..	..	..	..	..	..	..	..	.. 1,090,600	55
QP35 APR 1968	..	..	..	..	..	..	..	..	.. 1,127,800	55
QP36 MAY 1968	..	..	..	..	..	..	..	..	.. 1,398,000	55

Change to PVA gum (No. U12(2))

QP37 MAY 1968	..	..	..	..	..	..	..	.. *(incl. in* QP36)	55

II. Orange-red cover as Type F. Birds Series. PVA gum (No. U12(2))

QP38 JUNE 1968 (Kingfisher) (issued 4.6.68)	..	..	..	..	.. 1,212,000	55
QP39 JULY 1968 (Kingfisher)	..	..	..	..	..	.. 1,195,000	1·00
QP40 AUG 1968 (Peregrine Falcon)	..	..	..	..	..	.. 1,223,800	55

Change to one centre phosphor band. PVA gum (No. U13)

QP41 SEPT 1968 (Peregrine Falcon) (issued 16.9.68)	..	..	..	.. 1,010,200	55
QP42 OCT 1968 (Pied Woodpecker)	..	..	..	..	.. 1,277,800	55
QP43 NOV 1968 (Pied Woodpecker)	..	..	..	..	.. 1,006,200	55
QP44 DEC 1968 (Great Crested Grebe)	..	..	..	..	.. 975,600	55
QP45 JAN 1969 (Barn Owl)	..	..	..	..	..	.. 1,017,000	55

Change to 4d. bright vermilion with one centre phosphor band. PVA gum
    (No. U14)

QP46 FEB 1969 (Barn Owl) (issued 20.2.69)	..	..	..	..	.. 1,035,200	55
QP47 MAR 1969 (Jay)	..	..	..	..	..	..	.. 1,424,400	55
QP48 MAY 1969 (Jay)	..	..	..	..	..	..	.. 533,800	55
QP49 JULY 1969 (Puffin)	..	..	..	..	..	..	.. 498,400	55
QP50 SEPT 1969 (Puffin)	..	..	..	..	..	..	.. 506,200	55

Change to cover Type F printed in black

QP51 NOV 1969 (Cormorant)	..	..	..	..	..	.. 472,600	55
QP52 JAN 1970 (Cormorant)	..	..	..	..	..	.. 487,800	55
QP53 APR 1970 (Wren)	..	..	..	..	..	..	.. 512,800	55
QP54 AUG 1970 (Golden Eagle)	..	..	..	..	..	.. 570,600	55
QP55 OCT 1970 (Golden Eagle)	..	..	..	..	..	.. 754,800	55

10/- Booklets

Composition. Panes of six: 24 × 4d., 6 × 3d., 6 × 1d.
Bright purple cover as Type E. Explorers Series. PVA gum (Nos. U2, U9, U12)

XP4 MAY 1968 (Livingstone) (issued 25.3.68)	..	..	..	..	.. 713,200	1·00
XP5 AUG 1968 (Livingstone)	..	..	..	..	..	.. 39,497	1·25

New composition. Panes of six: 12 × 5d., 12 × 4d. and pane 4 × 1d. and 2 × 4d.
    arranged *se-tenant* vertically
Yellow-green cover as Type E. Explorers Series. PVA gum (Nos. U3, U13, U17)

XP6 SEPT 1968 (Scott) (issued 16.9.68)	..	..	..	..	.. 1,513,400	1·10

Change to 4d. bright vermilion but *se-tenant* pane comprises 1d. with two
    phosphor bands and 4d. with one left side phosphor band. PVA gum (Nos. U2,
    U14, U16, U17)

XP 7 FEB 1969 (Mary Kingsley) (issued 6.1.69)	..	..	..	.. 2,338,200	85
XP 8 MAY 1969 (Mary Kingsley)	..	..	..	..	.. 1,165,200	85
XP 9 AUG 1969 (Shackleton)	..	..	..	..	..	.. 1,765,600	85
XP10 NOV 1969 (Shackleton)	..	..	..	..	..	.. 1,176,000	85

Change to cover Type F

XP11 FEB 1970 (Frobisher)	..	..	..	..	..	.. 490,200	85
XP12 NOV 1970 (Captain Cook)	..	..	..	..	..	.. 737,400	85

Type X

£1 Booklet ("Stamps for Cooks")

Composition. Panes of fifteen: 15 × 5d., 30 × 4d. and pane 6 × 4d., 6 × 1d. and 3 × 5d. arranged
  se-tenant vertically
Full colour cover showing "Baked, Stuffed Haddock" Type X, size 6 × 2⅞ *in.*
Contains 12 recipes on interleaving pages and on *se-tenant* label attached to all panes
Pane of fifteen 5d. has two phosphor bands, panes of fifteen 4d. have one centre phosphor
  band but *se-tenant* pane has two phosphor bands on 1d. and 5d. and one side band on 4d.
  (three stamps with band at left and three stamps with band at right)

ZP1	(no date) (issued 1.12.69) (Sewn with thread)	..	..	..	..	..	374,902	1·75
ZP1*a*	As last but booklet is bound with two wire staples instead of being sewn	..	10,848	3·50
s.	Each stamp overprinted "Specimen". Stapled	..	..	..	..	..

Section D.   Machin Decimal Issues with Violet Phosphor Bands

Type G

The 25p, 30p and 50p booklets are as
Type F but without the design inscription.
This is no longer necessary as the designs
and background information are given on
the inside of the front cover. Each series is
also numbered.

NOTE. All booklets in this Section are fully interleaved.

10p Booklets

Composition. Panes of four: 2 × 2p *se-tenant* vertically with 2 × ½p and 2 × 1p
  se-tenant vertically with 2 × 1½p
Orange-yellow cover Type G (Nos. U37, U39, U41, U42)
British Pillar Box Series designed by Ronald Maddox

DN46 FEB 1971 (No. 1 1855 type) (issued 15.2.71)	15
DN47 APR 1971 (No. 1 1855 type)	15
DN48 JUNE 1971 (No. 2 1856 type)	15
DN49 AUG 1971 (No. 2 1856 type) (issued 14.7.71)	15

In No. DN47 the pillar box is in slightly reduced size and in Nos. DN48/9 the
description is given on the inside front cover instead of on the front.
In No. DN49 the values are arranged *se-tenant* horizontally instead of vertically.

25p Booklets

Composition. Panes of six: 5 × 2½p with one label, 4 × 2½p with two labels, 5 × 1½p with one label

Dull purple cover as Type F (Nos. U37, U44)

Veteran Transport Series designed by David Gentleman

DH39 FEB 1971 (No. 1 Knife-board omnibus) (issued 15.2.71)   4

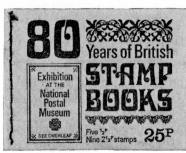

Type H
Issued to publicise the National Postal Museum Exhibition
of 80 Years of British Stamp Books

Change to dull purple cover Type H

DH40 APR 1971 (issued 19.3.71)   4

Change back to dull purple cover as Type F

Veteran Transport Series continued

DH41 JUNE 1971 (No. 2 B-type omnibus)   4

30p Booklets

Composition. Panes of six: 2 panes of 5 × 3p with one label

Bright purple cover as Type F (No. U46)

British Birds Series designed by Harry Titcombe

DQ56 FEB 1971 (No. 1 Curlew) (issued 15.2.71)   5

Change to bright purple cover Type H

DQ57 APR 1971 (issued 19.3.71)   5

Change back to bright purple cover as Type F

British Birds Series continued

DQ58 JUNE 1971 (No. 2 Lapwing)   5
DQ59 AUG 1971 (No. 2 Lapwing) (issued 23.7.71)   5

    No. DQ59 has the label imperforate in the binding margin.

50p Booklets

Composition. Panes of six: 6 × 3p, 4 × 3p *se-tenant* horizontally with 2 × 2½p (side band), 5 × 2½p (centre band) with one label, 5 × ½p with one label

Turquoise-green cover as Type F (Nos. U37, U44, U45, U46)

British Flowers Series designed by Rosalie Southall

DX13 FEB 1971 (No. 1 Large Bindweed) (issued 15.2.71)   7
DX14 MAY 1971 (No. 2 Primrose) (issued 24.3.71)   7
DX15 AUG 1971 (No. 3 Honeysuckle) (issued 28.6.71)   7